WAVE MECHANICS

AND ITS

APPLICATIONS

N. F. MOTT

*Cavendish Professor of Experimental Physics in
the University of Cambridge*

AND

I. N. SNEDDON

*Simson Professor of Mathematics in the
University of Glasgow*

NEW YORK

Published in the United Kingdom by Constable and Company Limited, 10 Orange Street, London W.C. 2.

This Dover edition, first published in 1963, is an unabridged and unaltered republication of the work first published by the Clarendon Press, Oxford University, in 1948. This edition is published by special arrangement with the Oxford University Press.

Library of Congress Catalog Card Number: 63-19510

Manufactured in the United States of America

Dover Publications, Inc.
180 Varick Street
New York 14, N.Y.

PREFACE

THIS book is intended for the student of physics or chemistry who wishes to use quantum mechanics. Not much space, therefore, is devoted to the foundations of the subject; in particular no attempt is made to present the foundations in their most general form, as is done in the classical treatises of Dirac and of Pauli, for example. Schrödinger's wave equation for a single particle in an electrostatic field is shown to follow from diffraction experiments; generalizations of the equation for the magnetic field, the many-body problem, for the spin, and for relativistic velocities are introduced as and when the physical subjects under discussion make it necessary. This treatment, though it lacks the elegance of the more general formulation, has the advantage of keeping close to experimental fact. It should appeal to the research worker who wants to learn the subject in order to explain new facts of physical science, rather than to the man whose interest is in the logical basis of quantum mechanics, and in the improvements necessary in those parts that remain unsatisfactory.

We are grateful to Dr. A. F. Devonshire and Dr. K. Guggenheimer who have read parts of the book in manuscript or in proof, and made suggestions for its improvement.

N. F. M.
I. N. S.

April 1948

CONTENTS

CONTENTS

INTRODUCTION

QUANTUM or Wave Mechanics is the name given to a system of equations which must be used instead of Newton's Laws of Motion in order to calculate the behaviour of atoms and electrons and other ultimate particles of matter. Newton's laws have proved adequate for the mathematical description of a very wide class of phenomena, including, for instance, the motion of the planets round the sun and the motion of projectiles under the influence of gravity and air resistance. When, however, they are applied to the behaviour of electrons, and in particular to the motion of electrons within the atom, the answer that they give is not in agreement with experiment. Consequently it has been necessary to invent a new system of equations which gives as completely as possible an answer which does fit the facts. These equations, while profoundly different from Newton's laws, give very nearly the same results except when applied to particles of extremely small mass such as electrons; this will be shown in Chapter I of this book. Therefore it must not be thought that two different sets of equations exist, one for atoms and electrons and one for the heavier bodies of everyday experience; Newton's laws can be considered a special case of the more general quantal† laws.

The first step in the development of the new system of mechanics is due to the German physicist Max Planck, who in 1900 made the assumption that the energy of light was quantized, in order to explain the spectrum of black-body radiation.‡ He introduced into physics a new constant of nature, Planck's constant. In 1905 Albert Einstein made use of Planck's assumption to account for the photoelectric effect. In 1913 Niels Bohr, the great Danish leader of theoretical physics who was working at that time with Rutherford in Manchester, made use of the idea of quantization and of Planck's constant to give a quantitative theory§ of the line spectrum of hydrogen. In this theory, the outlines of which are given in Chapter II of this book, Newton's Laws of Motion were accepted as the correct equations for the electrons in atoms. In the hydrogen atom the single electron was therefore assumed to revolve round the positively charged nucleus in circular or elliptic orbits. The new assumption was that only certain of these orbits were allowed,

---

† The word 'quantal' has been introduced as an adjective to describe that which pertains to the quantum or to quantum mechanics.

‡ M. Plank, *Ver. d. Deut. Phys. Gesellschaft*, **2**, 237 (1900).

§ N. Bohr, *Phil. Mag.* **26**, 1 476, 857 (1913).

those for which the angular momentum was an integral multiple of $h/2\pi$, h denoting Planck's constant.

In the hands of Niels Bohr in Copenhagen, Arnold Sommerfeld in Munich, and a number of other investigators, a fairly detailed theory of atomic and molecular spectra was developed along these lines;† this was known as the Quantum Theory. The theory was brilliantly successful in many directions and its formulation was the work of a man of genius; nevertheless it became apparent in a very few years that it, too, gave the wrong answer in many cases, and between 1924 and 1927 the completely new system of equations which we call Quantum Mechanics was put forward. In this system Newtonian mechanics is abandoned completely and the quantization of Bohr's theory appears as a consequence of the equations. These developments were carried out under the guidance and inspiration of Niels Bohr, by a large number of investigators—in particular, de Broglie in France,‡ Schrödinger in Switzerland, Heisenberg, Pauli, and Born in Germany,§ and by Dirac in England.‖ The theory was originally presented in two different forms, the 'Matrix Mechanics' and the 'Wave Mechanics'. Both formulations are mathematically equivalent and lead to the same results. In most of this book the methods of Wave Mechanics will be used, because they are most suitable for the applications of the theory to the simpler problems of physics and chemistry.

We shall not attempt in this book to follow closely the historical development of the subject. Before introducing the equations of quantum mechanics, we shall give an outline of the experimental facts which have made the development of these equations necessary. We shall then show how these facts force us to invent new laws of motion quite different from Newton's laws. These laws will then be developed and applied to a number of physical phenomena.

† See, for example, N. Bohr, 'On the quantum theory of line spectra', *D. Kgl. Danske Vid.-Selsk. Skrifter, Nat. Math.* iv, 1 (1918); *Über die Quantentheorie der Linienspektren* (Braunschweig, 1923).

‡ L. de Broglie, *Ann. de Physique*, **3**, 22 (1925).

§ W. Heisenberg, *Zeits. f. Physik*, **33**, 879 (1925); M. Born and P. Jordan, ibid. **34**, 858 (1925); M. Born, P. Jordan, and W. Heisenberg, ibid. **35**, 557 (1926); E. Schrödinger, *Ann. der Physik*, **79**, 361, 489, 734 (1925).

‖ P. A. M. Dirac, *Proc. Roy. Soc.* A, **109**, 642 (1925); **112**, 661 (1926); **113**, 621 (1927); **114**, 243, 710 (1927).

I

THE SCHRÖDINGER EQUATION

1. The wave nature of matter

1.1. *Interaction of matter and radiation*

ONE of the most obvious facts about light is that opaque bodies cast shadows, and that in casting shadows light appears to travel in straight lines. It was this fact which led Sir Isaac Newton to put forward his corpuscular theory of light, according to which energy is conveyed away from a source of light in the form of the kinetic energy of a stream of particles. The reason why the corpuscular theory was abandoned, and replaced by the wave theory, will be familiar to every reader of this book, namely that light shows interference. The interference is shown in its simplest form in Fig. 1. A point source of light S is separated from a screen CD by an opaque screen EF with pin-holes at A and B, SA being equal to SB. The pin-holes will both act as sources of light. If the nature of light

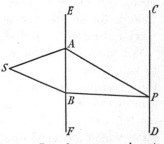

FIG. 1. Interference experiment.

were corpuscular, the illumination on the screen CD from the pin-holes A and B could be added together; thus the illumination at all points on the screen is greater when both holes are open than when one is. Since, however, light is propagated as a wave motion, this is not the case; the two sources reinforce each other at points P such that $PA - PB$ is zero or an integral multiple of a wave-length, but interfere destructively if $PA - PB$ differs from this by a half wave-length, so that the two sources of light spreading from A and B are out of phase.

All direct ways of measuring the wave-length of light, such as the use of the diffraction grating, are based on the interference principle. This is true also of methods for measuring the wave-length of X-rays by crystal spectroscopy.

Maxwell's theory of the electromagnetic field has shown us what it is that oscillates in a light wave. According to this theory, it is the electric vector E, defined as the force that would act on a unit positive electric charge at any point, and the magnetic vector H defined in an analogous way. A plane polarized wave, moving in the z-direction and with its electric vector in the x-direction, will have the form

$$E_x = A \sin 2\pi(\nu t - z/\lambda), \qquad E_y = E_z = 0.$$

$$H_y = A \sin 2\pi(\nu t - z/\lambda), \qquad H_x = H_z = 0.$$

Here ν is the frequency and λ the wave-length; if the wave is in a vacuum the wave velocity is c (= 3×10^{10} cm./sec.), so that

$$\nu\lambda = c.$$

We now know that electromagnetic waves can exist with a great variety of wave-lengths between several kilometres and that of the hardest γ-radiation, less than 10^{-12} cm. Down to values of the order 10^{-12} cm., measurements have been made by methods of crystal spectroscopy, though for shorter wave-lengths there is no direct evidence for the wave-nature of the radiation.

For radiation of the wave-lengths used in radio transmission, that is to say, greater than a few centimetres, analysis based on Maxwell's theory appears completely satisfactory, both as regards the transmission of the waves and their reaction on the receiving aerials.† In the receiving aerials currents are induced; these can be calculated in two ways which are mathematically equivalent; either by considering the electric vector E as being responsible for setting up an electromotive force along the aerial, or the magnetic flux threading the circuit as inducing a current in it.

When we turn to radiation of shorter wave-lengths, that is to say, to light and to X-rays, the position of the wave theory in general and Maxwell's theory in particular is less satisfactory. It appears to be correct when applied to problems of propagation such as reflection, diffraction, and refraction of radiation; in fact, as already emphasized, the facts of diffraction and interference compel the adoption of a wave theory. But it does not correctly describe what happens when light is observed, or more precisely when light gives up its energy to matter. When this happens, phenomena *always* occur which suggest that light consists of a stream of particles rather than a continuous train of waves. An appreciation of this dual nature of light is essential for an understanding of quantum mechanics, and we must consider it in some detail.

Leaving out of consideration the human eye, the most important

† Quantum effects with centimetre waves have, however, been observed, especially connected with nuclear spins. Cf. the report by J. B. M. Kellogg and S. Millman, *Rev. Mod. Phys.* **18**, 323 (1946).

ways in which light and radiations of shorter wave-length are observed and measured are:

1. Photography;
2. Photo-conductivity, or the property that light of suitable wave-length has of making certain solids and liquids conduct;
3. The photo-electric effect, or the property that light and especially ultra-violet light has of releasing electrons from the surfaces of solids or from gas molecules.

Modern research (cf. Chap. VIII) has shown that the primary action of light on photographic emulsions is to make the halide grains photo-conductors; in discussing the quantum nature of light, therefore, it need not be considered separately. The photo-electric effect shows most clearly the properties of light which we wish to emphasize, and this will be discussed first.

What happens when light falls on the surface of a metal or of some other conducting material is briefly as follows: if the *frequency* of the light is too small, there is no emission of electrons. As the frequency is increased, emission begins at a definite frequency ν_0. If the frequency ν is greater than ν_0, electrons will be emitted with kinetic energies less than or equal to a maximum value W_{max} given by

$$W_{max} = h(\nu - \nu_0).$$

h is here Planck's constant. This equation and the experimental facts on which it is based are perhaps the logical basis for the definition of this constant.

These facts show that, when light gives up its energy to matter by ejecting photo-electrons, it behaves as though it were a stream of particles each of energy $h\nu$. The energy $h\nu_0$ will represent the minimum energy necessary to eject an electron from the surface. All this was pointed out by Einstein in 1905; the hypothesis of the quantization of light had already been introduced by Planck to explain the facts about black-body radiation.

The phenomenon of photo-conductivity points in the same direction. All photo-conducting substances show a lower limit ν_0 above which the frequency of the radiation must lie if the effect is to occur. On the basis of Einstein's hypothesis $h\nu_0$ will be the minimum energy that an electron must absorb in order to escape from the molecules or atoms of the solid into a free state in which it can move through it. The nature of this free state need not concern us here and will be discussed in a later chapter. The important thing to notice is that a lower limit of *frequency* exists below which the effect does not occur. The existence of a lower limit is common to all photo-electric and photo-chemical effects and in fact to every mechanism whereby light gives up energy to matter except that of inducing currents in conductors. Here there is no lower limit, as we know from the behaviour of radio waves which induce currents in aerials, the energy of which can be dissipated as heat or absorbed in a receiver. This apparent escape from the quantized nature of light is connected with the existence of free electrons in metals.

We must examine further the nature of these light quanta, and since they move with the velocity c, equal to 3×10^{10} cm./sec., we must make use of the formulae of the Principle of Relativity in discussing their properties. According to this principle, the energy of a particle of mass m moving with velocity v is

$$mc^2 \Big/ \sqrt{\left(1 - \frac{v^2}{c^2}\right)}.$$

For small values of v/c this reduces to $mc^2 + \frac{1}{2}mv^2$; the second term is the familiar kinetic energy, the first represents the energy that would be liberated if the particle were annihilated. Now, from this formula it is apparent at once that since a light quantum moves with velocity c and has finite energy, its mass must be zero. A light quantum therefore must be thought of simply as a little bundle of energy, and when it loses its energy it has no mass or other measurable attribute, and can be considered to cease to exist.

The question arises whether a light quantum can give up part of its energy to matter, or whether it always gives up all or none as in the photo-electric effect. The effects associated with the names of Raman[†] and of Compton[‡] show that it can. We cannot discuss these fully until we have treated the quantization of atomic energy levels; briefly we may say that under certain conditions light after being scattered by gas molecules may have a component with lower frequency than the original. In terms of the quantum hypothesis, part of the energy of each quantum is absorbed by each molecule.

Another formula from the Principle of Relativity is useful, namely that connecting kinetic energy (W) with momentum (p). This is

$$W = c\sqrt{(m^2c^2 + p^2)}.$$

For light quanta, for which m vanishes, this gives

$$W = cp.$$

† C. V. Raman and R. S. Krishnan, *Nature*, **121**, 501 (1928).
‡ A. H. Compton, *Phys. Rev.* **21**, 483 (1923); P. Debye, *Phys. Zeits.* **24**, 161 (1923).

Therefore the momentum of a light quantum is $h\nu/c$. This formula gives an easy way of calculating the pressure of light, since it shows that if light falls on a totally absorbing surface the momentum transmitted is equal to the energy absorbed divided by c. Thus

$$c \times \text{pressure} = \text{energy absorbed per unit area per unit time.}$$

Also the above formula for the momentum of a light quantum has been applied to explain the Compton effect.

A beam of light can thus be described in two ways: (1) as a beam of particles, each of energy W and momentum p; (2) as a wave of frequency ν and wave-length λ. Instead of the wave-length it is often convenient to introduce the wave-number K, equal to the reciprocal of λ,

$$K = 1/\lambda.$$

Like the momentum p, K is a vector; for the wave amplitude can be written

$$\sin 2\pi(K_x x + K_y y + K_z z - \nu t),$$

so the quantity $K_x x + K_y y + K_z z$ is scalar; that is to say, it is independent of the coordinate axes chosen. Thus since (x, y, z) is a vector, so is (K_x, K_y, K_z).

Now since the same beam of light can be described alternatively by two vectors, $\mathbf{p}$ or $\mathbf{K}$, the momentum or the wave-number, it must necessarily be assumed that

$$\mathbf{p} = \text{const.}\,\mathbf{K}. \tag{1}$$

From the formulae already given ($p = h\nu/c, K = 1/\lambda = \nu/c$) it follows that the constant is h.

We may go farther; in the principle of relativity the momentum $\mathbf{p}$ and the energy divided by c form together what is known as a 4-vector; thus $(p_x, p_y, p_z, W/c)$ are components of a vector in the space-time continuum. So are $(K_x, K_y, K_z, \nu/c)$, the four numbers specifying the state of a wave. If the same physical event is to have a particle and a wave description it follows that each component of the one vector must be proportional to the corresponding component of the other. Thus

$$W = h\nu, \qquad \mathbf{p} = h\mathbf{K},$$

where h is some constant. These are equations which we have already established on experimental and theoretical grounds, with h equal to Planck's constant.

This curious dual property of light must now be defined more clearly; if we wish to calculate the *path* of a light beam, through any series of slits or gratings, we must use the wave theory. The wave theory gives us at all points of space a value for the electric and magnetic vectors E and H and predicts that the energy density there will be

$$\frac{E^2+H^2}{8\pi}. \tag{2}$$

But when we come to investigate how light reacts with matter we find that it usually gives up its energy in quanta $h\nu$, and always acts as though it were a stream of particles. Formula (2), in fact, gives only the energy density averaged over a long time in a steady beam. In other words, the average number of light quanta per unit volume in the beam is

$$\frac{1}{h\nu}\frac{E^2+H^2}{8\pi}.$$

In general, whether we are dealing with a steady beam or not, we can say that the *probability* that a light quantum is at a given instant in the volume element $dxdydz$ is

$$\frac{1}{h\nu}\frac{E^2+H^2}{8\pi}\,dxdydz.$$

This dual nature of light was quite unexpected, and was forced on theoretical physics by overwhelming experimental evidence. It has never been 'explained'. On the other hand, it has been found that this dual nature is not confined to light, but is common to electrons, atoms, and in fact all material particles. It has then to be accepted as a fundamental law of nature, on which any scheme of mechanics must be built up.

1.2. *Wave properties of material particles*

The evidence that cathode-rays consist of particles, the electrons, need not be reviewed here. Our whole system of thought about atoms is based on it, as is witnessed by the confidence with which such a statement is made as that the Uranium atom contains 92 extra-nuclear electrons. All the arguments of this book will be based on the assumption that the electron is a particle of mass m and charge e and that it can only be created and destroyed under rather special conditions peculiar to high-voltage laboratories, stellar interiors, and β-active nuclei.

The discovery that beams of electrons, and indeed beams of heavier particles, ions or molecules or neutrons, have wave properties was made between 1927 and 1928, by Davisson and Germer[†] and by G. P. Thomson[‡] for electrons and later by Stern and his collaborators[§] for particles

[†] C. Davisson and L. H. Germer, *Phys. Rev.* **30**, 707 (1927).
[‡] G. P. Thomson, *Proc. Roy. Soc.* A, **117**, 600 (1928).
[§] F. Knauer and O. Stern, *Zeits. f. Physik*, **53**, 786 (1929), I. Estermann and O. Stern, ibid. **61**, 115 (1930).

of atomic mass. The wave effects—at any rate the most striking ones, were shown when electron beams were reflected or scattered by crystalline substances, diffraction phenomena extremely similar to those with X-rays being obtained. These phenomena enabled the wave-length λ of the waves to be determined in terms of the energy W or momentum p of the particles; the latter can of course be determined for charged particles from the accelerating voltage or the deflexion in a magnetic field. The experiments showed that the relation was as follows:

$$\lambda = h/p. \tag{3}$$

This is often written

$$\lambda = h/mv,$$

but (3) is correct even for particles moving with relativistic velocities.[†] It will be noticed that (3) is the same relation as that which holds between the momentum of a light quantum and the wave-length of the corresponding light wave.

The magnitude of the wave-length is of the order 10^{-8} cm. or less for fast electrons, and thus of the order of magnitude of the diameter of any atom.

In a famous and interesting paper published in 1924 before the experimental discovery of the dual nature of electrons, de Broglie[‡] argued that if such dual properties existed, (3) must be true. His argument was the one already put forward in § 1.1; if $\mathbf{K}$, ν are the wave number and frequency of the wave, $\mathbf{p}$, W the momentum and energy of the particle, both form 4-vectors in the space-time continuum. Therefore, since all components of $(\mathbf{K}, \nu)$ must be known if $(\mathbf{p}, W)$ is known and vice versa, we must have

$$\mathbf{p} = h\mathbf{K}, \qquad W = h\nu,$$

where h is some constant. The facts already known about light quanta suggested that the constant would be Planck's constant.

We shall return in § 4 to a consideration of the equation $W = h\nu$.

We see, then, that just as for light quanta, when we wish to calculate the path of a beam of electrons (at any rate through crystals), we have to treat the beam as a wave. The intensity of the wave will be proportional to the density of electrons in the beam; more exactly it gives the probability of finding an electron at some point. However, unlike the position with regard to light, where Maxwell's theory of E and H

---

† For the experimental evidence for this, cf. J. V. Hughes, *Phil. Mag.* **19**, 129 (1935); see also S. C. Curran, ibid. **24**, 953 (1937).

‡ L. de Broglie, *Dissertation* (Masson, Paris, 1924); see also *Phil. Mag.* **47**, 446 (1924); *Ann. de Physique*, **3**, 22 (1925).

already existed, nothing was known about the electron waves. A theory had to be built up from the beginning to fit the facts.

In the literature the wave amplitude is denoted by ψ and is called the wave function. As we have seen, the only way these waves can make their presence felt is by the relation between the wave intensity and the density of electrons. The simplest assumption that we can make is that the density of electrons is proportional to the wave intensity. Since we know nothing *a priori* about these waves, it is simplest to choose the units in which ψ is measured so that the density is *equal* to the wave intensity. Thus

$$|\psi|^2 = \text{number of electrons per unit volume,}$$

or $\quad |\psi|^2\,dxdydz = $ the probability that an electron is in the volume element $dxdydz$.

The wave function ψ is a complex quantity, and may therefore be written

$$\psi = f + ig, \tag{4}$$

where f and g are real functions of position and time. The intensity of the wave, and hence the average number of particles per unit volume at any point, is taken to be equal to the square of the modulus of the wave function, which is written $\psi^*\psi$ or $|\psi|^2$ and defined by

$$\psi^*\psi = |\psi|^2 = f^2 + g^2.$$

It is often a stumbling-block to the beginner in this subject that a physical quantity, the wave function, should be represented by a complex function. The reason is as follows. We know *a priori* nothing about the wave function, but we should expect, by analogy with the case of light waves, that the type of expression which in other wave systems represents the energy density would in this case give the particle density. But the energy density in any wave system is always given by the sum of the square of *two* independent functions whose magnitudes define the state of the wave. For a light wave they are E and H and the energy density is $(E^2 + H^2)/8\pi$. For elastic waves they are the displacement and velocity of the medium. Thus for the waves associated with an electron or other material particles, it is reasonable to assume that the state of the wave is defined by two quantities f and g at any point, and it is convenient to combine them into a single function ψ by means of equation (4).

It may be noted that Maxwell's equations for the electromagnetic field in free space may be treated in the same way; the equations are

$$-c\,\mathrm{curl}\,E = \frac{\partial H}{\partial t}, \qquad c\,\mathrm{curl}\,H = \frac{\partial E}{\partial t},$$

and if ψ is written for $E+iH$, both equations become

$$c \operatorname{curl} \psi = i \frac{\partial \psi}{\partial t}.$$

It will be convenient at this stage to make a further assumption about the form of a plane wave. A plane wave travelling, say, along the x-axis has, for any type of wave motion, the form

$$A \sin 2\pi(Kx - \nu t + \epsilon),$$

where K is the wave number and ν the frequency. In a plane polarized light wave E and H are in phase; thus the energy density is proportional to

$$\sin^2 2\pi(Kx - \nu t + \epsilon)$$

and fluctuates with time at any point. There is no reason to think that any such fluctuation occurs in the wave associated with an electron; it would in fact be difficult to understand what physical significance could be ascribed to a rapid fluctuation of the probability that an electron would be found at a certain point. It is therefore reasonable to suppose that f and g are 90° out of phase, so that

$$f = A \cos 2\pi(Kx - \nu t),$$
$$g = A \sin 2\pi(Kx - \nu t),$$

and $$f^2 + g^2 = A^2,$$

which keeps a steady value independent of time. Making use of the complex function ψ we see that a plane wave is represented by

$$\psi = A e^{2\pi i(Kx - \nu t)}.$$

We shall represent a wave going in the other direction by

$$\psi = A e^{2\pi i(-Kx - \nu t)}.$$

In the remainder of this book we shall follow the accepted convention and use always the complex wave function ψ, and shall not refer again to the real and imaginary parts, f and g.

1.3. *The connexion with Newtonian mechanics*

We have seen that when we wish to calculate the path of a beam of electrons or of any other material particles, we must postulate the existence of a train of waves ψ of wave-length h/p; the intensity $|\psi|^2$ gives us the average number of electrons per unit volume in any part of the wave. The necessity for this procedure is shown by the behaviour of electrons in passing through crystals, where scattering centres (the atoms) have diameters comparable with the wave-length. In the absence of crystal diffraction, however, Newton's Laws of Motion have been entirely successful in accounting for the behaviour of beams of charged particles, in particular their deflexion by electric and magnetic fields. It would be very unsatisfactory if we had to assume that Newton's laws were valid in the latter case and wave mechanics in the former. Actually, wave mechanics is perfectly general and includes Newtonian mechanics as a special case. In this section we shall show, for the case of deflexion of a beam of electrons by an electric field, that wave mechanics gives the same result as classical Newtonian mechanics so long as the field remains sensibly constant over the whole width of the beam. The case of magnetic fields is treated in §8.

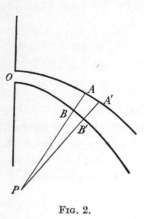

Fig. 2.

The electron beam is supposed to enter the field at O in Fig. 2, where the kinetic energy is W. The field is supposed to be conservative, so that at any point of space a potential energy function $V(x,y,z)$ can be defined, equal to the work done to take the electron from O to the point (x,y,z) considered. The kinetic energy there will be

$$W - V(x,y,z).$$

From the wave point of view the wave-length of the de Broglie waves must be h/p. Since at any point (x,y,z)

$$p^2 = 2m(W-V),$$

it follows that the wave-length λ at that point is given by

$$h/\sqrt{\{2m(W-V)\}}. \tag{5}$$

The wave-length therefore varies continuously from point to point, and therefore the problem of determining the path of the beam is that of determining the path in a medium of continuously varying refractive index. This can be done quite generally, for any type of wave motion, as follows:

We require at each point along the path of the beam the curvature of the beam due to the refraction. In Fig. 2 let AB, $A'B'$ be lines drawn along the intersection of two successive wave fronts with the plane of the paper. They will meet at P, the centre of curvature of the beam.

If λ is the wave-length at any point, say at BB', then the wave-length AA' on the other side of the beam may be written

$$\lambda + \frac{\partial \lambda}{\partial n}t,$$

where t is the width AB of the beam and $\partial/\partial n$ denotes differentiation along BA. Also denoting PB by R, PA by $R+t$, we have from the similar triangles PBB', PAA'

$$\frac{R+t}{R} = \left(\lambda + \frac{\partial \lambda}{\partial n}t\right)\Big/\lambda,$$

or

$$\frac{1}{R} = \frac{1}{\lambda}\frac{\partial \lambda}{\partial n}. \tag{6}$$

This formula gives the radius of curvature R of the beam in terms of the rate of change of λ, or in other words, the rate of change of the refractive index.

In our case, using formula (5) for the wave-length, (6) gives

$$\frac{1}{R} = \frac{1}{2(W-V)}\frac{\partial V}{\partial n}. \tag{7}$$

But this is exactly the formula that we should obtain using Newtonian mechanics. This may be seen as follows: according to Newtonian mechanics, the curvature of the orbit of the particles in the beam can be obtained by equating the centrifugal force mv^2/R to the force normal to the trajectory exerted by the field on the particles. This is equal to $\partial F/\partial n$. We have therefore

$$\frac{mv^2}{R} = \frac{\partial V}{\partial n}.$$

But since mv^2 is equal to $2(W-V)$, this is identical with (7).

So long, therefore, as the field remains sensibly constant across the width of the beam, a calculation of the path according to the principles of wave mechanics will give the same result as a calculation according to Newtonian mechanics.

A beam must necessarily have a width large compared with the wave-length. It is not difficult to see, therefore, that the condition for the applicability of Newtonian mechanics is that the kinetic energy of the particles should change by only a small proportion in a distance comparable with a wave-length. If this condition is not fulfilled diffraction effects characteristic of wave motion will occur. These are discussed in the next sections.

2. The wave equation of Schrödinger

In this section we shall derive Schrödinger's equation for the wave function ψ associated with a particle or beam of particles, all with the same energy, moving in an electrostatic or other field of force. The total energy of each particle will be denoted by W, and its potential energy in the field of force by $V(x, y, z)$, as in the last section. Therefore we have

kinetic energy of each particle $= W - V(x, y, z)$.

Now a beam of waves moving in either direction along the z-axis has the form

$$\psi = A e^{2\pi i(\pm Kz - vt)},$$

and both expressions for ψ satisfy the equation

$$\frac{d^2\psi}{dz^2} + 4\pi^2 K^2 \psi = 0. \tag{8}$$

Conversely, equation (8) means that ψ has the form of a wave of wave-number K moving in one direction or other along the z-axis, or else that ψ is given by the superposition of two such waves

$$\psi = [A e^{2\pi i Kz} + B e^{-2\pi i Kz}] e^{-2\pi i vt}.$$

It will be remembered (cf. p. 9) that the time factor is always of the form $e^{-2\pi i vt}$. More generally, a wave of wave-number K moving in the direction given by the direction cosines (l, m, n) will have the form

$$\psi = A e^{2\pi i K(lx + my + nz) - 2\pi i vt}. \tag{9}$$

Remembering that $l^2 + m^2 + n^2 = 1$, it will easily be verified that (9) satisfies the equation

$$\nabla^2 \psi + 4\pi^2 K^2 \psi = 0, \tag{10}$$

where ∇^2 denotes the operator

$$\nabla^2 = \frac{\partial^2}{\partial x^2} + \frac{\partial^2}{\partial y^2} + \frac{\partial^2}{\partial z^2}.$$

Conversely, the most general solution of (10) can be formed by the superposition of any number of waves of the type (9), with the same wave-length but different directions and amplitudes. Equation (10), therefore, when applied to a wave function, means simply that the wave-length is $1/K$.

Now we know from direct experiment that the relation between the kinetic energy $W - V$ of a particle and the wave-number K is

$$K^2 = 2m(W - V)/h^2. \tag{11}$$

If we substitute for K in equation (10) we obtain the well-known equation of Schrödinger†

$$\nabla^2\psi + \frac{8\pi^2 m}{h^2}(W-V)\psi = 0. \tag{12}$$

If V is constant, or varying very slowly from place to place, this expresses nothing more than what we already know about the wave function. It is, however, a new assumption that ψ will satisfy this equation even when significant changes in V occur in distances comparable with λ, as, for example, within the atom. This assumption will be made; it is justified first because of its simplicity, but ultimately because it gives results in agreement with experiment.

In what follows we shall write this equation in the form

$$\nabla^2\psi + \frac{2m}{\hbar^2}(W-V)\psi = 0 \quad (\hbar = h/2\pi).$$

3. Motion of electrons in one dimension

In this and in the next section we shall discuss some simple problems which illustrate the conditions under which Newtonian and wave mechanics give different results, and what the nature of the difference is.

In particular, our analysis shows that when particles move in fields such that $W-V$ changes appreciably in a distance comparable with a wave-length, the results differ from classical mechanics. To show this we consider the extreme case of a discontinuous 'potential jump', where the kinetic energy of the particles changes discontinuously. This may be thought of as the limiting form of a very strong field acting over a very short distance. We shall show that if a beam of particles is incident on a potential jump, some are reflected and some transmitted. According to Newtonian mechanics they would be all transmitted or all reflected, according as to whether the height of the jump V_0 was greater or less than the kinetic energy W.

3.1. The effect of potential jumps on the motion of an electron

We consider first the effect of a potential jump on the motion of an electron, i.e. we consider the solutions of the one-dimensional Schrödinger equation when the potential function is given by

$$V(x) = \begin{cases} V_0 & (x < 0), \\ V_1 & (x > 0). \end{cases}$$

† E. Schrödinger, *Ann. der Physik*, **79**, 361 (1926). See also E. Schrödinger, *Collected Papers on Wave Mechanics* (London, 1928).

There are then two cases to consider according as $V_1 \gtrless W$, where W is the energy of the electron.

CASE (i). $V_1 < W$. The differential equations governing the motion of the particle are then

$$\frac{d^2\psi}{dx^2} + \alpha^2\psi = 0 \quad (x < 0),$$

$$\frac{d^2\psi}{dx^2} + \beta^2\psi = 0 \quad (x > 0),$$

where $\qquad \alpha^2 = \frac{2m}{\hbar^2}(W - V_0), \qquad \beta^2 = \frac{2m}{\hbar^2}(W - V_1).$

The wave function to the left of the potential step may be taken as

$$\psi = (e^{i\alpha x} + Ae^{-i\alpha x})e^{-2\pi i\nu t} \quad (x < 0),$$

consisting of an incident wave $e^{i(\alpha x - 2\pi\nu t)}$ of unit amplitude and a reflected wave of unknown amplitude A. When $x > 0$ we have a solution

$$\psi = Be^{i\beta x - 2\pi i\nu t},$$

representing a wave transmitted through the potential jump.

The fact that there is a finite discontinuity in the potential function V occurring in the Schrödinger equation means that ψ'' suffers a finite discontinuity at $x = 0$. The increase in ψ' in crossing the origin is then

$$\lim_{\epsilon \to 0} \int_{-\epsilon}^{\epsilon} \psi'' \, dx = \lim_{\epsilon \to 0} \epsilon\{\psi''(-\epsilon) + \psi''(\epsilon)\} = 0,$$

so that ψ, ψ' are continuous at $x = 0$. Thus there are two equations

$$1 + A = B,$$

$$\alpha(1 - A) = \beta B$$

for the determination of the constants A and B. It follows immediately that

$$A = \frac{\alpha - \beta}{\beta + \alpha}, \qquad B = \frac{2\alpha}{\beta + \alpha}.$$

Now the velocity of the particles in the incident and the reflected beam is

$$v = \left\{\frac{2(W - V_0)}{m}\right\}^{\frac{1}{2}} = \frac{\alpha\hbar}{m},$$

so that in an incident beam of unit amplitude the number of electrons crossing unit area in unit time is $\alpha\hbar/m = N_i$. The number of particles in the reflected beam is

$$N_r = \frac{\alpha\hbar}{m} AA^* = \frac{\alpha\hbar}{m}\left(\frac{\beta - \alpha}{\beta + \alpha}\right)^2 = N_i\left(\frac{v' - v}{v' + v}\right)^2,$$

where $v' = \beta \hbar/m$ is the velocity of the transmitted beam. Similarly the number of electrons in the transmitted beam is

$$N_t = \frac{\beta \hbar}{m} BB^* = \frac{\beta \hbar}{m}\left(\frac{2\alpha}{\beta+\alpha}\right)^2 = N_i \frac{4vv'}{(v'+v)^2}.$$

From these expressions it follows immediately that

$$N_i = N_r + N_t,$$

so that, as we would expect, the total number of particles is constant.

This analysis shows the fundamental difference between Newtonian and wave mechanics. According to Newtonian mechanics, it would of course follow that $N_t = 1$.

CASE (ii). $V_1 > W$. In this case the equation for the wave-function ψ in the region $x > 0$ is

$$\frac{d^2\psi}{dx^2} = \gamma^2\psi,$$

where $\hbar^2\gamma^2 = 2m(V_1 - W)$; for the transmitted wave we then take the exponentially decreasing solution

$$\psi = Be^{-\gamma x - 2\pi i \nu t}. \tag{13}$$

The boundary conditions at $x = 0$ give

$$1 + A = B, \qquad i\alpha(1 - A) = -\gamma B.$$

Solving for A we find
$$A = \frac{\alpha - i\gamma}{\alpha + i\gamma},$$

so that
$$AA^* = 1,$$

showing that the amplitude of the reflected wave is equal to the amplitude of the incident wave. Thus all the electrons are reflected. If the theory had not predicted this it would have needed revision.

3.2. The tunnel effect

We have seen in the last section that the wave function of a beam of electrons reflected by a potential jump does not vanish at the point $x = 0$ where, according to the Newtonian interpretation, the electrons should be reflected. From this point onwards, according to the formula (13), the wave function decays rapidly and is proportional to $e^{-\gamma x}$.

We shall now consider the incidence of a beam of electrons upon a 'potential barrier' bounded by sharp potential jumps. We shall take for the potential energy of the particles

$$V(x) = \begin{cases} 0 & (x < 0), \\ V_0 & (0 < x < a), \\ 0 & (x > a), \end{cases}$$

and shall suppose that the kinetic energy W is less than V_0. The Schrödinger equation then assumes the form

$$\psi'' + \alpha^2\psi = 0 \quad (x < 0, x > a), \qquad \psi'' = \gamma^2\psi \quad (0 < x < a),$$

where $\alpha\hbar = \sqrt{(2mW)}$, $\gamma\hbar = \sqrt{\{2m(V_1 - W)\}}$. Then, just as before, the solution of the wave equation for $x < 0$ will be taken to consist of an incident and reflected wave

$$\psi = (e^{i\alpha x} + Ae^{-i\alpha x})e^{-2\pi i\nu t},$$

and the solution for $x > a$, a transmitted wave

$$\psi = Be^{i\alpha x - 2\pi i\nu t}.$$

Within the potential barrier, for $0 < x < a$, the general solution is

$$\psi = (Ce^{\gamma x} + De^{-\gamma x})e^{-2\pi i\nu t}.$$

The boundary conditions are as before that ψ and ψ' shall be continuous; these conditions at $x = 0$ give

$$1 + A = C + D, \qquad i\alpha(1 - A) = \gamma(C - D),$$

and at $x = a$

$$Ce^{\gamma a} + De^{-\gamma a} = Be^{i\alpha a},$$

$$\gamma(Ce^{\gamma a} - De^{-\gamma a}) = ia Be^{i\alpha a}.$$

Eliminating A, C, D from these equations we obtain

$$B = 2 \bigg/ \left[2\cosh\gamma a + i\left(\frac{\gamma}{\alpha} - \frac{\alpha}{\gamma}\right)\sinh\gamma a \right].$$

If we define as *transmission coefficient*, or transparency, T, the ratio of the number of electrons crossing unit area per unit time in the incident and transmitted beams, we have

$$T = BB^* = 4 \bigg/ \left[4\cosh^2\gamma a + \left(\frac{\gamma}{\alpha} - \frac{\alpha}{\gamma}\right)^2\sinh^2\gamma a \right].$$

If γa is large both $\cosh\gamma a$ and $\sinh\gamma a$ are approximately equal to $\frac{1}{2}e^{\gamma a}$ and the transparency of the potential barrier becomes

$$T = 4e^{-2\gamma a} \bigg/ \left[1 + \frac{1}{4}\left(\frac{\gamma}{\alpha} - \frac{\alpha}{\gamma}\right) \right].$$

In most cases the amplitude of the wave which 'penetrates' the 'potential barrier' between $x = 0$ and $x = a$ will be very small. Nevertheless these arguments show that, according to wave mechanics, if a beam of electrons is incident on a potential barrier of the type described, a small proportion of the total current will penetrate through it. This prediction of wave mechanics has been termed the 'tunnel effect'.

The tunnel effect has several important applications. It applies of course to protons and to heavier particles as well as to electrons, but for heavy particles the proportion that will go through potential barriers of atomic dimensions is negligible and the tunnel effect is unimportant. For protons and α-particles it is, however, of great importance in the theory of the nucleus and of radioactivity.† Electrons will in practice pass freely through potential barriers a few electron volts high and of

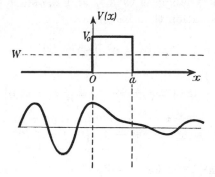

FIG. 3 a. The rectangular barrier.

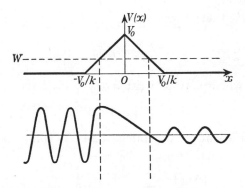

FIG. 3 b. The triangular barrier.

thickness up to about ten atomic diameters. This is the reason why an electric current will flow between two metals in contact, in spite of the layers of oxide or grease with which a metal surface is normally contaminated, and the reason why electrons can pass between metallic electrodes and ions in solution.

The wave equation for a triangular barrier can also be solved

† G. Gamow, *Structure of Atomic Nuclei*, chap. v (Oxford, 1937).

exactly. Consider a triangular barrier defined by the potential function (Fig. 3 b)

$$V = \begin{cases} 0 & (x < -V_0/k) \\ V_0 + kx & (-V_0/k < x < 0) \\ V_0 - kx & (0 < x < V_0/k) \\ 0 & (x > V_0/k). \end{cases}$$

The altitude of the triangle is thus V_0 and the slope of the sides $\pm k$. The Schrödinger equation then becomes

$$\psi'' + \alpha^2 \psi = 0 \quad \left(|x| \geqslant \frac{V_0}{k}\right) \tag{14a}$$

$$\psi'' - (\beta^2 + 2\kappa x)\psi = 0 \quad \left(-\frac{V_0}{k} \leqslant x \leqslant 0\right) \tag{14b}$$

$$\psi'' - (\beta^2 - 2\kappa x)\psi = 0 \quad \left(0 \leqslant x \leqslant \frac{V_0}{k}\right), \tag{14c}$$

where $\alpha^2 = 2mW/\hbar^2$, $\beta^2 = 2m(V_0 - W)/\hbar^2$, and $\kappa = mk/\hbar^2$.

If we substitute $\quad \xi = (2\kappa)^{\frac{1}{3}}(x + \beta^2/2\kappa)$

in equation (14 b) then it becomes

$$\frac{d^2\psi}{d\xi^2} = \xi\psi,$$

the solution of which may be written†

$$\psi = c_1 \mathrm{Ai}(\xi) + c_2 \mathrm{Bi}(\xi),$$

where $\mathrm{Ai}(\xi)$, $\mathrm{Bi}(\xi)$ are the Airy integral and its companion function

$$\mathrm{Ai}(\xi) = \frac{1}{\pi} \int_0^\infty \cos(\xi z + \tfrac{1}{3}z^3) \, dz,$$

$$\mathrm{Bi}(\xi) = \frac{1}{\pi} \int_0^\infty \{e^{z\xi - \frac{1}{3}z^3} + \sin(z\xi + \tfrac{1}{3}z^3)\} \, dz.$$

Similarly the substitution

$$\eta = (2\kappa)^{\frac{1}{3}}\left(-x + \frac{\beta^2}{2\kappa}\right)$$

† H. Jeffreys and B. S. Jeffreys, *Methods of Mathematical Physics*, 447 (Cambridge, 1946).

reduces the equation (14 c) to the same form. We may then write for
the wave function

$$\psi = e^{i\alpha x} + A e^{-i\alpha x} \qquad \left(x < -\frac{V_0}{k} \right)$$

$$\psi = C \operatorname{Ai}(\xi) + D \operatorname{Bi}(\xi) \qquad \left(-\frac{V_0}{k} \leqslant x < 0 \right)$$

$$\psi = E \operatorname{Ai}(\eta) + F \operatorname{Bi}(\eta) \qquad \left(0 \leqslant x < \frac{V_0}{k} \right)$$

$$\psi = B e^{i\alpha x} \qquad \left(x > \frac{V_0}{k} \right).$$

If we apply the conditions that ψ and ψ' are continuous at $x = \pm V_0/k$
and at $x = 0$, we obtain six equations for the six constants A, B, C,
D, E, F. Solving these equations we obtain an expression for B in
terms of the Airy integrals and companion functions with arguments
$(\beta^3/2\kappa)^{\frac{2}{3}}$ and $-(\alpha^3/2\kappa)^{\frac{2}{3}}$. If κ is small in comparison with α^3 and β^3 we
can replace the Airy integrals by their asymptotic expansions†

$$\operatorname{Ai}(z) \sim \frac{1}{2\sqrt{\pi}} z^{-\frac{1}{4}} \exp(-\tfrac{2}{3}z^{\frac{3}{2}}), \quad \operatorname{Bi}(z) \sim \frac{1}{\sqrt{\pi}} z^{+\frac{1}{4}} \exp(\tfrac{2}{3}z^{\frac{3}{2}})$$

to obtain finally $T = BB^* = \exp(-4\beta^3/3\kappa)$

for the transparency of the triangular barrier. If we introduce the
width l of the barrier at the height of penetration, so that

$$\frac{l}{2V_0/k} = \frac{V_0 - W}{V},$$

we have

$$l = \frac{2(V_0 - W)}{k} = \frac{\beta^2}{\kappa},$$

and the formula for the transparency becomes

$$T = \exp(-\tfrac{4}{3}\beta l). \qquad (15)$$

3.3. The WKB method

A solution of the Schrödinger equation

$$\frac{d^2\psi}{dx^2} + \frac{2m}{\hbar^2}(W - V)\psi = 0$$

appropriate to the case where $W - V$ is everywhere positive and where
$W - V$ changes by a small amount in a distance comparable with the
wave-length $h\{2m(W-V)\}^{-\frac{1}{2}}$ can be obtained using a formula due

† H. and B. S. Jeffreys, loc. cit., p. 476.

originally to Jeffreys.† The Schrödinger equation may be written in the form
$$\psi'' + f(x)\psi = 0,$$

with $f(x) = 2m(W-V)/\hbar^2$ a slowly varying function of x. If we write the solution of this equation in the form

$$\psi = \exp i\alpha(x),$$

then in the case where $f(x)$ is a constant $\alpha(x)$ is simply $f^{\frac{1}{2}}x$ or $\int_0^x f^{\frac{1}{2}}\,dx$. If f is not a constant, then α satisfies the differential equation

$$i\alpha'' - \alpha'^2 + f = 0.$$

If we assume that α is also a slowly varying function of x so that

$$\alpha'' \ll \alpha'^2, \tag{16}$$

then we have
$$\alpha = \pm \int_{x_0}^x f^{\frac{1}{2}}\,dx.$$

For a second approximation we substitute this solution in the term $i\alpha''$ in the differential equation for α and obtain

$$\alpha'^2 = f \pm i\frac{d}{dx}f^{\frac{1}{2}}.$$

Extracting the square root and using the fact that f' is small in comparison with f we obtain the equation

$$\alpha' = \pm f^{\frac{1}{2}} + \frac{1}{2}if^{-\frac{1}{2}}\frac{d}{dx}(f^{\frac{1}{2}}),$$

which may be integrated to give

$$\alpha = \pm \int_{x_0}^x f^{\frac{1}{2}}\,dx + \frac{1}{2}i\log f^{\frac{1}{2}},$$

giving
$$\psi = Cf^{-\frac{1}{4}}\exp\left(\pm i\int_{x_0}^x f^{\frac{1}{2}}\,dx\right), \tag{17}$$

where C is a constant.

This solution is of course valid only in those regions for which the condition (16) is satisfied. Using the first approximation for α we see that this condition is equivalent to

$$\left|\frac{d}{dx}\left(\frac{1}{\alpha'}\right)\right| = \left|\frac{d}{dx}(f^{-\frac{1}{2}})\right| \ll 1.$$

† H. Jeffreys, *Proc. Lond. Math. Soc.* (2), **23**, 428–36 (1924); *Phil. Mag.* **33**, 451–6 (1942).

According to equation (17) the total number N of electrons crossing unit area in unit time is

$$N = \psi\psi^* v = CC^* f^{-\frac{1}{2}}\{2m(W-V)\}^{\frac{1}{2}} = CC^*,$$

which is a constant, as it ought to be.

In the preceding analysis it was assumed that the function $f(x)$ was positive in the range considered. If $f(x) < 0$ we find that the solution can be written in the form

$$\psi = (-f)^{-\frac{1}{4}}\exp\left(\pm\int_{x_0}^{x}(-f)^{\frac{1}{2}}dx\right).$$

Jeffreys also gives formulae for connecting up solutions at a zero of the function $f(x)$, which we may take to be at $x = x_0$. Suppose for definiteness that

$$f(x) < 0, \quad x > x_0; \qquad f(x) > 0, \quad x < x_0,$$

then the connecting formulae can be written as

$$(f)^{-\frac{1}{4}}\exp[\pm i(L+\tfrac{1}{4}\pi)] \longleftrightarrow (-f)^{-\frac{1}{4}}[\exp M \pm \tfrac{1}{2}i\exp(-M)], \qquad (18)$$

where

$$M = \int_{x_0}^{x}(-f)^{\frac{1}{2}}dx, \qquad L = \int_{x}^{x_0}f^{\frac{1}{2}}dx.$$

This method of approximating to the solutions of a second-order linear equation was first applied to Schrödinger's equation by Wentzel,[†] Kramers,[‡] and Brillouin[§] and is known usually as the WKB method. Higher approximations may be obtained by writing the solution of the wave equation in the form

$$\psi = \exp\left\{\frac{i}{\hbar}\int_{x_0}^{x}\chi\,dx\right\},$$

where χ is a power series in $(\hbar/i)$,

$$\chi = \sum_{m=0}^{\infty}\left(\frac{\hbar}{i}\right)^{m}\chi_m$$

with coefficients χ_m which are functions of x. By substituting in the differential equation and equating powers of $\hbar$ it is found that

$$\chi_0 = \{2m(W-V)\}^{\frac{1}{2}}, \qquad \chi_1 = -\frac{1}{2}\frac{\chi_0'}{\chi_0} = \frac{V'}{4(W-V')}$$

† G. Wentzel, *Zeits. f. Physik*, **38**, 518–29 (1926).
‡ H. A. Kramers, ibid. **39**, 828–40 (1926).
§ L. Brillouin, *Comptes rendus*, **183**, 24–6 (1926).

in agreement with the formula (17), and that

$$\chi_2 = -\frac{\chi_1^2 + \chi_1'}{2\chi_0} = -\frac{5V'^2}{32(2m)^{\frac{1}{2}}(W-V)^{\frac{5}{2}}} - \frac{V''}{8(2m)^{\frac{1}{2}}(W-V)^{\frac{3}{2}}},$$

and similarly for χ_3, χ_4,... to any desired degree of accuracy.

A rigorous treatment of this method of approximation has been given recently by Kemble[†] and Titchmarsh.[‡]

The condition (16) for the validity of this method is that

$$\frac{d}{dx}\left\{\frac{2m}{\hbar^2}(V-W)\right\}^{-\frac{1}{2}} \ll 1. \tag{19}$$

A further condition is that in the neighbourhood of a zero $x = x_1$ of $V - W$, the function $V'(x)(x-x_1)$ shall be a good approximation to $V - W$.

3.4. *The transparency of potential barriers by WKB method*

In the theory of α-decay it is of interest to study the motion of a particle in a field whose potential is of the form shown in Fig. 4.[§]

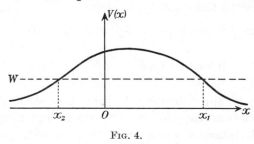

Fig. 4.

From the formula (17) the solution representing a wave going from left to right in the region $x > x_1$ is

$$\psi_3 = \left\{\frac{2m}{\hbar^2}(W-V)\right\}^{-\frac{1}{4}}\exp\left[i\int_{x_2}^{x}\left\{\frac{2m}{\hbar^2}(W-V)\right\}^{\frac{1}{2}}dx\right].$$

From the connexion formula (18) it follows that the wave function for the region $x_1 < x < x_2$ which connects up with ψ_3 at $x = x_2$ is

$$\psi_2 = e^{-\frac{1}{4}i\pi}\left\{\frac{2m}{\hbar^2}(V-W)\right\}^{-\frac{1}{4}}\{e^{M_2}+\tfrac{1}{2}ie^{-M_2}\},$$

where

$$M_2 = \int_{x}^{x_2}\left\{\frac{2m}{\hbar^2}(V-W)\right\}^{\frac{1}{2}}dx.$$

† E. C. Kemble, *Phys. Rev.* **48**, 549 (1935).

‡ E. C. Titchmarsh, *Eigenfunction Expansions associated with Second-order Differential Equations*, chap. viii (Oxford, 1946).

§ G. Gamow, *Zeits. f. Physik*, **51**, 204 (1928); E. Condon and R. W. Gurney, *Phys. Rev.* **33**, 127 (1929).

Writing
$$M_2 = \left(\int_{x_1}^{x_2} - \int_{x_1}^{x} \right) \left\{ \frac{2m}{\hbar^2}(V-W) \right\}^{\frac{1}{2}} dx = A - M_1$$

we may put the expression for ψ_2 in the form

$$\psi_2 = e^{-\frac{1}{4}i\pi} \left\{ \frac{2m}{\hbar^2}(V-W) \right\}^{-\frac{1}{4}} \{ e^{A-M_1} + \tfrac{1}{2} i e^{-A+M_1} \}.$$

The solution joining this at $x = x_1$ is

$$\psi_1 = \left\{ \frac{2m}{\hbar^2}(W-V) \right\}^{-\frac{1}{4}} \{ e^{-iL_1}(e^A + \tfrac{1}{4}e^{-A}) - i e^{iL_1}(e^A - \tfrac{1}{4}e^{-A}) \},$$

where
$$L_1 = \int_{x}^{x_1} \left\{ \frac{2m}{\hbar^2}(W-V) \right\}^{\frac{1}{2}} dx.$$

The wave function ψ_1 represents an incident wave

$$\psi_i = -i \left\{ \frac{2m}{\hbar^2}(W-V) \right\}^{-\frac{1}{4}} (e^A - \tfrac{1}{4}e^{-A}) e^{iL_1}$$

and a reflected wave ψ_r; the wave function ψ_3 represents the wave transmitted through the potential barrier. The transparency of the barrier measured as the ratio of the current density on either side is

$$T = v_3 \psi_3 \psi_0^* / v_1 \psi_i \psi_i^* = (e^A - \tfrac{1}{4}e^{-A})^{-2}.$$

If $e^A \gg e^{-A}$, as in the case of a high wide barrier, then

$$T = \exp\left[-2 \int_{x_1}^{x_2} \left\{ \frac{2m}{\hbar^2}(V-W) \right\}^{\frac{1}{2}} dx \right]. \tag{20}$$

This differs slightly from a formula given by Gamow,[†] who calculates not the ratio of current densities but that of probability densities. The derivation given here is due to B. Jeffreys.[‡]

For a triangular barrier of the type considered in § 3.2 we have from (20)

$$T = \exp\left[-2 \int_{-\frac{1}{2}l}^{0} \left\{ \frac{2mk}{\hbar^2}(\tfrac{1}{2}l+x) \right\}^{\frac{1}{2}} - 2 \int_{0}^{\frac{1}{2}l} \left\{ \frac{2mk}{\hbar^2}(\tfrac{1}{2}l-x) \right\}^{\frac{1}{2}} dx \right],$$

where
$$l = 2(V_0 - W)/k = \beta^2/\kappa.$$

Thus
$$T = \exp\left\{ -\frac{8}{3} \left(\frac{2mk}{\hbar^2} \right)^{\frac{1}{2}} (\tfrac{1}{2}l)^{\frac{3}{2}} \right\} = \exp(-\tfrac{4}{3}\beta l),$$

in agreement with equation (15).

A comprehensive account of the determination of the transparency of a potential barrier is given in Kemble's book.[§] The application of

† G. Gamow, *Structure of Atomic Nuclei*, p. 94, equation (25) (Oxford, 1937).

‡ B. Jeffreys, *Proc. Camb. Phil. Soc.* **38**, 401 (1942).

§ E. C. Kemble, *Fundamental Principles of Quantum Mechanics* (New York, 1937).

the results of calculations of this type to the theory of α-decay is given in the monograph by Gamow, but the treatment of barrier problems given there is unsatisfactory since the asymptotic expansions are employed at points where they become infinite.

The penetration of particles into potential barriers in several dimensions has been considered by Kapur and Peierls.†

4. Frequency and group velocity of the waves associated with material particles

For any kind of wave motion there exists a definite relation between the frequency ν and the wave-length λ. For light waves in a vacuum, for instance, this relation is

$$\nu = c/\lambda.$$

In general we may write $\qquad \nu = v/\lambda,$

where v is the 'wave velocity', which may be a constant, or may be itself a function of the frequency, as is the case for light waves in a dispersive medium.

The wave velocity is the velocity with which the crest of each wave travels. The group velocity is the velocity of a wave pulse or of a wave front. For instance, if a stone is dropped into water, the front of the disturbance travels out with the group velocity. The time taken for a sound to reach our ears is equal to the distance of the source divided by the group velocity. All direct ways of measuring the velocity of light give this quantity, and it is also the speed with which radar pulses are propagated.

The group and wave velocities are equal only if the wave velocity is independent of frequency (as for light in a vacuum). In general the formula for the group velocity V_G is‡

$$V_G = \frac{d\nu}{d(1/\lambda)} = -\lambda^2 \frac{d\nu}{d\lambda}.$$

In terms of our usual notation, $K = 1/\lambda$

$$V_G = \frac{d\nu}{dK}. \qquad (21)$$

Since $\nu = vK$ this gives $\qquad V_G = v + K\frac{dv}{dK}.$

Formula (21) is most easily proved by considering the velocity of

† P. L. Kapur and R. Peierls, *Proc. Roy. Soc.* A, **163**, 606 (1937).

‡ C. A. Coulson, *Waves*, p. 132 (Edinburgh, 1941).

the wave groups formed when two wave trains of nearly equal frequency are superimposed. For let these two wave trains have the amplitudes

$$A \sin 2\pi(Kx - \nu t)$$

and $$A \sin 2\pi(K'x - \nu't).$$

On adding these we obtain

$$2A \sin 2\pi \left(\frac{K+K'}{2}x - \frac{\nu+\nu'}{2}t \right) \cos 2\pi \left(\frac{K-K'}{2}x - \frac{\nu-\nu'}{2}t \right).$$

If K, K' are nearly equal this represents a train of wave groups; each wave moves with the wave velocity $(\nu+\nu')/(K+K')$, but each group moves with the velocity

$$\frac{\nu-\nu'}{K-K'},$$

which, if ν and ν' are nearly equal, tends to $d\nu/dK$.

The same formula can be shown to give the velocity of a single wave pulse.

The application of the concept of group velocity to wave mechanics is as follows: suppose that a beam of particles is incident with velocity V on a screen, in which there is a hole which can be closed by a shutter. The shutter is closed to begin with, then opened for a time t_0, and then closed again. Obviously a beam of length Vt_0 will pass through the hole and travel as a whole with velocity V. According to the concepts of wave mechanics, how-

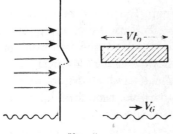

Fig. 5.

ever, we must describe the whole phenomenon in terms of the wave function ψ. A continuous train of waves falls on the screen; when the shutter is opened a train of waves of limited length, that is to say a wave group or wave packet passes through, and as usual the intensity of the wave is equal to the density of electrons in the beam. This wave group must travel with the group velocity of the waves; thus if wave mechanics is to give a correct description of observed phenomena, the group velocity of the waves must be equal to the actual velocity of the particles that they represent.

Up to the present in this book, in considering steady beams of particles, we have not had occasion to define the frequency of the waves associated with them. Now, however, we must do so. The group velocity, by equation (21), is equal to dv/dK. The velocity V of the particles is equal to hK/m. We have therefore

$$\frac{dv}{dK} = V = hK/m. \tag{22}$$

We can integrate this equation and obtain

$$v = \tfrac{1}{2}hK^2/m + \text{const}.$$

If we substitute for K in terms of V, we find

$$v = \tfrac{1}{2}mV^2/h + \text{const}.$$

We thus see that, apart from an unknown constant independent of V, hv is equal to the kinetic energy of the particles with which the waves are associated.

We have next to consider the value of this constant. It will be realized that a steady beam of particles moving for an indefinite time through a field of force must be represented by a wave of constant frequency. It is natural to take a point where the potential energy is zero and to define hv as the kinetic energy there. We see therefore that

$$hv = W, \tag{23}$$

where W is the total energy of each particle. This is the formula which we shall use for the frequency. It must be realized, however, that the point where the potential energy vanishes is in fact arbitrary; for instance that of a particle acted on by gravity may be considered zero on the earth's surface, or at an infinite distance. The total energy of a particle, therefore, does contain an arbitrary constant; all that has physical meaning is the change in the energy.

It is rather disconcerting to find that the frequency of these waves also contains an arbitrary constant; it suggests that, though the equations of wave mechanics are correct in their description of how matter actually behaves, these waves have not the same kind of physical reality as sound or electromagnetic waves. This view will be confirmed by the considerations of the next section.

The derivation of equation (23) is non-relativistic. A relativistic derivation can be given. We know that $K = p/h$, where p is the momentum of a particle; and the relation between velocity V and momentum p is

$$p = mV/\sqrt{(1-V^2/c^2)}.$$

We therefore have

$$\frac{dv}{dK} = V = cp/\sqrt{(m^2c^2+p^2)} = chK/\sqrt{(m^2c^2+h^2K^2)}.$$

On integrating we obtain

$$\nu = c\sqrt{(m^2c^2+h^2K^2)}/h+\text{const.}$$
$$= c\sqrt{(m^2c^2+p^2)}/h+\text{const.}$$
$$= W/h+\text{const.}$$

We see that as before $h\nu$ is equal to the total energy W of the particle, the kinetic energy together with energy of the rest mass, and also an arbitrary constant.

The derivation given here of the formula (23) for the frequency is based on experiment, or rather it shows that if the equation were not satisfied wave mechanics would give an incorrect description of the commonest facts. It may be compared with the derivation from the principle of relativity given in § 1.2. This derivation shows that the arbitrary constant should be zero.

5. The wave equation for non-stationary phenomena

The wave equation which we have considered already, namely

$$\nabla^2\psi+\frac{8\pi^2m}{h^2}(W-V)\psi = 0, \qquad (24)$$

is applicable to steady beams of particles each particle having energy W; the particle density $|\psi|^2$ does not then vary with time. In the phenomena considered in the last section $|\psi|^2$ does vary with the time; a more general wave equation is therefore required.

This wave function must be of the first order in the time, and thus linear in the operator $\partial/\partial t$. The reason is that in any form of wave motion, if the displacement and velocity of the medium are known, the further motion is determinate. In electromagnetic waves the same is true of E and H. We have seen that the real and imaginary parts of ψ are analogous to E and H. Thus if ψ is given at any moment its future behaviour should be calculable from the wave equation. It follows that this equation must be linear in $\partial/\partial t$.

The most general form of the wave equation for a particle moving in a field of potential energy V will be made up by superimposing wave functions of the type

$$\psi = \psi_W(x,y,z)e^{-2\pi iWt/h}, \qquad (25)$$

where ψ_W satisfies equation (24). This follows from the assumption made on p. 12 about the form of the time factor, and from equation (23) for the frequency. The functions which are to be superimposed will have different amplitudes and values of W. It will easily be seen that

$$\frac{\partial \psi}{\partial t} = -\frac{2\pi i W}{h}\psi.$$

The equation linear in $\partial/\partial t$, from which W has been eliminated and which (25) satisfies, is therefore

$$\frac{h}{2\pi i}\frac{\partial \psi}{\partial t} = \frac{h^2}{8\pi^2 m}\nabla^2\psi - V\psi. \tag{26}$$

This then is the general equation† satisfied by the wave function ψ.

We must now use this equation to show that wave mechanics will give the same results as classical Newtonian mechanics when the field of force in which the electrons move does not vary much in a distance comparable with the wave-length. This is almost implicit in what has gone before; we have shown in § 1.3 that a continuous beam of waves under these conditions follows the same path as a beam of particles according to classical mechanics, and also that the velocity of a wave packet is the classical velocity of the particles. The following more formal proof may, however, be of interest.

If ψ represents a wave group or wave packet, the quantity

$$\bar{x} = \int x\psi\psi^* \, dxdydz \Big/ \int \psi\psi^* \, dxdydz$$

will represent the average x-coordinate of the electrons, information about whose position is given by the wave function ψ. It will be sufficient if we show that $\bar{x}$, $\bar{y}$, $\bar{z}$ satisfy the classical equations of motion. We shall in fact prove that

$$m\frac{\partial^2 \bar{x}}{\partial t^2} = -\int \frac{\partial V}{\partial x}\psi\psi^* \, dxdydz,$$

which shows that the wave packet follows the Newtonian path as closely as its finite size will allow.

The proof makes use of Green's theorem in the form

$$\int (A\nabla^2 B - B\nabla^2 A) \, dx = 0$$

if the integral is over all space and A and B tend to zero outside a finite region.

We first multiply equation (26) by $x\psi^*$ and integrate over all space;

† For a discussion of the relation of this equation to other wave equations occurring in physics and of the analogy between wave mechanics and physical optics see Condon and Morse, *Quantum Mechanics*, p. 10 (New York, 1929); K. K. Darrow, *Rev. Mod. Phys.* **6**, 23 (1934).

and then multiply the complex conjugate equation by $x\psi$ and integrate over all space; we then subtract the two equations and obtain

$$\frac{h}{2\pi i}\frac{\partial \bar{x}}{\partial t} = \frac{h^2}{8\pi^2 m}\int (\psi^* x\nabla^2\psi - \psi x\nabla^2\psi^*)\,d\tau.$$

The integral on the right can be replaced by

$$\int \{\psi^* x\nabla^2\psi - \psi\nabla^2(x\psi^*)\}\,d\tau + 2\int \psi\frac{\partial\psi^*}{\partial x}\,d\tau.$$

We thus obtain, since the first term vanishes by Green's theorem,

$$m\frac{\partial \bar{x}}{\partial t} = \frac{hi}{2\pi}\int \psi\frac{\partial\psi^*}{\partial x}\,d\tau. \qquad (27)$$

If we differentiate further with respect to the time we obtain

$$m\frac{\partial^2\bar{x}}{\partial t^2} = \frac{hi}{2\pi}\int \left(\frac{\partial\psi}{\partial t}\frac{\partial\psi^*}{\partial x} + \psi\frac{\partial^2\psi^*}{\partial x\partial t}\right)d\tau$$

$$= \frac{hi}{2\pi}\int \left(\frac{\partial\psi}{\partial t}\frac{\partial\psi^*}{\partial x} - \frac{\partial\psi^*}{\partial t}\frac{\partial\psi}{\partial x}\right)d\tau$$

by partial integration of the second term on the right-hand side. If we now substitute for $\partial\psi/\partial t$ and $\partial\psi^*/\partial t$ from (26), we obtain for the right-hand side

$$-\frac{h^2}{8\pi^2 m}\int \left(\nabla^2\psi\frac{\partial\psi^*}{\partial x} + \nabla^2\psi^*\frac{\partial\psi}{\partial x}\right)d\tau + \int V\left(\psi\frac{\partial\psi^*}{\partial x} + \psi^*\frac{\partial\psi}{\partial x}\right)d\tau.$$

The first term vanishes by Green's theorem and the second gives

$$-\int \frac{\partial V}{\partial x}\psi\psi^*\,d\tau.$$

We thus obtain the classical equation of motion in the required form.

We shall also verify that the equation (26) predicts the conservation of matter; since $|\psi|^2 d\tau$ is equal to the probability that the particle is in the volume element $d\tau$, it follows that

$$\int |\psi|^2 d\tau$$

integrated over all space must be equal to the number of particles described by the wave function; it will be equal to unity if the wave function is used to describe a single particle. It should therefore be possible to deduce from the wave equation that

$$\frac{\partial}{\partial t}\int |\psi|^2 d\tau = 0. \qquad (28)$$

If this were not so, the prediction of the equation would not accord with common experience, and it would have to be modified.

The proof is as follows: the left-hand side of (28) may be written

$$\int \left(\psi \frac{\partial \psi^*}{\partial t} + \psi^* \frac{\partial \psi}{\partial t} \right) d\tau.$$

If we substitute for $\partial \psi / \partial t$ and $\partial \psi^* / \partial t$ from equation (26), we obtain

$$\frac{hi}{4\pi m} \int (\psi^* \nabla^2 \psi - \psi \nabla^2 \psi^*) \, d\tau. \tag{29}$$

Integrated over all space this gives zero by Green's theorem, which is what we set out to prove.

If we integrate over a finite volume (29) is equal to

$$\frac{hi}{4\pi m} \int (\psi^* \operatorname{grad} \psi - \psi \operatorname{grad} \psi^*)_n \, dS,$$

where dS is an element of the surface bounding the volume, the integration is over the whole surface and the suffix n denotes that the component of the vector within the brackets normal to the surface should be taken. This suggests that the vector

$$\frac{hi}{4\pi m} (\psi^* \operatorname{grad} \psi - \psi \operatorname{grad} \psi^*) \tag{30}$$

should denote the number of particles crossing unit area per unit time. Multiplied by the charge on each particle it would give the current.

It will easily be verified that if ψ has the form of a plane wave $A \exp(i\mathbf{K}\mathbf{r})$, (30) is equal to AA^*v, where $v (= hK/m)$ is equal to the velocity of the particles.

6. The uncertainty principle

In § 4 it was shown that if two plane waves of wave-number K, K' are superimposed, a series of wave groups is formed, and that the length of each group, from one minimum to the next, is equal to the distance between adjacent zeros of

$$\cos 2\pi \left(\frac{K - K'}{2} x - \frac{v - v'}{2} t \right).$$

This distance is equal to $1/(K - K')$.

If we analyse a single wave group, the same relation is valid approximately. If a wave group of length Δx and apparent wave-number K_0 is analysed into its Fourier components, that is to say into a series of monochromatic waves, the wave numbers of these waves will be found clustered about the mean value K_0 in a range of order ΔK given by the relation

$$\Delta x \, \Delta K \sim 1. \tag{31}$$

This can be shown most simply as follows: we may represent the wave group at any instant of time by

$$\psi = e^{2\pi i K_0 x} e^{-x^2/\sigma^2}; \tag{32}$$

the exponential function $\exp(-x^2/\sigma^2)$ is chosen as a simple and convenient function which tends to zero rapidly as x increases to values greater than σ. Thus $\Delta x \sim 2\sigma$. If we analyse this function into plane waves it will take the form

$$\psi = \int_{-\infty}^{\infty} A(K) e^{2\pi i K x} \, dK. \tag{33}$$

It may easily be verified by direct integration that if we take

$$A(K) = \pi^{\frac{1}{2}} \sigma \exp[-(K-K_0)^2 \pi^2 \sigma^2],$$

(32) and (33) are identical. $A(K)$ is thus very small except in a range ΔK given by

$$\Delta K = 2/\pi\sigma.$$

Thus $\Delta x \, \Delta K = 4/\pi$, which is of order unity. Equation (31) is therefore verified.

It will be seen, therefore, that the shorter the length of a wave group the greater is the spread in the values of the wave-number, and thus in wave-length or frequency. This is of course a well-known and important principle in radio reception where too selective a receiver distorts short pulses or musical notes of high pitch, and also in optics where the breadth of a spectral line, and thus the spread in frequency, depends on the time during which the atom emits the wave and thus on the length of the wave train.

The application of these principles to quantum mechanics is as follows: we return to the idealized experiment shown in Fig. 5 in which a beam of particles moving with velocity V falls on a screen with a slit in it, which can be opened or closed by a shutter; the shutter is opened or closed for a short time t_0, and a cloud of particles of length Δx equal to Vt_0 passes through. The density of particles in this group is determined by the wave function ψ. Following the principles described in the last paragraph, this wave function can be analysed into plane waves of wave-number lying in a range ΔK about that of the original wave incident on the screen, where $\Delta K \sim 1/\Delta x$. Since a wave of wave-number K describes a beam of particles of velocity hK/m, it follows that, whereas the beam of particles falling on the screen had a well-defined velocity V, the velocities of those that pass through the screen have a spread of velocities ΔV defined by

$$\Delta V \, \Delta x \sim h/m;$$

or, in terms of the momentum p,

$$\Delta p \, \Delta x \sim h. \tag{34}$$

This relation is known as the Uncertainty Principle, and was first formulated by Heisenberg.†

The principle shows that, if wave mechanics is valid, and if it is always possible to describe a beam of electrons by a wave function, then any attempt to form a beam of electrons of finite and known length Δx, as for example with slits and shutters, will necessarily disturb the momentum p of each particle by an unknown amount, the spread Δp being given by (34).

The principle, however, goes further, and leads to a formulation of wave mechanics more general than that considered up to this point. Let us suppose that at a given instant of time measurements are made in any way of the position and of the momentum of a particle, and that the accuracy of the measurements are such that its position lies between $x - \frac{1}{2}\Delta x$ and $x + \frac{1}{2}\Delta x$, and the momentum between $p - \frac{1}{2}\Delta p$ and $p + \frac{1}{2}\Delta p$. Then the equations of either Newtonian or of wave mechanics will enable the future position of the particle to be predicted, with certain uncertainties arising from the inaccuracy of the original measurement. The procedure according to wave mechanics will be as follows: we must write down a wave-function ψ which embodies the *knowledge* which, as a result of measurements, we have obtained about the position and momentum of the particle. The wave function will have the form of a wave group of length Δx and will be made up of waves with wave numbers in the range $\Delta p/h$. The wave equation (26), being linear in the time, will enable the form of ψ at any future time to be calculated. $|\psi|^2 \, dx$ will then give the probability that the position of the particle at that time lies between x and $x + dx$.

If the accuracy of measurement is such that $\Delta x \, \Delta p \sim h$ the wave function will have the form of the wave group written down in equation (33). If $\Delta x \, \Delta p > h$ (as is certain to be the case in practice) it is possible to imagine a number of these functions superimposed, with random phases and values of K_0 distributed over the range ΔK; the form of the wave function will be analogous to that of a wave pulse of white light. But if $\Delta x \, \Delta p$ is much less than h, it is impossible to write down a wave function at all which represents the results of the measurement. We must conclude, assuming that wave mechanics will always describe correctly the motion of a particle, that it is impossible to determine simultaneously the position and the momentum of a particle with errors less than those given by the uncertainty relation (34). This limitation, moreover, must not be one which is temporarily imposed by the clumsiness of the measuring instruments now available, but must lie deep in the nature of things; for were it possible to overcome it, the whole edifice of wave mechanics would fall to the ground, and a direct contradiction would arise between the deductions made from experiments on electron diffraction and the result of our hypothetical experiment.

It is therefore of great interest to examine the hypothetical experiments by which we could determine position and momentum simultaneously, and to show that they do in fact yield an uncertainty of the predicted amount. The most famous of these demonstrations is the 'Gamma ray microscope' first discussed by Heisenberg. The argument put forward is as follows: A beam of electrons is supposed to be travelling along the x-axis with known velocity V and momentum p. It is desired to observe an electron and to measure its position; for this purpose it is imagined that a microscope will be used, and since the utmost accuracy is required a short wave-length should be chosen. The position can then be determined to an accuracy given by

$$\Delta x = \lambda f/a, \tag{35}$$

where a is the aperture, λ the wave-length, and f the distance from the electron to the lens.

Radiation cannot be scattered by an electron without disturbing the electron; radiation is scattered by free electrons according to the rules of the Compton effect, according to which the momentum lost by the light quantum when scattered is transferred to the electron. Thus if a quantum of frequency ν, and hence momentum $h\nu/c$ is scattered through an angle θ, momentum

$$h\nu(1-\cos\theta)/c$$

is transferred to the electron. Thus we cannot observe the electron without disturbing it. Moreover, we disturb it by an unknown amount, since owing to the finite aperture of the lens, θ is not known exactly. In Fig. 6, θ may lie between ABC and ABC'. There is thus an uncertainty a/f in θ, and hence, since $\theta \sim 90°$, of

$$h\nu a/cf$$

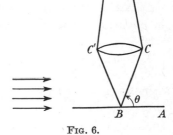

FIG. 6.

in the momentum transferred to the electron. Since $\lambda = c/\nu$ this may be written

$$\Delta p = ha/f\lambda,$$

where Δp is the uncertainty in the momentum of the electron after the measurement has been made. We see that

$$\Delta p\,\Delta x = h,$$

as we expect.

7. Wave functions for the momentum of a particle

It is implicit in what we have said already that if at a given instant of time a particle is described by a wave-function $\psi(x)$, deductions can be made about the momentum p of the particle as well as about its position x. In this section we shall show in detail how this can be done. We shall confine ourselves to particles moving in one dimension; the generalization to more complex systems is straightforward.

With regard to the spatial coordinate, we have seen that:

(*a*) The probability that x lies between the values x' and $x'+dx'$ is

$$|\psi(x')|^2\,dx'.$$

(*b*) The mean or most probable value of x is $\bar{x}$ given by

$$\bar{x} = \int x|\psi(x)|^2\,dx.$$

We require similar information about the momentum p. We want in fact a function $g(p)$ such that $|g(p')|^2\,dp'$ is the probability that p lies between the values p' and $p'+dp'$, and

$$\bar{p} = \int p|g(p)|^2\,dp$$

is the mean value of p.

It is clear from the considerations of the last section that $g(p)$ will be equal to the appropriate Fourier component of $\psi(x)$. We may thus set†

$$g(p) = A \int\limits_{-\infty}^{\infty} e^{-ipx/\hbar}\psi(x)\,dx. \tag{36}$$

The constant A will be determined by the condition that

$$\int |g(p)|^2\,dp = 1.$$

This gives $A = 1/\sqrt{(2\pi\hbar)}.$

The proof is as follows. Consider the integral

$$\int\limits_{-p_0}^{p_0} |g(p)|^2\,dp.$$

† $\hbar$ is written for $h/2\pi$.

It may be written

$$\iiint e^{ip(x-x')/\hbar}\psi(x)\psi(x')\,dpdxdx',$$

which, on integrating with respect to p, gives

$$\iint \frac{2\hbar}{x-x'}\sin\left\{\frac{p_0(x-x')}{\hbar}\right\}\psi(x)\psi(x')\,dxdx'.$$

Integrating with respect to x' and making p_0 tend to infinity, and making use of the equation

$$\int_{-\infty}^{\infty} \frac{\sin x}{x}\,dx = \pi,$$

we obtain
$$2\pi\hbar \int |\psi(x)|^2\,dx.$$

The function $\exp(-ipx/\hbar)/\sqrt{(2\pi\hbar)}$ is known as a 'transformation function', by means of which we can transform the wave function giving information about x into a wave function giving information about p.

The mean value of the momentum p is given by

$$\bar{p} = \int p|g(p)|^2\,dp. \tag{37}$$

It is often desirable to express $\bar{p}$ in terms of the wave-function $\psi(x)$ for spatial coordinates. We shall now show that

$$\bar{p} = \frac{\hbar}{i}\int \psi^*\frac{\partial\psi}{\partial x}\,dx.$$

The proof is as follows:

The quantity $\bar{p}$ defined by (37) may be written

$$\bar{p} = \frac{1}{2\pi\hbar}\iiint pe^{ip(x-x')/\hbar}\psi(x)\psi^*(x')\,dxdx'dp.$$

We carry out the p-integration between the limits $\pm p_0$; writing $p_0/\hbar = k_0$, and $x-x' = \xi$, this gives

$$\bar{p} = \frac{\hbar}{\pi i}\iint \left[\frac{k_0\cos k_0\xi}{\xi} + \frac{\sin k_0\xi}{\xi^2}\right]\psi(x)\psi^*(x')\,dxdx'.$$

After partial integration with respect to x, we obtain

$$\bar{p} = \frac{\hbar}{\pi i}\iint \frac{\sin k_0(x-x')}{x-x'}\frac{\partial\psi(x)}{\partial x}\psi^*(x')\,dxdx'.$$

Carry out the integration with respect to x', we find as before

$$\bar{p} = \frac{\hbar}{i}\int \psi^*(x)\frac{\partial\psi(x)}{\partial x}\,dx.$$

This identification of the momentum p with the operator $(\hbar/i)\partial/\partial x$ has consequences of importance. It enables one to find the average value of other quantities, for instance the energy of a particle. Thus in classical mechanics the energy $H(p, x)$ of a particle moving in one dimension is given by

$$H = \frac{p^2}{2m} + V(x).$$

Replacing p by $(\hbar/i)\partial/\partial x$, we see that the mean value $\overline{W}$ of the energy is given by

$$\overline{W} = \int \psi^* H \psi \, dx$$

$$= \int \psi^* \left[-\frac{\hbar^2}{2m} \frac{d^2}{dx^2} + V(x) \right] \psi \, dx. \tag{38}$$

If ψ is the solution of a Schrödinger equation for known energy W,

$$\frac{\hbar^2}{2m} \frac{d^2\psi}{dx^2} + (W - V)\psi = 0, \tag{39}$$

(38) is then a trivial result, obtainable by multiplying both sides of (39) by $\psi(x)$ and integrating over all x. Equation (38) is applicable for systems described by any wave functions.

It will be noticed that if p denotes the operator $(\hbar/i)\partial/\partial x$, then

$$(px - xp)\psi = \frac{\hbar}{i}\psi.$$

In some formulations of quantum mechanics† the quantum conditions are introduced in this way, as

$$px - xp = \frac{\hbar}{i}. \tag{40}$$

It there appears that for any two dynamical variables f and g for which

$$fg - gf = 0$$

it is possible to measure them both simultaneously with unlimited accuracy. Such variables are said to 'commute'. If, however, $fg \neq gf$, the two quantities cannot be determined simultaneously.

In finding the mean value of any quantity which contains terms of the form px, an ambiguity arises, since, if p is replaced by $(\hbar/i)\partial/\partial x$,

$$px\psi \neq xp\psi.$$

† e.g. P. A. M. Dirac, *Quantum Mechanics*, 3rd ed. (Oxford, 1947).

In such cases we replace px by $\frac{1}{2}(px+xp)$, and thus $px\psi$ by

$$\frac{1}{2}\frac{\hbar}{i}\left(\frac{\partial}{\partial x}(x\psi)+x\frac{\partial\psi}{\partial x}\right),$$

i.e. by

$$\frac{\hbar}{i}\left(x\frac{\partial\psi}{\partial x}+\tfrac{1}{2}\psi\right).$$

More generally, a classical term

$$f(x)p\psi$$

is replaced by

$$\frac{1}{2}\frac{\hbar}{i}\left\{f\frac{\partial\psi}{\partial x}+\frac{\partial}{\partial x}(f\psi)\right\}.$$

With this convention, operators have the 'Hermitian' property; this is defined as follows: If ϕ and ψ are any wave functions vanishing at infinity and $L(p,x)$ any real function of p and q,

$$\int \psi^* L\phi \, dx = \int \phi L^*\psi^* \, dx. \tag{41}$$

For terms of the type p^2 the proof is obvious; for terms of the type $f(x)p$ we have for the difference of the two sides of (41)

$$\frac{\hbar}{2i}\int\psi^*\left\{f\frac{\partial\phi}{\partial x}+\frac{\partial}{\partial x}(f\phi)\right\}dx+\frac{\hbar}{2i}\int\phi\left\{f\frac{\partial\psi^*}{\partial x}+\frac{\partial}{\partial x}(f\psi^*)\right\}dx$$

$$=\frac{\hbar}{i}\int\frac{d}{dx}(\psi^*f\phi)\,dx=0.$$

In the next section it will be shown that the Hermitian property is necessary if the predictions from wave mechanics are to be in accord with the facts.

8. Hamiltonian equations of motion

In the preceding sections a method has been given whereby the wave functions of a particle can be set up, which will give information about the momentum p and the positional coordinate x. For certain purposes it may be necessary to consider more complicated dynamical systems, such as rigid bodies (for certain purposes molecules can be so treated) or numbers of interacting particles. For such systems we shall make use of generalized positional coordinates $q_1, q_2,..., q_n$, where n is the number of degrees of freedom of the system, and Hamilton's equations of motion. We require a wave function $\psi(q_1,q_2,...)$ of *all* the coordinates, the interpretation of which will be that

$$|\psi(q_1,q_2,...,q_n)|^2 \, dq_1\,dq_2...dq_n$$

is the probability that, at the instant of time considered, the coordinate q_1 lies between q_1 and q_1+dq_1, q_2 between q_2 and q_2+dq_2, and so on.

We require also an equation linear in the time of the type of (26), to determine ψ at all subsequent times if it is given initially.

The Hamiltonian equations on which we shall base the theory are as follows: A 'Hamiltonian function' $H(p_r, q_r)$ $(r = 1,..., n)$ of the positional coordinates q_r and momenta p_r is set up; the equations of motion are then

$$\frac{\partial p_r}{\partial t} = -\frac{\partial H}{\partial q_r}, \qquad \frac{\partial q_r}{\partial t} = \frac{\partial H}{\partial p_r}. \tag{42}$$

The Hamiltonian function and momenta p_r are defined as follows: first the kinetic energy T and potential energy V are written down as functions of q_r, $\dot{q}_r$. The Lagrangian function is then defined by

$$L = T - V$$

The generalized momentum p_r is then defined by

$$p_r = \frac{\partial L}{\partial \dot{q}_r} \tag{43}$$

and the Hamiltonian function by

$$H = \sum p_r \dot{q}_r - L,$$

where the $\dot{q}_r$ are to be eliminated by means of (43).

Where V does not contain the time explicitly H is equal to the energy of the system. Thus for a particle in a field of force

$$H = \frac{1}{2m}(p_x^2 + p_y^2 + p_z^2) + V.$$

The generalized Schrödinger equation that will replace (26) is

$$-\frac{\hbar}{i}\frac{\partial \psi}{\partial t} = H(p, q)\psi, \tag{44}$$

where p_r is to be understood for $(\hbar/i)\partial/\partial q_r$. This is suggested, first because it reduces to (26) for the case of a particle moving in a field, and also because it leads to the classical Hamiltonian equations of motion (42) for the centre of gravity of a wave packet. This will now be proved.

The mean value $\bar{p}_r$ of p_r is given by

$$\bar{p}_r = \int \psi^* p_r \psi \, dq,$$

and thus

$$\frac{\partial \bar{p}_r}{\partial t} = \int (\dot{\psi}^* p_r \psi + \psi^* p_r \dot{\psi}) \, dq = \int \left\{ H^* \psi^* \frac{\partial \psi}{\partial q_r} - \psi^* \frac{\partial}{\partial q_r}(H\psi) \right\} dq,$$

on substituting for $\dot{\psi}$, $\dot{\psi}^*$ from (44) and writing $p_r = (\hbar/i)\partial/\partial q_r$. The right-hand side gives

$$\int \left\{ \frac{\partial \psi}{\partial q_r} H^* \psi^* - \psi^* H \frac{\partial \psi}{\partial q_r} - \psi^* \frac{\partial H}{\partial q_r} \psi \right\} dq.$$

The first two terms vanish by the Hermitian property (41) and we are left with

$$\bar{p}_r = -\int \psi^* \frac{\partial H}{\partial q_r} \psi \, dq.$$

Examples of systems for which a wave equation must be deduced from a Hamiltonian function are:

(a) *Motion of a system consisting of two or more particles.* If their spatial coordinates are (x_1, y_1, z_1) and (x_2, y_2, z_2), a wave function $\psi(x_1, y_1, z_1 ; x_2, y_2, z_2)$ will describe the system, and

$$|\psi|^2 \, dx_1 \, dy_1 \, dz_1 \, dx_2 \, dy_2 \, dz_2,$$

will give the probability that the first particle is at the point (x_1, y_1, z_1) in the volume element $dx_1 \, dy_1 \, dz_1$ and at the same time the second particle is at the point (x_2, y_2, z_2).

(b) *Motion of an electron in a magnetic field.* In this case there is no potential energy function, and so the definition of H given above cannot be used. Nevertheless a Hamiltonian function can be set up so that equations (42) are valid. This function is

$$\frac{1}{2m}\left\{\left(p_x + \frac{eA_x}{c}\right)^2 + \left(p_y + \frac{eA_y}{c}\right)^2 + \left(p_z + \frac{eA_z}{c}\right)^2\right\} + V,$$

where Λ is the vector potential defined so that the magnetic field **H** satisfies

$$\mathbf{H} = \operatorname{curl} \mathbf{A}.$$

That this is the correct Hamiltonian may be verified as follows: Hamilton's equations give

$$\dot{p}_r = -\frac{e}{mc} \sum_s \left(p_s + \frac{eA_s}{c}\right)\frac{\partial A_s}{\partial q_r} - \frac{\partial V}{\partial q_r}$$

and

$$\dot{q}_r = \frac{1}{m}\left(p_r + \frac{eA_r}{c}\right), \tag{45}$$

where the suffix r can have the three values x, y, z and q_x is written for x. Substituting in the first of these equations, we find

$$\dot{p}_r = -\frac{e}{c} \sum_s \dot{q}_s \frac{\partial A_s}{\partial q_r} - \frac{\partial V}{\partial q_r},$$

while the second gives, on differentiating with regard to the time

$$m\ddot{q}_r = \dot{p}_r + \frac{e}{c} \sum_s \frac{\partial A_r}{\partial q_s}\dot{q}_s$$

$$= \frac{e}{c} \sum_s \dot{q}_s\left[\frac{\partial A_s}{\partial q_r} - \frac{\partial A_r}{\partial q_s}\right] - \frac{\partial V}{\partial q_r}.$$

This, in vector form, may be written

$$m\dot{\mathbf{v}} = -\operatorname{grad} V + \frac{e}{c}[\mathbf{vH}],$$

which gives the classical equation of motion.

In most physical applications $\mathbf{H}$ may be considered small, and the Hamiltonian becomes

$$\frac{1}{2m}(p_x^2 + p_y^2 + p_z^2) + \frac{e}{mc}(A_x p_x + A_y p_y + A_z p_z) + V,$$

from which the wave equation can be written down in the usual way. As we saw above, $(\mathbf{Ap})\psi$ has to be replaced by

$$\frac{\hbar}{i}\,\tfrac{1}{2}\{(\mathbf{A}\operatorname{grad}\psi) + \operatorname{div}(\mathbf{A}\psi)\},$$

and if div $\mathbf{A}$ vanishes this gives

$$\frac{\hbar}{i}(\mathbf{A}\operatorname{grad}\psi).$$

The Schrödinger equation is thus

$$-\frac{\hbar}{i}\frac{\partial\psi}{\partial t} = -\frac{\hbar^2}{2m}\nabla^2\psi + \frac{\hbar e}{mci}(\mathbf{A}\operatorname{grad}\psi) + V\psi. \tag{46}$$

II
STATIONARY STATES

9. The old quantum theory

IT was Niels Bohr in 1913 who first brought forward the hypothesis that the energy of an atom is quantized. This hypothesis means that the total energy of the electrons in an atom cannot have any arbitrary value, but must have one of a series of discrete values, of which one is the lowest and is thus the energy of the normal state of the atom. Bohr's hypothesis was made in order to explain a series of experimental facts, and a theory (the old quantum theory) was built up in accord with many of these facts, based on a few assumptions such as the quantization of angular momentum. It is, of course, one of the most striking successes of Schrödinger's equation that the quantization of energy follows from it naturally and without the introduction of special hypotheses.

The experimental facts on which the quantization of energy rests are widespread and of very different type. We may mention first the fact, fundamental to crystallography and indeed to chemistry, that atoms and molecules seem to have each a characteristic size.† It is useful to think of many atoms and ions, especially those having the 'rare gas' configuration of electrons such as K^+ or Cl^-, as behaving much like elastic spheres when brought into contact with each other. This behaviour seems quite incompatible with the picture of the atom that we owe to Rutherford, that of a number of electrons moving in the field of a positive nucleus; the dimensions of such an atom would depend entirely on the speed with which the electrons were moving and hence on their energy, and could be very small for large negative values of the energy.

A second piece of evidence of the same type is provided by the specific heats of monatomic gases which at constant volume approximate closely to $\frac{3}{2}R$. This means that the whole of the thermal energy of the molecules of the gas consists of translational energy, and that the internal degrees of freedom do not make any contribution. It follows that the electrons in the molecules cannot normally give or receive energy on collision with other molecules, and this in its turn implies that the minimum amount of internal energy that a molecule can take up is too large to

---

† See, for instance, the tables of ionic radii given by V. M. Goldschmidt (*Trans. Faraday Soc.* **258,** 1929) or W. H. and W. L. Bragg, *The Crystalline State* (London, 1933).

be transferred in a collision at ordinary temperatures. This shows
that the energy must be quantized.

Since the hypothesis was originally put forward, numerous experiments have been carried out in which molecules of gases have been
bombarded by electrons and it has been shown that the energy lost
by a colliding electron must have one of a series of discrete values,
unless enough energy is lost to ionize the molecule. We may thus take
it as an established experimental fact that for any gaseous atom or
molecule of given type there exists a definite state of greatest stability
(the 'normal state'), in which the atom will normally be found; and
that if it absorbs energy, either from light, a colliding electron, or in
any other way, it will absorb an amount equal to one of the terms of
a definite series. The atom is then left in an 'excited state'. The series
tends to a definite limit, the ionization energy, I. Any amount of
energy greater than I can be absorbed, an electron being then ejected
from the atom.

The energies of an atom in the normal or excited states are usually

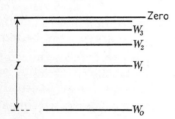

FIG. 7. Energy levels of an atom.

defined with the convention that the
total energy is zero when one electron
is removed from the atom and is at rest.
The energies W_0 of the normal state and
$W_1, W_2,...$ of the excited states are then all
negative. They are shown schematically
in Fig. 7. The ionization energy is equal
to $-W_0$ and the first excitation energy,
that is to say, the smallest energy that
can be absorbed by an atom in the normal state, is equal to $|W_0-W_1|$.

Further strong evidence for the existence of stationary states in
atoms is the fact that the optical emission and absorption spectra
consist of lines. The mere existence of line spectra proves that the
energy must be quantized, since we know that when light of frequency
ν receives or gives up its energy to matter, it does so in quanta of
amount $h\nu$. It follows that an atom can only change its energy by one
of a series of definite values. Further it is found that in the line
spectrum of a given atom, groups of three lines of frequencies ν_1, ν_2, ν_3
such that

$$\nu_1+\nu_2 = \nu_3$$

are frequent. In terms of the theory of stationary states, this will mean
that the three lines correspond to transitions between states $W_a, W_b, W_c,$

$$h\nu_1 = W_a-W_b, \qquad h\nu_2 = W_b-W_c, \qquad h\nu_3 = W_a-W_c.$$

From an examination of the line spectra of atoms it is in fact usually possible to determine the relative values of the stationary states, all emission lines being ascribed to transitions between a series of states as shown in Fig. 7. Absorption lines in a cold gas, where all atoms are in the ground state, correspond to transitions between the ground state only and the excited states.

In the line spectrum of atomic hydrogen the frequencies of the lines were found experimentally to conform to a simple formula; the frequencies can be expressed as

$$\frac{\nu}{c} = R\left(\frac{1}{n_1^2} - \frac{1}{n_2^2}\right).$$

On the left we have the wave-number (the reciprocal of the wavelength); on the right n_1 and n_2 are integers and R is a constant, known as Rydberg's constant. It is equal to

$$R = 109,677 \text{ cm.}^{-1}$$

From this fact we can deduce that the hydrogen atom has a series of energy levels, and that the energy of the nth level is given by

$$W_n = -hcR/n^2 \quad (n = 1, 2, ...),$$

subject to the convention already made that the energy should be zero when an electron is just removed from the atom.

The hydrogen atom is a particularly simple structure, consisting as it does of a single electron moving in the field of a heavy positively charged nucleus. According to Newtonian mechanics the electron ought to move round the nucleus in circular or elliptic orbits; the energy could have any value from zero to minus infinity. Niels Bohr in his original theory assumed that the orbits were in fact Newtonian, but that only a restricted series of orbits were possible. Confining ourselves to circular orbits, we shall now show what this limitation must be if the observed series of energy levels is to be obtained.

Suppose that an electron with charge e and mass m moves round an infinitely heavy nucleus carrying an identical charge of opposite sign. If the radius of the orbit is r and the velocity of the electron is v, then the electrostatic attraction between them, e^2/r^2, will be just balanced by the centrifugal force mv^2/r; we thus have

$$\frac{e^2}{r} = mv^2. \tag{1}$$

The potential energy of the system is $-e^2/r$, and the kinetic energy $\frac{1}{2}mv^2$; adding these together we see that the total energy is

$$\tfrac{1}{2}mv^2 - e^2/r,$$

which by (1) is equal to $-\frac{1}{2}e^2/r$. But we know from experiment that this is equal to $-hcR/n^2$, where n is an integer; it follows that

$$\frac{1}{2}\frac{e^2}{r} = \frac{hcR}{n^2},$$

or that
$$r = n^2 e^2/2hcR. \tag{2}$$

It follows that the radii of the allowed orbits are proportional to the square of an integer.

Again, from (1),
$$v = \left(\frac{2hcR}{m}\right)^{\frac{1}{2}}\frac{1}{n}, \tag{3}$$

and multiplying (2) and (3) we obtain for the angular momentum

$$mvr = \frac{me^2}{(2mhcR)^{\frac{1}{2}}}\, n.$$

Now Bohr's assumption was that the angular momentum should be quantized; and the elementary derivation given here shows that, if it is assumed that the electron moves in a circular orbit obeying Newtonian mechanics, this can be deduced from known experimental facts. There was no *a priori* reason to quantize the angular momentum in preference to any other constant of the motion such as the energy; Bohr's choice of the angular momentum could only be justified by its results.

Bohr also pointed out that, to within the limits of experimental error to which these quantities were known, $me^2/(2mhcR)^{\frac{1}{2}}$ was equal to $h/2\pi$. Planck's constant had the right dimensions and had already been used for the quantization of light; there was, however, no reason *a priori* why the multiplying factor should be $1/2\pi$ rather than anything else.

The assumption made by Bohr in building up a system of atomic mechanics was thus that the angular momentum Ω of an electron in an atom or of any rotating system should be a multiple of $h/2\pi$ or $\hbar$,

$$\Omega = nh/2\pi \quad (n = 1, 2, 3, ...).$$

This assumption had a series of striking successes of which a few will be enumerated here.

9.1. *Allowance for the rotation of the nucleus about the centre of gravity*

According to the above analysis, the value of the Rydberg constant for an infinitely heavy nucleus should be

$$R = 2\pi^2 e^4/mh^3 c.$$

For an electron of mass m revolving round a nucleus of mass M, it will easily be seen that R is given by

$$R = 2\pi^2 e^4 / m^* h^3 c,$$

with

$$m^* = m \Big/ \left(1 + \frac{m}{M}\right).$$

The change (one part in 2,000) is too small to be detectable, since although R is known sufficiently accurately the other constants m, e, h are not. However, a check on the theory can be obtained by observing the lines of ionized helium. In ionized helium a single electron moves round a nucleus of charge $2e$ and mass approximately $4M$, if M is the mass of the proton. Thus the line spectrum of ionized helium should, according to the theory, be given by the formula

$$\nu/c = 4R_{\text{He}}/n^2,$$

where

$$\frac{R_{\text{He}}}{R_{\text{H}}} = \left(1 + \frac{m}{M}\right) \Big/ \left(1 + \frac{m}{4M}\right) \simeq 1 + \frac{3m}{4M}.$$

Experimental values of the two Rydberg constants are

$$R_{\text{He}} = 109,722, \qquad R_{\text{H}} = 109,677,$$

enabling a value of m/M equal to $1/1843$ to be obtained, in reasonable agreement with values obtained from other sources.

9.2. *Structure of atoms other than hydrogen*

Although the old quantum theory was not able to yield exact quantitative results in agreement with experiment for atoms more complicated than hydrogen, it was able to give an extremely valuable qualitative picture of atomic structure. A theory comprehending elliptic as well as circular orbits was built up, and the interaction between the electrons was taken into account in a qualitative way. Much of the old theory, in particular the concept of the inner K, L, and M shells in a heavy atom, has been incorporated into the new theory, but since the concept of orbits has been completely discarded, we shall in this book build up the whole theory of atomic structure on a basis of wave mechanics; this will be done in Chapter VI. The very great service rendered by the old theory must, however, be stressed.

9.3. *Rotational energy levels of molecules*

A diatomic molecule rotating about its centre of gravity may be treated approximately as a rigid body of moment of inertia I, say. If its angular velocity is ω, then Bohr's hypothesis gives

$$I\omega = nh/2\pi \quad (n = 1, 2, 3, ...).$$

The kinetic energy is $\frac{1}{2}I\omega^2 = n^2 h^2 / 8\pi^2 I$.

This formula was used with fair success to account for the rotational terms in the band spectra of hydrogen (cf. Chap. V) and also to account for the drop at low temperatures of the rotational specific heat of hydrogen.† The formula has been slightly modified by the wave mechanical derivation (Chap. V) according to which the kinetic energy of rotation is

$$n(n+1)h^2/8\pi^2 I.$$

9.4. *Vibrational energy*

It was assumed before the introduction of wave mechanics that the quantized energy values of any vibrating system with one degree of freedom and natural frequency ν would be given by the formula

$$W = nh\nu,$$

it being supposed that a light wave was just a special case of a vibrating system, and that the formula valid for light would be valid for other systems. This formula was useful in accounting for the vibrational terms in the band spectra of molecules, and for the specific heats of solids at low temperatures. It is replaced according to wave mechanics by the formula

$$W = (n+\tfrac{1}{2})h\nu.$$

10. The concept of stationary states in wave mechanics

It can be shown as a quite general consequence of wave mechanics that the energy of any particle which moves in a limited space, from which it cannot escape, must be quantized. Thus electrons bound in atoms, or atoms as a whole vibrating about fixed positions in a solid, will have quantized energy values, while a free electron in an electron beam can have any arbitrary energy. This will most easily be seen if we consider a very idealized case, that of an electron shut up in a box with perfectly reflecting sides. We need consider motion in one dimension only; we thus suppose that the electron moves along the x-axis from $x = 0$ to $x = a$, and at these two extremities, where the walls are, the wave function vanishes. The wave function must then have the form

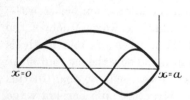

FIG. 8. Wave functions for electrons in a box.

$$\psi = A \sin(\pi n x/a)e^{-2\pi i \nu t},$$

† Cf. R. H. Fowler, *Statistical Mechanics*, 2nd ed. p. 82 (Cambridge, 1936).

where n is an integer and A a constant. Substituting into the Schrödinger equation

$$\frac{d^2\psi}{dx^2} + \frac{2mW}{\hbar^2}\,\psi = 0,$$

we see that W has the series of values

$$W_n = \frac{\pi^2\hbar^2 n^2}{2ma^2}. \tag{4}$$

We thus have a series of solutions

$$\psi_n = A\sin(\pi nx/a)e^{-iW_n t/\hbar}$$

which represent standing waves in the box. We also see that wave functions only exist corresponding to electrons with energies given by (4). If an electron could exist in the box with any other energy, it would not be possible to describe it by a wave function. Thus, if wave mechanics is to be universally applicable to the behaviour of electrons, it follows that the energy of an electron in a box must be quantized.

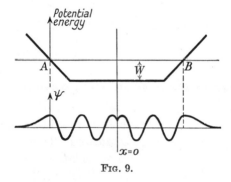

Fig. 9.

It will be noticed that the quantum-number n has the following physical meaning; $n-1$ is the number of nodes or zeros in the wave function between the two extremities.

Suppose that we now consider an electron shut up in a box bounded not by perfectly reflecting sides but by an electrostatic field which pushes the electron back when it tries to get out. The potential energy of an electron in this field is shown in Fig. 9. Suppose that the electron has an arbitrary energy W. The wave function in the neighbourhood of the points A and B, where the 'classical' electron would try to get out, is as described in Chap. I, § 3.2; in the regions where the classical electron cannot go ψ will decay exponentially, while within the box it will oscillate. If we started to draw the wave function from either end, taking the solutions that decay exponentially instead of increasing exponentially, the two solutions will not in general join up in the middle; only for a discrete series of energy values W_n will they do so, and these will be the quantized values that the energy of the electron must have.

An electron in a hydrogen atom is held in a box very much of this type. The potential energy of such an electron plotted along a line passing through the nucleus is shown in the upper part of Fig. 10: an electron with the energy represented by the horizontal line AB can move freely between the points A, B, where it will suffer total reflection. The wave function will be as shown below; it will oscillate in the region between A and B and die away exponentially outside. Clearly, only for a series of energies W_n will such a solution of the Schrödinger equation be obtainable.

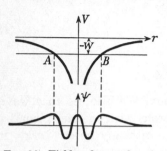

FIG. 10. Field and wave function for hydrogen atom.

10.1. *Quantization with several degrees of freedom*

We return now to the motion of an electron in a box with perfectly reflecting walls, but now consider motion in three dimensions. Let the boundaries of the box be given by

$$0 < x < a,$$
$$0 < y < b,$$
$$0 < z < c,$$

and let the wave function vanish on these boundaries. Then the Schrödinger equation

$$\nabla^2 \psi + \frac{2mW}{\hbar^2} \psi = 0$$

has solutions†
$$\psi = A \sin \frac{\pi n_1 x}{a} \sin \frac{\pi n_2 y}{a} \sin \frac{\pi n_3 z}{a}$$

for the values of the energy given by

$$W = \frac{\pi^2 \hbar^2}{2m} \left(\frac{n_1^2}{a^2} + \frac{n_2^2}{b^2} + \frac{n_3^2}{c^2} \right).$$

We see that the allowed values of the energy are defined by three quantum numbers (n_1, n_2, n_3), and that each quantum number (minus one) is equal to the number of nodal planes that the wave function has perpendicular to the appropriate axis in space.

† Here and in subsequent work we omit the time factor.

It may happen that the wave equation will have two or more solutions for one value of the energy. This will be the case, for example, if two of the sides of the box are equal. Thus if a is equal to b, the two wave functions with quantum numbers

$$(n_1, n_2, n_3), \quad (n_2, n_1, n_3) \qquad (n_1 \neq n_2)$$

are solutions of the wave equation corresponding to the same value of the energy. The solutions in this case are said to be 'degenerate'.

It is instructive to consider the energy levels of an electron in a cubic box of side a. The ground state (111) is non-degenerate; the next three (211), (121), (112) all have the same energy, so the energy level has a threefold degeneracy. The next level is (122), (212), (221), and the next (311), etc., also with threefold degeneracy. After (222) comes (123), etc., giving a sixfold degeneracy.

It will be noticed that when two or more degenerate levels exist, ψ_1 and ψ_2, then a linear combination of them

$$A\psi_1 + B\psi_2$$

is also a solution of the wave equation.

10.2. *Electron moving in a closed path*

The following idealized problem is instructive, although it does not refer to any actual physical phenomenon.

A particle of mass m is supposed to move with velocity v on the circumference of a circle of radius a. We denote by x the distance measured along the circumference of the circle from some arbitrary point P. The wave function describing the motion of the particle will then be

$$\psi = A e^{\pm imvx/\hbar}.$$

But clearly this function must be single-valued in x; on going round the circumference of the circle we must return to the same value of ψ.

Thus

$$\frac{mv(2\pi r)}{\hbar} \cdot \frac{1}{2\pi}$$

must be an integer. Thus the velocity is quantized, and has values

$$v = n\hbar/mr.$$

This may be written in the form

$$mvr = n\hbar.$$

This shows that the angular momentum, in this particular case, is quantized according to Bohr's condition (cf. § 9).

11. Wave functions for the simple harmonic oscillator†

11.1. *The simple harmonic oscillator in one dimension*

One of the simplest and most important examples in the theory of stationary states is that of the linear oscillator. A particle of mass M is held to a fixed point P by a restoring force equal to $-px$, where x is the displacement from P. According to Newtonian mechanics, it will then vibrate about P with arbitrary amplitude and energy, and with frequency ν given by

$$\nu = \frac{1}{2\pi}\sqrt{\frac{p}{M}}.$$

Our problem is to find the energies of vibration allowed by wave mechanics, and the associated wave functions. We shall find that the energies are given by

$$W_n = (n+\tfrac{1}{2})h\nu \quad (n = 1, 2, 3,...).$$

Before writing down and solving the Schrödinger equation we shall obtain an approximation to the energies by a simple method. The potential energy of the particle is $\tfrac{1}{2}px^2$. This is plotted in Fig. 11. If the energy of the particle is W, it can move according to Newtonian mechanics between the points A and B, that is to say, over a distance $2x_0$ given by

$$AB = 2\sqrt{(2W/p)} = 2x_0.$$

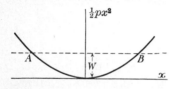

FIG. 11. Potential energy of harmonic oscillator.

The average kinetic energy may be taken to be

$$\int\limits_{-x_0}^{x_0} (W - \tfrac{1}{2}px^2)\, dx \bigg/ \int\limits_{-x_0}^{x_0} dx = \tfrac{2}{3}W.$$

Thus the average wave-length is $h/\sqrt{(4MW/3)}$. If n half-waves are fitted into the length AB, we have

$$\tfrac{1}{2}nh/\sqrt{(4MW/3)} = 2\sqrt{(2W/p)}.$$

This gives
$$W = 0{\cdot}94nh\nu,$$

an answer of the correct order of magnitude.

We shall now write down the wave equation and obtain the solution. The wave equation is

$$\frac{d^2\psi}{dx^2} + \frac{2m}{\hbar^2}(W - \tfrac{1}{2}px^2)\psi = 0.$$

If we introduce a new variable

$$y = \left(\frac{Mp}{\hbar^2}\right)^{-\frac{1}{4}}x, \tag{5}$$

† Cf. E. Schrödinger, *Ann. der Physik*, **79**, 489 (1926).

the equation becomes
$$\frac{d^2\psi}{dy^2} + (\lambda - y^2)\psi = 0, \tag{6}$$

where $\lambda = 2W/h\nu$. We have to find for what values of λ solutions of (6) exist which decay exponentially to zero as y tends to ∞.

The solution is obtained by making the substitution
$$\psi = e^{-\frac{1}{2}y^2} f(y).$$

Substituting into (6), we obtain
$$\frac{d^2f}{dy^2} - 2y\frac{df}{dy} + (\lambda - 1)f = 0.$$

If we now express f by a power series
$$f = \sum_{n=0}^{\infty} A_n y^n,$$

we obtain the recurrence relation
$$(n+2)(n+1)A_{n+2} = (2n+1-\lambda)A_n. \tag{7}$$

It is thus clear that the equation has two independent solutions of the form
$$\begin{aligned} &1 + A_2 y^2 + A_4 y^4 + \ldots, \\ &y + A_3 y^3 + A_5 y^5 + \ldots, \end{aligned} \tag{8}$$

and that the coefficient A_n can be determined from (7) in either case.

Two cases now arise; first, if $2n+1-\lambda$ does not vanish for any integral value of n, then f is given by a power series which is clearly divergent. For large n
$$\frac{A_{n+2}}{A_n} \to \frac{2}{n}.$$

For large n, therefore, successive terms have the same ratio to each other as those of the expansion of $\exp(2y^2)$. It follows that for large x, the function f tends to infinity as $\exp(2y^2)$, and thus that our wave function ψ tends to infinity as $\exp(\frac{3}{2}y^2)$.

If
$$\lambda = 2n+1, \tag{9}$$

where n is a positive integer, the series (8) terminates and f is a polynomial. It is only in these cases that our solution ψ tends to zero as x tends to ∞.

Equation (9) at once gives us the allowed values of the energy
$$W_n = (n+\tfrac{1}{2})h\nu \quad (n = 0, 1, 2, \ldots).$$

The corresponding wave functions are
$$\begin{aligned} \psi_0(y) &= A_0 \exp(-\tfrac{1}{2}y^2), \\ \psi_1(y) &= A_1 y \exp(-\tfrac{1}{2}y^2), \\ \psi_2(y) &= A_2 (2y^2 - 1)\exp(-\tfrac{1}{2}y^2). \end{aligned}$$

The multiplying constants A_n are arbitrary; but it is convenient to choose them so that the functions are 'normalized', i.e. so that $\int |\psi|^2 dx = 1$. In that case

$$A_0 = \pi^{-\frac{1}{4}}, \quad A_1 = (4/\pi)^{\frac{1}{4}}, \quad A_2 = (1/4\pi)^{\frac{1}{4}}.$$

The functions $f_n(y)$ are called Hermitian polynomials, and their properties are discussed in a number of text-books.† f_n is defined by

$$f_n(x) = (-1)^n e^{x^2} \frac{d^n}{dx^n}(e^{-x^2}).$$

Some of the wave functions are plotted against x (our original variable) in Fig. 12. We plot also $|\psi|^2$, which gives the probability that the particle will be found in any unit interval. It will be seen that for the higher states the particle is more likely to be found towards the boundaries of its vibration than at the centre, where its velocity is highest.

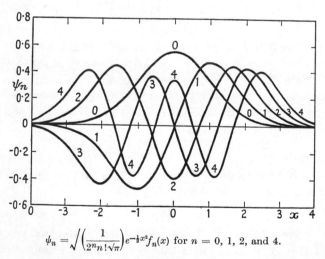

$$\psi_n = \sqrt{\left(\frac{1}{2^n n! \sqrt{\pi}}\right)} e^{-\frac{1}{2}x^2} f_n(x) \text{ for } n = 0, 1, 2, \text{ and } 4.$$

Fig. 12. Normalized wave functions of linear oscillator.

It is worth noting here that, according to wave mechanics, even in the state of lowest energy, an oscillator still has some energy, namely the 'zero point' energy $\frac{1}{2}h\nu$. This is a result characteristic of wave mechanics.

---

† For instance, Courant and Hilbert, *Methoden der mathematischen Physik*, Bd. 1 (Berlin, 1924). Cf. also Appendix to this book (pp. 376 et seq).

11.2. *The bounded harmonic oscillator*

In the above analysis we imposed the boundary condition that the wave-function ψ vanishes at infinity. If we replace this condition by the one that the wave function vanishes at the walls of an enclosure we may obtain the energy levels of a 'bounded' harmonic oscillator. This problem has been treated by several authors.† It is found that the effect of enclosing the oscillator is to displace its energy levels towards higher energies, the displacement increasing with decreasing dimensions of the enclosure. Thus if we write $\xi_0 = \frac{1}{2}l(4cm/\hbar^2)^{\frac{1}{4}}$, where $\psi(x) = 0$ at $x = \pm\frac{1}{2}l$ then

$$\frac{dW_n}{d\xi_0} > 0,$$

where W_n is the energy of the nth state. The formula for W_n is complicated but reduces to a simple form for $\xi_0^2 \gg (n-\frac{1}{2})$, when it becomes

$$W_n = (n-\tfrac{1}{2})\hbar\omega + \left(\frac{8}{\pi}\right)^{\frac{1}{2}}\hbar\omega \frac{e^{-\frac{1}{2}\xi_0^2}\xi_0^{2q-1}}{(q-1)!},$$

and for $\xi_0^2 \ll n-\frac{1}{2}$, when it reduces to

$$W_n = \frac{\pi^2 n^2}{4\xi_0^2}\hbar\omega,$$

showing that as $\xi_0 \to 0$, $W_n \to \infty$.

11.3. *Simple harmonic oscillator in three dimensions*

Suppose that the restoring force is $-p_1 x$ for displacements in the x-direction, $-p_2 y$ for displacements in the y-direction, and so on. The potential energy V is given by

$$V = -\tfrac{1}{2}(p_1 x^2 + p_2 y^2 + p_3 z^2).$$

The Schrödinger equation is separable; if we write

$$\psi = \psi_1(x)\psi_2(y)\psi_3(z),$$

then ψ is a solution if

$$\frac{d^2\psi_1}{dx^2} + \frac{2m}{\hbar^2}(W_1 - \tfrac{1}{2}p_1 x^2)\psi_1 = 0, \quad \text{etc.}$$

and

$$W = W_1 + W_2 + W_3.$$

If ν_1, ν_2, ν_3 are the frequencies for vibration in the three directions, the energy values are

$$\frac{W}{h} = \nu_1(n_1+\tfrac{1}{2}) + \nu_2(n_2+\tfrac{1}{2}) + \nu_3(n_3+\tfrac{1}{2}).$$

† F. C. Auluck, *Proc. Nat. Inst. Sci. India*, **7**, 133, 383 (1941); **8**, 147 (1942); F. C. Auluck and D. S. Kothari, *Science and Culture*, **6**, 370 (1940); *Proc. Camb. Phil. Soc.* **41**, 175 (1946); S. Chandrasekhar, *Astrophys. J.* **97**, 268 (1943).

12. The wave mechanical treatment of the hydrogen atom[†]

In this section we shall treat the motion of an electron in a central field of force, and in particular in the Coulomb field of a charged positive nucleus. We shall first treat the nucleus as of infinite mass; the correction for its finite mass will be made in Chapter V. Denoting by r the distance of the electron from the nucleus, we thus write $V(r)$ for the potential energy of the electron in the field of the nucleus. If the electron moves in the field of a positively charged nucleus of charge Ze, then

$$V(r) = -Ze^2/r.$$

The Schrödinger equation is

$$\nabla^2\psi + \frac{2m}{\hbar^2}(W-V)\psi = 0. \tag{10}$$

In this section we show that, for negative values of W, solutions exist which tend exponentially to zero outside the atom if W has one of the values

$$W_n = -\frac{mZ^2e^4}{2n^2\hbar^2}. \tag{11}$$

This is the same series of values that was given by Bohr's original theory. Solutions bounded at infinity exist for all positive values of W; these correspond to the ionized state of the atom and will be discussed in Chapter IX.

The first step in the solution of equation (10) is to transform it to spherical polar coordinates θ, ϕ. The equation transforms[‡] into

$$\frac{1}{r^2}\frac{\partial}{\partial r}\left(r^2\frac{\partial\psi}{\partial r}\right) + \frac{1}{r^2\sin\theta}\frac{\partial}{\partial\theta}\left(\sin\theta\frac{\partial\psi}{\partial\theta}\right) + \frac{1}{r^2\sin^2\theta}\frac{\partial^2\psi}{\partial\phi^2} + \frac{2m}{\hbar^2}(W-V)\psi = 0. \tag{12}$$

This is solved by setting

$$\psi = R(r)\Theta(\theta)\Phi(\phi),$$

where R, Θ, Φ are functions to be determined. It can easily be verified that ψ satisfies (10) if R, Θ, Φ satisfy the following equations

$$\frac{d^2\Phi}{d\phi^2} + u^2\Phi = 0, \tag{13}$$

$$\frac{1}{\sin\theta}\frac{d}{d\theta}\left(\sin\theta\frac{d\Theta}{d\theta}\right) + \left\{l(l+1) - \frac{u^2}{\sin^2\theta}\right\}\Theta = 0, \tag{14}$$

$$\frac{1}{r^2}\frac{d}{dr}\left(r^2\frac{dR}{dr}\right) + \left\{\frac{2m}{\hbar^2}(W-V) - \frac{l(l+1)}{r^2}\right\}R = 0. \tag{15}$$

† E. Schrödinger, *Ann. der Physik*, **79**, 361 (1926).
‡ C. E. Weatherburn, *Advanced Vector Analysis*, p. 15 (London, 1944).

where u^2 and $l(l+1)$ are arbitrary constants which have been written in this form for reasons which will appear below.

Now Φ must be a single-valued function of the azimuthal angle ϕ; that is to say, when ϕ is increased by 2π or any multiple of 2π, Φ must be unchanged. Thus u in (13) must be an integer, and we have for the general solution

$$\Phi = A\cos u\phi + B\sin u\phi,$$

where A and B are arbitrary constants. It will be convenient to ascribe to u positive and negative integral values and take the general solution to be

$$\Phi = Ae^{iu\phi}.$$

The equation (14) is the well-known equation of which the solution is the associated Legendre polynomial $P_l^u(\cos\theta)$. If l is integral and

$$l \geqslant |u|,$$

then there exists one solution $P_l^u(\cos\theta)$ which is bounded in the range $0 \leqslant \theta \leqslant \pi$. For other values of l no bounded solution exists.

Values of $P_l^u(\cos\theta)$ are (we write $P_l^0 = P_l$)

$$P_0(\cos\theta) = 1,$$
$$P_1(\cos\theta) = \cos\theta, \qquad P_1^1(\cos\theta) = \sin\theta,$$
$$P_2(\cos\theta) = \tfrac{3}{2}\cos^2\theta - 1.$$

We thus see that solutions of Schrödinger's equation can be classified conveniently according to the value of l. If $l = 0$ the solution is a function of r only, and thus spherically symmetrical. The solution is non-degenerate (except for certain special forms of $V(r)$, of which the Coulomb form is one). The states corresponding to such solutions are known as s-states.† It will be shown below that the angular momentum corresponding to such states is zero.

If $l = 1$, the function $\Theta\Phi$ can have either of the three forms

$$\cos\theta, \qquad \sin\theta\, e^{i\phi}, \qquad \sin\theta\, e^{-i\phi}.$$

These three independent solutions necessarily correspond to the same energy value; therefore any combination of them would give a solution, for instance,

$$\cos\theta, \qquad \sin\theta\cos\phi, \qquad \sin\theta\sin\phi,$$

i.e. $$z/r, \qquad x/r, \qquad y/r.$$

Thus three independent solutions with $l = 1$ have each a nodal plane passing through the origin. The states corresponding to $l = 1$ are called p-states.

---

† The letters s, p, d, f, now used to describe states with $l = 0, 1, 2, 3$ were originally introduced before the advent of the quantum theory to describe certain series of lines. s stands for sharp, p for principal, d for diffuse, f for fundamental.

Similarly the states corresponding $l = 2$ are called d-states.

In general there are $2l+1$ different values of u corresponding to a given value of l; the state corresponding to a given value of l shows a $(2l+1)$-fold degeneracy.

We turn now to the equation (15) for the radial part of the wave function. We shall take $V(r)$ to be either a Coulomb field, or a field of the type

$$V(r) = -Z(r)e^2/r,$$

where Z tends to unity as r tends to infinity, and to some larger value Z_0 as r tends to zero. We shall see in Chapter VI that this is a good approximation to the field in a heavy atom with one valence electron, such as an alkali atom.

We first substitute in (15)

$$R(r) = f(r)/r;$$

we then obtain
$$\frac{d^2f}{dr^2} + \left\{ \frac{2m}{\hbar^2}(W-V) - \frac{l(l+1)}{r^2} \right\} f = 0. \tag{16}$$

This equation is of the same type as the Schrödinger equation for the motion of an electron in one dimension.

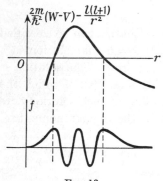

FIG. 13.

The type of solution can be seen by plotting against r the quantity enclosed in curly brackets. If W is negative but $|W|$ is small enough, it will appear as shown in Fig. 13. Where it is positive f will oscillate, where it is negative f will tend exponentially to zero. The quantum state will be defined by the number of nodes in the wave function; four are shown in the figure. They will appear in the wave-function ψ as nodal surfaces of spherical form.

We denote the total number of nodal surfaces in the wave-function ψ by $n-1$, and call n the *principal quantum number*. n is then equal to unity for the ground state, which has no nodes. Since l is the number of nodal surfaces passing through the origin, $n-l-1$ is the number of nodes in $f(r)$, i.e. the number shown as 4 in Fig. 13. We would expect the value of the energy associated with a given quantum state to depend primarily on n. Actually for the pure Coulomb field $(V = -Z_0 e^2/r)$, the analysis given below shows that the energy is actually independent of l, and depends only on the principal quantum number n according to (11). This is not the case for any other field; for the field described above the energy with $l = 0$ is the lowest. The scheme of energy levels is shown schematically† in Fig. 14.

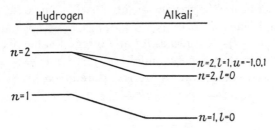

Fig. 14. Levels for hydrogen and alkali atoms.

We turn now to the solution of equation (10) for the particular case when V is equal to $-Ze^2/r$. If we set

$$r = \frac{1}{\hbar}\sqrt{(2m|W|)}\,x$$

the equation becomes

$$\frac{d^2f}{dx^2} + \left\{ -1 + \frac{\alpha}{x} - \frac{l(l+1)}{x^2} \right\} f = 0, \tag{17}$$

where

$$\alpha = \frac{1}{\hbar} Ze^2 \sqrt{\frac{2m}{|W|}}.$$

For large x, f will behave like $e^{\pm x}$, and as we require the solution which behaves like e^{-x}, we set

$$f = e^{-x}g(x).$$

We obtain, substituting into (17),

$$\frac{d^2g}{dx^2} - 2\frac{dg}{dx} + \left\{ \frac{\alpha}{x} - \frac{l(l+1)}{x^2} \right\} g = 0. \tag{18}$$

We attempt to find a solution of (18) of the form

$$g = x^\sigma \sum_{s=0}^{\infty} A_s x^s. \tag{19}$$

For σ this gives

$$\sigma(\sigma-1) = l(l+1),$$

whence $\sigma = l+1$ or $-l$. We require a solution that vanishes at the origin since R must remain finite; therefore we take the first solution. Substituting (19) into (18) we then obtain the following recurrence relation for A_s:

$$A_s[(s+l+1)(s+l) - l(l+1)] = A_{s-1}[2(s+l) - \alpha].$$

† In an actual atom the lowest levels will be forbidden for the valence electron by the exclusion principle.

If s is very large, and $2(s+l)-\alpha$ does not vanish for any integral value of s, then
$$A_s/A_{s-1} \sim 2/s.$$

The ratio of successive terms in the series is thus the same as the ratio of successive terms in the expansion of e^{2x}. Thus g tends to infinity as e^{2x} and f, and hence ψ, as e^x.

If, however, $2(s+l)-\alpha$ vanishes for any integral value of s, the series terminates. $g(x)$ is thus a polynomial and $f(x)$ tends exponentially to zero. The allowed energy values are therefore given by
$$\alpha = 2(s+l) \quad (s = 1, 2, 3, ...),$$
i.e.
$$W = -\frac{Z^2 e^4 m}{2\hbar^2}\frac{1}{(s+l)^2}.$$

We see that the energies depend only on a *single* quantum number n defined by
$$n = s+l.$$

If $n = 1$, we must have $l = 0$, if $n = 2$, $l = 0$ or $l = 1$, and so on.

The wave functions will be written down in a normalized form below.

$n = 1, l = 0, u = 0$
$$\psi = \pi^{-\frac{1}{2}}(Z/a)e^{-r/a},$$

$n = 2, l = 0, u = 0$
$$\psi = \frac{1}{4\sqrt{(2\pi)}}\left(\frac{Z}{a}\right)^{\frac{3}{2}}\left(2 - \frac{r}{a}\right)e^{-r/2a},$$

$n = 2, l = 1, n = -1, 0, +1$
$$\psi = \frac{1}{4\sqrt{(2\pi)}}\left(\frac{Z}{a}\right)^{\frac{3}{2}}\frac{r}{a}e^{-r/2a}\frac{1}{\sqrt{2}}\frac{\cos\theta}{\sin\theta}e^{\pm i\phi}.$$

A very full account of the normalized wave function for hydrogen can be obtained from a number of text-books, for example, Pauling and Wilson, *Introduction to Quantum Mechanics* (New York, 1935).

The problem of the hydrogen atom enclosed in a sphere (the proton being at the centre of the sphere) has been treated by Sommerfeld and Welker† who find that when the radius of the sphere is less than 1·835 times the radius of the first Bohr orbit, the energy of the system is positive, so that the electron is exerting a pressure on the walls of the sphere.

12.1. *Interpretation of the wave functions*

The wave function for an electron in an atom must be interpreted in the same way as for a free electron; $|\psi(x,y,z)|^2 dxdydz$ gives the probability that the electron will be found in the volume element $dxdydz$

† A. Sommerfeld and H. Welker, *Ann. der Physik*, **32**, 56 (1938).

at the point (x, y, z). It is here assumed that the wave function is normalized, i.e. that

$$\int |\psi(x, y, z)|^2 \, dx \, dy \, dz = 1.$$

An equivalent interpretation is the statement that

$$e|\psi(x, y, z)|^2$$

is the charge density in the atom averaged over a time long compared with the period of the electronic motion.

Some further points about the wave functions are worth noting. The wave functions of the s-states are spherically symmetrical; it will be shown later that they correspond to states of zero angular momentum. They have a maximum at $r = 0$, which shows that the electron has a large probability of penetrating into the interior of the atom.

The wave functions of the p-states all have a nodal plane through the nucleus and $R(r)$ vanishes there; this means that the electron has small probability of being found near the nucleus. For d-states, where two nodal planes pass through the nucleus and $R(r)$ behaves like r^2, the probability is smaller still.

12.2. *The momentum density functions*

We saw in Chapter I that, if the probability that an electron moving on a line lies between x' and $x' + dx'$ is $|\psi(x')|^2 dx'$, then the probability that its momentum p lies between p' and $p' + dp'$ is

$$|g(p')|^2 \, dp',$$

where
$$g(p) = \frac{1}{h^{\frac{1}{2}}} \int \psi(x) e^{-ipx/\hbar} \, dx. \tag{20}$$

It is clear that this result may be extended readily to the case of an electron moving in three-dimensional space. Thus if $\psi(\mathbf{r})$ is its wave function in xyz-space it follows by repeated application of (20) that its wave function in momentum space is

$$\chi(\mathbf{p}) = \frac{1}{h^{\frac{1}{2}}} \int \psi(\mathbf{r}) e^{-i(\mathbf{p} \cdot \mathbf{r})/\hbar} \, d\tau, \tag{21}$$

where $d\tau$ denotes a volume element and $(\mathbf{p} \cdot \mathbf{r})$ denotes the scalar product $p_x x + p_y y + p_z z$.

By means of this formula we can evaluate the distribution of momentum in the various states of the hydrogen atom. Thus for the ground state

$$\psi(\mathbf{r}) = \left(\frac{1}{\pi a^3}\right)^{\frac{1}{2}} e^{-r/a}.$$

Thus, using the result

$$\int e^{-\alpha r + i(\boldsymbol{\beta} \cdot \mathbf{r})} d\tau = \frac{8\pi\alpha}{(\alpha^2 + \beta^2)^2},$$

we obtain for the wave function in momentum space

$$\chi(p) = \frac{2}{\pi} \frac{(2\hbar^5 a^3)^{\frac{1}{2}}}{(\hbar^2 + a^2 p^2)^2},$$

so that the momentum density function is

$$|\chi(p)|^2 = \frac{8a^3\hbar^5}{\pi^2(\hbar^2 + a^2 p^2)^4}.$$

The density functions for the other states can be evaluated in a similar way. Pauling and Podolsky[†] have calculated the momentum function for hydrogen-like atoms, but very little theoretical work has been done on momentum distributions in atoms. The momentum distribution of electrons in atoms and molecules is of importance in electron scattering and will be considered later (Chap. VII).

12.3. *The continuous spectrum*

Solutions of the Schrödinger equation for the hydrogen atom also exist for positive values of the energy W. These correspond to the ionized state of the atom, and behave at infinity like $r^{-1}\sin(kr+\epsilon)$. They will be discussed further in Chapter IX.

13. The rigid rotator

A further problem which can be solved by elementary methods is that of finding the rotational energy levels of a diatomic molecule. We treat the molecule as a rigid rod, able to rotate about its centre of gravity with moment of inertia I. Then if θ, ϕ are the spherical polar coordinates defining its position in space, the Schrödinger equation is

$$\frac{\hbar^2}{2I}\left[\frac{1}{\sin\theta}\frac{\partial}{\partial\theta}\left(\sin\theta\frac{\partial\psi}{\partial\theta}\right) + \frac{1}{\sin^2\theta}\frac{\partial^2\psi}{\partial\phi^2}\right] + W\psi = 0.$$

We solve as before by setting

$$\psi = \Theta(\theta)\Phi(\phi),$$

and obtain

$$\Phi = e^{\pm iu\phi}$$

and

$$\frac{\hbar^2}{2I}\left[\frac{1}{\sin\theta}\frac{\partial}{\partial\theta}\left(\sin\theta\frac{\partial\Theta}{\partial\theta}\right) + \frac{u^2\Theta}{\sin^2\theta}\right] + W\Theta = 0.$$

[†] L. Pauling and B. Podolsky, *Phys. Rev.* **34**, 109 (1929).

This has bounded solutions $P_l^\mu(\cos\theta)$, if

$$W = \hbar^2 l(l+1)/2I. \tag{22}$$

This differs from the corresponding solution obtained from the old quantum theory in that l^2 is replaced by $l(l+1)$.

The bounded rigid rotator has been considered by Sommerfeld and Hartmann.†

14. Schrödinger's equation in invariant form‡

The invariant form of the Schrödinger equation may be obtained from the kinetic energy by a simple process. Suppose that in terms of generalized coordinates q^i ($i = 1,...,n$) the kinetic energy T of a dynamical system may be written in the form

$$T = \sum_{i,j}^{n} a_{ij}\dot{q}^i\dot{q}^j,$$

then we may consider the quantities a_{ij} to be the metric tensor of a coordinate space of n dimensions. Thus in rectangular Cartesian coordinates the a_{ij} then represent masses and the a^{ij} the inverses of these masses. In this space the invariant form of the Laplacian operator is

$$\frac{1}{\sqrt{a}}\sum_{i,j}\frac{\partial}{\partial q^j}\left(\sqrt{a}\,a^{ij}\frac{\partial}{\partial q^j}\right).$$

The other invariants in the wave equation can be constructed similarly. We can write the Schrödinger equation in the invariant form

$$\left[\sum_{k,j} -\frac{\hbar^2}{\sqrt{a}}\frac{\partial}{\partial q^k}\left(\sqrt{a}\,a^{kj}\frac{\partial}{\partial q^k}\right)+V\right]\Psi+\frac{\hbar}{i}\frac{\partial\Psi}{\partial t} = 0. \tag{23}$$

14.1. Symmetrical top molecules

If a molecule has an axis of symmetry this axis will be one of the principal axes of inertia. If a molecule (such as CH_3Cl) has a threefold axis the moments of inertia about any three axes $\xi\xi'$, $\eta\eta'$, $\zeta\zeta'$ lying in a plane normal to the axis of symmetry are equal. Since the momental ellipsoid intersects this plane in an ellipse, and since no ellipse can have three equal diameters at angles of $120°$ unless it degenerates into a circle, the curve of intersection must be a circle and the momental ellipsoid an ellipsoid of revolution. Thus a molecule of the type with a threefold axis behaves dynamically like a symmetrical top. Furthermore, there are molecules of lower symmetry (or no symmetry at all)

† A. Sommerfeld and H. Hartmann, *Ann. der Physik*, **37**, 333 (1940).
‡ Cf. E. Schrödinger, ibid. **79**, 748 (1926).

in which it so happens that two of the principal moments of inertia are equal; they, too, behave like symmetrical tops.

For this reason the wave equation for a symmetrical top is of interest in quantum mechanics.†

To describe the motion of a symmetrical top we make use of Euler's angles θ, ϕ, χ. θ denotes the angle between the z-axis in space and the axis of symmetry Oz' of the top, ϕ and χ the angles between the line of nodes on the line of intersection of the planes xOy, $x'Oy'$ and the lines Ox, Ox' respectively. If A and C denote the moments of inertia of the top about Ox' and Oz' respectively, then the kinetic energy T of the top is given in terms of the generalized momenta p_θ, p_ϕ, p_χ by the equation

$$2T = \frac{1}{A} p_\theta^2 + \left(\frac{\cos^2\theta}{A\sin^2\theta} + \frac{1}{C}\right) p_\phi^2 + \frac{1}{A\sin^2\theta} p_\chi^2 - \frac{2\cos\theta}{A\sin^2\theta} p_\phi p_\chi.$$

The Schrödinger equation for this system is then, by equation (23),

$$\frac{\partial^2\psi}{\partial\theta^2} + \frac{\cos\theta}{\sin\theta}\frac{\partial\psi}{\partial\theta} + \left(\frac{A}{C} + \frac{\cos^2\theta}{\sin\theta} + \frac{1}{C}\right)\frac{\partial^2\psi}{\partial\phi^2} + \frac{1}{\sin^2\theta}\frac{\partial^2\psi}{\partial\chi^2} -$$
$$- \frac{2\cos\theta}{\sin^2\theta}\frac{\partial^2\psi}{\partial\chi\partial\phi} + \frac{2AW}{\hbar^2}\psi = 0. \quad (24)$$

This equation is separable if we write

$$\psi = \Theta(\theta)\frac{\sin}{\cos}(n\phi + m\chi), \quad (25)$$

where m and n must be chosen to be integers if ψ returns to the same value when ϕ and χ are increased by integral multiples of 2π. Substituting from equation (25) into equation (24) we obtain

$$\frac{d^2\Theta}{d\theta^2} + \cot\theta\frac{d\Theta}{d\theta} - (m\operatorname{cosec}\theta - n\cot\theta)^2\Theta + \sigma\Theta = 0, \quad (26)$$

where we have written $\quad \sigma = \frac{2AW}{\hbar^2} - \frac{A}{C}n^2. \quad (27)$

If we make the substitutions

$$u = \tfrac{1}{2}(1+\cos\theta), \qquad \Theta = u^{\frac{1}{2}|m+n|}(u-1)^{\frac{1}{2}|m-n|}U,$$

then equation (26) can be brought to the form

$$u(u-1)\frac{d^2U}{du^2} + \{\gamma - (\alpha+\beta+1)u\}\frac{dU}{du} - \alpha\beta U = 0, \quad (28)$$

† F. Reiche, *Zeits. f. Physik*, **39**, 444 (1926); R. de L. Kronig and I. I. Rabi, *Phys. Rev.* **29**, 262 (1927); D. M. Dennison, ibid. **28**, 318, 891 (1928).

where
$$2\alpha = |m+n|+|m-n|+1+(1+4\sigma+4n^2)^{\frac{1}{2}},$$
$$2\beta = |m+n|+|m-n|+1-(1+4\sigma+4n^2)^{\frac{1}{2}}, \tag{29}$$
$$\gamma = |m+n|+1.$$

It follows immediately from the definitions (29) and the fact that m and n are integers that $\gamma-1$ is a positive integer and that
$$\alpha+\beta-\gamma \geqslant 0.$$

Originally θ lay in the interval $0 \leqslant \theta \leqslant \pi$ so that $0 \leqslant u \leqslant 1$; if U is to be finite in this interval β must be zero or a negative integer. This will only be so if
$$\sigma = j(j+1)-n^2, \tag{30}$$
where
$$j = \tfrac{1}{2}\{|m+n|+|m-n|\}, \quad \tfrac{1}{2}\{|m+n|+|m-n|\}+1, \quad ...,$$

as is easily seen from (29). Hence j must be zero or a positive integer. Eliminating σ from equations (27) and (30) we have finally for the energy levels
$$W_{jn} = \tfrac{1}{2}\hbar^2\left[\frac{j(j+1)}{A}+\left(\frac{1}{C}-\frac{1}{A}\right)n^2\right], \tag{31}$$

which is Dennison's formula for the energy levels of the rotational motion of simple molecules. This formula can also be derived in a semi-classical way.[†]

The wave mechanical theory of a symmetric top which in addition to the usual three degrees of rotational freedom has also a degree of torsional freedom between two of its principal parts is of interest, since certain molecules, the simplest of which probably are ethylene (C_2H_4) and ethane (C_2H_6), are thought to behave in this manner. In this case two angles ϕ_1 and ϕ_2 are required in place of the ϕ above; ϕ_1 denotes the angle between the line of nodes and an x-axis fixed in the lower part of the top, and ϕ_2 is similarly defined for an axis fixed in the upper part. The angle of twist is then $\phi_2-\phi_1$ and the potential energy, which was zero in the case of the rigid top, is now of the form
$$V = L\{1-\cos m(\phi_2-\phi_1)\}.$$

The energy levels for this system have been investigated by Nielsen,[‡] to whose paper the reader is referred for further details.

[†] See, for instance, G. Herzberg, *Infra Red and Raman Spectra of Polyatomic Molecules* (New York, 1945), pp. 24–6.

[‡] H. A. Nielsen, *Phys. Rev.* **40**, 445 (1932).

III

PROPERTIES OF THE WAVE FUNCTIONS

15. The orthogonal property

THIS property is of great importance for the further development of wave mechanics. It will be explained first for particles moving in one dimension (along the x-axis). It will be supposed that the particle is described by a wave-function $\psi(x)$ satisfying the Schrödinger equation

$$\frac{d^2\psi}{dx^2} + \frac{2m}{\hbar^2}\{W - V(x)\}\psi = 0. \tag{1}$$

It will be supposed that a set of solutions exists either satisfying the boundary conditions that ψ tends to zero as x tends to $\pm\infty$, or that ψ vanishes at the extremities of some range of x. (An alternative boundary condition which is of importance in Chapter VIII is that $\partial\psi/\partial x$ vanishes at the extremities of some range of x.) Then the orthogonal property states that, if ψ_1, ψ_2 are solutions of (1) corresponding to different characteristic values of W, W_1, and W_2,

$$\int \psi_1^* \psi_2 \, dx = 0, \tag{2}$$

the integration being over the range of x considered.

The proof is as follows: from (1) we have the Schrödinger equation

$$\frac{d^2\psi_1}{dx^2} + \frac{2m}{\hbar^2}(W_1 - V)\psi_1 = 0$$

and therefore

$$\frac{d^2\psi_2^*}{dx^2} + \frac{2m}{\hbar^2}(W_2 - V)\psi_2^* = 0.$$

Multiplying the first equation by ψ_2^* and the second by ψ_1 and subtracting, we have

$$\frac{2m}{\hbar^2}(W_1 - W_2)\psi_2^*\psi_1 + \left(\psi_2^*\frac{d^2\psi_1}{dx^2} - \psi_1\frac{d^2\psi_2^*}{dx^2}\right) = 0. \tag{3}$$

If we integrate from x_1 to x_2 the second term gives

$$\left[\psi_2^*\frac{d\psi_1}{dx} - \psi_1\frac{d\psi_2^*}{dx}\right]_{x_1}^{x_2}.$$

The boundary conditions for ψ are that either ψ or $d\psi/dx$ should vanish; the term in square brackets therefore vanishes and it follows that

$$\int \psi_2^*\psi_1 \, dx = 0.$$

If the particle moves in three dimensions, we have

$$\nabla^2\psi_1 + \frac{2m}{\hbar^2}(W_1 - V)\psi_1 = 0$$

with a corresponding equation for ψ_2. We obtain as before

$$\psi_2^* \nabla^2 \psi_1 - \psi_1 \nabla^2 \psi_2^* + \frac{2m}{\hbar^2}(W_1 - W_2)\psi_1 \psi_2^* = 0.$$

On integrating over the space in which the electron moves, the first term gives

$$\int \left(\psi_2^* \frac{\partial \psi_1}{\partial n} - \psi_1 \frac{\partial \psi_2^*}{\partial n} \right) dS,$$

where the variable n denotes the normal component of the vector and dS an element of the surface bounding the space. Since either ψ or $\partial \psi / \partial n$ vanishes at all points on this surface, it follows that

$$\iiint \psi_2^* \psi_1 \, dx \, dy \, dz = 0.$$

If the system contains degenerate states, i.e. a number of states ψ_1, $\psi_2, \ldots, \psi_s$ which have all the same energy, it is always possible to obtain linear combinations of these,

$$\psi_{s'}^1 = \sum_s c_{s's} \psi_s,$$

which are orthogonal to each other. Thus all the wave functions of the system which correspond to bound states may be considered orthogonal to each other.

15.1. *Expansion of an arbitrary function in terms of wave functions*

For the discussions of this section it will be convenient to consider only systems for which all the energy values are quantized. This will be the case for a particle in a box with rigid reflecting walls (Chap. II) or for a simple harmonic oscillator. It will not be the case for the hydrogen atom, unless we suppose the atom to be shut up in a large box with rigid reflecting walls.

Suppose then a particle moves in a field of potential $V(x, y, z)$ and that the quantized energy-values W_n and corresponding wave-functions ψ_n are given by

$$\nabla^2 \psi_n + \frac{2m}{\hbar^2}(W_n - V)\psi_n = 0,$$

where ψ_n satisfies certain boundary conditions (i.e. that ψ_n should tend to zero as r tends to infinity). Suppose that $f(x, y, z)$ is any arbitrary continuous function satisfying the same boundary conditions. Then it may be shown that $f(x, y, z)$ can be expanded in the form

$$f(x, y, z) = \sum_n A_n \psi_n(x, y, z). \tag{4}$$

For a proof the reader is referred to Courant and Hilbert, loc. cit.

The expansion is clearly a generalization of Fourier's theorem, the functions $\psi_n(x, y, z)$ taking the place of the sines and cosines in a Fourier expansion. The coefficients can be found in the same way as Fourier coefficients. Using the orthogonal relation

$$\int \psi_n^* \psi_{n'} \, d\tau = 0 \quad (n \neq n')$$

and assuming the wave functions to be normalized, so that

$$\int \psi_n^* \psi_n \, d\tau = 1,$$

then if both sides of (4) are multiplied by ψ_n^* and an integration is carried out over all space, we find

$$A_n = \int f \psi_n^* \, d\tau.$$

The expansion (4) has an important physical interpretation. Supposing $f(x, y, z)$ is a wave function describing the state of a particle at a given instant of time. Then if the expansion (4) is made, the coefficients A_n will have the following physical significance; A_n is the probability that if the energy of the particle were determined, it would be equal to W_n.

The assumption that the coefficients A_n can be interpreted in this way is a new one, and is not inherent in the arguments developed up to this point. It is similar to the assumption made in Chapter I, that the Fourier component of a wave function gives information about the momentum of a particle.

It will easily be verified that

$$\sum_n |A_n|^2 = 1.$$

16. Transformation functions

In the last section we showed that if a particle is described by a wave-function $f(x)$, then

$$\left| \int \psi_n^* f \, d\tau \right|^2$$

gives the probability that particle has energy W_n. In section 7 it was shown that

$$\left| \frac{1}{h^{\frac{1}{2}}} \int e^{-ipx/\hbar} f \, dx \right|^2 dp$$

gives the probability that the momentum lies between p and $p+dp$. The functions

$$\psi_n(x), \qquad h^{-\frac{1}{2}} e^{ipx/\hbar}$$

are known as 'transformation functions'; they can be used to obtain information about the energy or the momentum from a wave function giving information about the position of a particle. In this section this procedure will be generalized, and a method will be given whereby information about any dynamical variable can be obtained.

Let the dynamical variable under consideration be denoted by $L(p, x)$, a function of the momentum and spatial coordinates. Besides the momentum p and energy $p^2/2m + V(x)$, the most important variable that we shall have to consider is the angular momentum

$$yp_z - zp_y, \qquad zp_x - xp_z, \qquad xp_y - yp_x.$$

In this section, however, L will be assumed to be a quite general function of p and x.

If, as in §7, we replace p by the operator $(\hbar/i)\partial/\partial x$, then L can be regarded as an operator. We may thus set up a differential equation

$$\left[L\left(\frac{\hbar}{i}\frac{\partial}{\partial x}, x\right) - L' \right] g_L(x) = 0, \tag{5}$$

which, if $g_L(x)$ is subject to appropriate boundary conditions, will define a set of characteristic functions g_L which satisfy the boundary conditions if and only if L' has one of a series of characteristic values. For example, if L is the energy

$$L = p^2/2m + V,$$

(5) is the usual Schrödinger equation. If L is the momentum p, the equation takes the form

$$\frac{\hbar}{i}\frac{\partial g}{\partial x} - p'g = 0$$

with solutions

$$g = Ae^{ip'x/\hbar}.$$

It will now be shown that the functions $g_L(x)$, the characteristic solutions of (5), are the required transformation functions; in other words that, if a particle is in a state described by a wave function $\psi(x)$,

$$\left| \int g_{L'}^*(x)\psi(x)\, dx \right|^2$$

is the probability that the variable L has the value L'.

First of all, let us consider $g_{L'}(x)$ as a wave function. Then, if a particle is in a state described by a wave function $g_{L'}(x)$, the average value of L is

$$\int g_{L'}^*(x) L\left(\frac{\hbar}{i}\frac{\partial}{\partial x}, x\right) g_{L'}(x)\, dx.$$

If the wave functions are normalized, this by (5) is equal to L'. Further, making use of (5) we can easily show that

$$\int g_{L'}^*(x)[L - L']^2 g_{L'}(x)\, dx = 0,$$

where L as before denotes the operator $L\left(\frac{\hbar}{i}\frac{\partial}{\partial x}, x\right)$. It follows that if

the particle is in a state described by $g_{L'}(x)$, then the value of L is
certainly L'. The functions $g_{L'}$ stand in the same relation to the variable
L as the wave-functions $\psi_n(x)$ do to the energy $\frac{1}{2}p^2/m+V$.

Suppose now that the particle is in a state described by *any* wave-
function $\psi(x)$. We can, as in the last section, expand ψ in a series

$$\psi(x) = \sum A_{L'} g_{L'}(x).$$

As before, $|A_{L'}|^2$ will give the probability that the variable L has the
value L'. But, by the orthogonal property of the functions $g_{L'}$,

$$A_{L'} = \int \psi(x) g_L^*(x)\, dx.$$

This shows that the functions $g_{L'}(x)$ are the required transformation
functions.

16.1. *Formulation of problems in momentum space*

A useful method of solution of quantum mechanical problems consists
in a transformation of the Schrödinger equation to momentum space.
This method has particular advantages when applied to the solution
of problems in theoretical nuclear physics.† The transformation of the
Schrödinger equation to momentum space is equivalent to applying
the method of Fourier transforms to the solution of the equation. In
this section an outline of the method will be given; for a rigorous
mathematical theory of the representation of the Schrödinger equation
in momentum space reference should be made to a paper by Gordon.‡

For simplicity we shall consider a system with only one degree of
freedom, the extension to higher degrees of freedom being purely
formal. If we denote the coordinate and momentum of the system by
x, p respectively, the Schrödinger equation may be written in the form

$$\left\{\frac{p^2}{2m} + V(x)\right\}\psi = W\psi.$$

According to the theory we have developed above the momentum p is
interpreted as a differential operator $(\hbar/i)\partial/\partial x$ and the potential energy
$V(x)$ acts on the wave function ψ as an ordinary multiplier. It is easily
shown by integration by parts that

$$\int_{-\infty}^{\infty} e^{ipx/\hbar}\left(\frac{\hbar}{i}\frac{\partial}{\partial x}\right)^2 \psi\, dx = p^2 \int_{-\infty}^{\infty} e^{ipx/\hbar}\psi\, dx,$$

† Nils Svartholm, *The Binding Energies of the Lightest Atomic Nuclei* (thesis, Lund, 945).

‡ W. Gordon, *Skand. Matem. Kongr. Stockholm*, 249 (1934).

so that when the problem is transposed from the ordinary space x to the momentum space p by means of the transformation

$$\chi(p) = \frac{1}{h^{\frac{1}{2}}} \int\limits_{-\infty}^{\infty} e^{ipx/\hbar} \psi(x)\, dx$$

we may write the Schrödinger equation in the form

$$\left(\frac{p^2}{2m} - W\right)\chi(p) + \frac{1}{h^{\frac{1}{2}}} \int\limits_{-\infty}^{\infty} V(x) e^{ipx/\hbar} \psi(x)\, dx = 0.$$

By the Fourier inversion theorem

$$\psi(x) = \frac{1}{h^{\frac{1}{2}}} \int\limits_{-\infty}^{\infty} e^{-ip'x/\hbar} \chi(p')\, dp',$$

so that

$$\frac{1}{h^{\frac{1}{2}}} \int\limits_{-\infty}^{\infty} V(x) e^{ipx/\hbar} \psi(x)\, dx = \frac{1}{h} \int\limits_{-\infty}^{\infty} \chi(p')\, dp' \int\limits_{-\infty}^{\infty} V(x) e^{i(p-p')x/\hbar}\, dx.$$

Writing

$$v(p-p') = \frac{1}{h} \int\limits_{-\infty}^{\infty} V(x) e^{i(p-p')x/\hbar}\, dx,$$

we obtain

$$\left(\frac{p^2}{2m} - W\right)\chi(p) + \int\limits_{-\infty}^{\infty} v(p-p')\chi(p')\, dp' = 0.$$

The solutions of this equation differ according as W is positive or negative. If W is negative and we write

$$\phi(p) = (p^2 - 2mW)^{\frac{1}{2}}\chi(p),$$

$$K(p, p') = -2m(p^2 - 2mW)^{-\frac{1}{2}}(p'^2 - 2mW)^{-\frac{1}{2}}v(p-p');$$

we then obtain the homogeneous integral equation

$$\phi(p) = \int\limits_{-\infty}^{\infty} K(p, p')\phi(p')\, dp'.$$

Approximate solutions of this integral equation may be constructed by means of the Gauss–Hilbert variational principle and the method of iterated functions due to Kellog.†

In certain cases, however, it is possible to obtain exact solutions of this equation. For example if

$$V(x) = V_0 e^{-a|x|/\hbar},$$

† O. D. Kellog, *Math. Ann.* **86**, 14 (1922).

then
$$\int_{-\infty}^{\infty} e^{i(p-p')x/\hbar} V(x)\, dx = \frac{2V_0 a\hbar}{a^2+(p-p')^2},$$

so that if we write $p_0^2 = -2mW$, $\lambda = -2V_0 m/a^2$ the integral equation for the wave-function $\chi(p)$ reduces to

$$(p^2+p_0)^2\chi(p) = \frac{\lambda}{\pi} \int_{-\infty}^{\infty} \frac{a^3}{a^2+(p-p')^2}\, \chi(p')\, dp'.$$

If we assume a solution of this equation of the form

$$\chi(p) = \sum_{n=0}^{\infty} \frac{c_n p}{p^2+(an+p_0)^2},$$

then by direct substitution and use of the result

$$\frac{1}{\pi} \int_{-\infty}^{\infty} \frac{a^3}{a^2+(p-p')^2} \frac{p'}{p'^2+\nu^2}\, dp' = \frac{a^2 p}{p^2+(a+\nu)^2}$$

we obtain the relation

$$\sum_{n=0}^{\infty} c_n p\left[1 - \frac{(an+p_0)^2-p_0^2}{p^2+(an+p_0^2)}\right] = \lambda a^2 \sum_{n=1}^{\infty} c_{n-1} \frac{p}{p^2+(an+p_0^2)}.$$

Both sides of this equation represent the same function if the coefficients c_n satisfy the relations

$$c_n = -\frac{\lambda a^2}{(an+p_0)^2-p_0^2}\, c_{n-1},$$

$$\sum_{n=0}^{\infty} c_n = 0.$$

Substituting from the former of these equations into the latter we obtain the relation

$$c_0 + c_0 \sum_{n=1}^{\infty} \frac{(-\lambda)^n}{n!} \cdot \frac{1}{(1+2p_0/a)...(n+2p_0/a)} = 0,$$

which may be written in the form

$$\lambda^{-p_0/a} J_{2p_0/a}(2\sqrt{\lambda}) = 0,$$

$J_n(z)$ denoting the Bessel function of order n. In this transcendental equation λ and a are known, so the equation may be used to find p_0, i.e. the possible values of the energy, W, of the system. Once p_0 has been determined in this way the wave function $\chi(p)$ can be obtained as an infinite series.

17. The elements of perturbation theory

17.1. *Perturbation theory for non-degenerate states*

In this section, following the considerations of § 8, we shall write the symbol H for the operator

$$H = -\frac{\hbar^2}{2m}\nabla^2 + V.$$

If the solutions of a Schrödinger equation

$$(H - W)\psi = 0 \tag{6}$$

are known, together with the corresponding discrete energy values W_n, then it is possible to calculate the change in the energy values that results if H is changed by a *small* amount U. The term U is called the perturbation, and the analysis by which this is done is known as perturbation theory. Examples are: the change in the energy of the stationary states due to an electric or magnetic field, the interaction between the electrons in a two-electron atom, and so on.

The first-order perturbation may be obtained as follows: let ψ_n and W_n be the wave function and energy value of a non-degenerate solution of equation (6). The perturbed equation is

$$(H + U - W)\psi = 0. \tag{7}$$

Let us write

$$W = W_n + w,$$
$$\psi = \psi_n + f.$$

Then retaining in (7) only small quantities of the first order in U, w, and f we have

$$(H - W_n)f + (U - w)\psi_n = 0. \tag{8}$$

Now let us expand f in the form

$$f = \sum A_{n'}\psi_{n'}.$$

Equation (8) becomes

$$\sum_{n'} A_{n'}(W_{n'} - W_n)\psi_{n'} + (U - w)\psi_n = 0.$$

If we multiply by ψ_n^* and integrate over all spatial coordinates q we obtain

$$w = \int \psi_n^* U\psi_n \, dq, \tag{9}$$

which is the required result. The coefficient $A_{n'}$ in the perturbed wave function can be obtained in the same way:

$$A_{n'} = \frac{\int \psi_{n'}^* U\psi_n \, dq}{W_n - W_{n'}}. \tag{10}$$

As an example, we take an electron moving in a central field with potential energy function Ze^2/r, and try the effect on the ground state of changing Z to $Z+1$. Then

$$U = -e^2/r$$

and

$$w = \int_0^\infty e^{-2Zr/a}\frac{e^2}{r}r^2\,dr \bigg/ \int_0^\infty e^{-2Zr/a}r^2\,dr,$$

where

$$a = \hbar^2/mZe^2.$$

On evaluating this gives

$$w = \frac{mZe^4}{\hbar^2},$$

which may be compared with the exact value

$$\frac{me^4}{2\hbar^2}\{(Z+1)^2 - Z^2\} = \frac{me^4}{\hbar^2}(Z+\tfrac{1}{2}).$$

It will be noticed that formula (9) predicts a big change in the energy if $|\psi|^2$ is large in regions where the perturbing field is large. Thus, for example, a change in the field near the nucleus of an atom will lead to a much larger change in the energy of the s-states than the p-states, for which ψ vanishes at the nucleus.

17.2. *Matrix elements*

The quantity defined by

$$(n'|U|n'') = \int \psi_{n'}^* U\psi_{n''}\,dq$$

is termed the 'matrix element' of U with respect to the two states n', n''. It occurs in (10) for the first time in this book.

From any dynamical variable $L(p,q)$ and any set of transformation functions $g_n(q)$ a matrix may be formed, of which the element n, n' is

$$\int g_n^*(q)L\left(\frac{\hbar}{i}\frac{\partial}{\partial q}, q\right)g_{n'}(q)\,dq.$$

For the Hermitian operators which occur in quantum mechanics, it follows that

$$(n|U|n') = \text{complex conjugate of } (n'|U|n),$$

and also that the diagonal elements are real.

17.3. *Perturbation theory for degenerate states*

Let us suppose that the unperturbed system satisfying equation (6) has states ψ_a, ψ_b with the same energy. Then the perturbation will in general split the degenerate energy value into two with energies $W+w_1$, $W+w_2$ and wave-functions ψ_1+f_1, ψ_2+f_2 where

$$\psi_1 = A_1\psi_a + B_1\psi_b,$$
$$\psi_2 = A_2\psi_a + B_2\psi_b. \tag{11}$$

In practice there are two ways of finding the coefficients A_1, B_1, etc., and the energies w_1, w_2. As before, if we insert ψ_1 into the wave equation we have
$$(U-w)\psi_1+(H-W)f_1 = 0.$$

Since ψ_1, ψ_2 are orthogonal, and $\int \psi_2 H f_1 \, dq$ vanishes,
$$\int \psi_2 U\psi_1 \, dq = 0. \tag{12}$$

Thus, if we can choose ψ_1, ψ_2 by inspection such that ψ_1, ψ_2 are orthogonal and (12) is satisfied, then the energies can be obtained from
$$w_1 = \int \psi_1^* \, U\psi_1 \, dq, \qquad w_2 = \int \psi_2^* \, U\psi_2 \, dq.$$

Alternatively, inserting (11) into (8), multiplying by ψ_a, and integrating over all q we find
$$A_1(U_{aa}-w)+B_1 U_{ab} = 0.$$
Similarly
$$A_1 U_{ba}+B_1(U_{bb}-w) = 0.$$

Eliminating A_1, B_1 and remembering that $U_{ab} = U_{ba}^*$, we obtain the following quadratic equation for w_1, w_2:
$$(U_{aa}-w)(U_{bb}-w) = |U_{ab}|^2. \tag{13}$$

18. The Rayleigh–Schrödinger method

18.1. *Unperturbed system non-degenerate*

In the preceding analysis we retained only small quantities of the first order in U, w, f. In some problems, however, it happens that the matrix element
$$(n|U|n) = \int \psi_n^* \, U\psi_n \, d\tau$$

vanishes, so it is necessary to examine terms of higher order. Suppose, for instance, that it is possible to expand the perturbation U in the form
$$U = \lambda H_1+\lambda^2 H_2+\lambda^3 H_3+\ldots, \tag{14}$$

where λ is a parameter, and that ψ_n, W_n are the wave function and energy value of a *non-degenerate* solution of equation (6); then we may assume that the solution of equation (7) may be written in the form
$$\psi = \psi_n+\lambda\phi_n+\lambda^2\chi_n+\lambda^3\theta_n+\ldots \tag{15}$$

with corresponding energy value
$$W = W_n+\lambda w_n+\lambda^2 \varpi_n+\ldots. \tag{16}$$

Substituting from equations (14), (15), and (16) into equation (7) and rearranging in powers of λ we obtain
$$(H-W_n)\psi_n+\lambda[(H_1-w_n)\psi_n+(H-W_n)\phi_n]+$$
$$+\lambda^2[(H_2-\varpi_n)\psi_n+(H_1-w_n)\phi_n+(H-W_n)\chi_n]+\ldots = 0.$$

The term devoid of λ is identically equal to zero by equation (6). Equating to zero the coefficients of λ we obtain the set of equations

$$(H_1-w_n)\psi_n+(H-W_n)\phi_n = 0 \tag{17}$$

$$(H_2-\varpi_n)\psi_n+(H_1-w_n)\phi_n+(H-W_n)\chi_n = 0, \tag{18}$$

$$\cdot \quad \cdot \quad \cdot \quad \cdot \quad \cdot \quad \cdot \quad \cdot \quad \cdot \quad \cdot$$

If we expand ϕ_n in the form

$$\phi_n = \sum_i a_{ni}\psi_i,$$

then

$$(H-W_n)\phi_n = \sum_i a_{ni}(W_i-W_n)\psi_i;$$

multiplying both sides of this equation by ψ_n^*, integrating, and making use of the equation

$$\int \psi_n^*\psi_i \, d\tau = \delta_{ni},$$

we can obtain the result $\int \psi_n^*(H-W_n)\phi_n \, d\tau = 0$, so that, from equation (17),

$$\int \psi_n^*(H_1-w_n)\psi_n \, d\tau = 0.$$

From this it follows that $\quad w_n = (n|H_1|n).$ \hfill (19)

Furthermore,

$$\int \psi_j^*(H-W_n)\phi_n \, d\tau = \sum_l a_{nl} \int \psi_j^*(H-W_n)\psi_l \, d\tau$$

$$= a_{nj}(W_j-W_n)$$

$$= - \int \psi_j^*(H_1-w_n)\psi_n \, d\tau$$

$$= -(j|H_1|n),$$

giving

$$a_{nj} = - \frac{(j|H_1|n)}{W_j-W_n} \quad (j \neq n),$$

and we have

$$\phi_n = - {\sum_j}' \frac{(j|H_1|n)}{W_j-W_n}\psi_j, \tag{20}$$

the dash on the summation sign denoting that the term $j = n$ is omitted.

Substituting from equations (19) and (20) into equation (18), we obtain the equation

$$(H_2-\varpi_n)\psi_n+{\sum_j}' \frac{(j|H_1|n)}{W_n-W_j}\{H_1-(n|H_1|n)\}\psi_j+(H-W_n)\chi_n = 0. \tag{21}$$

If we write

$$\chi_n = \sum_i b_{ni}\psi_i,$$

then it can easily be shown that

$$\int \psi_n^*(H-W_n)\chi_n \, d\tau = 0,$$

so that, multiplying equation (21) throughout by ψ_n^* and integrating, we obtain

$$\varpi_n = (n|H_2|n) + \sum_j{}' \frac{(j|H_1|n)(n|H_1|j)}{W_n - W_j}. \tag{22}$$

Similarly, multiplying both sides of (21) by ψ_l^* ($l \neq n$), we obtain

$$b_{nl} = \frac{(l|H_2|n)}{W_n - W_l} + \sum_j{}' \frac{(l|H_1|j)(j|H_1|n)}{(W_n - W_j)(W_n - W_l)}. \tag{23}$$

Generally only these earlier terms of the expansion are used in actual calculations; the higher terms become increasingly complicated. The final values for the perturbed wave function and energy value are thus

$$\psi = \psi_n + \lambda \sum_j{}' \frac{(j|H_1|n)}{W_n - W_j} \psi_j +$$

$$+ \lambda^2 \sum_l{}' \left\{ \frac{(l|H_2|n)}{W_n - W_l} + \sum_j{}' \frac{(l|H_1|j)(j|H_1|n)}{(W_n - W_j)(W_n - W_l)} \right\} \psi_l + O(\lambda^3) \tag{24}$$

and

$$W = W_n + \lambda(n|H_1|n) + \lambda^2 \left\{ (n|H_2|n) + \sum_j{}' \frac{(n|H_1|j)(j|H_1|n)}{W_n - W_j} \right\} + O(\lambda^3). \tag{25}$$

In cases for which the elementary method fails, i.e. $(n|U|n) = 0$, we have

$$\lambda(n|H_1|n) + \lambda^2(n|H_2|n) + \ldots = 0,$$

so that the formula for W reduces to

$$W = W_n + \lambda^2 \sum_j{}' \frac{(n|H_1|j)(j|H_1|n)}{W_n - W_j}$$

$$= W_n + \sum_j{}' \frac{(n|U|j)(j|U|n)}{W_n - W_j}. \tag{26}$$

This method of obtaining an expression for the energy of the perturbed system was devised by Schrödinger;[†] it is the natural extension to wave mechanics of Rayleigh's method[‡] of approximating to the modes of vibration of a continuous solid. The procedure adopted above is also analogous to the methods of Newcomb and Linstedt[§] for the solution of the equations of dynamics in terms of trigonometric series.

18.2. *Degenerate systems*

When the unperturbed system is degenerate the procedure is the same in principle. Suppose, for instance, that there are k independent

† E. Schrödinger, *Ann. der Physik*, **80**, 437 (1926).
‡ Lord Rayleigh, *The Theory of Sound*, vol. i, p. 113 (1894).
§ H. Poincaré, *Méthodes nouvelles de la mécanique céleste.*

wave functions of equation (6) corresponding to the energy value W_n. Denote these wave functions by

$$\psi_n^{(1)}, \ \psi_n^{(2)}, \ \psi_n^{(3)},..., \ \psi_n^{(k)},$$

and suppose that they are normalized and orthogonal to each other and to all other eigenfunctions. Then the set of k wave functions

$$\psi_{n,m} = \sum_{j=1}^{k} a_{mj} \psi_n^{(j)} \tag{27}$$

$(m = 1, 2,..., k)$ correspond to the energy W_n and satisfy the orthogonality and normalization property

$$\int \psi_{n,m}^* \psi_{n,p} \, d\tau = \delta_{mp},$$

provided the coefficients a_{mj} are chosen to satisfy the relation

$$\sum_{j=1}^{k} a_{mj}^* a_{pj} = \delta_{mp}. \tag{28}$$

If we now assume a solution of equation (7) in the form

$$\psi = \psi_{n,m} + \lambda \phi_{n,m} + \lambda^2 \chi_{n,m} + ...,$$

then as before we have, on equating the coefficient of λ to zero,

$$(H_1 - w_n)\psi_{n,m} + (H - W_n)\phi_{n,m} = 0. \tag{29}$$

If we write $\phi_{n,m}$ as a series of the $\psi_n^{(i)}$ wave functions, say

$$\phi_{n,m} = \sum \alpha_{mj} \psi_n^{(j)}, \tag{30}$$

and replace $\psi_{n,m}$ by the expansion (27), then we obtain the equation

$$\sum_{j=1}^{k} a_{mj}\{(i|H_1|j) - \delta_{ij} w_n\} = 0 \quad (i = 1, 2,..., k) \tag{31}$$

by a procedure similar to that employed in the non-degenerate case. In equation (31) $(i|H_1|j)$ now denotes the matrix element

$$(i|H_1|j) = \int \psi_n^{(i)*} H_1 \psi_n^{(j)} \, d\tau.$$

The set of equations (31) determines the constants a_{mj}. To determine the k values of the energy into which W_n is split by the perturbation we eliminate the a_{mj} from equation (31) to obtain the determinantal equation

$$\begin{vmatrix} (1|H_1|1) - w_n & (1|H_1|2) & . & . & . & (1|H_1|k) \\ (2|H_1|1) & (2|H_1|2) - w_n & . & . & . & (2|H_1|k) \\ . & . & . & . & . & . \\ (k|H_1|1) & (k|H_2|2) & . & . & . & (k|H_1|k) - w_n \end{vmatrix} = 0. \tag{32}$$

The determinant on the left-hand side of this equation has, of course,

k rows and k columns. In general the equation will have k distinct roots. Corresponding to each of these roots w_m, there will be a set of coefficients a_{mj} determined from the equations (31). These coefficients will, in turn define a unique wave-function $\psi_{n,m}$ defined by equation (27). The perturbation will then, in general, split up the energy W_n into k separate energy levels $W_n + w_m$ $(m = 1, 2, ..., k)$ and will determine a unique set of wave-functions $\psi_{n,m}$. Once these $\psi_{n,m}$ are known the coefficients α_{mj} in the expansion (30) for the wave function $\phi_{n,m}$ can be determined as in the non-degenerate case.

18.3. *A modified form of the Schrödinger theory*

There are many problems in quantum mechanics in which the solutions of the unperturbed Schrödinger equation for the higher values of W are not known with any accuracy. We shall see later (§§ 25, 33) that the wave functions of the helium atom and the hydrogen molecule are known accurately for only the very lowest energy states. If, however, we wished to determine the wave function of such a system perturbed from its normal state by means of equation (24) above, we would require to know all the eigenfunctions, not only the one which is perturbed. It is, however, possible to increase the accuracy of such calculations by transforming the series on the right-hand side of equation (24) to a form which is more rapidly convergent.

We may write

$$H_1 \psi_n = \sum_j (j|H_1|n)\psi_j = \sum_j{}' (j|H_1|n)\psi_j + w_n \psi_n,$$

so that

$$\frac{(H_1 - w_n)\psi_n}{W_n} + \sum_j{}' \frac{W_j(j|H_1|n)}{W_n(W_n - W_j)}\psi_j = \sum_j{}' \left\{\frac{1}{W_n} + \frac{W_j}{W_n(W_n - W_j)}\right\}\psi_j(j|H_1|n)$$

$$= \sum_j{}' \frac{(j|H_1|n)}{W_n - W_j}\psi_j.$$

Thus equation (20) can be put in the form

$$\phi_n = \frac{(H_1 - w_n)\psi_n}{W_n} + \sum_j{}' \frac{W_j(j|H_1|n)}{W_n(W_n - W_j)}\psi_j. \tag{33}$$

Substituting from equations (19) and (33) into equation (18) we obtain

$$(H_2 - \varpi_n)\psi_n + \frac{(H_1 - w_n)^2 \psi_n}{W_n} + \sum_j{}' \frac{W_j(j|H_1|n)}{W_n(W_n - W_j)}(H_1 - w_n)\psi_j +$$

$$+ (H - W_n)\chi_n = 0.$$

Multiplying both sides of this equation by ψ_n^* and making use of the result

$$\int \psi_n^*(H_1-w_n)^2\psi_n \, dq = (n|H_1^2|n)-(n|H_1|n)^2$$

we obtain finally

$$\varpi_n = (n|H_2|n)+\frac{(n|H_1^2|n)-(n|H_1|n)^2}{W_n}+\sum_j{}'\frac{W_j(n|H_1|j)(j|H_1|n)}{W_n(W_n-W_j)}. \quad (34)$$

The integral $(n|H_1^2|n)$ is as easy to evaluate as $(n|H_1|n)$ and the series usually converges much more rapidly than those involved in (25) and (26). In the case in which $(n|U|n) = 0$ we get for the energy of the perturbed system

$$W = W_n+\frac{(n|U^2|n)}{W_n}+\sum_j{}'\frac{W_j(n|U|j)(j|U|n)}{W_n(W_n-W_j)}. \quad (35)$$

18.4. Lennard-Jones's form of perturbation theory

A method of obtaining the results of the Schrödinger perturbation theory which has the advantage of indicating exactly what is neglected in the above analysis and also of dispensing with the assumption that the perturbation is small has been devised by Lennard-Jones.†

If we assume that the solutions ψ_n of equation (6) corresponding to an energy-value W_n are non-degenerate, then we may write the solution of equation (7) in the form

$$\psi = \sum_i a_i\psi_i; \quad (36)$$

then

$$U\psi = \sum_i a_i U\psi_i = \sum_i a_i \sum_j (j|U|j)\psi_j. \quad (37)$$

Substituting from equations (36) and (37) into equation (7) we have

$$\sum_i a_i(W_i-W)\psi_i+\sum_{i,j} a_i(i|U|j)\psi_j = 0,$$

and equating coefficients of ψ_i we obtain

$$a_i(W-W_i) = \sum_j a_j(j|U|i), \quad (38)$$

$(j = 1, 2,...)$, the series on the right-hand side having an infinite number of terms. The set of equations (38) determine the coefficients a_i and the possible values of W. To determine the possible values of W we eliminate the a's from this system of equations to obtain the determinantal equation

$$\begin{vmatrix} (1|U|1)-(W-W_1) & (1|U|2) & . & . & . \\ (2|U|1) & (2|U|2)-(W-W_2) & . & . & . \\ . & . & . & . & . \end{vmatrix} = 0, \quad (39)$$

† J. E. Lennard-Jones, *Proc. Roy. Soc.* A, **129**, 604 (1930).

the determinant on the left-hand side having an infinite number of rows and columns. The values of W_1, W_2,...., and the wave-functions ψ_1, ψ_2,... being known, the matrix elements $(i|U|j)$ may be calculated by quadratures. When equation (39) has been solved for W the wave function may be obtained from equation (36), after the coefficients a_i have been found from (38) or from the expansion of a determinant of the type

$$\psi = \begin{vmatrix} \psi_1 & \psi_2 & . & . & \psi_i & . & . & . \\ (2|U|1) & (2|U|2)-(W-W_2) & . & . & (2|U|i) & . & . & . \\ . & . & . & . & . & . & . & . \\ (i|U|1) & (i|U|2) & . & . & (i|U|i)-(W-W_i) & . & . & . \\ . & . & . & . & . & . & . & . \end{vmatrix}$$

the values of W already found being inserted.

For definiteness, suppose we wish to determine the perturbation of W_1. Then as a first approximation to the solution of equation (39) we may neglect all the matrix elements $(i|U|j)$ except $(1|U|1)$ and obtain

$$W = W_1 + (1|U|1)$$

in agreement with equation (19). To obtain a second approximation we neglect all those matrix elements $(i|U|j)$ which do *not* lie in the first row or the first column of the determinant on the left side of equation (39). In this way we get the equation

$$\begin{vmatrix} (1|U|1)-(W-W_1) & (1|U|2) & (1|U|3) & . & . & . \\ (2|U|1) & (2|U|2)-(W-W_2) & 0 & . & . & . \\ (3|U|1) & 0 & (3|U|3)-(W-W_3) & . & . & . \\ . & . & . & . & . & . \end{vmatrix} = 0.$$

Expanding this bordered determinant we obtain

$$\{(1|U|1)-(W-W_1)\}(W_2-W)(W_3-W)...- $$
$$ -\sum_j{}' \frac{(1|U|j)(j|U|1)}{W_j-W}(W_2-W)(W_3-W)... = 0$$

by means of a well known theorem on determinants. Dividing throughout by the infinite product $(W_2-W)(W_3-W)...$ and rearranging the terms, we obtain as our second approximation

$$W = W_1 + (1|U|1) + \sum_j{}' \frac{(1|U|j)(j|U|1)}{W-W_j}, \tag{40}$$

in agreement with equation (25) except that now W appears in place of W_1 in each denominator on the right-hand side. Equation (40) must be solved by the method of successive approximations,

$$W = W_1 + (1|U|1)$$

being taken as a first approximation.

The theory for degenerate states can be developed in precisely the same way.

18.5. *Rotating polar molecules in an electric field*

As an example of the application of the second-order perturbation theory to a particular problem, we consider the solution of the Schrödinger equation for rotating molecules subject to an electric field of strength F—a problem of some interest in the theory of dielectrics.† If we treat the molecule as a rigid body symmetrical about an axis we may then write the wave equation in the form‡

$$\frac{\hbar^2}{2I}\left\{\frac{1}{\sin\theta}\frac{\partial}{\partial\theta}\left(\sin\theta\frac{\partial\psi}{\partial\theta}\right)+\frac{1}{\sin^2\theta}\frac{\partial^2\psi}{\partial\phi^2}\right\}+(W+\mu F\cos\theta)\psi = 0,$$

where I is the moment of inertia of the molecule about its axis of symmetry and μ is the permanent electric moment of the molecule. We saw previously that the unperturbed wave equation ($F = 0$) has bounded solutions

$$\psi_l^{(u)} = c_{ul}P_l^u(\cos\theta)e^{iu\phi},$$

where c_{ul} is a constant and

$$W = \frac{\hbar^2}{2I}l(l+1).$$

Moreover, if the wave functions ψ are to be normalized to unity we must take

$$c_{ul} = \left(\frac{4\pi}{2l+1}\right)^{\frac{1}{2}}\left\{\frac{(l+u)!}{(l-u)!}\right\}^{\frac{1}{2}}.$$

In the notation of the previous sections we have

$$U = \mu F\cos\theta$$

and

$$(i|U^{(u)}|j) = \int \psi_i^{(u)}U\psi_j^{(u)}\,d\tau = 2\pi\mu Fc_{ui}c_{uj}\int_0^1 P_i^u(\mu)P_j^u(\mu)\mu\,d\mu.$$

Now it can be shown§ that the integral on the right vanishes unless $j = i\pm1$, and that

$$(i|U^{(u)}|i-1) = (i-1|U^{(u)}|i) = \frac{(i+u)^{\frac{1}{2}}(i-u)^{\frac{1}{2}}}{(2i-1)^{\frac{1}{2}}(2i+1)}\mu F.$$

† Cf. P. J. W. Debye, *Polare Molekeln*, chap. ix (Leipzig, 1929).
‡ Cf. Chap. II, § 14, above.   § Cf. Appendix.

Thus $(l|U|l) = 0$ and we must use equation (26) to find the perturbation in W_l; the series on the right-hand side of (26) reduces simply to two terms to give

$$W = W_l + \frac{(l|U|l-1)^2}{W_l - W_{l-1}} + \frac{(l|U|l+1)^2}{W_l - W_{l+1}}$$

$$= \frac{\hbar^2}{2I}\left[l(l+1) + \frac{K^2}{2}\left\{\frac{(l+u)(l-u)}{l(2l-1)(2l+1)} - \frac{(l+1+u)(l+1-u)}{(l+1)(2l+1)(2l+3)}\right\}\right],$$

where we have written $K = 2I\mu F/\hbar^2$. In particular the perturbation of the lowest energy level ($u = l = 0$) is

$$W = -\frac{\hbar^2}{2I}\cdot\frac{K^2}{6}.$$

These results have been derived by Lennard-Jones using the determinantal method.[†] This method is also applicable in the case of large electric fields when K can no longer be assumed to be small.

18.6. *Wigner's perturbation method*

It often happens that the infinite series in equation (25) diverges in cases in which the lowest energy value itself is finite. In such cases the Rayleigh-Schrödinger method is, of course, inapplicable. Wigner[‡] has given an approximate formula for the lowest energy which can be proved to converge at least in certain simple cases. Suppose we wish to determine the energy of the lowest state of the system whose wave equation is

$$(H_0 + \lambda H_1)\psi = W\psi, \tag{41}$$

when the energy values W_n and the wave-functions ψ_n ($n = 1, 2, ...$) of the equation with $\lambda = 0$ are known. Assume a solution of (41) of the form

$$\psi = \left(\psi_1 + \lambda\sum_{j=2} a_j\psi_j\right)\left(1 + \lambda^2\sum_j a_j a_j^*\right)^{-\frac{1}{2}} \tag{42}$$

for the lowest state. Using the result

$$H_1\psi_j = \sum_i (i|H_1|j)\psi_i$$

it is easily seen that for the wave function (42)

$$\int \psi^* H_1 \psi \, d\tau$$
$$= \frac{(1|H|1) + \lambda\sum_{j=2}\{(1|U|j)a_j + (j|U|1)a_j^*\} + \lambda^2\sum_{j=2}\sum_{k=2}(j|U|k)a_k a_j^*}{1 + \lambda^2\sum_j a_j a_j^*}.$$

† J. E. Lennard-Jones, loc. cit., § 6.
‡ E. Wigner, *Math. u. naturw. Anz. der ungar. Akad. d. Wiss.* **53**, 477 (1935).

Similarly it is easily shown that

$$\int \psi^* H_0 \psi \, d\tau = W_1 + \lambda^2 \frac{\sum_j (W_j - W_1) a_j^* a_j}{1 + \lambda^2 \sum_j a_j^* a_j} \, .$$

Adding the two integrals and writing

$$E_j = W_j + \lambda(j|H_1|j), \tag{43}$$

we obtain for the energy of the perturbed system

$$W = \int \psi^* (H_0 + \lambda H_1) \psi \, d\tau =$$

$$E_1 + \lambda^2 \frac{\sum_j \{(E_j - E_1) a_j^* a_j + (1|H_1|j) a_j + (j|H_1|1) a_j^*\} + \lambda \sum_{j=2} \sum_{k=2} (j|H_1|k) a_j^* a_k}{1 + \lambda^2 \sum_{j=2} a_j^* a_j} \, . \tag{44}$$

Neglecting λ^3 and higher powers of λ we obtain

$$\left(1 + \lambda^2 \sum_{j=2} a_j^* a_j\right)(W - E_1) = \lambda^2 \sum_j \{(E_j - E_1) a_j^* a_j + (1|H_1|j) a_j + (j|H_1|1) a_j^*\}.$$

Differentiating this equation with respect to a_k^* and setting $\partial W / \partial a_k^*$ to zero we obtain the relation

$$a_k(W - E_1) = (E_k - E_1) a_k + (k|H_1|1),$$

which may be solved to give

$$a_k = \frac{(k|H_1|1)}{W - E_k} \, . \tag{45}$$

Substituting from equation (45) into equation (44) and neglecting powers of λ higher than the third, we obtain the equation

$$W - E_1 = \lambda^2 \sum_k \frac{(1|H_1|k)(k|H_1|1)}{W - E_k} + \lambda^3 \sum_{k,l} \frac{(1|H_1|k)(k|H_1|l)(l|H_1|1)}{(W - E_k)(W - E_l)} \tag{46}$$

for the determination of the energy W.

The value of W obtained from this equation is always too high. Continuing this process Wigner obtains the equation

$$W - E_1 = \sum_{j=1}^{2n} T_{j+1}(W), \tag{47}$$

where

$$T_{j+1}(W) = (\lambda)^{j+1} \sum_{\mu_1} \cdots \sum_{\mu_j} \frac{(1|H_1|\mu_1)(\mu_1|H_1|\mu_2)\dots(\mu_{j-1}|H_1|\mu_j)}{(W - E_{\mu_1})(W - E_{\mu_2})\dots(W - E_{\mu_j})} \, . \tag{48}$$

This equation for W can be solved by successive approximations. The series (48) converges in many cases in which the Rayleigh–Schrödinger perturbation theory leads to divergent results. It can converge even in the case of a continuous spectrum which has been made discrete by imposing a finite boundary on the problem (as in the bounded linear oscillator § 11.2, above). The series (48) was first obtained by Brillouin,† who obtained it by an intuitive consideration of the equations of the Schrödinger method.

† L. Brillouin, *Journ. d. Phys.* **4,** 1 (1933).

IV

EFFECT OF A MAGNETIC FIELD AND THE ELECTRONIC SPIN

19. Effect of a magnetic field on the energy levels of atoms

19.1. Effect of a magnetic field

IN this chapter we shall consider the effect on a hydrogen or alkali atom of a magnetic field. It will be shown that the observed phenomena cannot be explained by the assumption of the point electron, and that we have to introduce the assumption of the 'spinning electron'. This assumption amounts to the following: the electron, besides its positional coordinates, has a fourth degree of freedom; a quantum number σ_z is introduced to describe this fourth degree of freedom. In the absence of a magnetic field the energy levels are unaltered by the spin, but in a magnetic field H the spin introduces an additional term into the energy

$$\frac{e\hbar}{2mc} H\sigma_z, \qquad \sigma_z = \pm 1.$$

All energy levels are thus split. In addition the spin makes an addition to the resolved part of the angular momentum of the system along the magnetic field equal to

$$\pm \tfrac{1}{2}\hbar.$$

In this chapter these hypotheses will be introduced in order to explain the experimental facts. In Chapter XI it will be shown that, in order to obtain a consistent quantal theory of the electron obeying the principle of relativity, it was necessary to assume that the electron had these properties. This striking advance in the theory of the electron was due to Dirac (1928). In this theory the properties of the spin and the relativistic correction to the earlier non-relativistic theory are intimately connected, and it is no longer true to say that the spin does not affect the levels except in a magnetic field.

The effect of a magnetic field on the energy levels of atoms can be investigated by the following methods:

(a) Experiments of the type carried out originally by Stern and Gerlach† (1924). In these a beam of atoms is passed through an in-homogeneous magnetic field. Suppose the ground state of the atom is

---

† For further details of this method, see any book on magnetism, e.g. E. C. Stoner, *Magnetism and Matter* (London, 1934).

split by a field H in the z-direction into a number of states, with energies differing from the original state by

$$\mu H u,$$

where u is a quantum number having a number of discrete values. Then the force on an atom in the state u is

$$\mu u \frac{\partial H}{\partial z}.$$

The beam is thus split by an inhomogeneous field. The number of beams into which it is split gives the number of possible values of u, and the magnitude of the splitting gives the magnitude of $\mu \partial H/\partial z$.

(b) *The Zeeman effect.* Emission or absorption lines in the line spectra of elements are frequently split by a magnetic field into a number of components. On the quantal interpretation this means that the energy levels are split. Unlike the Stern–Gerlach experiment, the Zeeman effect gives information about the excited as well as the ground state.

(c) *Paramagnetic salts.* The susceptibility of a salt containing N magnetic ions or atoms per unit volume is, if interaction between them can be neglected,

$$\frac{N}{\nu} \frac{2\mu^2}{kT} \sum u^2,$$

where the summation is over the ν states of the ion. μ and u refer of course to the ground state of the ion. For the derivation of this formula, cf. Stoner, loc. cit.

It will first be necessary to evaluate the angular momentum of an electron in a hydrogen-like atom.

19.2. *The orbital angular momentum*

In this section it will be shown that if an electron or other particle is described by a wave function

$$\psi(x,y,z) = R(r)\Theta(\theta)e^{iu\phi}/\sqrt{(2\pi)}, \qquad (1)$$

where $R(r)$, $\Theta(\theta)$ are any normalized functions of r and θ, the component of the angular momentum along the axis of spherical polar coordinates is $u\hbar$.

In Newtonian mechanics the components of the angular momentum M_x, M_y, M_z, are given by

$$\begin{aligned}
M_x &= yp_z - zp_y, \\
M_y &= zp_x - xp_z, \qquad (2) \\
M_z &= xp_y - yp_x.
\end{aligned}$$

Let us take the z-direction as the direction of spherical polar coordinates. Then we can show in an elementary way that the mean value $\bar{M}_z$ of M_z is $u\hbar$, for, by (2)

$$\bar{M}_z = \frac{\hbar}{i} \int \psi^* \left(x \frac{\partial \psi}{\partial y} - y \frac{\partial \psi}{\partial x} \right) d\tau.$$

Transferring to polar coordinates this gives

$$\bar{M}_z = \frac{\hbar}{i} \int \psi^* \frac{\partial \psi}{\partial \phi} d\tau,$$

and if ψ is of the form (1) this reduces to

$$\bar{M}_z = u\hbar.$$

To show that M_z for a particle in the state corresponding to the wave function (1) actually has the value $u\hbar$, we must make use of the transformation theory of § 16. We need a series of transformation functions $g_{M_z}(x, y, z)$; then

$$\left| \int g_{M_z'}^*(x, y, z) \psi(x, y, z) d\tau \right|^2 \tag{3}$$

will give the probability that M_z has the value M_z'. These transformation functions are defined by the equation

$$\frac{\hbar}{i} \left(x \frac{\partial g}{\partial y} - y \frac{\partial g}{\partial x} \right) - M_z' g = 0;$$

in polar coordinates this gives

$$\frac{\hbar}{i} \frac{\partial g}{\partial \phi} - M_z' g = 0.$$

The normalized solution is

$$g = e^{iu'\phi}/\sqrt{(2\pi)},$$

where

$$M_z' = u'\hbar,$$

and the condition that g must be single-valued shows that u must be integral.

Making use of (1), it will be seen that (3) vanishes unless $u = u'$. Thus if an electron is in a state corresponding to the wave function (1), the angular momentum has the value $u\hbar$.

19.3. *The total angular momentum*

In this section it will be shown that if an electron is in a state with wave-function

$$R(r)\Theta(\theta)e^{iu\phi}/\sqrt{(2\pi)} \tag{4}$$

the total angular momentum is

$$\sqrt{\{l(l+1)\}}\hbar.$$

The total angular momentum M is given in Newtonian mechanics by

$$M^2 = M_x^2 + M_y^2 + M_z^2.$$

In quantum mechanics, M_x^2 is represented by the operator

$$-\hbar^2\left(y\frac{\partial}{\partial z} - z\frac{\partial}{\partial y}\right)\left(y\frac{\partial}{\partial z} - z\frac{\partial}{\partial y}\right)$$

$$= -\hbar^2\left(y^2\frac{\partial^2}{\partial z^2} + z^2\frac{\partial^2}{\partial y^2} - 2yz\frac{\partial^2}{\partial y\partial z} - y\frac{\partial}{\partial y} - z\frac{\partial}{\partial z}\right).$$

M^2 is therefore represented by the sum of three such terms. We have to transform to spherical polar coordinates. This can be done as follows: it is easily verified that

$$\bar{M}^2 = \hbar^2\left[-r^2\nabla^2 + \left(\sum_{x,y,z} x\frac{\partial}{\partial x}\right)^2 + \sum_{x,y,z} x\frac{\partial}{\partial x}\right]$$

$$= \hbar^2[-r^2\nabla^2 + (\mathbf{r}\,\mathrm{grad})^2 + (\mathbf{r}\,\mathrm{grad})]$$

$$= \hbar^2\left[-r^2\nabla^2 + r^2\frac{\partial^2}{\partial r^2} + 2r\frac{\partial}{\partial r}\right]$$

$$= \hbar^2\left[\frac{1}{\sin\theta}\frac{\partial}{\partial\theta}\left(\sin\theta\frac{\partial}{\partial\theta}\right) + \frac{1}{\sin^2\theta}\frac{\partial^2}{\partial\phi^2}\right].$$

The transformation function $q_{M^2}(\theta, \phi)$ is thus given by

$$\frac{1}{\sin\theta}\frac{\partial}{\partial\theta}\left(\sin\theta\frac{\partial g}{\partial\theta}\right) + \frac{1}{\sin^2\theta}\frac{\partial^2 g}{\partial\phi^2} + \frac{M'^2}{\hbar^2}g = 0.$$

With the boundary conditions that g must be single-valued and bounded the solutions are

$$P_l^{u'}(\cos\theta)e^{iu'\phi}$$

with

$$M'^2/\hbar^2 = l(l+1), \tag{5}$$

and l a positive integer. It follows as in the last section that, for an electron in the state with wave function (4), M^2 (the square of the total angular momentum) has the value $l(l+1)\hbar^2$.

19.4. Energy levels in a magnetic field

We shall now calculate the energy levels of an electron in an atom when subjected to a magnetic field, without taking account of the spin. The Schrödinger equation is (cf. p. 40)

$$\nabla^2\psi + \frac{2ie}{\hbar c}(\mathbf{A}\,\mathrm{grad}\,\psi) + \frac{2m}{\hbar^2}(W - V)\psi = 0.$$

The second term is to be treated as a 'perturbation', according to the methods of the perturbation theory.

For the magnetic field we take

$$H_x = 0, \qquad H_y = 0, \qquad H_z = H.$$

This has the vector potential

$$A_x = -\tfrac{1}{2}Hy, \qquad A_y = \tfrac{1}{2}Hx, \qquad A_z = 0.$$

Our perturbing term therefore becomes

$$U = \frac{ieH\hbar}{2mc}\left(x\frac{\partial \psi}{\partial y} - y\frac{\partial \psi}{\partial x}\right),$$

or, introducing polar coordinates with the z-axis as axis of coordinates,

$$U = i\hbar w\frac{\partial \psi}{\partial \phi},$$

with

$$w = eH/2mc.$$

Since the wave functions of the electrons are of the form

$$R(r)\Theta(\theta)e^{iu\phi}/\sqrt{(2\pi)},$$

it is clear that all matrix elements of U vanish except the diagonal ones, and that

$$(u'|U|u'') = i\hbar w\frac{1}{2\pi}\int_0^{2\pi} e^{-iu'\phi}\frac{\partial}{\partial \phi}e^{iu''\phi}\,d\phi.$$

A state of azimuthal quantum number l is thus split into $2l+1$ states with energies displaced by

$$\frac{e\hbar}{2mc}Hu \quad (u = -l, -(l-1),..., l). \tag{6}$$

This result was also obtained on the Bohr theory. It is easily verified on the classical theory that an electron revolving in an orbit with angular momentum I has magnetic moment $eI/2mc$. If I is equal to $l\hbar$, the magnetic moment is $le\hbar/2mc$. If we now assume that the resolved part of the angular momentum along the field is also quantized and equal to $u\hbar$ ($u = -l,..., l-1, l$), then it follows that the resolved part of the magnetic moment is $ue\hbar/2mc$. Formula (6) for the energy change follows.

A magnetic moment equal to $e\hbar/2mc$ is called a *Bohr magneton* and denoted by μ_B.

We see therefore that s-states ($l = 0$) should not be split by a magnetic field, apart from the electronic spin to be considered below; p-states are split into three states separated by an energy interval $\mu_B H$.

If an atom has two states with energies W_1, W_2, transitions between which give rise to a line of the emission spectrum of frequency ν_0 given by

$$h\nu_0 = W_2 - W_1,$$

then according to the above theory the frequency of the line in a field H will be given by $\nu_0 + \Delta\nu$, where

$$\Delta\nu = \frac{eH}{4\pi mc}\Delta u. \tag{7}$$

A selection rule proved in Chapter X shows that $\Delta u = 0$ or ± 1. Thus any lines (except s–s transitions which are actually forbidden) should split into three lines separated by frequency intervals $eH/4\pi mc$.

Splitting of this type is known as the Normal Zeeman Effect; it is actually shown only for singlet terms, e.g. parhelium. The formula for $\Delta\nu$ does not contain h, and should thus be derivable from the classical theory of a vibrating electron. The proof of this is instructive, and is given below.

Suppose that an electron is held in position by a restoring force $-pr$ when it is displaced a distance r. Then, in the absence of a field, it will vibrate in any direction with frequency ν given by

$$\nu = \frac{1}{2\pi}\sqrt{\frac{p}{m}}.$$

Suppose now a magnetic field H is introduced in the z-direction; the electron can still vibrate in this direction with its frequency unaltered, but the vibrations perpendicular to the field will clearly be affected. The normal modes of the vibration are thus circular orbits in a plane perpendicular to the field. If r is the radius of such an orbit, we have for the components of force on the electron

$$\begin{array}{ll}
\text{restoring force} & -pr, \\
\text{centrifugal force} & m\omega^2 r, \\
\text{force due to field} & \pm He\omega r/c,
\end{array}$$

where ω is the angular velocity $(= 2\pi\nu)$. Thus

$$p - m\omega^2 = \pm He\omega/c,$$

giving approximately

$$\omega = \sqrt{\frac{p}{m}} \pm \frac{eH}{2mc}.$$

Formula (6) for the frequencies follows, as does information about the polarization of the three components (circular polarization of the outer components and disappearance of central component if the emitting gas is viewed parallel to the field, linear polarization of all three if the gas is viewed perpendicular to it).

20. The electronic spin

Many experimental facts have made necessary the introduction of the assumption of the electronic spin. These include the gyromagnetic effect, the anomalous Zeeman effect, the results of the Stern–Gerlach experiment, and the existence of doublets in the spectra of the alkalis. In general it may be said that the number of states of the single-electron system (e.g. alkali, silver, or hydrogen atoms) is twice as great as it would be without spin. This is especially striking in the case of the ground state, which is an s-state ($l = 0$) and should therefore be non-degenerate. The original Stern–Gerlach experiment showed, however, a splitting of the ground state of silver into two, with a separation given by ($e\hbar H/2mc$). On these grounds alone a spin must be introduced.

We may obtain a formula for the component of angular momentum as follows. For electrons without spin we have deduced from the properties of the Legendre polynomial $P_l^u(\cos\theta)$ the following properties of the orbital angular momentum:

(a) The total angular momentum is $\sqrt{\{l(l+1)\}}\hbar$.

(b) The component of angular momentum along the axis of coordinates has the value $\hbar u$ where u has ($2l+1$) integral values.

Since experiment shows a twofold splitting of the energy states due to the spin, then if s is the quantum number giving the angular momentum of the spin, it is reasonable to assume that $(2s+1) = 2$ and thus that $s = \frac{1}{2}$. Hence it follows that

(a) The total angular momentum of a spinning electron is
$$\sqrt{\{s(s+1)\}}\hbar = \tfrac{1}{2}\sqrt{3}\,\hbar.$$

(b) The component of angular momentum in the direction of the field is S_z where
$$S_z = \pm\tfrac{1}{2}\hbar.$$

From the experimental point of view we may determine the component of angular momentum in the direction of a magnetic field H by means of the gyromagnetic effect. This measures the change in the angular momentum of a bar of magnetic material when the direction of magnetization is reversed; the bar thereby receives a small impulse causing it to rotate about the field. If the magnetism is due to orbital motion and not to spins, we have for the ratio
$$\frac{\text{angular momentum}}{\text{magnetic moment}} = \frac{2mc}{e}.$$

For spins the ratio is halved.

The first experimental measurements of the gyromagnetic effect were carried out with ferromagnetic materials; we have here no *a priori* evidence as to whether the magnetism is due to orbital or spin motion. The observed values of the ratio ($\frac{1}{2}.2mc/e$) show that the magnetism is due to spin.

20.1. *Doublets of the alkali atoms and anomalous Zeeman effect*

Owing to the spin, all states of the alkali-like atoms except the s-states are doublets; the s-states in the absence of a magnetic field are not split, and so have a twofold degeneracy. This can be seen in a general way as follows: the electron, since it is moving in an electric field e/r^2, is acted on by a magnetic field of order ev/cr^2. In this field the energy of the electronic spin is of order

$$\frac{e\hbar}{2mc}\frac{ev}{cr^2},$$

which, if r is of the order of the radius of the hydrogen atom ($\hbar^2/me^2$), gives a separation of the order

$$\frac{v^2}{c^2} \times \text{total energy,}$$

or about one part in 10,000 of the total energy. In s-states, however, there is no axis of symmetry for the motion and hence no change of energy due to the spin.

Calculations of the doublet separation can be made (*a*) on the basis of the Pauli-Darwin theory of the next section; (*b*) on the basis of the Dirac theory of the electron (Chap. XI). The latter is, of course, the more complete theory and should give a correct result.

The effect of the spin on the magnetic moment of an atom and hence in the Zeeman effect can also be worked out on the basis of either of the above theories, for a single electron moving in a central force. We give below a more elementary derivation due to Landé,† which is applicable also in a many-electron atom, where several electrons may combine together to give a total spin angular momentum S. Let also L be the total angular momentum due to orbital motion, and J the resultant angular momentum of the whole atom. Then the vectors S, L, and J will form a triangle as shown in Fig. 15. The component μ of the magnetic moment along J will be given by

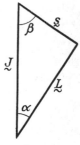

Fig. 15.

$$\mu = \frac{e}{2mc}(2S\cos\beta + L\cos\alpha),$$

since the spin gives two Bohr magnetons for each quantum $\hbar$ of angular momentum. We thus have

$$\mu = \frac{e}{2mc}Jg,$$

† A. Landé, *Zeits. f. Physik*, **19**, 112 (1923).

where
$$g = \left(1 + \frac{S\cos\beta}{J}\right).$$

The quantity g is called the Landé g-factor. Since

$$\cos\beta = \frac{S^2 + J^2 - L^2}{2SJ},$$

we find
$$g = \left[1 + \frac{S^2 + J^2 - L^2}{2J^2}\right].$$

Putting in the quantum mechanical value for the angular momentum in terms of the quantum numbers, we find

$$g = \left[1 + \frac{s(s+1) + j(j+1) - l(l+1)}{2j(j+1)}\right]. \tag{8}$$

If the atom is now placed in a magnetic field H, the component of the angular momentum along the field will take up the following values

$$j, j-1, \ldots, -j \times \hbar,$$

giving $2j+1$ terms if j is integral or $2j$ if j is half an odd integer. In either case the energy interval between two adjacent terms is

$$\Delta W = \frac{e\hbar H}{2mc} g. \tag{9}$$

21. Wave functions for the spin

Wave functions describing the spin may be introduced in the following way. We take an arbitrary direction in space, for instance the z-axis of Cartesian coordinates. If a magnetic field H is applied in this direction, an electron in an atom will be found to have changed its energy by $\pm\mu_B H$, where μ_B is the Bohr magneton ($e\hbar/2mc$). Which value the energy should have is the only information that we may hope to obtain about the spin; we therefore introduce a variable σ_z, which can take only the values ± 1 so that the energy of the electron in the field is

$$-\sigma_z \mu_B H \quad (\sigma_z = \pm 1).$$

$\frac{1}{2}\hbar\sigma_z$ is then the component of angular momentum along the field. The complete wave function of an electron will then be

$$\psi(x, y, z; \sigma_z) \quad (\sigma_z = \pm 1).$$

The interpretation of this wave function is that

$$|\psi(x, y, z; +1)|^2 d\tau$$

is the chance that the electron described by the wave-function ψ is in the volume element $d\tau$ and that its spin would give an energy $-\mu_B H$

if a field were set up in the z-direction, with a similar interpretation if $\sigma_z = -1$.

Since the interaction between the spin forces and the orbital motion of the electron is small, it is a good approximation to take $\psi(x, y, z; \sigma_z)$ in the form

$$\psi(x, y, z)\chi(\sigma_z) \quad (\sigma_z = \pm 1),$$

where $\psi(x, y, z)$ is the solution of a Schrödinger wave equation for an electron without spin, and $\chi(\sigma_z)$ is a function of the spin coordinates only.

In a magnetic field along the z-axis, the spin can have two *stationary* states. If the energy is $-\mu_B H$ we shall denote the spin wave function by

$$\chi_\alpha(\sigma_z),$$

where $\quad \chi_\alpha(1) = 1, \qquad \chi_\alpha(-1) = 0.$

If the spin energy is $\mu_B H$, we denote the corresponding wave function by

$$\chi_\beta(\sigma_z),$$

where $\quad \chi_\beta(1) = 0, \qquad \chi_\beta(-1) = 1.$

Problems involving the spin are of two types:

(a) Those involving the symmetry of the wave function in the many-body problem. These may be handled by the use of the wave-functions χ_α, χ_β without the introduction of a wave equation.

(b) Problems involving the interaction of the spin with a magnetic field; for these we need to set up a wave equation.

In the next two sections, therefore, we will show how to build up a wave equation for the electron with spin. This equation was first obtained, by somewhat different methods, by Darwin† and Pauli.‡ It is a non-relativistic and therefore only an approximation to Dirac's relativistic equation (Chap. XI). It is nevertheless worth while to develop this approximate equation for the following reasons: no satisfactory relativistic equation has been given for the interaction of two electrons in an atom; also the more elementary theory still has to be applied to nuclear particles (e.g. the proton and heavier nuclei) which have mechanical and magnetic moments but certainly do not obey the Dirac equation.

The extra term in the energy of an electron due to its spin should be, according to classical mechanics,

$$(\boldsymbol{\mu}\mathbf{H}) + \frac{1}{c}(\boldsymbol{\mu}[\mathbf{E}\mathbf{v}]). \tag{10}$$

† C. G. Darwin, *Proc. Roy. Soc.* A, **116**, 227 (1927).
‡ W. Pauli, *Zeits. f. Physik*, **43**, 601 (1927).

Here μ denotes the magnetic moment of the electron, $\mathbf{H}$ the magnetic field and $\mathbf{E}$ the electric field in which the electron moves, and $\mathbf{v}$ its velocity. It will be noted that $[\mathbf{Ev}]/c$ is the apparent magnetic field due to the motion of the electron through the electric field $\mathbf{E}$.

Since $\mu = (e/mc)\mathbf{S}$, where $\mathbf{S}$ is the angular momentum, (10) becomes

$$\frac{e}{mc}\Big\{(\mathbf{SH}) + \frac{1}{c}(\mathbf{S}[\mathbf{Ev}])\Big\}. \tag{11}$$

To set up the wave equation for an electron with spin, therefore, we should add (11) to the Hamiltonian function. Our first difficulty, however, is that we do not yet know how $\mathbf{S}$ should operate on ψ. We have shown in previous chapters that the angular momentum due to orbital motion appears in the Hamiltonian as an operator $x\dfrac{\partial}{\partial y} - y\dfrac{\partial}{\partial x}$, etc., but we are now concerned with the internal degrees of freedom of the electron, and we do not wish to introduce coordinates to specify its orientation in space when in fact only the two values of σ_z are observable.

We shall therefore make use of the methods of matrix mechanics, here introduced for the first time.

21.1. *Matrix mechanics*

The matrix corresponding to any dynamical variable $L(p, q)$ and any set of transformation functions $g_n(q)$ has already been defined. We write

$$(n'|L|n'') = \int g_n^*(q) L(p, q) g_{n'}(q)\, dq,$$

where p is, as usual, to be replaced by the operator $-i\hbar\partial/\partial q$. The aggregate of numbers $(n'|L|n'')$ for all values of n', n'' is said to form a matrix, which may be written thus (if n takes the values 1, 2, 3...)

$$\begin{pmatrix} (1|L|1) & (1|L|2) & . & . & . \\ (2|L|1) & (2|L|2) & . & . & . \\ . & . & . & . & . & . \end{pmatrix}.$$

As proved in Chapter I, § 7, the matrix elements have the Hermitian property
$$(n'|L|n'') = (n''|L|n')^*.$$

The diagonal elements $(n'|L|n')$ are real.

An important property of these matrices is that, if $L(p, q)$, $M(p, q)$ are any two dynamical variables, then

$$(n'|LM|n'') = \sum_{n'''} (n'|L|n''')(n'''|M|n''). \tag{12}$$

This is easily proved as follows: the right-hand side of (12) may be written

$$\sum_{n'''} \int \int g_{n'}^*(q) L(p,q) g_{n'''}(q) g_{n'''}^*(q') M(p',q') g_{n'}(q') \, dq dq'. \tag{13}$$

But since the functions $g_n(q)$ form a complete set of orthogonal functions, we can expand any function $F(q)$ in terms of them; thus

$$F(q) = \sum_n A_n g_n(q),$$

where

$$A_n = \int F(q) g_n^*(q) \, dq.$$

Thus

$$F(q) = \sum_n \int F(q') g_n^*(q') g_n(q) \, dq'. \tag{14}$$

Applying (14) to (13) we see that (13) is equal to

$$\int g_{n'}^*(q) L M g_{n'}(q) \, dq,$$

or, in other words, to the left-hand side of (12), which is what we set out to prove.

It will be seen from (14) that

$$\left. \begin{aligned} \sum_n g_n^*(q') g_n(q) &= 0 \quad (q \neq q') \\ &= \infty \quad (q = q') \end{aligned} \right\} \tag{15}$$

and that the series behaves like the 'δ-function', $\delta(x)$ introduced by Dirac. This has the property that

$$\int f(x') \delta(x-x') \, dx' = f(x).$$

A further theorem of importance, and the one that we shall use in the development of the theory of the spin, is the following: suppose a system has the Schrödinger equation

$$H(p,q)\psi(q) - W\psi(q) = 0 \tag{16}$$

from which the allowed energy values W are determined. Then if $g_n(q)$ is any transformation function and

$$\chi(n') = \int g_{n'}^*(q) \psi(q) \, dq,$$

so that $|\chi(n')|^2$ is the probability that, for the system in the state ψ, the variable n has the value n', then (16) is equivalent to

$$\sum_{n''} (n'|H|n'') \chi(n'') - W\chi(n') = 0. \tag{17}$$

The proof follows the same lines as that given above, as follows: we have

$$\sum_{n''} (n'|H|n'')\chi(n'') = \sum_{n''} \int\int g_{n'}^*(q)H(p,q)g_{n'}(q)g_{n''}^*(q')\psi(q')\,dq dq'$$

$$= \int g_{n'}^*(q)H(p,q)\psi(q)\,dq$$

$$= W \int g_{n'}^*(q)\psi(q)\,dq,$$

which proves the desired theorem.

As an example of this procedure, the function $g_n(q)$ may be the transformation functions relating the z-component $u\hbar$ of the angular momentum to the polar coordinate ϕ, so that

$$g = e^{iu\phi}/\sqrt{(2\pi)}.$$

21.2. *Matrices for the spin moment*

In dealing with the electronic spin, the matrix form of the wave equation (17) is very convenient, and saves us from the necessity of introducing internal coordinates of the spherical polar type to describe the rotation of the electron. The coordinate n in this case will be the z-component S_z of the angular momentum which is known to take the values $\pm\frac{1}{2}\hbar$ only.

It is convenient as before to introduce the quantity σ_z such that $\frac{1}{2}\sigma_z\hbar$ is the component of the angular momentum in the z-direction, and

$$-\frac{e\hbar}{2mc}\sigma_z H$$

the energy in a magnetic field. Then

$$\sigma_z = \pm 1.$$

Corresponding to our wave functions $\chi(n)$, we then describe the spin by the wave function already introduced

$$\chi(\sigma_z).$$

Any quantity L in the Hamiltonian must thus be expressible as a matrix

$$(\sigma_z'|L|\sigma_z''),$$

and $L\chi$ denotes

$$\sum_{\sigma_z''} (\sigma_z'|L|\sigma_z'')\chi(\sigma_z'').$$

We thus have to find a matrix expression for the spin angular momentum **S** of the electron which occurs in (11).

Consider the *orbital* angular momentum M of a particle in a state with quantum number l. We can then form the matrix of the angular momentum

$$(u'|M_x|u'') = \frac{\hbar}{i}\int\int P_l^{u'}(\cos\theta)e^{-iu'\phi}\left(y\frac{\partial}{\partial z} - z\frac{\partial}{\partial y}\right)P_l^{u''}(\cos\theta)e^{iu''\phi}\sin\theta\,d\theta d\phi.$$

For the z-component the evaluation is elementary;

$$
\begin{aligned}
(u'|M_z|u'') &= \frac{\hbar}{i} \int P_l^{u'}(\cos\theta)e^{-iu'\phi}\frac{\partial}{\partial\phi}P_l^{u''}(\cos\theta)e^{iu''\phi}\sin\theta\,d\theta d\phi \\
&= \frac{\hbar}{i}u' \quad (u'=u'') \\
&= 0 \quad (u'\neq u''),
\end{aligned}
\left.\begin{aligned}\end{aligned}\right\} \tag{18}
$$

and direct evaluation gives for the other elements

$$
\left.\begin{aligned}
(u+1|M_x|u) &= \tfrac{1}{2}\hbar\sqrt{\{(l-u)(l+1+u)\}} = (u|M_x|u+1), \\
(u+1|M_y|u) &= -\tfrac{1}{2}\hbar i\sqrt{\{(l-u)(l+1+u)\}} = -(u|M_y|u+1)
\end{aligned}\right\} \tag{19}
$$

with all the other components of the matrix vanishing.

These forms are deduced for *orbital* motion, and thus for integral values of l and u. We shall, nevertheless, obtain matrices for the spin angular momentum **S** by setting $l=\tfrac{1}{2}$, $u=S_z=\pm\tfrac{1}{2}$ in these formulae. Introducing as before the matrix

$$
\sigma = (\sigma_z'|\sigma|\sigma_z'') = 2S/\hbar
$$

we obtain thus the following values:

$$
\sigma_x = \begin{pmatrix}0 & 1 \\ 1 & 0\end{pmatrix}, \qquad \sigma_y = \begin{pmatrix}0 & -i \\ i & 0\end{pmatrix}, \qquad \sigma_z = \begin{pmatrix}1 & 0 \\ 0 & -1\end{pmatrix}. \tag{20}
$$

An alternative way of obtaining these matrices is by means of the relation

$$
M_x M_y - M_y M_x = -\frac{\hbar}{i}M_z,
$$

which is easily verified if **M** has the form of the operator (2). It is therefore true also as a matrix equation if **M** refers to the orbital motion. Let it be assumed that the same equation also applies to angular momentum of the spin. In that case, if we write as before $\mathbf{M}=\tfrac{1}{2}\hbar\boldsymbol{\sigma}$ we have

$$
\sigma_x\sigma_y - \sigma_y\sigma_x = 2i\sigma_z, \tag{21a}
$$

$$
\sigma_z\sigma_x - \sigma_x\sigma_z = 2i\sigma_y, \tag{21b}
$$

$$
\sigma_y\sigma_z - \sigma_z\sigma_y = 2i\sigma_x. \tag{21c}
$$

Since

$$
\sigma_z = \begin{pmatrix}1 & 0 \\ 0 & -1\end{pmatrix}
$$

the equations (21 b) and (21 c) show that the diagonal elements of σ_y and σ_z vanish. For the other elements we obtain from (21 b)

$$
(-1|\sigma_x|1) = i(-1|\sigma_y|1) \tag{22a}
$$

and from (21 a)

$$
(-1|\sigma_x|1)(1|\sigma_y|-1) - (-1|\sigma_y|1)(1|\sigma_x|-1) = -2i. \tag{22b}
$$

Using the Hermitian relation, that

$$(1|\sigma_y|-1) = (-1|\sigma_y|1)^*,$$

and substituting from (22), we find

$$|(-1|\sigma_x|1)|^2 = 1.$$

This gives for σ_x
$$\sigma_x = \begin{pmatrix} 0 & 1 \\ 1 & 0 \end{pmatrix} e^{i\alpha},$$

where α is an arbitrary phase. The value of this phase will not affect any quantities that we may have to compare with experiment. σ_y may be found in a similar way.

It should also be noted that the three matrices σ_x, σ_y, σ_z together with the unit matrix

$$I_2 = \begin{pmatrix} 1 & 0 \\ 0 & 1 \end{pmatrix}$$

form the basis of an algebra of 2×2 matrices; for any arbitrary matrix of this type

$$\begin{pmatrix} a & b \\ c & d \end{pmatrix}$$

can be written as a linear combination

$$\begin{pmatrix} a & b \\ c & d \end{pmatrix} = \tfrac{1}{2}(a+d)I_2 + \tfrac{1}{2}(a-d)\sigma_z + \tfrac{1}{2}(b+c)\sigma_x + \tfrac{1}{2}i(b-c)\sigma_y$$

of σ_x, σ_y, σ_z, and I_2.

Furthermore, if we write χ_α and χ_β in matrix form we have

$$\chi_\alpha = \begin{pmatrix} 1 \\ 0 \end{pmatrix}, \qquad \chi_\beta = \begin{pmatrix} 0 \\ 1 \end{pmatrix},$$

so that
$$\sigma_x \chi_\alpha = \begin{pmatrix} 0 & 1 \\ 1 & 0 \end{pmatrix}\begin{pmatrix} 1 \\ 0 \end{pmatrix} = \begin{pmatrix} 0 \\ 1 \end{pmatrix} = \chi_\beta.$$

In this way we may establish all of the relations

$$\left.\begin{array}{ll} \sigma_x \chi_\alpha = \chi_\beta, & \sigma_x \chi_\beta = \chi_\alpha \\ \sigma_y \chi_\alpha = i\chi_\beta, & \sigma_y \chi_\beta = -i\chi_\alpha \\ \sigma_z \chi_\alpha = \chi_\alpha, & \sigma_z \chi_\beta = -\chi_\beta \end{array}\right\}. \tag{23}$$

21.3. Pauli's wave equation for an electron with spin

The wave equation can now be written down. For a point electron, for a magnetic field **H** and electrostatic potential energy V, it is

$$-\frac{\hbar^2}{2m}\nabla^2\psi + V\psi + \frac{e\hbar}{mci}(\mathbf{A}\,\mathrm{grad}\,\psi) = W\psi. \tag{24}$$

The additional terms in the energy due to spin are (eq. (11))

$$\frac{e}{mc}(\mathbf{HS}) + \frac{e}{mc^2}(\mathbf{S}[\mathbf{Ev}]).$$

Replacing $\mathbf{v}$ by $\mathbf{p}/m$ and $\mathbf{S}$ by $\tfrac{1}{2}\hbar\boldsymbol{\sigma}$ we have to add to the left-hand side of (24)

$$\frac{e\hbar}{2mc}\left\{(\mathbf{H}\boldsymbol{\sigma})\psi + \frac{\hbar}{mci}(\boldsymbol{\sigma}[\mathbf{E}\,\mathrm{grad}\,\psi])\right\}. \tag{25}$$

ψ is of course of the form $\psi(x, y, z, \sigma'_z)$, and

$$\sigma\psi = \sum_{\sigma''_z=1,-1}(\sigma'_z|\sigma|\sigma''_z)\psi(x, y, z, \sigma''_z).$$

With this Hamiltonian we shall solve the following problem.

Suppose that a beam of atoms in ^2S states is passed through an inhomogeneous magnetic field (Stern–Gerlach experiment), the field being in the zx-plane such that $H_x = H\cos\theta$, $H_z = H\sin\theta$. The beam will be separated into two by the field. Let the wave functions of the spins in these two states be

$$\chi'_\alpha = A\chi_\alpha(\sigma_z) + B\chi_\beta(\sigma_z),$$
$$\chi'_\beta = A'\chi_\alpha(\sigma_z) + B'\chi_\beta(\sigma_z).$$

Our problem is to find A and B, and hence the numbers of atoms that would be found parallel and antiparallel to a field if it were suddenly switched to the z-direction.

The conditions that the two functions χ_α and χ_β should be normal and orthogonal gives

$$A^*A' + B^*B' = 0,$$
$$AA^* + BB^* = A'A'^* + B'B'^* = 1.$$

We thus set

$$A = \cos\lambda\,e^{i\mu}, \qquad B = \sin\lambda\,e^{i\nu},$$
$$A' = -\sin\lambda\,e^{i\mu}, \qquad B' = \cos\lambda\,e^{i\nu}. \tag{26}$$

Further, since χ'_α, χ'_β represent the two *stationary* states in the field H, the non-diagonal matrix element $\chi'^*_\alpha(H\sigma)\chi'_\beta$ must vanish. This gives

$$(A^*A' - B^*B')H_z + (A^*B' + B^*A')H_x = 0.$$

Substituting from (26) we see that $\mu = \nu$ and

$$H_z\sin 2\lambda = H_x\cos 2\lambda.$$

Thus $$\tan 2\lambda = H_x/H_z = \tan\theta,$$

and thus $$\lambda = \tfrac{1}{2}\theta.$$

Thus the relative numbers of electrons that will point parallel and antiparallel to a field suddenly imposed along the z-axis are

$$\cos^2\tfrac{1}{2}\theta, \qquad \sin^2\tfrac{1}{2}\theta.$$

22. Evaluation of the doublet separation in alkali atoms and the anomalous Zeeman effect

The Schrödinger equation for a point electron in the absence of a magnetic field is

$$-\frac{\hbar^2}{2m}\nabla^2\psi + V\psi = W\psi. \tag{27}$$

The perturbing terms due to a magnetic field H along the z-axis and to the spin are

$$U\psi = \frac{e\hbar}{2mc}\left\{H\left(\frac{1}{i}\frac{\partial\psi}{\partial\phi} + \sigma_z\psi\right) + \frac{\hbar}{mci}(\sigma[\mathbf{E}\,\mathrm{grad}\,\psi])\right\}. \tag{28}$$

For a given value of l, there are $2l+1$ solutions of (27) all with the same energy, and $2(2l+1)$ solutions when the spin coordinate is introduced. These will be split into $2(2l+1)$ non-degenerate states by the perturbing term (28). Fortunately the $2(2l+1)$ unperturbed wave functions can be split into pairs ψ_a, ψ_b such that the non-diagonal elements of U with respect to states in different pairs vanish. Each pair corresponds to a given value of the z-component j_z of the total angular momentum; the wave functions are

$$\psi_a = R(r)\Theta(\theta)e^{iu\phi}\chi_\alpha(\sigma_z'),$$

$$\psi_b = R(r)\Theta(\theta)e^{i(u+1)\phi}\chi_\beta(\sigma_z').$$

For these $j_z = u+\frac{1}{2}$. It will easily be verified that elements of the type $(j_z'|U|j_z'')$ vanish if $j_z' \neq j_z''$.

Neither ψ_a nor ψ_b is the correct wave function for our state, unless a strong field is applied sufficiently great to break down the spin-orbit interaction and orient the spin along the z-axis instead of along L; our wave functions will be of the form

$$A\psi_a + B\psi_b,$$

$$A'\psi_a + B'\psi_b$$

and the contribution w to the energies will be given (cf. p. 73) by the quadratic equation

$$(U_{11}-w)(U_{22}-w) = |U_{12}|^2. \tag{29}$$

The matrix elements can be evaluated as follows: E is given by

$$eE_x = -\frac{x}{r}\frac{dV}{dr},$$

and thus

$$\frac{\hbar e}{i}[\mathbf{E}\,\mathrm{grad}\,\psi] = -\frac{1}{r}\frac{dV}{dr}\mathbf{M}\psi,$$

where **M** is the orbital angular momentum. Thus, if we write

$$\frac{\hbar^2}{2mc^2} \int_0^\infty \frac{1}{r} \frac{dV}{dr} \{R(r)\}^2 r^2 \, dr = P,$$

we have for the matrix elements of

$$\frac{e\hbar^2}{2m^2c^2i} (\boldsymbol{\sigma}[\mathbf{E} \, \mathrm{grad}])$$

with respect to the wave functions ψ_a, ψ_b,

$$P \begin{pmatrix} u & \sqrt{\{l(l+1)-u(u+1)\}} \\ \sqrt{\{l(l+1)-u(u+1)\}} & -(u+1) \end{pmatrix},$$

making use of the relations (19) for the matrix elements of **M**.

Equation (29) thus becomes

$$\{w-\mu H(u+1)-Pu\}\{w-\mu Hu+P(u+1)\} = P^2\{l(l+1)-u(u+1)\}.$$

$$(30)$$

If H vanishes, this gives

$$w^2+Pw = P^2 l(l+1),$$

whence $$w = Pl \quad \text{or} \quad w = -P(l+1).$$

The doublet separation is thus

$$(2l+1)P.$$

Since P is of order $1/c^2$, we do not expect a non-relativistic theory to give a quantitatively correct theory; compare the value given by the Dirac equation, Chap. XI, § 56.2.

Turning now to the shift of the levels given by a magnetic field, we see at once from (30) that a strong field ($H\mu \gg P$) gives

$$w = \mu H(u+1) \quad \text{or} \quad \mu Hu.$$

In this case the spin-orbital coupling is broken down (Paschen-Back effect). For weak fields

$$\frac{1}{\mu}\left(\frac{\partial w}{\partial H}\right)_{H\to 0} = (2u+1)\frac{w+P}{2w+P}$$

$$= j_z \frac{l+1}{l+\frac{1}{2}} \quad \text{or} \quad j_z \frac{l}{l-\frac{1}{2}}.$$

The Landé g-factor is thus given by

$$g = (l+1)/(l+\tfrac{1}{2}), \qquad j = l+\tfrac{1}{2},$$
$$g = (l+1)/(l-\tfrac{1}{2}), \qquad j = l-\tfrac{1}{2}.$$

It will easily be verified that the usual factor reduces to this form when $s = \frac{1}{2}$ (i.e. for one electron).

V

THE TWO-BODY PROBLEM

23. Introduction

In this chapter we consider the problem of two particles, moving in one another's field and also in some external field. Problems in this category are: the hydrogen atom when the motion of the nucleus is taken into account, the helium atom and the hydrogen molecule, the scattering of α-particles by helium nuclei. The most interesting features of the problem arise when the two particles are identical, i.e. two electrons or two α-particles; in this case we shall find that only half the mathematically possible solutions correspond to states that occur in nature.

We shall first develop the theory without taking into account the electronic spin. We shall suppose that we have two interacting particles, with masses m_1, m_2, and that their coordinates are

$$\mathbf{r}_1 = (x_1, y_1, z_1), \qquad \mathbf{r}_2 = (x_2, y_2, z_2).$$

Then we have seen in § 8 that the state of the system will be defined by a wave function $\psi(\mathbf{r}_1 \mathbf{r}_2)$ of the coordinates of *both* particles, and that the interpretation of ψ is that

$$|\psi(\mathbf{r}_1 \mathbf{r}_2)|^2 d\tau_1 d\tau_2$$

is the probability that the first particle is at the point $\mathbf{r}_1$ in the volume element $d\tau_1$, and at the same time the second particle is in the volume element $d\tau_2$ at the point $\mathbf{r}_2$. The equation satisfied by ψ is

$$i\hbar \frac{\partial \psi}{\partial t} = \frac{\hbar^2}{2m_1} \nabla_1^2 \psi + \frac{\hbar^2}{2m_2} \nabla_2^2 \psi - V(\mathbf{r}_1 \mathbf{r}_2)\psi, \qquad (1)$$

here

$$\nabla_1^2 = \frac{\partial^2}{\partial x_1^2} + \frac{\partial^2}{\partial y_1^2} + \frac{\partial^2}{\partial z_1^2},$$

$$\nabla_2^2 = \frac{\partial^2}{\partial x_2^2} + \frac{\partial^2}{\partial y_2^2} + \frac{\partial^2}{\partial z_2^2},$$

and $V(\mathbf{r}_1 \mathbf{r}_2)$ is the potential energy of the system when the first particle is at $\mathbf{r}_1$ and the second particle at $\mathbf{r}_2$.

23.1. *The hydrogen atom with motion of the nucleus*

We denote by $\mathbf{r}_1$, $\mathbf{r}_2$ the coordinates of the nucleus and electron respectively, and by m_1, m_2 their masses. The potential energy of the system is $-e^2/r$, where

$$r = |\mathbf{r}_1 - \mathbf{r}_2| = \sqrt{\{(x_1 - x_2)^2 + (y_1 - y_2)^2 + (z_1 - z_2)^2\}}$$

is the distance between the electron and the nucleus. To solve equation (1) we introduce the coordinates of the centre of gravity of the system

$$\mathbf{R} = (m_1\mathbf{r}_1 + m_2\mathbf{r}_2)/(m_1 + m_2)$$

and the distance between the particles

$$\mathbf{r} = \mathbf{r}_1 - \mathbf{r}_2.$$

The equation then transforms into

$$i\hbar \frac{\partial\psi}{\partial t} = \frac{\hbar^2}{2M}\nabla_R^2\psi + \frac{\hbar^2}{2m}\nabla_r^2\psi + \frac{e^2\psi}{r}, \tag{2}$$

where

$$\nabla_R^2 = \frac{\partial^2}{\partial X^2} + \frac{\partial^2}{\partial Y^2} + \frac{\partial^2}{\partial Z^2},$$

and

$$M = m_1 + m_2, \qquad m = m_1 m_2/(m_1 + m_2). \tag{3}$$

The equation is now separable. If we write

$$\psi = \psi_1(\mathbf{R})\psi_2(\mathbf{r}),$$

ψ is a solution of the equation if ψ_1, ψ_2 satisfy the equations

$$i\hbar \frac{\partial\psi_1}{\partial t} = \frac{\hbar^2}{2M}\nabla^2\psi_1,$$

$$i\hbar \frac{\partial\psi_2}{\partial t} = \frac{\hbar^2}{2m}\nabla^2\psi_2 - V\psi_2.$$

The first is the equation for the wave function of a free particle of mass M; the solutions represent the motion of the hydrogen atom as a whole. The second equation is the Schrödinger equation for the hydrogen atom; from it we deduce that the energy levels of the hydrogen atom are given by

$$W_n = -\frac{me^4}{2\hbar^2}\frac{1}{n^2},$$

where m is not the mass m_2 of the electron but

$$m_2 \Big/ \Big(1 + \frac{m_2}{m_1}\Big).$$

The same result was obtained on the old quantum theory (§ 9).

23.2. *Rotational and vibrational states of the diatomic molecule*

Suppose the Schrödinger equation for the electrons in a diatomic molecule to be solved for the case when the distance between the two nuclei is r. The energy of the electrons in the lowest quantized state will be a function of r; we may denote it by $W(r)$. If we add to this the potential energy of the nuclei in one another's field, we get an expression for the total energy that the system would have if the nuclei were held rigidly at rest at a distance r apart. We denote this energy by $V(r)$. For stable molecules we expect a curve with a minimum, as shown in Fig. 16.

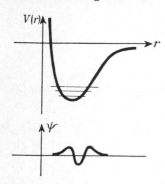

In considering the rotational and vibrational states of a molecule, and hence the motion of the nuclei, it may be shown† that it is a good approximation to treat the nuclei according to Schrödinger's equation as moving under a mutual interaction with potential energy $V(r)$. In that case the Schrödinger equation is formally the same as that discussed in the last section, if m_1, m_2 are the masses of the nuclei. The solution is in fact

$$\psi_1(\mathbf{R})\psi_2(\mathbf{r}),$$

FIG. 16. Energy of a molecule as a function of the inter-atomic distance R.

where $\psi_1(\mathbf{R})$ describes the motion of the centre of gravity as before, and $\psi_2(\mathbf{r})$ is of the form

$$P_K^u(\cos\theta)e^{iu\phi}L(r)e^{-iWt/\hbar}, \tag{4}$$

where $L(r)$ satisfies

$$\frac{1}{r^2}\frac{\partial}{\partial r}\left(r^2\frac{\partial L}{\partial r}\right)+\left[\frac{2m}{\hbar^2}\{W-V(r)\}-\frac{K(K+1)}{r^2}\right]L=0.$$

The approximation usually made in describing the levels is that for the lower vibrational states only the form of V near the minimum need be considered, and so V may be written

$$V = V_0+\tfrac{1}{2}p(r-r_0)^2.$$

In a crude approximation, assuming the amplitude of the vibrations to be small compared with r_0, we replace $K(K+1)/r^2$ by $K(K+1)/r_0^2$. The energy values are then

$$W = h\nu(n+\tfrac{1}{2})+\frac{\hbar^2 K(K+1)}{2mr_0^2} \quad \left(\nu=\frac{1}{2\pi}\sqrt{\frac{p}{m}}\right). \tag{5}$$

The first term gives the vibrational energy, the second the rotational energy.

These energies are in general small compared with electronic energies, containing as they do the large nuclear mass m in the denominator either as $m^{\frac{1}{2}}$ or m. The interval between the rotational levels is in general less than that between the vibrational.

† M. Born and J. R. Oppenheimer, *Ann. d. Physik*, **84**, 457 (1927).

In the case where the diatomic molecule is built up of two atoms of the same kind, as for example in the hydrogen molecule H_2, the wave functions $\psi(r_1 r_2)$ have certain symmetry characteristics which, as we shall see in the next section, assume great importance. Suppose we interchange the positions of the two particles. Then R, the position of the centre of gravity, is unchanged, as is also r, the distance between them. θ, however, defined by

$$\cos\theta = (z_1 - z_2)/r,$$

is changed to $\pi - \theta$, and ϕ is changed to $\pi + \phi$. It will be seen from the definitions of the spherical harmonics that $P_K^u(\cos\theta)e^{iu\phi}$ and hence $\psi(r_1 r_2)$ changes sign if K is odd but is unchanged if K is even. Thus

$$\psi(r_1 r_2) = \psi(r_2 r_1) \qquad (K \text{ even}),$$
$$\psi(r_1 r_2) = -\psi(r_2 r_1) \quad (K \text{ odd}).$$

24. Symmetry characteristics of the wave functions

It will now be shown that the symmetry characteristic proved above for the wave functions describing the positions of the nuclei of a molecule is a general property of the wave functions describing non-degenerate states, with quantized energy levels, of any atomic system consisting of two identical particles. We denote by q_1 the group of coordinates $(x_1, y_1, z_1, \sigma_1)$ describing the position and spin orientation of the first particle, and by q_2 that of the second; if the particle has no spin, as for the α-particle for example, the σ-coordinate is omitted. Then we shall show that for all non-degenerate states either

$$\psi(q_1 q_2) = \psi(q_2 q_1),$$

or
$$\psi(q_1 q_2) = -\psi(q_2 q_1). \qquad (6)$$

States of the first type are called symmetrical, those of the second type anti-symmetrical.

The proof is elementary; ψ satisfies a wave equation of the type

$$\{H_0(p_1 q_1;\ p_2 q_2) - W\}\psi(q_1 q_2) = 0. \qquad (7)$$

The Hamiltonian H_0 is necessarily symmetrical; therefore by interchanging the suffixes 1 and 2 we see that $\psi(q_2 q_1)$ is a solution of the same equation as $\psi(q_1 q_2)$. But the solution is non-degenerate; in other words, only one solution of the equation exists. Therefore

$$\psi(q_1 q_2) = A\psi(q_2 q_1),$$

where A is a numerical constant. Interchanging q_1 and q_2 on the right-hand side of this equation we obtain

$$\psi(q_2 q_1) = A^2\psi(q_2 q_1).$$

Thus
$$A^2 = 1$$
and
$$A = \pm 1.$$

We have thus proved that all solutions satisfy one or other of the relations (6).

We shall now show that if a system is originally in a state described by a wave function of given symmetry it will remain in a state of that symmetry; that is to say, transitions between symmetrical and anti-symmetrical states are impossible. Again the proof is elementary. Whatever the perturbing influence to which the system is subjected, it must be represented by a symmetrical Hamiltonian; thus if the perturbing field is such that the potential energy of an electron in it is $V(q)$, the perturbing terms to be added to the Hamiltonian are $V(q_1) + V(q_2)$. Thus the change with time of the wave function is determined by the equation

$$\frac{\hbar}{i} \frac{\partial \psi}{\partial t} = H\psi,$$

where H is a symmetrical Hamiltonian containing the perturbing functions.

It follows that if ψ is initially symmetrical, the change $\delta\psi$ that will occur in a time interval δt is symmetrical; and if ψ is initially anti-symmetrical, so is $\delta\psi$. The symmetry of ψ therefore remains unchanged.

To proceed further, we must appeal to experiment and point out the remarkable fact that in nature, in the energy spectrum of a system of two particles, only the energy levels corresponding to states of one symmetry are observed, for instance in the optical spectrum. For electrons and also for protons, both of which have a spin of $\frac{1}{2}\hbar$, only the anti-symmetrical states are observed; for α-particles, which have no spin, only the symmetrical states. We shall show below the evidence for this statement; we shall discuss first some of its consequences.

First of all it follows that, in describing pairs of particles in the free state as well as in the bound state, we must use a wave function of the required symmetry. If we did not, we could predict the formation of quantized states of the type which are not in fact observed. Suppose then we perform a measurement on one particle, the results of the measurement being describable by a wave function $u(q)$. Suppose we perform another measurement on another particle, and describe the results of this measurement by $v(q)$. Then we might think that the correct wave function to describe the system consisting of the pair of particles would be

$$u(q_1)v(q_2),$$

where q_1 is the coordinate of the first particle and q_2 of the second. We know, however, that this is not correct. If the particles are electrons the correct wave function must be

$$u(q_1)v(q_2)-u(q_2)v(q_1).\qquad(8)$$

If they are α-particles the sign must be reversed, giving

$$u(q_1)v(q_2)+u(q_2)v(q_1).\qquad(9)$$

At first sight this is rather surprising, because having made the appropriate measurement we *know* that particle 1 is in the state u. It is therefore necessary to introduce a slightly different interpretation of the wave function $\psi(q_1 q_2)$ which describes the state of two identical particles. This interpretation is as follows:

$$|\psi(q_1' q_2')|^2 \, dq_1' \, dq_2'$$

is equal to the probability that a particle has coordinates q_1, lying between q_1' and $q_1'+dq_1'$ and the other particle has coordinates q_2 lying between q_2' and $q_2'+dq_2'$. No attempt is made to state which particle is at which position, and the suffixes 1, 2 refer to two volume elements in space, rather than to the coordinates of two particles.

With this interpretation it is obvious that $|\psi(q_1 q_2)|^2$ must be a symmetrical function of $q_1 q_2$; and thus that our system of two particles must be described either by the anti-symmetrical wave function (8) or by the corresponding symmetrical one (9). Thus, unless in our formulation of quantum mechanics we exclude either the symmetrical or the anti-symmetrical functions, the theory becomes ambiguous; we do not know whether to describe the result of our two measurements by (8) or by (9). It is therefore *necessary* to exclude either symmetrical or anti-symmetrical functions; to determine which should be excluded for particles of a given type we still have to appeal to experiment.

Particles which must be described by symmetrical wave functions are said to obey the Einstein–Bose statistics, and particles which must be described by an anti-symmetrical wave function to obey the Fermi–Dirac statistics.

For *quantized* systems, zero-order wave functions can be shown to be of the types (8) or (9) by applying perturbation theory as in § 17.3. Suppose, for example, that we consider two electrons in an atom. Then if the interaction between them is neglected or considered small, we can retain the concept of separate stationary states for the individual electrons. Suppose that these states have wave functions $\psi_n(q)$. Then a state in which one electron is in the state n and another in the state n' can be described by either of the two wave functions

$$\psi_n(1)\psi_{n'}(2) \quad \text{or} \quad \psi_n(2)\psi_{n'}(1),$$

both of which give the same energy. The state is therefore degenerate. When, however, the interaction between the two electrons is taken into account, the energy will in general split; if this occurs, the correct wave functions of zero order will be

$$\frac{1}{\sqrt{2}}\{\psi_n(1)\psi_{n'}(2)\pm\psi_n(2)\psi_{n'}(1)\}.$$

That this is the case follows from the proposition already proved, that solutions of the Schrödinger equation for non-degenerate quantized energy levels must be symmetrical or anti-symmetrical. It also follows from the methods of § 17. If we set for the wave function

$$A\psi_n(1)\psi_{n'}(2)+B\psi_n(2)\psi_{n'}(1)$$

and introduce a perturbing energy $V(12)$, we find that the shift w in the energy is given by

$$(V_a-w)^2 = |V_b|^2, \tag{10}$$

so that
$$w = V_a \pm V_b,$$

where
$$V_a = \int \psi_n^*(1)\psi_{n'}^*(2)V(12)\psi_n(1)\psi_{n'}(2)\,dq_1\,dq_2,$$

$$V_b = \int \psi_n^*(1)\psi_{n'}^*(2)V(12)\psi_n(2)\psi_{n'}(1)\,dq_1\,dq_2.$$

It will easily be seen that the two wave functions of zero order corresponding to these two values of w are those given by (8) and (9).

24.1. *Introduction of the spin coordinates*

The electron (and, as we shall see, the proton) has a spin of $\frac{1}{2}\hbar$ and can thus be described by a wave function $\chi(\sigma_z)$, where σ_z takes the values ± 1 only. For ease of notation the suffix z will be dropped in this section.

If we introduce a strong magnetic field H which will break down any coupling between spin and orbital motion, or between one spin and another, then the wave functions describing the two stationary states of each electron will be the functions already introduced, $\chi_\alpha(\sigma)$, $\chi_\beta(\sigma)$, defined by

$$\chi_\alpha(\sigma) = 1, \qquad \chi_\beta(\sigma) = 0 \quad (\sigma = 1),$$

$$\chi_\alpha(\sigma) = 0, \qquad \chi_\beta(\sigma) = 1 \quad (\sigma = -1).$$

A pair of electrons will then have four stationary states, described by wave functions

$$\left.\begin{array}{c}
\chi_\alpha(\sigma_1)\chi_\alpha(\sigma_2) \\
\chi_\alpha(\sigma_1)\chi_\beta(\sigma_2)+\chi_\alpha(\sigma_2)\chi_\beta(\sigma_1) \\
\chi_\alpha(\sigma_1)\chi_\beta(\sigma_2)-\chi_\alpha(\sigma_2)\chi_\beta(\sigma_1) \\
\chi_\beta(\sigma_1)\chi_\beta(\sigma_2)
\end{array}\right\}. \tag{11}$$

These states have energies $2\mu H$, 0, 0, $-2\mu H$. The suffixes 1, 2 refer to the spin coordinates of the two particles; as already emphasized, no attempt must be made to associate either suffix with a particular particle. It will be seen that three of these functions are symmetrical and one anti-symmetrical.

In the same way, if we are setting up wave functions for (e.g. nuclear) particles with spin $s\hbar$, so that for each particle there are $2s+1$ stationary states, there will be $(2s+1)^2$ states in all. Of these, in $2s+1$ both particles will be in the same state, and the wave function will be symmetrical. Of the remaining $2s(2s+1)$ states, half will be symmetrical and half anti-symmetrical. There are thus

$$\left.\begin{array}{ll}
s(2s+1) & \text{anti-symmetrical states} \\
(s+1)(2s+1) & \text{symmetrical states}
\end{array}\right\}. \tag{12}$$

When the interaction between the spins is taken into account, it may no longer be a good approximation to express the spin wave functions as products or sums of products of the form (11). Nevertheless, the property proved above must persist; if $s\hbar$ is the angular momentum of each particle, the system of two particles will, for each orbital state, have $(2s+1)^2$ states of the spin, of which $(s+1)(2s+1)$ will be described by symmetrical wave functions $\chi_S(\sigma_1\sigma_2)$ and $s(2s+1)$ by anti-symmetrical wave functions $\chi_A(\sigma_1\sigma_2)$.

When therefore we come to consider the stationary states with quantized energy values of two particles with spin, the position is as follows: first of all, the wave functions must be found for two particles without spin; these will be of the form $\psi_S(\mathbf{r}_1\mathbf{r}_2)$, $\psi_A(\mathbf{r}_1\mathbf{r}_2)$; some, denoted by the suffix S, are symmetrical, others, denoted by the suffix A, anti-symmetrical. The complete wave function for the positional and spin coordinates may have either of the four forms

$$\left.\begin{array}{l}
\psi_S(\mathbf{r}_1\mathbf{r}_2)\chi_S(\sigma_1\sigma_2) \\
\psi_A(\mathbf{r}_1\mathbf{r}_2)\chi_A(\sigma_1\sigma_2)
\end{array}\right\} \text{symmetrical}, \tag{13}$$

$$\left.\begin{array}{l}
\psi_S(\mathbf{r}_1\mathbf{r}_2)\chi_A(\sigma_1\sigma_2) \\
\psi_A(\mathbf{r}_1\mathbf{r}_2)\chi_S(\sigma_1\sigma_2)
\end{array}\right\} \text{anti-symmetrical}. \tag{14}$$

The first two are symmetrical, the second two anti-symmetrical in the complete group of coordinates $(\mathbf{r}, \sigma)$ that describes the state of the particle. Thus either the first two types, or the second two types, must be excluded. To find out which, we must make use of the observed properties.

We may anticipate the findings of the next section and state here that for protons and electrons only anti-symmetrical functions may be used, for α-particles and in general for nuclei with an even number of heavy particles (nucleons) as constituents, only symmetrical functions.

We have seen that transitions between states symmetrical and anti-symmetrical in the whole group of coordinates $(\mathbf{r}\,\sigma)$ associated with a particle are absolutely forbidden. Transitions between states of the two types, for example

$$\psi_S(\mathbf{r}_1\,\mathbf{r}_2)\chi_A(\sigma_1\,\sigma_2),$$
$$\psi_A(\mathbf{r}_1\,\mathbf{r}_2)\chi_S(\sigma_1\,\sigma_2), \tag{15}$$

while not absolutely forbidden, have nevertheless very low intensities. The matrix element of any perturbing function $V(\mathbf{r}_1\,\sigma_1;\ \mathbf{r}_2\,\sigma_2)$ vanishes with respect to these two functions; it will be shown in Chapter X that this matrix element determines the transition probabilities. To obtain a finite transition probability, therefore, more accurate wave functions than the approximate ones (15) must be used; in other words, the effect on the wave functions of the spin-orbit interaction must be taken into account. In particular, for nuclei, since the magnetic moment of the nucleus is about 1,000 times less than for the electron, the probability of these transitions is very small indeed.

24.2. *Application to diatomic molecules*

The considerations of this section are valid only for *homonuclear* molecules such as H_2 in which the two nuclei are identical. If the element consists of a number of isotopes, they do *not* apply to the case where the two nuclei have different masses.

We denote by $\mathbf{r}_1$, $\mathbf{r}_2$ the spatial coordinates of the two nuclei, and by σ_1, σ_2 their spin coordinates. The orbital wave functions $\psi(\mathbf{r}_1\,\mathbf{r}_2)$ have already been found; they are of the form

$$\psi_K(\mathbf{r}_1\,\mathbf{r}_2) = P_K^u(\cos\theta)e^{iu\phi}L(r),$$

where (r, θ, ϕ) are the spherical polar coordinates of the vector $\mathbf{r}_1 - \mathbf{r}_2$. It has already been shown that ψ_K is anti-symmetrical if K is odd, symmetrical if K is even.

If then we limit ourselves to anti-symmetrical wave functions, we see that for a given orbital state the spin wave functions will give rise to $(s+1)(2s+1)$ states if K is odd, $s(2s+1)$ if K is even. If we are limited to symmetrical wave functions, these numbers are reversed. Let us then consider transitions between two electronic states of a diatomic molecule; the energy levels corresponding to the two states will be, according to formula (5),

$$W_1 + h\nu_1(n+\tfrac{1}{2}) + \hbar^2 K(K+1)/2I_1,$$
$$W_2 + h\nu_2(n'+\tfrac{1}{2}) + \hbar^2 K'(K'+1)/2I_2,$$

where I_1, I_2 are the moments of inertia of the two states. The usual selection rule for diatomic molecules is

$$K - K' = 0 \quad \text{or} \quad \pm 1,$$

but for homonuclear transitions $K - K' = \pm 1$ is excluded by the arguments of the last section. Therefore the rotational structure of a band is given by the formula

$$h\nu = h\nu_0 + K(K+1)\left[\frac{\hbar^2}{2I_1} - \frac{\hbar^2}{2I_2}\right]. \tag{16}$$

Also, if a gas containing diatomic molecules is in thermal equilibrium, there will be differing numbers of molecules in states with odd and even K, the numbers being in the ratio $s:(s+1)$ or $(s+1):s$. Further, this ratio will not be altered when the molecule is excited by electronic bombardment or in any other way, since the probability of transition from odd to even states is so small. Thus, finally, we see that the *intensities* of the lines given by formula (16) should alternate, odd lines and even lines having intensities in the ratio $s/(s+1)$ or $(s+1)/s$.

Turning now to the results of observations on diatomic molecules, it is found that for the molecules He_2, C_2, and O_2 the lines with odd K are not observed; therefore these nuclei must have no spin and obey Bose–Einstein statistics (symmetrical wave functions). Also for N_2 the odd states have half the intensity that the even states have. Therefore the nitrogen nucleus has a spin of unity ($s = 1$) and again obeys the Bose–Einstein statistics.

It should be pointed out that these relations hold only when the molecule is formed from the common isotope, e.g. He_4, C_{12}, or O_{16}. No such alternation of intensity is expected or observed for molecules of the type $O_{16}O_{17}$, for example (for which the rotational levels are slightly displaced on account of the changed moment of inertia).[†]

It is significant that nuclei of even atomic weight always obey Bose–

[†] Cf. R. T. Birge and A. S. King, *Phys. Rev.* **34**, 376 (1929).

Einstein statistics, as far as known. This is to be expected if they are built up of heavy particles (protons and neutrons) only.

For hydrogen, lines corresponding both to odd and to even values of K occur; but lines for which K is odd have three times the intensity of the lines for which K is even. This shows that hydrogen nuclei (protons) obey Fermi–Dirac statistics (anti-symmetrical wave functions) and have a spin of one-half quantum ($s\hbar$ where $s = \frac{1}{2}$).

Results for many other nuclei can be found in any book on nuclear physics, for example the review by Seaborg, *Rev. Mod. Phys.* **16**, 1 (1944).

The arguments given above show that transitions between the two forms of hydrogen (those with odd and even values of K) will proceed at a very slow rate. This means that if hydrogen gas in equilibrium at some temperature is heated or cooled to some new temperature, it will take a very long time to reach equilibrium. This gives rise to anomalies in the specific heat of hydrogen gas at low temperatures. The two forms of hydrogen (K even, K odd) are called para- and ortho-hydrogen. The one form can only be changed into the other by a catalyst which dissociates the molecule and allows the atoms to recombine after being mixed up.†

24.3. *The helium atom: general principles*

Considering first the orbital motion, and hence the wave functions for the spatial coordinates, we expect to have a series of symmetrical wave functions $\psi_S(\mathbf{r}_1 \mathbf{r}_2)$ with associated energies W_S and anti-symmetrical wave functions $\psi_A(\mathbf{r}_1 \mathbf{r}_2)$ with energies W_A. The ground state will be a symmetrical function. Including spin coordinates, the anti-symmetrical functions are of the type

$$\left.\begin{array}{ll} \psi_S(\mathbf{r}_1\mathbf{r}_2)\chi_A(\sigma_1\sigma_2), & \text{one spin state,} \\ \psi_A(\mathbf{r}_1\mathbf{r}_2)\chi_S(\sigma_1\sigma_2), & \text{three spin states.} \end{array}\right\} \tag{17}$$

If electrons obey Fermi–Dirac statistics (as they do!) we expect therefore to find in helium two sets of energy levels, between which optical transitions are extremely weak. One set of these, known as the par-helium levels, will have symmetrical orbital wave functions and will thus include the ground state; these states have zero spin moment (anti-parallel spins) and are not split by the spin. The other set (ortho-helium) with anti-symmetrical levels will be split into *three* states by the spin and thus give a triplet series.

† Cf. for example, R. H. Fowler, *Statistical Mechanics*, 2nd ed. (Cambridge, 1936), p. 850.

The spin wave functions (17) are wave functions for *stationary states* only if a strong external magnetic field is applied, sufficiently great to break down the spin-orbital coupling and produce a Paschen–Back effect. The spin wave functions in the absence of an external field will be combinations of these wave functions. For a mathematical treatment of this case, a derivation of the triplet separation and of the Landé g-factor, cf. for example H. Bethe, *Handb. d. Physik*, **24**/1, p. 393 (1933).

Methods of obtaining the orbital or spatial wave functions are given in Chapter VI.

24.4. *Collisions between identical particles*

The symmetry characteristics of the wave function affect the intensity of scattering when one particle collides with another of identical type, for example when α-particles are scattered by helium gas. The wave equation for the two particles (equation (2)) can as before be solved in the form

$$\psi_1(\mathbf{R})\psi_2(\mathbf{r}),$$

where $\mathbf{R}$ is the coordinate of the contro of gravity and $\mathbf{r}$ is the vector joining the position of the two particles. If we refer the system to moving axes with respect to which the centre of gravity is at rest,

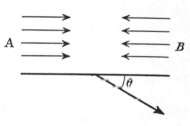

Fig. 17. Collision between identical particles.

$\psi_1(\mathbf{R})$ is a constant; we thus consider two streams of particles impinging with equal and opposite velocities, as in Fig. 17. The function $\psi_2(\mathbf{r})$ satisfies the differential equation

$$\nabla^2\psi_2+\frac{2m^*}{\hbar^2}\{W-V(r)\}\psi_2 = 0,$$

where $V(r)$ is the interaction energy and m^* is the 'reduced mass', in this case half the mass of either particle. As will be shown in Chapter IX, a solution $\psi(\mathbf{r}_1\mathbf{r}_2)$ can be obtained which for large r has the form

$$\psi \sim e^{ikz}+\frac{e^{ikr}}{r}f(\theta). \tag{18}$$

With this unsymmetrical wave function we should interpret $|f(\theta)|^2$ as the number per unit solid angle scattered from beam A and $|f(\pi-\theta)|^2$ as the number scattered in the same direction from beam B. The total intensity of scattering would thus be

$$|f(\theta)|^2+|f(\pi-\theta)|^2. \tag{19}$$

The function (18), however, does not have the desired symmetry. Suppose, for instance, that we are dealing with α-particles; for these the spin is zero and the wave function must be symmetrical. Since an interchange of the coordinates of the two particles changes z into $-z$ and θ into $\pi-\theta$, the correct wave function is

$$\psi(\mathbf{r_1\,r_2})+\psi(\mathbf{r_2\,r_1}) \sim 2\cos kz+\frac{e^{ikr}}{r}[f(\theta)+f(\pi-\theta)],$$

and the total intensity of scattering in the direction θ is, instead of (19),

$$|f(\theta)+f(\pi-\theta)|^2. \tag{20}$$

There is no possibility, theoretical or experimental, of distinguishing between knocked-on and scattered particles; (20) gives the total number.

It is particularly to be observed that when $\theta = 90°$ formula (20) gives just twice as many scattered particles as the unsymmetrical wave function (19).

If the velocity of the particles is not too high, the electrostatic repulsion between the particles alone is responsible for the scattering. Under these conditions, as shown in Chapter IX, $|f(\theta)|^2$ reduces to the form given by classical mechanics, namely

$$|f(\theta)|^2 = \left(\frac{Z^2e^2}{2mv^2}\right)^2 \operatorname{cosec}^4 \tfrac{1}{2}\theta,$$

and thus the quantum mechanical formula (20) gives just twice the classical value at 90°.

In order to verify this prediction of quantum mechanics that for identical particles without spin the scattering would be twice the classical, experiments were carried out by Chadwick,[†] who bombarded helium with α-particles; it is then to be expected that twice the classical scattering will occur at 45° (since in the actual system the centre of gravity is not at rest). In Fig. 18 a is shown the ratio of the observed number of scattered particles between 40° and 50° to the number to be expected classically. It will be seen that at low velocities this ratio tends to 2; at higher velocities the scattering is determined by the structure of the α-particle.

For Coulomb scattering the function $f(\theta)$ has the form[‡]

$$\frac{Ze^2}{2mv^2}\operatorname{cosec}^2 \tfrac{1}{2}\theta \exp\left[-i\frac{Z^2e^2}{\hbar v}\log(1-\cos\theta)+\text{const.}\right].$$

The phase factor, which contains Planck's constant h and is therefore

† J. Chadwick, *Proc. Roy. Soc.* A, **128**, 114 (1930).

‡ Cf. Mott and Massey, *Theory of Atomic Collisions* (Oxford, 1933), p. 35.

a consequence typically of quantum mechanics, does not affect the collision between particles that are not identical. As is evident from

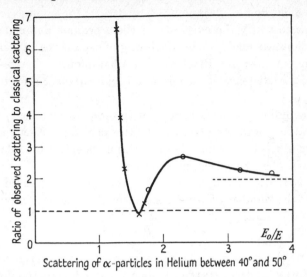

FIG. 18*a*. Ratio of observed scattering of α-particles in helium to classical Coulomb scattering. *E* is the energy of the particle, and E_0 that of the original particle from a polonium source.

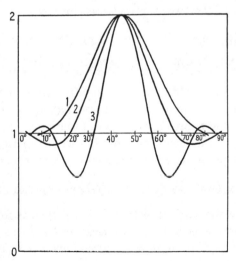

FIG. 18*b*. Theoretical value of ratio shown in Fig. 18*a*. Curve 1, $v = 8 \times 10^8$, curve 2, $v = 4 \times 10^8$, curve 3, $v = 2 \times 10^8$ cm./sec.

formula (20), however, it does do so in the case of identical particles; the ratio of the scattering given by (20) and by the (classical) formula

(19) is plotted in Fig. 18 b for values of the velocity equal to 2×10^8, 4×10^8 and 8×10^8 cm. per sec. The smaller the velocity, the more rapid are the oscillations.

In order to verify the existence of these peaks a detailed statistical investigation was made of the scattering of α-particles by helium in an expansion chamber by Blackett and Champion.† The results fully confirmed the existence of the minimum round about $35°$ for $v \sim 2 \times 10^8$ cm./sec.

If the colliding particles have spin (protons or electrons) the treatment is rather more complicated. In this chapter a discussion will be given only of the case where the particles have spin $\frac{1}{2}$ (angular momentum $\frac{1}{2}\hbar$) and obey Fermi–Dirac statistics.

If the particles have opposite spins, they may be treated as distinguishable; the number of particles scattered in the direction θ will be given by (19), namely

$$|f(\theta)|^2 + |f(\pi - \theta)|^2. \tag{21}$$

If they have the same spin, the wave function in the spatial coordinates must be anti-symmetrical; the number of particles scattered will therefore be

$$|f(\theta) - f(\pi - \theta)|^2. \tag{22}$$

Taking the mean of the two, the scattered intensity is

$$\tfrac{1}{2}\{|f(\theta)|^2 + |f(\pi - \theta)|^2 + |f(\theta) - f(\pi - \theta)|^2\},$$

i.e.

$$\tfrac{1}{4}\{|f(\theta) + f(\pi - \theta)|^2 + \tfrac{3}{4}|f(\theta) - f(\pi - \theta)|^2\}.$$

This formula may be obtained in a slightly different way. Suppose that a measurement is made which shows that one electron is in the neighbourhood of the point A, with wave function $\psi_A(\mathbf{r})$ and with spin wave function $\chi_\alpha(s)$; the second electron has wave functions $\psi_B(\mathbf{r})$, $\chi_\beta(s)$. Then the wave function describing the pair of particles is

$$\psi_A(\mathbf{r}_1)\chi_\alpha(s_1)\psi_B(\mathbf{r}_2)\chi_\beta(s_2) - \psi_A(\mathbf{r}_2)\chi_\alpha(s_2)\psi_B(\mathbf{r}_1)\chi_\beta(s_1).$$

If the spins are in the same direction ($\alpha = \beta$), then it follows that the spatial wave function is anti-symmetrical and that the scattering is given by (22). If they are in opposite directions it may be written

$$\tfrac{1}{2}\{\psi_A(1)\psi_B(2) - \psi_A(2)\psi_B(1)\}\{\chi_\alpha(1)\chi_\beta(2) + \chi_\beta(1)\chi_\alpha(2)\} +$$

$$+ \tfrac{1}{2}\{\psi_A(1)\psi_B(2) + \psi_A(2)\psi_B(1)\}\{\chi_\alpha(1)\chi_\beta(2) - \chi_\beta(1)\chi_\alpha(2)\}.$$

† P. M. S. Blackett and F. C. Champion, *Proc. Roy. Soc.* A, **130**, 380 (1931).

From this it follows that the scattering is given by

$$\tfrac{1}{2}|f(\theta)+f(\pi-\theta)|^2+\tfrac{1}{2}|f(\theta)-f(\pi-\theta)|^2,$$

which is identical with (21).

24.5. *The Pauli principle*

The Pauli principle, as originally formulated, stated that no two electrons in an atom could have the same set of four quantum numbers.

The Pauli principle follows from the more general statement that the wave function $\psi(\mathbf{r}_1\sigma_1,\ \mathbf{r}_2\sigma_2,\ \mathbf{r}_3\sigma_3\ldots)$ of *all* the electrons in an atom, or in any other system, must be anti-symmetrical in the coordinates of any two electrons. When the interaction between the electrons is small enough for it to be possible to represent the orbital wave function by a product of functions of the coordinates of individual particles, the Pauli principle results. This may be seen as follows.

It is simplest to consider an atom in a strong magnetic field sufficient to produce a Paschen–Back effect, so that there is no coupling between the spin and the orbital motion. Suppose that the n individual electrons are in orbital states a, b, c,..., n with wave functions $\psi_a(\mathbf{r})$, $\psi_b(\mathbf{r})$.... If the total spin along the field is $s\hbar$, this means that $\tfrac{1}{2}n+s$ spins are oriented along the field and $\tfrac{1}{2}n-s$ in the other direction. Thus there are $n!/(\tfrac{1}{2}n-s)!(\tfrac{1}{2}n\mid s)!$ ways in which a spin wave function $\chi_\alpha(\sigma)$ or $\chi_\beta(\sigma)$ can be associated with an orbital wave function $\psi_a(\mathbf{r})$. Let the series of functions

$$\psi_a(\mathbf{r})\chi_a(\sigma),\qquad \psi_b(\mathbf{r})\chi_b(\sigma),\qquad \psi_c(\mathbf{r})\chi_c(\sigma),\quad \ldots \qquad (23\,a)$$

represent one of these ways; the suffixes a, b, c, must when appended to χ denote α or β. Then, as long as none of these wave functions is the same, we can form an anti-symmetrical wave function in the form of the determinant

$$\begin{vmatrix} \psi_a(\mathbf{r}_1)\chi_a(\sigma_1) & \psi_a(\mathbf{r}_2)\chi_a(\sigma_2) & \cdot & \cdot & \cdot \\ \psi_b(\mathbf{r}_1)\chi_b(\sigma_1) & \psi_b(\mathbf{r}_2)\chi_b(\sigma_2) & \cdot & \cdot & \cdot \\ \cdot & \cdot \quad \cdot \quad \cdot \quad \cdot \quad \cdot \quad \cdot \quad \cdot \quad \cdot \quad \cdot & & & \end{vmatrix}. \qquad (23\,b)$$

If, however, any of the individual wave functions $(23\,a)$ are the same, $(23\,b)$ vanishes and no anti-symmetrical wave function is possible. This proves the Pauli principle.

The function $(23\,b)$ is not the correct zero-order wave function of the system; to obtain this we must add together all of the $n!/(\tfrac{1}{2}n-s)!(\tfrac{1}{2}n+s)!$ functions of the type $(23\,b)$ which do not vanish, with coefficients which have to be determined. Methods by which this can be done are described in Chapter VI.

25. The helium atom: methods of obtaining wave functions

In this section we discuss only the wave functions in the spatial coordinates; we have therefore to solve the Schrödinger equation

$$\nabla_1^2\psi+\nabla_2^2\psi+\frac{2m}{\hbar^2}\Big\{W+\frac{2e^2}{r_1}+\frac{2e^2}{r_2}-\frac{e^2}{|\mathbf{r}_1-\mathbf{r}_2|}\Big\}\psi = 0. \tag{24}$$

As has been shown already, we expect to obtain a series of symmetrical wave functions $\psi_S(\mathbf{r}_1\mathbf{r}_2)$ with corresponding energy values, which with the introduction of the spin remain singlet terms, and a series of anti-symmetrical wave functions $\psi_A(\mathbf{r}_1\mathbf{r}_2)$, which become triplet terms.

25.1. *Perturbation method of obtaining energy levels*

In order to obtain approximate values for the energy levels it is convenient to consider both electrons moving in some field $V(r)$; the Schrödinger equation

$$\nabla^2\psi+\frac{2m}{\hbar^2}\{W-V(r)\}\psi = 0 \tag{25}$$

is then solved, and characteristic energies W_n and wave functions obtained; wave functions of zero order for the helium atom are then taken to be

$$\frac{1}{\sqrt2}\{\psi_n(1)\psi_{n'}(2)\pm\psi_n(2)\psi_{n'}(1)\}$$

with energy $W_n+W_{n'}$; and the remaining term in the potential energy in (24),

$$U(\mathbf{r}_1\mathbf{r}_2) = -\frac{2e^2}{r_1}-\frac{2e^2}{r_2}+\frac{e^2}{|\mathbf{r}_1-\mathbf{r}_2|}-V(r_1)-V(r_2),$$

is treated as a perturbation and the change in the energy is calculated by the methods of Chapter III. In his original paper on the helium atom, Heisenberg[†] took for $V(r)$

$$V(r) = -\frac{2e^2}{r}+v(r) \quad \begin{cases}v(r) = e^2/r_0 & (r < r_0) \\ \quad\;\;= e^2/r & (r > r_0),\end{cases}$$

where r_0 is some suitably chosen radius; clearly each electron will move in the field of a doubly charged nucleus for small r and that of a singly charged nucleus for large r. This form of $V(r)$ is not, however, the best possible choice (cf. § 25.2).

The change in the energy due to the perturbing term $U(\mathbf{r}_1\mathbf{r}_2)$ is then (we write $\psi(1)$ for $\psi(\mathbf{r}_1)$)

$$\tfrac12\int\!\!\int|\psi_n(1)\psi_{n'}(2)\pm\psi_n(2)\psi_{n'}(1)|^2U(\mathbf{r}_1\mathbf{r}_2)\,d\tau_1\,d\tau_2,$$

† W. Heisenberg, *Zeits. f. Physik*, **39**, 499 (1927).

which reduces to $J_{nn'} \pm K_{nn'}$, where

$$J_{nn'} = \iint U(\mathbf{r}_1 \mathbf{r}_2) |\psi_n(1)\psi_{n'}(2)|^2 \, d\tau_1 d\tau_2$$

and
$$K_{nn'} = \iint U(\mathbf{r}_1 \mathbf{r}_2) \psi_n(1)\psi_n^*(1)\psi_n(2)\psi_n^*(2) \, d\tau_1 d\tau_2.$$

The integral K is called the 'exchange' integral. The ground state of helium has the wave function of zero order $\psi_0(1)\psi_0(2)$ and there is thus no splitting of the energy value when interaction between the electrons is taken into account; when, however, one electron is excited the pair of wave functions of zero order

$$\psi_0(1)\psi_n(2) \pm \psi_0(2)\psi_n(1)$$

are possible, with energies to the first order

$$W_0 + W_n + J_{0n} \pm K_{0n}.$$

The terms with the positive sign form the series of levels (singlets) which include the ground state.

25.2. *Choice of the field $V(r)$; the Hartree method of the self-consistent field*

It has been shown by Hartree† that the best field $V(r)$ for the calculation of the wave functions of zero order, at any rate for the ground state of helium, may be obtained as follows: if $\psi(r)$ is the wave function for the ground state of an electron moving in the field $V(r)$, and thus the solution of (25), $V(r)$ is given by

$$V(r) = -\frac{2e^2}{r} + \int |\psi(r')|^2 \frac{e^2}{|\mathbf{r}-\mathbf{r}'|} \, d\tau'. \tag{26}$$

This field is termed the self-consistent field; it can only be obtained by a series of successive approximations, since ψ cannot be calculated until an estimate of V is made, which must then be modified using the value of ψ obtained.

It will be seen that $V(r)$ is the potential energy of an electron in the field due to the nucleus and to a charge distribution (due to the other electron) of density $-e|\psi(r)|^2$ at any point at a distance r from the nucleus.

The self-consistent equation is thus

$$\nabla^2 \psi + \frac{2m}{\hbar^2}\{W - V(r)\}\psi = 0.$$

† D. R. Hartree, *Proc. Camb. Phil. Soc.* **24**, 89 (1928).

It will be noticed that W or $2W$ is not directly related either to the ionization potential or to the total energy of the atoms. The total energy of both electrons (minus the work required to remove them both) is

$$\iint \psi^*(1)\psi^*(2)H\psi(1)\psi(2)\,d\tau_1\,d\tau_2$$
$$= 2w - e^2 \iint \frac{1}{|\mathbf{r}_1 - \mathbf{r}_2|}\,|\psi(1)|^2|\psi(2)|^2\,d\tau_1\,d\tau_2.$$

It is important to realize that the Hartree approximation does not entirely neglect the influence of one electron on another; for instance, in helium the field $V(r)$ behaves as $-2e^2/r$ near the nucleus and as $-e^2/r$ at large distances, owing to the screening effect of the other electron. On the other hand, if one electron is on the right-hand side of the atom, the other electron is more likely to be on the left than on the right because of the repulsion between them. This fact is neglected in Hartree's approximation; to take it into account terms involving $|\mathbf{r}_1 - \mathbf{r}_2|$ must be introduced into the wave function.

The proof that the self-consistent field gives the best approximation for the ground state requires the following lemma:

Consider a Hamiltonian function $H(p \dots q \dots)$ from which a Schrödinger equation can be set up. Let $\psi(q \dots)$ be *any* function of the space coordinates q satisfying the normalizing condition

$$\int \psi^*\psi\,dq = 1. \tag{27}$$

Then, if the integral $\qquad W = \int \psi^*H\psi\,dq \tag{28}$

is formed, the lowest energy value W_0 corresponding to a characteristic solution of the Schrödinger equation

$$(H - W)\psi = 0$$

is equal to the lowest possible value of the integral (28) for all possible choices of ψ which obey (27).

The proof is as follows: suppose we vary ψ by adding to it a small arbitrary function $\delta\psi$ of q. Then since the integral (28) is a minimum, the change in its value will be zero to the first order. Thus

$$\int \delta\psi^*H\psi\,dq + \int \psi^*H\,\delta\psi\,dq = 0.$$

By the Hermitian property (cf. Chap. I) the two integrals are equal; we thus obtain

$$\int \delta\psi^*H\psi\,dq = 0.$$

This is valid for all functions $\delta\psi$ such that, by (27),

$$\int \delta\psi^*\psi\,dq = 0.$$

Using the method of undetermined multipliers, we see this is the case for a certain choice of a parameter λ if

$$\int \delta\psi^*(H\psi - \lambda\psi)\, dq = 0$$

for *all* functions $\delta\psi^*$. It follows that

$$H\psi - \lambda\psi = 0,$$

which gives us just the Schrödinger equation.

The other solutions of the Schrödinger equation also give minimum values of (28), ψ being varied in such a way as to keep the number of nodes or nodal surfaces in the wave function a constant.

The self-consistent or Hartree solution can now be shown to be the one which gives the minimum energy, and hence the best approximation to the wave functions when (in the case of an atom with two electrons) the wave function $\psi(\mathbf{r}_1, \mathbf{r}_2)$ is taken in the form of a simple product

$$\psi(\mathbf{r}_1)\psi(\mathbf{r}_2). \tag{29}$$

For if we substitute (29) in (28) above and vary ψ by $\delta\psi$ we obtain

$$\int \delta\psi(1)\Big\{\int \psi(2)H\psi(2)\, d\tau_2\Big\}\psi(1)\, d\tau_1 = 0$$

for any variations of $\psi(r)$ which satisfy

$$\int \psi(r)\, \delta\psi(r)\, d\tau = 0.$$

Using as before the method of undetermined multipliers, we obtain the following differential equation to determine $\psi(r)$:

$$\Big\{\int \psi(2)H\psi(2)\, d\tau_2\Big\}\psi(1) - W\psi(1) = 0. \tag{30}$$

The term in the curly brackets gives

$$\int \psi(2)H\psi(2)\, d\tau_2 = -\frac{\hbar^2}{2m}\nabla_1^2 + V(r_1) + A,$$

where $V(r)$ is defined by (26) and

$$A = \int \psi^*\Big\{-\frac{\hbar^2}{2m}\nabla^2 - \frac{2e^2}{r}\Big\}\psi_0\, d\tau.$$

Equation (30) thus becomes

$$\nabla^2\psi + \frac{2m}{\hbar^2}\{w - V(r)\}\psi = 0,$$

where $w = W - A$. This is Hartree's self-consistent equation for ψ. It will be noted that the total energy of the two electrons is given by $w = W - A$.

25.3. *The Fock equation*

If, in the approximation of zero order, the two electrons are not in the same state and thus if an excited state of the helium atom is under consideration, the wave functions derived by Hartree's method do not give the best possible approximation. If the wave functions concerned are $\psi_0(r)$, $\psi_n(r)$, Hartree's method would consist in making the integral

$$\iint \psi_0^*(1)\psi_n^*(2)H\psi_0(1)\psi_n(2)\,d\tau_1\,d\tau_2$$

a minimum. A better value for the energy will be obtained by using symmetrical or anti-symmetrical wave functions for the terms of ortho- and parhelium respectively and minimizing the integral

$$W = \iint [\psi_0^*(1)\psi_n^*(2)\pm\psi_0^*(2)\psi_n^*(1)]H[\psi_0(1)\psi_n(2)\pm\psi_0(2)\psi_n(1)]\,d\tau_1\,d\tau_2.$$

This was first pointed out by Fock,[†] and the resulting equations are called Fock's equations. These equations are, as may easily be shown by the methods of the last paragraph,

$$\left\{\frac{\hbar^2}{2m}\nabla^2+\frac{2e^2}{r}+W-H_{nn}-G_{nn}(r)\right\}\psi_0 = \pm\{H_{12}+G_{12}(r)\}\psi_n,$$

$$\left\{\frac{\hbar^2}{2m}\nabla^2+\frac{2e^2}{r}+W-H_{00}-G_{00}(r)\right\}\psi_n = \pm\{H_{12}+G_{12}(r)\}\psi_0,$$

where

$$H_{ik} = \int \psi_i^*\left\{-\frac{\hbar^2}{2m}\nabla^2-\frac{2e^2}{r}\right\}\psi_k\,d\tau,$$

$$G_{ik}(r_1) = \int \frac{e^2}{|\mathbf{r}_1-\mathbf{r}_2|}\psi_i^*(r_2)\psi_k(r_2)\,d\tau_2.$$

As in Hartree's equations, a solution can only be obtained by a method of successive approximations. An attempt to solve the equations for the excited s-states of helium has been given by L. P. Smith.[‡]

Further consideration of Hartree's and Fock's methods for atoms of more than two electrons is given in the next chapter.

26. The deuteron

A two-body problem of some importance in theoretical nuclear physics is that of determining the energy levels of the deuteron. The deuteron, consisting as it does of two elementary nuclear particles (or

---

† V. Fock, *Zeits. f. Physik.* **61**, 126 (1930). See also J. C. Slater, loc. cit., and Brillouin, *Actualités Scientifiques*, iv (Paris, 1934), who gives a detailed account of the two equations and of the relation between them.

‡ L. P. Smith, *Phys. Rev.* **42**, 176 (1932).

nucleons), one proton and one neutron, plays in nuclear physics a role similar to that assumed by the hydrogen atom in atomic physics. Further, since any two-body problem can be integrated explicitly if the force between the two particles is a known function of their distance apart, calculations on the deuteron are more suitable for quantitative comparison with the experimental results than any others in nuclear theory.

In order to deal with the two kinds of nucleons it is necessary to introduce a convenient formalism; this was first achieved by Heisenberg,[†] who introduced the *isotopic spin variable t* analogous to the spin variable s. Just as in the latter case $s = 1$ represents a particle with a spin in the direction of the z-axis and $s = -1$ a particle with spin in the opposite direction, $t = 1$ represents a neutron and $t = -1$ represents a proton. In precisely the same way there are *isotopic spin operators* $\tau = (\tau_x, \tau_y, \tau_z)$ corresponding to the Pauli spin operators $\sigma = (\sigma_x, \sigma_y, \sigma_z)$ defined above.

The wave function of the deuteron is thus a function not only of the space coordinates $\mathbf{r}^{(1)}$, $\mathbf{r}^{(2)}$ of the two particles but also of the spin coordinates $s^{(1)}$, $s^{(2)}$ and the isotopic spin coordinates $t^{(1)}$, $t^{(2)}$. Thus

$$\psi = \psi(\mathbf{r}^{(1)}, s^{(1)}, t^{(1)}; \mathbf{r}^{(2)}, s^{(2)}, t^{(2)}). \tag{31}$$

For the deuteron the wave function ψ may be written as a product

$$\psi = \phi(\mathbf{r}^{(1)}, \mathbf{r}^{(2)})\chi(s^{(1)}, s^{(2)}; t^{(1)}, t^{(2)}), \tag{32}$$

where ϕ is a function of the space variables and χ a function of the spin and isotopic spin variables. For nuclei containing more than two nucleons it is not possible to separate the space coordinates from the spin and isotopic spin variables in this way.

To fulfil the Pauli exclusion principle ψ must be an anti-symmetrical function. Thus either ϕ is symmetrical and χ is anti-symmetrical or ϕ is anti-symmetrical and χ is symmetrical. In the ground state we would expect the former of these conditions to hold. If we denote the spin wave functions by χ_α, χ_β, as above, and the corresponding isotopic spin functions by $\bar{\chi}_\alpha$, $\bar{\chi}_\beta$, then for the triplet state we have

$$\chi(^3S) = \chi_{\alpha_1}\chi_{\alpha_2}(\bar{\chi}_{\alpha_1}\bar{\chi}_{\beta_2} - \bar{\chi}_{\beta_1}\bar{\chi}_{\alpha_2}), \tag{33}$$

and for the singlet state

$$\chi(^1S) = (\chi_{\alpha_1}\chi_{\beta_2} - \chi_{\beta_1}\chi_{\alpha_2})(\bar{\chi}_{\alpha_1}\bar{\chi}_{\beta_2} + \bar{\chi}_{\beta_1}\bar{\chi}_{\alpha_2}). \tag{34}$$

Using the results (23) of Chapter IV we have

$$\sigma^{(1)}\chi_{\alpha_1} = (\chi_{\beta_1}, +i\chi_{\beta_1}, \chi_{\alpha_1}),$$

† W. Heisenberg, *Zeits. f. Physik*, **77**, 1 (1932).

and similarly for $\sigma^{(2)}\chi_{\alpha_2}$ so that

$$(\sigma^{(1)}.\sigma^{(2)})\chi_{\alpha_1}\chi_{\alpha_2} = (\sigma^{(1)}\chi_{\alpha_1}.\sigma^{(2)}\chi_{\alpha_2}) = \chi_{\alpha_1}\chi_{\alpha_2}. \tag{35}$$

The τ's and $\bar{\chi}$'s satisfy the same relations as the σ's and χ's, i.e.

$$\begin{aligned} \tau_x\bar{\chi}_\alpha = \bar{\chi}_\beta, \quad \tau_y\bar{\chi}_\alpha = +i\bar{\chi}_\beta, \quad \tau_z\bar{\chi}_\alpha = \bar{\chi}_\alpha \\ \tau_x\bar{\chi}_\beta = \bar{\chi}_\alpha, \quad \tau_y\bar{\chi}_\beta = -i\bar{\chi}_\alpha, \quad \tau_z\bar{\chi}_\beta = -\bar{\chi}_\beta \end{aligned} \Bigg\}, \tag{36}$$

so that $\qquad (\tau^{(1)}.\tau^{(2)})(\bar{\chi}_{\alpha_1}\bar{\chi}_{\beta_2}-\bar{\chi}_{\beta_1}\bar{\chi}_{\alpha_2}) = -3(\bar{\chi}_{\alpha_1}.\bar{\chi}_{\beta_2}-\bar{\chi}_{\beta_1}.\bar{\chi}_{\alpha_2}). \tag{37}$

Now according to the Møller–Rosenfeld meson theory[†] of nuclear forces the interaction between two nucleons is given by

$$U = (\tau^{(1)}.\tau^{(2)})[G^2+(\sigma^{(1)}.\sigma^{(2)})F^2]\frac{e^{-\lambda r_{12}}}{r_{12}} \tag{38}$$

where r_{12} denotes the distance between the two particles, F and G are two constants with the dimension of electric charge, and λ is a constant related to the mass, m, of the meson by the formula

$$\lambda = \frac{mc}{\hbar}. \tag{39}$$

If M denotes the mass of a nuclear particle, then transforming the Schrödinger equation to coordinates in which the centre of gravity is at rest, we obtain

$$\nabla^2\psi+\frac{M}{\hbar^2}(W-U)\psi = 0 \tag{40}$$

as the wave equation for the deuteron.

For the triplet state we have from equations (35) and (37) that

$$U\psi = -3(F^2+G^2)\frac{e^{-\lambda r}}{r}\psi,$$

and similarly for the singlet state it can be shown that

$$U\psi = (G^2-3F^2)\frac{e^{-\lambda r}}{r}\psi.$$

Thus in both cases we may write for the state $(l = 0)$ of the deuteron

$$\frac{d^2\phi}{dr^2}+\frac{2}{r}\frac{d\phi}{dr}+\frac{M}{\hbar^2}\left(W+B\frac{e^{-\lambda r}}{r}\right)\phi = 0.$$

Writing

$$r = \rho/\lambda, \quad B = b\left(\frac{m}{M}\right)\hbar c, \quad W = a\left(\frac{m}{M}\right)mc^2, \quad \phi = \frac{\Phi}{\rho},$$

we obtain the equation

$$\frac{d^2\Phi}{d\rho^2}+\left(a+b\frac{e^{-\rho}}{\rho}\right)\Phi = 0. \tag{41}$$

† C. Møller and L. Rosenfeld, *D. Kgl. Danske Vidensk. Selskab, Mek.-fys. Medd.* **17**, No. 8 (1940).

The differential equation (41) satisfied by the radial part of the wave function for the ground state of the deuteron has been studied in detail by A. H. Wilson.[†] The problem now is to determine a when b is known. Assuming a solution of equation (41) of the form

$$\Phi = \rho e^{-\frac{1}{2}\alpha\rho}, \tag{42}$$

so that $d^2\Phi/d\rho^2$ is equal to $\frac{1}{4}\alpha^2\Phi$, we have to determine the energy

$$\left(a+\frac{\alpha^2}{4}\right)\int_0^\infty \Phi\Phi^* \, d\rho = -b \int_0^\infty \frac{e^{-\rho}}{\rho}\Phi\Phi^* \, d\rho.$$

Now $$\int_0^\infty \Phi^*\Phi \, d\rho = \frac{2}{\alpha^3}, \qquad \int_0^\infty \frac{e^{-\rho}}{\rho}\Phi\Phi^* \, d\rho = \frac{1}{(1+\alpha)^2},$$

so that we obtain the relation

$$a = -\frac{b\alpha^3}{2(1+\alpha)^2} - \frac{1}{4}\alpha^2.$$

To obtain the best value of α we minimize a with respect to α. In this way we obtain the parametric equations

$$a = -\frac{\alpha^2(\alpha-1)}{4(\alpha+3)}, \qquad b = -\frac{(\alpha+1)^3}{\alpha(\alpha+3)}, \tag{43}$$

giving the relation between a and b. Wilson compares this solution with that obtained mechanically by means of a differential analyser. The results are summarized in the first three columns of the table below.

| | | b | |
a	Analyser	Wilson	Hulthén
0·00	−1·70	−2·00	−1·68
−0·25	−2·73	−2·81	−2·77
−0·50	−3·15	−3·23	−3·20
−0·75	−3·48	−3·54	−3·52
−1·00	−3·76	−3·83	−3·82

The second column gives the value of b, corresponding to the value of a on the left, as determined by the differential analyser. The third column was constructed by calculating b from equation (43) for the value of α necessary to give the prescribed value of a. It will be observed that these values of b lie close to each other except in the neighbourhood of $a = 0$. Wilson also computed the relations between a and b arising from taking a wave function of the form

$$\Phi = \rho(e^{-\frac{1}{2}\alpha\rho}-e^{-\frac{1}{2}\beta\rho})$$

[†] A. H. Wilson, *Proc. Camb. Phil. Soc.* **34**, 365 (1938).

containing two parameters α, β; but he found there was no marked improvement on that obtained from the wave function (42).

More recently Hulthèn[†] has employed an approximate wave function of the form

$$\Phi = e^{-\sqrt{(-MW)}\rho/\hbar\lambda}\{(1-e^{-\rho})-\gamma(1-e^{-\rho})^2\}, \qquad (44)$$

where γ is a parameter. The values of b resulting from this wave function are given in the final column of the table. The agreement with the exact solution obtained from the differential analyser is very close in this case (cf. Fig. 1 of a paper by Fröhlich, Ramsey, and Sneddon).[‡]

In calculating the binding energies of more complicated nuclei Hulthèn's wave function (44) is not much more accurate than Wilson's approximation (42) and the latter is easy to handle analytically. By means of these calculations and a similar one for H^3 it is possible to calculate the constants F, G, m of the Møller–Rosenfeld theory,[§] and to show that it leads to results in agreement with the observed angular dependence of the neutron-proton scattering.[‡] The value of the meson mass obtained in this way is about 220 electron masses, while cosmic-ray observations give a mean value of about 200 electron masses.[‖]

[†] L. Hulthèn, *Arkiv f. mat. astr. o. fys.* **28**, No. 5 (1942).

[‡] H. Fröhlich, W. Ramsey, and I. N. Sneddon, *Rep. Int. Cong. on Fundamental Particles*, Cambridge (1946), p. 166.

[§] H. Fröhlich, K. Huang, and I. N. Sneddon, *Proc. Roy. Soc.* A, **191**, 61 (1947).

[‖] W. F. G. Swann, *Reports Prog. Physics*, **10**, 46 (1944–5).

VI

ATOMS WITH MANY ELECTRONS

Introduction

IN the last chapter we discussed the quantum mechanics of monatomic systems next in order of complexity to the hydrogen atom, namely those in which two electrons move in the field of a heavy nucleus. We shall now consider some of the methods employed to extend the analysis to more complex monatomic systems, in which more than two planetary electrons revolve round a heavy nucleus. One of the most important methods of attack on this problem is omitted here because it requires a knowledge of the theory of groups. Accounts of the applications of the theory of groups to the discussion of complex atomic spectra† should be consulted for details of this method—one of the most powerful for the derivation of general results.

We shall be concerned here mainly with an account of the various methods of calculating the energy levels and wave functions of complex atoms. In many problems a knowledge of the wave functions of complex atoms is necessary for the determination of physical quantities such as the radial charge density; an account is given of methods of obtaining the wave functions numerically and of approximating to these wave functions by means of analytical expressions.

27. The wave functions of many-electron systems

27.1. *The Schrödinger equation in atomic units*

In order to avoid the frequent repetition of the constant $2m/\hbar^2$ it is convenient to express the Schrödinger equation in the atomic units first introduced by Hartree.‡ In this system of units the unit of length is chosen to be the radius of the lowest orbit in the Bohr theory of the hydrogen atom, $r_0 = \hbar^2/me^2$. Taking the unit of charge to be the electronic charge, $e = 4\cdot8025 \times 10^{-10}$ e.s.u., and the unit of mass to be the rest mass, m, of the electron ($9\cdot1067 \times 10^{-28}$ gm.), we find that r_0 has the value $0\cdot529 \times 10^{-8}$ cm.

From these quantities we derive the unit of energy

$$\epsilon = e^2/r_0 = me^4/\hbar^2 = 4\cdot354 \times 10^{-11} \text{ ergs} = 27\cdot20 \text{ eV}.$$

† See, for example, H. Weyl, *Gruppentheorie und Quantenmechanik* (Leipzig, 1928; Eng. trans. London, 1931); C. Eckart, *Rev. Mod. Phys.* **2**, 305 (1930); E. Wigner, *Gruppentheorie* (Braunschweig, 1931); B. van der Waerden, *Gruppentheoretische Methode in der Quantenmechanik* (Berlin, 1932).

‡ D. R. Hartree, *Proc. Camb. Phil. Soc.* **24**, 89 (1928).

The energy ϵ is twice the ionization potential of the hydrogen atom in the ground state. The unit of velocity is automatically fixed by the relation $\frac{1}{2}mv_0^2 = \epsilon$ once the units of energy and mass are fixed. It turns out to be the velocity of the electron in the ground state of the hydrogen atom (again, in the Bohr theory); i.e. we have as the unit of velocity

$$v_0 = e^2/\hbar = c/137\cdot0 = 2\cdot188\times10^8 \text{ cm./sec.}$$

The unit of time is then chosen to be

$$t_0 = r_0/v_0 = 2\cdot4188\times10^{-17} \text{ sec.}$$

In terms of atomic units the Schrödinger equation reduces to the simple form

$$\nabla^2\psi+2(W-V)\psi = 0. \tag{1}$$

27.2. *The wave functions of many-electron atoms*

Employing atomic units we may express the Schrödinger equation for a neutral atom containing Z electrons in the form

$$\left\{\tfrac{1}{2}\sum_{j=1}^{Z}\nabla_j^2+(W-V)\right\}\psi = 0, \tag{2}$$

where ∇_j^2 denotes the Laplacian operator

$$\frac{\partial^2}{\partial x_j^2}+\frac{\partial^2}{\partial y_j^2}+\frac{\partial^2}{\partial z_j^2}, \tag{3}$$

(x_j, y_j, z_j) being the rectangular Cartesian coordinates of the jth electron referred to the nucleus as origin. For the potential energy in the same units we have

$$V = -\sum_{j=1}^{Z}\frac{Z}{r_j}+\sum_{j>k}^{Z}\frac{1}{r_{jk}}, \tag{4}$$

where r_j denotes the distance of the jth electron from the nucleus and r_{jk} the distance between the jth and kth electrons. The Schrödinger equation (2) can seldom be solved exactly, but by making certain assumptions about the nature of the potential energy V approximate solutions of equation (2) may be obtained. Of these assumptions the simplest is that it is possible to construct a potential function of the type

$$V = \sum_{j=1}^{Z} V(\mathbf{r}_j), \tag{5}$$

which is a good approximation to the actual potential function V of equation (4). This is equivalent to considering the mutual repulsions of the electrons to be averaged out in such a way that each electron moves in a static field which is independent of the positions of the other electrons. Substituting from equation (5) into equation (2), we obtain

$$\sum_{j=1}^{Z} \{\tfrac{1}{2}\nabla_j^2 - V(\mathbf{r}_j)\}\psi + W\psi = 0. \tag{6}$$

An equation of this type may be solved by setting for ψ a product of n wave functions, $\psi(\mathbf{r}_j)$, each of which is a function of the coordinates of one electron only. Thus if $\psi_1(\mathbf{r}_1)$ is a solution of the wave equation

$$[\tfrac{1}{2}\nabla_1^2 + \{W_1 - V(\mathbf{r}_1)\}]\psi_1(\mathbf{r}_1) = 0, \tag{7}$$

and if $\psi_2(\mathbf{r}_2)$, $\psi_3(\mathbf{r}_3)$,..., $\psi_Z(\mathbf{r}_Z)$ are defined similarly, it can readily be shown that the product

$$\psi = \psi_1(\mathbf{r}_1)\psi_2(\mathbf{r}_2)...\psi_Z(\mathbf{r}_Z)$$

is a solution of the Schrödinger equation (6) corresponding to the energy

$$W = W_1 + W_2 + ... + W_Z.$$

If we now introduce the electron spin, we may associate either of the two spin wave-functions $\chi_\alpha(\sigma_j)$, $\chi_\beta(\sigma_j)$ with each of the spatial wave-functions $\psi(\mathbf{r}_j)$ so that the spin is considered as doubling the degeneracy. To denote that the wave functions are dependent on the four variables x, y, z, σ for each electron we introduce a vector $\mathbf{q}_j$ to denote the four quantities $\mathbf{r}_j$, σ_j. The wave functions corresponding to the jth electron are then written symbolically

$$\phi(\mathbf{q}_j) = \psi(\mathbf{r}_j)\chi(\sigma_j). \tag{8}$$

Thus if we include the electron spin there will be at least two (and, in the case of degenerate functions ψ, several) wave functions ϕ corresponding to each of the eigenvalues $W_1, W_2,..., W_k,...$ of the parameter W of equation (7). The ϕ wave functions corresponding to the eigenvalue W_k of the energy may be denoted by $\phi_k^{(\mu)}$, where the parameter μ ranges over the number of values appropriate to the degree of the degeneracy. A solution of the wave equation (6) is obtained by choosing any Z of the functions $\phi_k^{(\mu)}$, substituting in them the coordinates of the electrons, and forming the product. Thus, if from the class of functions $\phi_k^{(\mu)}$ we select a finite set which we shall denote simply by

$$\phi_1, \phi_2,..., \phi_Z,$$

then $\phi_{12...Z}$ defined by

$$\phi_{12...Z} = \phi_1(\mathbf{q}_1)\phi_2(\mathbf{q}_2)...\phi_Z(\mathbf{q}_Z) \tag{9}$$

is a solution of the wave equation (6) corresponding to the energy

$$W = W_1 + W_2 + ... + W_Z. \tag{10}$$

There are, of course, several ways in which the energy W can be distributed among the electrons, for instance, the wave-functions

$$\phi_{12...Z} = \phi_1(\mathbf{q}_1)\phi_2(\mathbf{q}_2)...\phi_Z(\mathbf{q}_Z)$$

and $$\phi_{21...Z} = \phi_2(\mathbf{q}_1)\phi_1(\mathbf{q}_2)...\phi_Z(\mathbf{q}_Z)$$

are quite distinct, although they correspond to the same value of the energy. In fact it is easily seen that there are $Z!$ distinct wave functions corresponding to the same value of the energy. If P denotes any permutation of the suffixes $1, 2,..., k,..., Z$, then the wave functions of such a set may be written symbolically as

$$P\phi_{12...k...Z} = P\Big\{ \prod_k \phi_k(\mathbf{q}_k)\Big\}.$$

Furthermore, if a_P is any constant, then the wave function

$$\Phi = \sum_P a_P P\phi_{12...k...Z} = \sum_P a_P P\Big\{ \prod_k \phi_k(\mathbf{q}_k)\Big\},$$

where the summation is taken over the $Z!$ different permutations P, is also a solution of the wave equation (6) for the same value of the energy W. Taking a_P to be $+1$ for even permutations and -1 for odd permutations we obtain the solution, *anti-symmetrical* in the q's,

$$\Phi = \begin{vmatrix} \phi_1(\mathbf{q}_1) & \phi_2(\mathbf{q}_1) & . & . & . & \phi_Z(\mathbf{q}_1) \\ \phi_1(\mathbf{q}_2) & \phi_2(\mathbf{q}_2) & . & . & . & \phi_Z(\mathbf{q}_2) \\ . & . & . & . & . & . \\ \phi_1(\mathbf{q}_Z) & \phi_2(\mathbf{q}_Z) & . & . & . & \phi_Z(\mathbf{q}_Z) \end{vmatrix}. \qquad (11)$$

This is the form that has to be used in the solution of problems involving atoms and molecules. The interchange of two electrons leaves $\Phi\Phi^*$ unaltered, as it must since it is impossible for us to distinguish between two electrons, and Φ vanishes, in accordance with the Pauli exclusion principle, if two of the electrons have their $\mathbf{q}$'s equal.[†] A wave function written in this way to include space and spin coordinates alike has many advantages over wave functions constructed in the space coordinates and the spin coordinates separately, especially in that it avoids many applications of the theory of groups which were a necessary consequence of this method of attack.

Some authors write the determinant (11) in the form

$$\Phi = \text{Det}\{\phi_1(\mathbf{q}_1)\phi_2(\mathbf{q}_2)...\phi_Z(\mathbf{q}_Z)\},$$

exhibiting only its leading term.

There may be several wave functions of the type (11) with the same

† P. A. M. Dirac, *Proc. Roy. Soc.* A, **112**, 661 (1926). See also J. C. Slater, *Phys. Rev.* **34**, 1293 (1929).

energy. For example, the excited states of a two-electron atom may be described by wave functions of the type

$$\Phi_1 = \begin{vmatrix} \psi_m(\mathbf{r}_1)\chi_\alpha(\sigma_1) & \psi_n(\mathbf{r}_1)\chi_\alpha(\sigma_1) \\ \psi_m(\mathbf{r}_2)\chi_\alpha(\sigma_2) & \psi_n(\mathbf{r}_2)\chi_\beta(\sigma_2) \end{vmatrix}$$

$$\Phi_2 = \begin{vmatrix} \psi_m(\mathbf{r}_1)\chi_\alpha(\sigma_1) & \psi_n(\mathbf{r}_1)\chi_\beta(\sigma_1) \\ \psi_m(\mathbf{r}_2)\chi_\alpha(\sigma_2) & \psi_n(\mathbf{r}_2)\chi_\beta(\sigma_2) \end{vmatrix}$$

$$\Phi_3 = \begin{vmatrix} \psi_m(\mathbf{r}_1)\chi_\beta(\sigma_1) & \psi_n(\mathbf{r}_1)\chi_\alpha(\sigma_1) \\ \psi_m(\mathbf{r}_2)\chi_\beta(\sigma_2) & \psi_n(\mathbf{r}_2)\chi_\alpha(\sigma_2) \end{vmatrix}$$

$$\Phi_4 = \begin{vmatrix} \psi_m(\mathbf{r}_1)\chi_\beta(\sigma_1) & \psi_n(\mathbf{r}_1)\chi_\beta(\sigma_1) \\ \psi_m(\mathbf{r}_2)\chi_\alpha(\sigma_2) & \psi_n(\mathbf{r}_2)\chi_\beta(\sigma_2) \end{vmatrix},$$

each corresponding to the energy $W_m + W_n$.

As long as we assume the potential to be of the type (5) any linear combination of the Φ's will be a solution of the Schrödinger equation. But if we use the correct form (4) the degeneracy will disappear either wholly or in part, and a first order approximation to the solution will be given by particular linear combinations of the Φ's. In the case of the helium atom, for instance, the approximate wave functions are $\Phi_2 - \Phi_3$, or any linear combination of Φ_1, Φ_4, and $\Phi_2 + \Phi_3$.

27.3. *The electron distribution function of a many-electron system*

In the non-degenerate case the approximate solution of the Schrödinger equation is a single determinant. In the degenerate case the approximate solutions are a restricted set of linear combinations of determinants. Even in this case, however, it is usually possible to choose some of the solutions to be single determinants. In this section therefore we shall consider the electron distribution when the solution is a single determinant.

If the wave function Φ of a many-electron system is expressed as a determinant of the form (11) and, as is consistent with the results of § 27.2, the functions ϕ are orthogonal to each other and normalized to unity, then the probability of finding one electron in the volume element $d\tau_1$, another one in the volume element $d\tau_2$, and so on, is

$$\rho \, dq_1 dq_2 \dots dq_Z.$$

Here $dq = d\tau d\sigma$ includes both space and spin coordinates and

$$\rho = \Phi^*\Phi = \begin{vmatrix} \phi_1^*(\mathbf{q}_1) & \cdot & \cdot & \cdot & \phi_Z^*(\mathbf{q}_1) \\ \phi_1^*(\mathbf{q}_2) & \cdot & \cdot & \cdot & \phi_Z^*(\mathbf{q}_2) \\ \cdot & \cdot & \cdot & \cdot & \cdot \\ \phi_1^*(\mathbf{q}_Z) & \cdot & \cdot & \cdot & \phi_Z^*(\mathbf{q}_Z) \end{vmatrix} \times \begin{vmatrix} \phi_1(\mathbf{q}_1) & \cdot & \cdot & \cdot & \phi_Z(\mathbf{q}_1) \\ \phi_1(\mathbf{q}_2) & \cdot & \cdot & \cdot & \phi_Z(\mathbf{q}_2) \\ \cdot & \cdot & \cdot & \cdot & \cdot \\ \phi_1(\mathbf{q}_Z) & \cdot & \cdot & \cdot & \phi_Z(\mathbf{q}_Z) \end{vmatrix}.$$

If we introduce the notation

$$\rho_{ij} = \sum_{k=1}^{Z} \phi_k^*(\mathbf{q}_i)\phi_k(\mathbf{q}_j), \tag{12}$$

the expression for the distribution function reduces to the form

$$\rho = \begin{vmatrix} \rho_{11} & \rho_{12} & \cdot & \cdot & \cdot & \rho_{1Z} \\ \rho_{21} & \rho_{22} & \cdot & \cdot & \cdot & \rho_{2Z} \\ \cdot & \cdot & \cdot & \cdot & \cdot & \cdot \\ \rho_{Z1} & \rho_{Z2} & \cdot & \cdot & \cdot & \rho_{ZZ} \end{vmatrix}. \tag{13}$$

The probability of finding m electrons in a certain prescribed configuration irrespective of the position of the other $(Z-m)$ may be obtained by integrating ρ over the coordinate spaces of the remaining $Z-m$ electrons. The integrations† must be carried out in such a way that each configuration appears only once; that is, $dq_{m+1}\,dq_{m+2}\ldots dq_Z$ must be replaced by $dq_{m+1}\,dq_{m+2}\ldots dq_Z/(Z-m)!$

Since the functions ϕ are normalized to unity we have

$$\int \rho_{ZZ}\,dq_Z = \sum_{k=1}^{Z} \int \phi_k^*(\mathbf{q}_Z)\phi_k(\mathbf{q}_Z)\,dq_Z = Z. \tag{14}$$

Similarly, by making use of the fact that the ϕ's form an orthogonal set, we can show that
$$\int \rho_{iZ}\rho_{Zj}\,dq_Z = \rho_{ij}. \tag{15}$$

Now if we denote by ρ_{Z-1} the determinant formed from ρ by removing the last row and the last column, and by Δ_{Z-1}^{ij} the cofactor of ρ_{ij} in the determinant ρ_{Z-1}, then expanding the determinant ρ in terms of the last row and column we obtain

$$\rho = \rho_{ZZ}\rho_{Z-1} - \sum_{i=1}^{Z} \sum_{j=1}^{Z} \rho_{iZ}\rho_{Zj}\Delta_{Z-1}^{ij}.$$

Integrating over the variables of the Zth electron and making use of equations (14) and (15) we obtain

$$\int \rho\,dq_Z = Z\rho_{Z-1} - (Z-1)\rho_{Z-1} = \rho_{Z-1},$$

showing that the effect of integration with respect to the coordinates of the Zth electron is merely that of removing the last row and column

---

† In the integrations we use $d\tau_i$ to denote $dx_i\,dy_i\,dz_i$ and dq_i for the volume element including spin. The integration over the spin variables is merely a sum: thus
$$\int dq_i = \int dx_i\,dy_i\,dz_i \sum_{\alpha,\beta}.$$

from the determinant. Carrying out the integrations with respect to the coordinates of the other electrons we obtain the relations

$$\int \rho \, dq_{Z-1} dq_Z = 2\rho_{Z-2},$$

$$\cdot \quad \cdot \quad \cdot \quad \cdot \quad \cdot \quad \cdot \quad \cdot \quad \cdot$$

$$\int \rho \, dq_S...dq_Z = (Z-S+1)! \, \rho_{S-1},$$

$$\cdot \quad \cdot \quad \cdot \quad \cdot \quad \cdot \quad \cdot \quad \cdot \quad \cdot$$

$$\int \rho \, dq_2...dq_Z = (Z-1)! \, \rho_{11}.$$

As previously explained, the probability of finding any one of the electrons in the volume element $d\tau_1$ is given by the sum of the distribution functions corresponding to the one-body problem, i.e.

$$d\tau_1 \int \rho \, \frac{dq_2...dq_Z}{(Z-1)!} = \rho_{11} d\tau_1 = \sum_{k=1}^{Z} \phi_k^*(\mathbf{r}_1)\phi_k(\mathbf{r}_1) \, d\tau_1.$$

27.4. *The energy of a many-electron system*

The Schrödinger equation for a system of Z electrons moving in the field of a nucleus of atomic number Z may be written in the form

$$(L-W)\Phi = 0, \tag{16}$$

where, in atomic units,

$$L = \sum_{j=1}^{Z} H_j + \sum_{j>k} \frac{1}{r_{jk}}, \tag{17}$$

and

$$H_j = -\left(\tfrac{1}{2}\nabla_j^2 + \frac{Z}{r_j}\right). \tag{18}$$

If we multiply both sides of equation (16) by Φ^*, substitute for Φ from equation (11), and integrate over the whole of the configuration space (i.e. over spin as well as spatial coordinates), we obtain the relation

$$W \int \rho \, d\tau = \sum_j \int H_j \rho \, d\tau + \sum_{j>k} \int \frac{\rho}{r_{jk}} \, d\tau, \tag{19}$$

where ρ is defined by equations (12) and (13). It should be noted that in this equation the operator H_j must be taken to act on ρ_{ij} but not on ρ_{ji}; this is a consequence of the fact that $H_j\rho$ is formed from the product $\Phi^*H_j\Phi$ in which H_j operates on Φ but not on Φ^*. The integrations can be performed by methods similar to those outlined in the preceding section. For example, we have

$$\frac{1}{(Z-2)!} \int \frac{\rho \, dq}{r_{jk}} = \int \frac{1}{r_{jk}} \begin{vmatrix} \rho_{jj} & \rho_{jk} \\ \rho_{kj} & \rho_{kk} \end{vmatrix} dq_j \, dq_k. \tag{20}$$

From the definition of the quantities ρ_{ij} we see that the right-hand side of this equation is equivalent to

$$\sum_{\lambda=1}^{Z} \sum_{\mu=1}^{Z} \int \phi_{\lambda}^{*}(\mathbf{q}_j)\phi_{\mu}^{*}(\mathbf{q}_k)\frac{1}{r_{jk}}\phi_{\lambda}(\mathbf{q}_j)\phi_{\mu}(\mathbf{q}_k)\,dq_j\,dq_k -$$

$$- \sum_{\lambda=1}^{Z} \sum_{\mu=1}^{Z} \int \phi_{\lambda}^{*}(\mathbf{q}_k)\phi_{\mu}^{*}(\mathbf{q}_j)\frac{1}{r_{jk}}\phi_{\lambda}(\mathbf{q}_j)\phi_{\mu}(\mathbf{q}_k)\,dq_j\,dq_k. \quad (21)$$

Since only certain of the orbital wave-functions ϕ_{λ} will have the same spin factors, they alone will give a non-zero result when the integrations over the spin variables are performed; the remainder are orthogonal and the integrals involving them vanish. Thus, if the spin wave functions are normalized to unity and if we write for the integrals over the spatial coordinates

$$(ab|G|cd) = \int \psi_a^{*}(\mathbf{r}_j)\psi_b^{*}(\mathbf{r}_k)\frac{1}{r_{jk}}\psi_c(\mathbf{r}_j)\psi_d(\mathbf{r}_k)\,d\tau_j\,d\tau_k, \quad (22)$$

we find that the first term of (21) may be written

$$\sum_{\lambda,\mu=1}^{Z} (\lambda\mu|G|\lambda\mu).$$

In the second term of (21), on the other hand, certain of the terms will vanish; it reduces to

$$\underset{\lambda,\mu=1}{\overset{Z}{S}} (\mu\lambda|G|\lambda\mu),$$

where the summation symbol $\underset{\lambda,\mu}{S}$ implies that the sum is taken over only those pairs of numbers λ, μ for which the corresponding orbital wave functions ϕ_{λ} and ϕ_{μ} have the same spin factor. Furthermore, since there are $\frac{1}{2}Z(Z-1)$ lines passing through Z points we have that

$$\sum_{j>k} \int \frac{\rho\,dq}{r_{jk}} = \frac{1}{2}Z(Z-1) \int \frac{\rho\,dq}{r_{jk}},$$

so that finally

$$\sum_{j>k} \int \frac{\rho\,dq}{r_{jk}} = \frac{1}{2}(Z!)\Big\{ \sum_{\lambda,\mu} (\lambda\mu|G|\lambda\mu) - \underset{\lambda,\mu}{S} (\mu\lambda|G|\lambda\mu)\Big\}. \quad (23)$$

The integrals $(ab|G|cd)$ occurring in equation (23) and defined by equation (22) are known as *generalized exchange integrals*.

The integrals involving ρ and H_j only may be evaluated in a similar fashion; we obtain

$$\left.\begin{array}{r}\displaystyle\int \rho\,dq = Z! \\[2mm] \displaystyle\sum_j \int H_j\rho\,dq = Z! \sum_{\lambda=1}^{Z} (\lambda|H|\lambda)\end{array}\right\}, \quad (24)$$

where

$$(\lambda|H|\lambda) = \int \psi_{\lambda}^{*}(\mathbf{r}_j)H_j\psi_{\lambda}(\mathbf{r}_j)\,d\tau_j, \quad (25)$$

$d\tau_j$ denoting as usual the volume element of the spatial coordinates. Substituting from (23) and (24) into equation (19) and dividing throughout by $Z!$ we obtain finally for the total energy of the system

$$W = \sum_{\lambda=1}^{Z} (\lambda|H|\lambda) + \tfrac{1}{2}\Big\{ \sum_{\lambda,\mu} (\lambda\mu|G|\lambda\mu) - \underset{\lambda,\mu}{S} (\mu\lambda|G|\lambda\mu) \Big\}, \qquad (26)$$

where the summation $\underset{\lambda,\mu}{S}$ is taken over those pairs of spatial wave functions ψ_λ and ψ_μ which have the same spin factors in Φ. W can be calculated from equation (26) only if the orbital wave functions of the system are known. Equation (26) shows, however, that the energy of a many-electron atom is made up of three components:

(i) the sum of the energies of each electron in the presence of the nucleus alone;

(ii) the sum of the Coulomb interactions of electrons in one orbital with those in another;

(iii) the sum of the exchange interactions between two electrons in different orbitals but possessing the same spin.

28. Variational methods of determining wave functions and energy values of many-electron atoms

28.1. *Fock's variational equations*

The Schrödinger wave equation (16) may easily be shown to be equivalent to the variation principle

$$\delta \int \Phi^*(H-W)\Phi \, dq = 0, \qquad (27)$$

δ denoting an arbitrary change of Φ subject to the normalizing condition. The integral is taken throughout the configuration space of all the coordinates (including those describing the spin) of all the electrons. By the methods of the calculus of variations we can establish that equation (27) reduces to

$$\int \delta\Phi^*(H-W)\Phi \, dq = 0,$$

which yields the variational equation

$$W \int \delta\Phi^*\Phi \, dq = \int \delta\Phi^* H\Phi \, dq. \qquad (28)$$

In the many-electron problem Φ is a determinant of the form (11), so that equation (28) takes the form

$$\int \Big(\sum_i \delta_i\Big)\Big(\sum_j H_j + \sum_{j>k} \frac{1}{r_{jk}}\Big)\rho \, dq = W \int \Big(\sum_i \delta_i\Big)\rho \, dq$$

$$= Z! \, W \sum_n \int \delta\psi_n^* \psi_n \, d\tau, \qquad (29)$$

where ρ is defined by equation (13). As before, the quantity H_j in equation (29) operates on the coordinates of the jth electron when they appear in terms such as ρ_{ij} but not when they occur in terms of the type ρ_{ji}. Contrariwise, δ_i operates only on ρ_{ij} and not on ρ_{ji}. With this convention we have

$$
\delta_i H_j \rho = \begin{vmatrix}
\rho_{11} & \rho_{12} & \cdot & \cdot & \cdot & H_j\rho_{1j} & \cdot & \cdot & \cdot & \rho_{1Z} \\
\rho_{21} & \rho_{22} & \cdot & \cdot & \cdot & H_j\rho_{2j} & \cdot & \cdot & \cdot & \rho_{2Z} \\
\cdot & \cdot & \cdot & \cdot & \cdot & \cdot & \cdot & \cdot & \cdot & \cdot \\
\delta_i\rho_{i1} & \delta_i\rho_{i2} & \cdot & \cdot & \cdot & \delta_i H_j\rho_{ij} & \cdot & \cdot & \cdot & \delta_i\rho_{iZ} \\
\cdot & \cdot & \cdot & \cdot & \cdot & \cdot & \cdot & \cdot & \cdot & \cdot \\
\rho_{Z1} & \rho_{Z2} & \cdot & \cdot & \cdot & H_j\rho_{Zj} & \cdot & \cdot & \cdot & \rho_{ZZ}
\end{vmatrix},
$$

and performing the integrations as in § 27.3 we find that if $i \neq j$

$$
\int \delta_i H_j \rho \, d\tau = (Z-2)! \int \begin{vmatrix} \delta_i\rho_{ii} & \delta_i H_j\rho_{ij} \\ \rho_{ji} & H_j\rho_{jj} \end{vmatrix} dq_i \, dq_j,
$$

which may be reduced to the form

$$
\int \delta_i H_j \rho \, d\tau
$$
$$
= (Z-2)! \left\{ \sum_{m,p=1}^{Z} (m|H|m) \int \delta\psi_p^*(r_i)\psi_p(r_i) \, d\tau_i - \underset{m,p}{S} (m|H|p) \int \delta\psi_p^*\psi_m \, d\tau_i \right\}.
$$

Similarly $\int \delta_i H_i \rho \, dq = (Z-1)! \sum \int \delta\psi^*(r_i)H\psi(r_i) \, d\tau_i,$

so that finally

$$
\int \left(\sum_i \delta_i \right)\left(\sum_j H_j \right)\rho \, dq
$$
$$
= Z! \sum_{p=1}^{Z} \int \delta\psi_p^* \left\{ H\psi_p - \overset{(p)}{\underset{m}{S}} (m|H|p)\psi_m + \sum_{m=1}^{Z} (m|H|m)\psi_p \right\} d\tau, \quad (30)
$$

where the summation $\overset{(p)}{\underset{m}{S}}$ extends over all those ψ's which have the same spin factor as ψ_p in the expression for Φ.

By a method similar to that employed in the last section for the evaluation of the integral $\sum_i \delta_i \int \dfrac{\rho \, d\tau}{r_{jk}}$ we can establish that, for $i \neq j, i \neq k$,

$$
\int \left(\sum_i \delta_i \right)\left(\sum_{j>k} \frac{1}{r_{jk}} \right)\rho \, dq
$$
$$
= \tfrac{1}{2}(Z!) \left\{ \sum_{l,m} (lm|G|lm) - \underset{l,m}{S} (lm|G|ml) \right\} \sum_{n=1}^{Z} \int \delta\psi_n^*\psi_n \, d\tau -
$$
$$
- (Z!) \left\{ \sum_{l,m,n} (lm|G|ln) - \underset{l,m,n}{S} (lm|G|nl) \right\} \int \delta\psi_n^*\psi_m \, d\tau, \quad (31)
$$

the summation $\underset{l,m,n}{S}$ being taken over those sets of spatial wave functions ψ which have the same spin factor in Φ. The result for $i = j$ or $i = k$ can be derived in a similar manner; it is found to be

$$\int \left(\sum_i \delta_i\right)\left(\sum_{j>i} \frac{1}{r_{ij}}\right)\rho \, dq = Z! \sum_{n=1}^{Z} \int \delta\psi_n^* \psi_n \, V(\mathbf{r}) \, d\tau - \underset{m,n}{S} \int \delta\psi_n^* \psi_m \, G_{mn}(\mathbf{r}) \, d\tau, \tag{32}$$

where
$$\left. \begin{aligned} G_{mn}(\mathbf{r}) &= \int \psi_m^*(\mathbf{r}')\psi_n(\mathbf{r}')\frac{d\tau'}{|\mathbf{r}'-\mathbf{r}|} \\ V(\mathbf{r}) &= \sum_n G_{nn}(\mathbf{r}) \end{aligned} \right\} . \tag{33}$$
and

Substituting from equations (26), (30), (31), and (32) into the variational equation (29) we obtain series of terms of the type $f\,\delta\psi_n^*$. Since we may treat the variations $\delta\psi_n^*$ as independent, we may take $f = 0$; in this way we obtain a set of equations of the type

$$[H+V(\mathbf{r})]\epsilon_n \psi_n(\mathbf{r}) - \underset{m}{\overset{(n)}{S}}\left\{G_{mn}(\mathbf{r})+(m|H|n)+ \sum_l (lm|G|ln)\right\}\psi_m+$$
$$+ \underset{l,m}{\overset{(n)}{S}} (lm|G|nl)\psi_m = 0, \quad (34)$$

where ϵ_n denotes the number of times, 1 or 2, ψ_n occurs in the wave-function Φ. The system of linear equations (34) for the determination of the functions ψ_n were first derived by Fock† by a different method; the derivation outlined above was given subsequently by Lennard-Jones.‡

Simple expressions for the summation symbols $\overset{(n)}{S}$ can be derived in certain special cases. For example, if the atom consists of p pairs of electrons and $q-p$ outer electrons possessing the same spin but different orbital quantum numbers, then when n refers to one of the orbitals in a closed shell ($n < p$) the wave function may be associated with either of the spin wave-functions χ_α, χ_β. In this case, then, $\epsilon_n = 2$ and

$$\underset{m}{\overset{(n)}{S}} = \sum_{m=1}^p + \sum_{m=1}^q, \qquad \underset{l,m}{\overset{(n)}{S}} = \sum_{l=1}^p \sum_{m=1}^p + \sum_{l=1}^q \sum_{m=1}^q . \tag{35}$$

On the other hand, if $p < n < q$, $\epsilon_n = 1$ and

$$\underset{m}{\overset{(n)}{S}} = \sum_{m=1}^q, \qquad \underset{l,m}{\overset{(n)}{S}} = \sum_{l=1}^q \sum_{m=1}^q . \tag{36}$$

By this method we have reduced the problem of solving the Schrödinger equation in $3n$ independent variables to that of determining the solutions of a system of n partial differential equations each with three

† V. Fock, *Zeits. f. Physik,* **61**, 126 (1930).
‡ J. E. Lennard-Jones, *Proc. Camb. Phil. Soc.* **27**, 469 (1930–1).

independent variables. The equations are not independent, but they lend themselves readily to solution by successive approximations.

28.2. *Hartree's method of the self-consistent field*

The simple method of calculating the field of an atom devised by D. R. Hartree and discussed in the last chapter for two-electron atoms may readily be extended to atoms containing many electrons. Each electron is assumed to possess a wave function which obeys a Schrödinger equation. The potential energy appearing in this equation is taken to be partly that due to the field of the nucleus and partly to the fields of the electrons in the other orbits. The latter fields are calculated by representing each electron by a uniform charge distribution of density $-e\psi\psi^*$, in accordance with the Schrödinger interpretation of the meaning of the wave function ψ. The ith electron thus moves in a field in which its potential energy is

$$V_i(\mathbf{r}) = -\frac{Ze^2}{r} + e^2 \sum_{j \neq i}^{Z} \int \frac{|\psi_j(\mathbf{r}')|^2}{|\mathbf{r}-\mathbf{r}'|}\, d\tau', \tag{37}$$

where we have considered a system of Z orbital electrons moving in the field of a nucleus of atomic number Z. The wave function ψ_i of this electron then satisfies the Schrödinger equation

$$[\nabla^2 + 2(W - V_i)]\psi_i = 0 \tag{38}$$

with $V_i(\mathbf{r})$ given by equation (37).

In applying this method to atoms containing many electrons Hartree has neglected the 'exchange' forces. Indeed Hartree's equations may be derived from the system of equations (34) by neglecting

(i) the coefficients of every ψ_m for which $m \neq n$;
(ii) the non-diagonal exchange integrals $(ln|G|nl)$.

Fock's equations (34) then reduce to

$$\left\{H + \sum_{l}' G_{ll}(\mathbf{r})\right\}\psi_n(\mathbf{r}) = \left\{(n|H|n) + \sum_{lm}' (lm|G|lm)\right\}\psi_n(\mathbf{r}), \tag{39}$$

the dash denoting that the term $l = n$ is omitted in the summation. It will be seen that $(n|H|n)$ is the energy of the nth electron in the field of the nucleus alone, $\sum_{l}' (ln|G|ln)$ is the averaged electrostatic energy due to the interactions between all the other electrons, and $\sum_{l}' G_{ll}(\mathbf{r})$ is the potential of the nth electron due to the Coulomb fields of all the other electrons averaged over their respective probability charge distributions. These equations may be solved numerically by smoothing out the fields $G_\mu(\mathbf{r})$ so as to make them spherically symmetrical, and adjusting them until the solutions of the equations for the ψ-functions reproduce the potential field.†

28.3. *Solutions of the Hartree–Fock equations*

The method of the self-consistent field as developed by Hartree and his collaborators is usually much easier to work with than the Fock method but, of course, it is not such a good approximation. In both

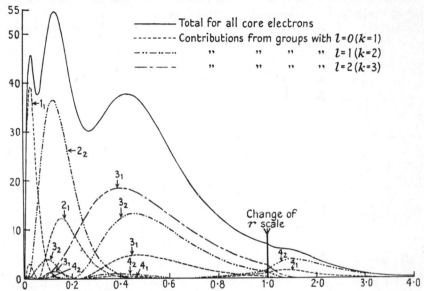

FIG. 19. Radial distribution of charge for Rb⁺ and contributions from different groups of core electrons. Radial density in electrons per atomic unit plotted against r in atomic units.

methods the solutions of the basic equations can be obtained only in a numerical form. Solutions of the Hartree equations of the self-consistent field and of the Fock equations have been derived for various atoms and ions. One way of representing graphically the results of these calculations is to calculate for each atom the radial charge density for a number of distances and then to illustrate the variation of this density by means of a diagram. Such a diagram is shown in Fig. 19; it shows the variation with distance of the radial charge density for the ion Rb⁺ and the contributions from the different groups of core electrons.‡ In this diagram the distance r is measured in atomic units

† D. R. Hartree, *Proc. Camb. Phil. Soc.* **24**, 111 (1927–8); see also J. A. Gaunt, ibid. 328.

‡ D. R. Hartree, ibid. 120.

and a different scale of r is used for $r < 1$ and $r > 1$. This is usual in diagrams of this type since a scale open enough to show the detail of the curves for $r < 1$ is unnecessarily open for $r > 1$ and the use of two uniform scales has seemed preferable to the distortion produced by a logarithmic scale. The regions of maximum charge corresponding to the K, L, and M shells are clearly evident on this diagram. There is, however, no peak corresponding to the N shell—only a flattening out of the curve; this is due to the fact that the contribution from the M-electrons is still appreciable in this region.

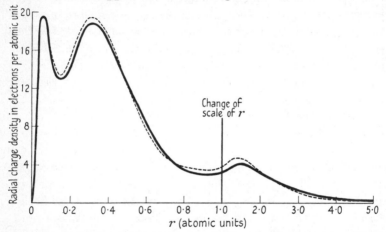

FIG. 20. Charge distribution in Cl⁻.   —— Hartree method, ... Fock method.

The same features are evident in the curve (Fig. 20) showing the variation of the radial charge density for the chlorine ion Cl⁻. For this ion both Hartree's and Fock's methods have been used† and the curves corresponding to both sets of calculations are shown. It will be noted from this diagram that the two curves have approximately the same shape but that for large values of r they differ appreciably. Indeed, if we denote by $\delta U(r)$ the difference between the radial charge densities in the two cases, then it can be shown that in the units chosen

$$\int_0^\infty r^2 \delta U(r)\, dr = 13\cdot 8,$$

and further that about 95 per cent. of this value comes from values of r greater than $3\cdot 4$ atomic units, which is the 'ionic radius'‡ of Cl⁻. It would thus be expected that the distortion of the wave functions by the presence of neighbouring atoms will be considerable in this region.

† D. R. and W. R. Hartree, *Proc. Roy. Soc.* A, **156**, 45 (1936).
‡ W. L. Bragg, *The Crystalline State*, chap. vii, p. 115 (1934).

If we calculate the diamagnetic susceptibility, χ, from these curves we find by the Hartree method (Hartree and Hartree, loc. cit) that

$$\chi = -41{\cdot}3 \times 10^{-6},$$

and by the Fock method that

$$\chi = -30{\cdot}4 \times 10^{-6}.$$

The observed value† is -25×10^{-6}, so that the use of the solutions of Fock's equations has reduced the discrepancy between the calculated and observed values of χ to about a third of the amount of the discrepancy when the results of the self-consistent field are used. The improvement which the solutions of the Fock equations makes to the calculated value of the electrical polarizability is also considerable. It seems then that the improvements effected by the use of the Fock equations—i.e. by the addition of 'exchange' terms to the Hartree equations—are substantial.

Solutions of the Hartree and of the Fock equations for other atoms and ions have been obtained by several authors. The results are given in the papers cited below. No attempt has been made to divide these papers into two classes depending on whether the Hartree or Fock equations formed the starting-point of the investigation, since it not infrequently happens that in the same paper the solutions of both types of equations have been derived for purposes of comparison and also for determining the relative speed of convergence of both methods.

D. R. Hartree	*Proc. Camb. Phil. Soc.* **24,** 111 (1928)	Li, Rb$^+$, Na$^+$, Cl$^-$.
	Proc. Roy. Soc. A, **141,** 283 (1933)	Cl$^-$, Cu$^+$.
	„ „ **143,** 506 (1933)	Cu$^+$, K$^+$, Cs.
	„ „ **150,** 96 (1935)	Al^{+3}, Fe$^-$, Rb$^+$.
	Phys. Rev. (2), **46,** 738 (1934)	Hg.
D. R. Hartree and M. M. Black	*Proc. Roy. Soc.* A, **139,** 311 (1933)	O in various stages of ionization.
D. R. and W. Hartree	*Proc. Roy. Soc.* A, **149,** 210 (1935)	Be, Ca, Hg.
	„ „ **150,** 9 (1935)	Be.
	„ „ **156,** 45 (1936)	Cl$^-$.
	„ „ **157,** 490 (1936)	Cu$^+$.
	„ „ **164,** 167 (1938)	Ca^{++}.
	„ „ **166,** 450 (1938)	K$^+$, A.
	Proc. Camb. Phil. Soc. **34,** 550 (1938)	Na$^-$, K$^-$.
J. MacDougall	*Proc. Roy. Soc.* A, **138,** 550 (1932)	Si^{+3}.
E. H. Kennard and E. Ramberg	*Phys. Rev.* (2), **46,** 1034 (1934)	Na.

† G. W. Brindley and F. F. Hoare, *Proc. Roy. Soc.* A, **152,** 342 (1935); E. C. Stoner, *Magnetism and Atomic Structure*, chap. ix, p. 4.

C. C. Torrance	Phys. Rev. (2), **46**, 388 (1934)	C.
L. P. Smith	Phys. Rev. (2), **42**, 176 (1932)	He.
V. Fock and M. J. Petrashen	Phys. Zeits. d. Sowjet. **6**, 368, (1934)	Na.
	Phys. Zeits. d. Sowjet. **8**, 547 (1935)	Li.
M. M. Black	Mem. Manchester Phil. Soc. **79**, 29 (1934–5)	Ag^+.
	Mem. Manchester Phil. Soc. **79**, 75 (1934–5)	Cr.
M. F. Manning and J. Millman	Phys. Rev. (2), **49**, 849 (1936)	W
M. F. Manning and Goldberg	Phys. Rev. (2), **53**, 662 (1938)	Fe.
W. S. Wilson and R. B. Lindsay	Phys. Rev. (2), **47**, 681 (1935)	He (excited state).
H. L. Donley	Phys. Rev. (2), **50**, 1012 (1936)	Si^{+2}, Si^{+3}
R. L. Mooney	Phys. Rev. (2), **55**, 557 (1939)	Cr^{++}.
W. Thatcher	Proc. Roy. Soc. A, **172**, 242 (1939)	K^{+2}, K^+.
D. R. and W. R. Hartree and B. Swirles	Phil. Trans. Roy. Soc. A, **238**, 229 (1939)	O
A. F. Stevenson	Phys. Rev. (2), **56**, 586 (1939)	He, O III.
A. Jucys	Proc. Roy. Soc. A, **173**, 59 (1939)	C^{+4}, C^{++}.
A. O. Williams	Phys. Rev. (2), **58**, 723 (1940)	Cu^+.
D. R. and W. R. Hartree and M. F. Manning	Phys. Rev. (2), **59**, 229 (1941) ,, ,, **60**, 857 (1941)	Ge^{++}, Ge Si IV, Si V.
M. T. Antunes	Phys. Rev. (2), **62**, 362 (1942)	Co.
D. R. Bates and H. S. W. Massey	Phil. Trans. Roy. Soc. A, **239**, 269 (1943)	O^-, O_2^-.

28.4. *Analytical atomic wave functions*

One of the simplest methods of determining the wave functions and energies of atoms which possess only a few electrons consists in constructing a wave-function Φ which has the correct symmetry properties but which contains certain parameters α, β, γ,... which are left unspecified. The most favourable values of these parameters are then determined by the variation method as follows. The function is substituted in the equation

$$\frac{\int \Phi^* H\Phi \, dq}{\int \Phi^* \Phi \, dq} = W(\alpha, \beta, \gamma ...) \qquad (40)$$

and the values of the parameters determined so as to make the energy W a minimum. In this way we obtain the system of equations

$$\frac{\partial W}{\partial \alpha} = \frac{\partial W}{\partial \beta} = \frac{\partial W}{\partial \gamma} = ... = 0 \qquad (41)$$

for the determination of the parameters α, β, γ,.... Wave functions constructed by this method have proved to be of great value in the approximate calculation of the properties of atoms containing many electrons.

This method was used by Hylleraas[†] to give a very good approximation to the observed ionization potential of helium. The form of wave function assumed by Hylleraas was

$$\Phi = [e^{-(\alpha r_1 + \beta r_2)} + e^{-(\beta r_1 + \alpha r_2)}]e^{-\gamma r_{12}},$$

corresponding to a helium atom in its ground state.

The wave functions for the atoms Li, Be, B, C, N, O, F, Ne have been derived by this method by Zener and Guillemin.[‡] For the 1s-orbitals Zener assumes a wave function of the form

$$\Phi = g_1 e^{-\gamma r}; \tag{42}$$

for the 2s-orbitals $\qquad \Phi = g_2(r - \alpha)r^{n^* - 2}e^{-\delta r}, \tag{43}$

and for the 2p-orbitals

$$\Phi = g_3 r^{n^* - 1}e^{-\delta r}Y_1(\theta, \phi). \tag{44}$$

Here $Y_1(\theta, \phi)$ denotes the surface spherical harmonic of the first degree, $\sqrt{(3/8\pi)}\sin\theta\, e^{\pm i\phi}$. The function (42) is of the same type as the wave function for the hydrogen atom in the ground state; the parameter γ may be regarded as allowing for the screening effect of the other electrons round the nucleus. For each atom the four parameters n^*, α, γ, δ are determined from the equations (40) and (41). The parameter n^* has been varied only in the cases of Li and Be; since for both of these atoms it has the hydrogenic value 2·0, Zener assumed it to retain this value in the other cases considered. It is found that for an atom of atomic number Z the parameter γ is given approximately by the formula

$$\gamma = Z - \tfrac{5}{16}. \tag{45}$$

The values of the remaining parameters are given in the accompanying table; by the use of these values the energies of the L-shell were determined with an error of one or two electron volts.

TABLE 1

	Li	Be	B	C	N	O	F	Ne
$\alpha(\pm 0 \cdot 02)$	0·18	0·15	0·10	0·07	0·05	0·05	0·05	0·05
$\delta(\pm 0 \cdot 01)$	0·63	0·96	1·26	1·59	1·92	2·24	2·56	2·88

† E. Hylleraas, *Zeits. f. Physik*, **65**, 209 (1930).
‡ V. Guillemin and C. Zener, ibid. **61**, 199 (1930); C. Zener, *Phys. Rev.* (2) **36**, 51 (1930).

Simple rules for obtaining the values of the four parameters γ, α, n^*, δ for most of the atoms in the periodic table have been given by Slater.[†] The charge densities derived from the functions (42), (43), and (44) with Slater's values for the parameters agree fairly well with those found by Hartree's method of the self-consistent field in the cases where that method has been applied.

For some purposes there is not sufficient flexibility in the Zener–Slater wave functions, and, in addition, the separate orbitals are not all mutually orthogonal. The method has been improved by Morse, Young, and Haurwitz[‡] and by Duncanson and Coulson[§] to remove these defects. These authors take the wave function of an atom to be the appropriate sum of determinantal wave functions in which the wave functions of the component orbits are assumed to be

$$\psi(1s) = \sqrt{(\mu^3 a^3/\pi)}e^{-\mu ar},$$

$$\psi(2s) = \sqrt{(\mu^5/3\pi N_1)}\{re^{-\mu r} - (3N_2/\mu)e^{-b\mu r}\},$$

$$\psi(2p_0) = \sqrt{(\mu^5 c^5/\pi)}r\cos\theta\, e^{-\mu cr},$$

$$\psi(2p_\pm) = \sqrt{(\mu^5 c^5/2\pi)}r\sin\theta\, e^{-\mu cr \pm i\phi}.$$

The numbers N_1 and N_2 are numerical constants; N_2 is determined by the condition that the wave-functions $\psi(2s)$, $\psi(1s)$ are orthogonal and N_1 is a normalizing constant. The energy is minimized to determine the remaining four constants a, b, c, μ; if we are concerned solely with atoms in their ground states an absolute minimum of the energy exists. The results obtained by Coulson and Duncanson for the ground states of the atoms Li to Ne are shown below. The quantity 2μ may be

TABLE 2

Element	$a\mu$	$b\mu$	$c\mu$	μ	Slater's value of μ
Li	2·69	2·26	..	0·658	0·650
Be	3·69	3·28	..	0·979	0·975
B	4·69	4·20	1·20	1·322	1·300
C	5·69	5·13	1·56	1·652	1·625
N	6·68	6·08	1·91	1·970	1·950
O	7·68	7·06	2·22	2·289	2·275
F	8·67	8·02	2·55	2·611	2·600
Ne	9·66	8·97	2·88	2·934	2·925

regarded as the effective nuclear charge for the $2s$-electron at large

† J. C. Slater, *Phys. Rev.* (2), **36**, 57 (1930).

‡ P. M. Morse, L. A. Young, and E. S. Haurwitz, ibid. **48**, 948 (1935).

§ W. E. Duncanson and C. A. Coulson, *Proc. Roy. Soc. Edin.* **62**, 37 (1944).

distances, and is seen to increase by about 0·35 for each extra electron. The formula

$$\mu = \tfrac{1}{3}(Z-1)$$

gives μ in terms of the atomic number Z to an accuracy of about 2 per cent.

29. The perturbation method of determining approximate wave functions of atoms[†]

29.1. *Non-degenerate cases*

In addition to the equations of Fock and Hartree, other approximate methods of determining the wave functions and energy levels of many-electron atoms have been devised. Suppose, for example, that the Schrödinger equation (in atomic units) for an atom containing many electrons is written in the form

$$(H-W)\Phi = 0, \tag{46}$$

where H denotes the Hamiltonian

$$H = -\tfrac{1}{2}\sum_{j=1}^{Z}\nabla_j^2 + V, \tag{47}$$

Z being the number of electrons. If the equation (46) cannot be solved directly, it is often possible to obtain an approximate solution from the solution of an equation which is separable and which does not differ greatly from (46). Suppose that the wave functions and characteristic values of the Schrödinger equation

$$(H'-W)\Phi = 0 \tag{48}$$

are known, where

$$H' = -\tfrac{1}{2}\sum_{j=1}^{Z}\nabla_j^2 + \sum_{j=1}^{Z} V_j'. \tag{49}$$

Here each of the functions V_j' is a spherically symmetrical function of $\mathbf{r}_j$. If a non-degenerate solution of the equation

$$\{\tfrac{1}{2}\nabla_j^2 + (W-V_j')\}\phi = 0 \tag{50}$$

can be obtained, the solution of equation (48) can be written as a determinant whose elements are solutions of equation (50); in most physical problems there is thus more than one wave function Φ_k for every characteristic value W_k of the wave equation (48). For simplicity we shall, however, assume, in the first instance, that there is only one solution Φ_k to each value of W_k and consider the degenerate case later. In the non-degenerate case the functions Φ_k then form an orthogonal set. Equation (48) may still have non-degenerate solutions even if the

[†] J. E. Lennard-Jones, *Proc. Roy. Soc.* A, **129**, 598 (1930); *Journ. Lond. Math. Soc.* **6**, 290 (1931).

solutions of (50) are degenerate. Provided the only degenerate solutions of (50) used in constructing Φ are complete sets, then Φ will be non-degenerate; e.g. for the helium atom in the ground state we construct Φ from the two $1s$-wave functions, and there is no other way of constructing Φ to give the same energy. Moreover, provided the solutions of (50) are chosen to be orthogonal, as they always can be, the functions Φ will be all orthogonal whether they are degenerate or not.

Let us write $$\int \Phi_k^* \Phi_l \, d\tau = (k|1|l), \tag{51}$$

where the integral is taken over all the coordinates, spatial and spin, then if the wave functions Φ_k are normalized to unity $(k|1|l)$ is merely the Kronecker delta† δ_{kl}; and $(k|1|l)$ always vanishes for $k \neq l$.

To obtain the approximate solution of equation (46) we observe that we have supposed equation (48) to be such that $\sum_{j=1}^{Z} V_j'$ does not differ greatly from V; we may thus write equation (46) in the form

$$(H' - W)\Phi = -v\Phi, \tag{52}$$

where $$v = V - \sum_{j=1}^{Z} V_j' \tag{53}$$

is small. It is assumed that the solution of equation (52) can be expressed as a linear combination

$$\Phi = \sum_k a_k \Phi_k$$

of the solutions of equation (48). Substituting this series in equation (52), multiplying by Φ_l^*, and integrating over the whole range of all the variables specifying the wave functions, we obtain a system of linear algebraic equations

$$\sum_k a_k \{(l|H'|k) - W(l|1|k) + (l|v|k)\} = 0 \quad (l = 1, 2, \dots) \tag{54}$$

for the determination of the coefficients a_k and the possible values of W. In these equations we have written, in the usual notation for matrix elements,

$$(l|A|k) = \int \Phi_l^* A \Phi_k \, dq.$$

It follows immediately from this definition and from that of H, H', v that

$$(l|H'|k) + (l|v|k) = (l|H|k),$$

which is the matrix element of the Hamiltonian of the equation (46) with respect to the wave functions of the Schrödinger equation (48).

† The Kronecker delta is defined by the relations $\delta_{kl} = 0$ $(k \neq l)$, $\delta_{kk} = 1$.

The system of algebraic equations (54) may then be written in the form
$$\sum_k a_k\{(l|H|k) - W(l|1|k)\} = 0. \tag{55}$$

In the general case the wave-function Φ is an *infinite* sum of terms of the form $a_k\Phi_k$ so that, in general, the system (55) consists of an infinite number of equations in an infinite number of unknowns. Eliminating the coefficients a_k from the set of equations (55) we obtain the determinantal equation

$$\begin{vmatrix} (1|H|1) - W(1|1|1) & (1|H|2) & (1|H|3) & . & . & . \\ (2|H|1) & (2|H|2) - W(2|1|2) & (2|H|3) & . & . & . \\ (3|H|1) & (3|H|2) & (3|H|3) - W(3|1|3) & . & . & . \\ . & . & . & . & . & . \end{vmatrix} = 0.$$

In the case where the wave-functions Φ_k are normalized to unity,
$$(l|1|k) = \delta_{lk};$$
also
$$(l|H'|k) = W_k\,\delta_{lk},$$
where W_k are the eigenvalues of equation (48). The determinantal equation then reduces to

$$\begin{vmatrix} (1|v|1) - (W - W_1) & (1|v|2) & (1|v|3) & . & . & . \\ (2|v|1) & (2|v|2) - (W - W_2) & (2|v|3) & . & . & . \\ (3|v|1) & (3|v|2) & (3|v|3) - (W - W_3) & . & . & . \\ . & . & . & . & . & . \end{vmatrix} = 0. \tag{56}$$

Since the number of equations of the system (56) is infinite, the determinant on the left-hand side has an infinite number of rows and columns. The eigenvalues W_k are known, and once the functions Φ_k are determined the matrix elements $(l|v|k)$ can be determined by quadratures, and the values of W found. Suppose, for definiteness, we wish to determine the change in the value of W_1. As a first approximation we assume
$$(l|v|k) = 0,$$
except when $l = 1$, $k = 1$, so that
$$W = W_1 + (1|v|1).$$
The second approximation is obtained by assuming $(l|v|k)$ to be zero except when either l or k is 1. Then

$$0 = \begin{vmatrix} (1|v|1) - (W - W_1) & (1|v|2) & (1|v|3) & . & . & . \\ (2|v|1) & W_2 - W & 0 & . & . & . \\ (3|v|1) & 0 & W_3 - W & . & . & . \\ . & . & . & . & . & . \end{vmatrix},$$

whence we obtain the equation

$$W = W_1 + (1|v|1) + \sum_{j \neq 1} \frac{(1|v|j)(j|v|1)}{W - W_j} \qquad (57)$$

for the determination of W. More accurate solutions are obtained by including more of the elements $(l|v|k)$ in the expansion of the determinant.

When the energy values have been determined by some numerical method, the corresponding wave-functions

$$\Phi = \sum_k a_k \Phi_k$$

are obtained from the solution of the set of equations (56). The wave function can thus be written as a determinant of the type

$$\Phi = \begin{vmatrix} \Phi_1 & \Phi_2 & . & . & . & \Phi_m & . & . & . \\ (2|v|1) & (2|v|2)-(W-W_2) & . & . & . & (2|v|m) & . & . & . \\ . & . & . & . & . & . & . & . & . & . & . & . & . & . & . \\ (m|v|1) & (m|v|2) & & . & . & . & (m|v|m)-(W-W_m) & . & . & . \\ . & . & . & . & . & . & . & . & . & . & . & . & . & . & . \end{vmatrix}$$

29.2. Degenerate cases

We now consider the case, which occurs most frequently in practice, in which there is more than one wave function Φ_k corresponding to each value of the energy W_k. Suppose there are α such functions associated with the same eigenvalue W_k of the energy; denote these wave functions by

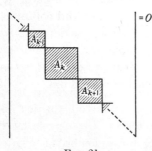

FIG. 21.

$$\Phi_k^1, \Phi_k^2, ..., \Phi_k^i, ..., \Phi_k^\alpha. \qquad (58)$$

If we denote by A_k the square of α^2 elements corresponding to the set of wave functions (58), then the determinantal equation (56) assumes the form shown in Fig. 21, where A_{k+1}, etc., are the square arrays corresponding in a similar way to the energies W_{k+1}, etc. It should of course be noted that the elements of the determinant *outside* the shaded squares do *not* in general vanish.

The determinant A_k can be transformed to one in which all the elements are zero except those on the diagonal by a method similar to that of changing the axes of a quadric in higher space. Since the wave functions $\Phi_k^i (i = 1, 2,..., \alpha)$ are degenerate it follows that the wave function

$$\Phi_{k,h}^1 = \sum_{i=1}^{\alpha} \beta_{ik} \Phi_k^i \qquad (59)$$

formed from a linear combination of the functions Φ_k^i will also correspond to the energy value W_k. The function (59) will be orthogonal to a similarly constructed wave-function

$$\Phi_{k,g}^1 = \sum_{i=1}^{\alpha} \beta_{ig} \Phi_k^i, \qquad (60)$$

provided that, when g is not equal to h,

$$\sum_{i=1}^{\alpha} \beta_{ih} \beta_{ig} = 0.$$

Thus if we can determine a set of α^2 coefficients β_{ih} such that

$$\sum_{i=1}^{\alpha} \beta_{ih} \beta_{ig} = 0,$$

the new set of wave functions $\Phi_{k,h}^1$ form an orthogonal set. With the set of wave functions so constructed the determinant A_k becomes a diagonal one. Similar transformations can be carried out for the square matrices $A_{k+1}...$, giving finally an equation of the type of Fig. 21 but now with the matrix A_k given by

$$A_k = \begin{pmatrix} (1|v|1)'-(W-W_k) & 0 & \cdot\;\;\cdot\;\;\cdot & 0 \\ 0 & (2|v|2)'-(W-W_k). & \cdot\;\;\cdot\;\;\cdot & 0 \\ \cdot\;\;\cdot\;\;\cdot\;\;\cdot\;\;\cdot\;\;\cdot & \cdot\;\;\cdot\;\;\cdot\;\;\cdot\;\;\cdot\;\;\cdot\;\;\cdot & \cdot\;\;\cdot & \cdot\;\;\cdot\;\;\cdot \\ 0 & 0 & \cdot\;\;\cdot\;\;\cdot & .(\alpha|v|\alpha)'-(W-W_n) \end{pmatrix},$$

the symbols $(g|v|h)'$ denoting the matrix elements

$$(g|v|h)' = \int \Phi_{k,g}^{1*} v \Phi_{k,h}^1 \, dq$$

and $A_{k+1}...$ of similar type.

The transformed determinantal equation may then be solved approximately by neglecting all the elements except those on the leading diagonal and successive approximations obtained by a variety of methods depending on the relative magnitudes of the elements neglected in the first step. Thus as a first approximation for the change in W_k we obtain

$$W = W_k + \int \Phi_{k,g}^{1*} v \Phi_{k,g}^1 \, dq,$$

where $g = 1, 2,..., \alpha$; as a second approximation we may omit every $(k|v|l)$ except those within the squares A_k, $A_{k+1},...$, and those of one row and column which intersect on the diagonal, and so on as in the case of non-degeneracy.

Since the potential function V in a real atom consists of electrostatic terms, it should be noted that

$$V = -\sum_j \frac{Z}{r_j} + \sum_{k<j} \frac{1}{r_{jk}},$$

so that the diagonal elements of the determinant on the left-hand side of equation (58) are given by expressions of the type

$$\frac{1}{Z!} \int H \begin{vmatrix} \rho_{11} & \rho_{12} & \cdot & \cdot & \cdot & \rho_{1Z} \\ \rho_{21} & \rho_{22} & \cdot & \cdot & \cdot & \rho_{2Z} \\ \cdot & \cdot & \cdot & \cdot & \cdot & \cdot \\ \rho_{Z1} & \rho_{Z2} & \cdot & \cdot & \cdot & \rho_{ZZ} \end{vmatrix} dq,$$

which can be evaluated to give

$$-\int \frac{Z}{r_j} \rho_{jj} \, dq_j + \frac{1}{2} \int \int \frac{1}{r_{jk}} \begin{vmatrix} \rho_{jj} & \rho_{jk} \\ \rho_{kj} & \rho_{kk} \end{vmatrix} dq_j \, dq_k$$

and can be expressed in terms of $(lm|G|lm)$ and $(lm|G|ml)$ as before.

To illustrate the general principles of the method by which the foregoing analysis may be used to obtain detailed information about the properties of real atoms, we shall outline the procedure for a particular case, that of carbon, in which there are six electrons. If each electron moved in the same field, assumed to be spherically symmetrical, the wave functions would be of the form

$$\psi_{n,l,m} = f_{n,l}(r) P_l^m(\cos\theta) e^{im\phi}, \tag{61}$$

n assuming integral values $1, 2,\dots$ and $|m| \leqslant l,\ l \leqslant n-1$. We thus obtain the wave functions including spin

$$n = 1,\, l = 0 \qquad \psi_{1,0,0}\chi_\alpha, \quad \psi_{1,0,0}\chi_\beta$$
$$n = 2,\, l = 0 \qquad \psi_{2,0,0}\chi_\alpha, \quad \psi_{2,0,0}\chi_\beta$$
$$n = 2,\, l = 1 \qquad \psi_{2,1,1}\chi_\alpha, \quad \psi_{2,1,1}\chi_\beta, \quad \psi_{2,1,0}\chi_\alpha, \quad \psi_{2,1,0}\chi_\beta$$
$$\psi_{2,1,-1}\chi_\alpha, \quad \psi_{2,1,-1}\chi_\beta$$

corresponding to the lowest energies.

The six wave functions for the construction of the wave function of the system of six electrons may then be taken as the first four of these wave functions together with any two of the last six (all of which correspond to the same energy). Corresponding to the lowest energy we can thus construct $6!/4!\,2! = 15$ wave functions each in the form of a determinant with six rows and six columns. We can construct similar wave functions for higher energies and then employ these wave functions as a basis for determining the properties of the real atom. The matrix elements of the Hamiltonian of the real atom are calculated with respect to these wave functions and the determinantal equation constructed in the manner described above. The fifteen degenerate wave functions lead to a square matrix of fifteen rows and columns, and the first step in the calculations is to determine such linear orthogonal combinations of the wave functions as will transform this square matrix into one with diagonal elements. This procedure is repeated for the other square matrices A_k and the roots of the determinantal equation determined by the method of successive approximations outlined above.

This cumbersome procedure can, however, be avoided by a method due to J. C. Slater based on the above analysis; this will be described in the next section.

29.3. *Slater's method for complex atoms*†

Slater's method of determining the values of the energy levels of complex atoms is based on the fact that the wave function (61) represents, not only a state of definite energy, but also one with definite angular momentum. The angular momentum about the z-axis $\theta = 0$ of a single electron defined by the wave function (61) is m measured in atomic units ($m\hbar$ in ordinary units). In the carbon atom we suppose as a first approximation that the six electrons move independently in the same central field and that the angular momentum of each electron is given by the value of m in the appropriate wave function. By assuming that the six electrons are moving in the same field we obtain the total angular momentum (in atomic units) merely by adding the m's appropriate to each of the electrons; thus denoting this quantity by M_z we have
$$M_z = \sum m. \tag{62}$$

The field in which the electrons move is not, of course, spherically symmetrical. The electrons exert forces on one another and it is no longer possible to determine the angular momentum of the *individual* electrons. These forces cannot, however, affect the *total* angular momentum; the value of M_z given by equation (62) therefore remains unaltered despite the interactions of the electrons.

In a similar way the total angular momentum due to the spins of the electrons is given by the formula
$$S_z = \sum s, \tag{63}$$
where s denotes the angular momentum in the z-direction due to the spin of a single electron moving in a spherically symmetrical field. In atomic units s assumes either of the values $\pm\frac{1}{2}$.

---

† J. C. Slater, *Phys. Rev.* **34**, 1283 (1929).

The values of M_z and S_z for the fifteen wave functions corresponding to the lowest energy of the carbon atom are shown in Fig. 22, the numbers of wave functions with the same values of M_z and S_z being shown in the circles which are joined to points whose coordinates are the appropriate values of S_z and M_z.

Now the Hamiltonian operator is not changed by a rotation about the θ-axis so that† the angular momentum commutes with the Hamiltonian H. Thus

$$M_z H - H M_z = 0. \tag{64}$$

A typical matrix element of $M_z H$ is by the definition of a matrix product

$$(m|M_z H|n) = \sum_l (m|M_z|l)(l|H|n)$$

$$= (m|M_z|m)(m|H|n),$$

since M_z is a diagonal matrix and therefore $(m|M_z|l) = 0$ if $m \neq l$. Also

$$(m|H M_z|n) = \sum_l (m|H|l)(l|M_z|n)$$

$$= (m|H|n)(n|M_z|n).$$

It follows at once that equation (64) is satisfied only if

$$(m|H|n) = 0,$$

when $(m|M_z|m) \neq (n|M_z|n)$. Similarly it can be shown that $(m|H|n) = 0$ when $(m|S_z|m)$ is not equal to $(n|S_z|n)$. Thus the elements of the determinant on the left-hand side of equation (58) are zero, except when the two wave functions defining the matrix element have the same values of the momenta M_z and S_z.

By means of this result and Fig. 22 we see that the matrix A_0 corresponding to the lowest energy of the electrons reduces to the form

$$A_0 = \begin{bmatrix} \cdot \\ \ \cdot \\ \ \ \cdot \\ \ \ \ \cdot \ \cdot \\ \ \ \ \ \cdot \ \cdot \\ \ \ \ \ \cdot \ \cdot \ \cdot \\ \ \ \ \ \cdot \ \cdot \ \cdot \\ \ \ \ \ \cdot \ \cdot \ \cdot \\ \ \ \ \ \ \ \cdot \ \cdot \\ \ \ \ \ \ \ \cdot \ \cdot \\ \ \ \ \ \ \ \ \cdot \\ \ \ \ \ \ \ \ \ \cdot \\ \ \ \ \ \ \ \ \ \ \cdot \end{bmatrix}, \tag{65}$$

the dots denoting the 25 of the 225 matrix elements which are not zero; the matrix A_0, thus consists of one square of three rows and

† See equation (29 a), Chap. XII.

columns, two of two rows and columns, and eight diagonal elements. The roots of the determinantal equation

$$|A_0| = 0 \tag{66}$$

may, or may not, be distinct. To determine which, if any, of these roots are multiple we consider next the total angular momentum M and the total spin momentum S.

Not only the component S_z but also the total spin S is a constant of the motion. Furthermore, if the total spin is S, S_z may assume any one of the $2S+1$ values

$$S,\ S-1,\ S-2,...,\ -(S-2),\ -(S-1),\ -S\,;$$

and if we neglect the interaction of the spins with the space coordinates

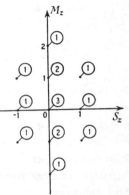

and the mutual interactions of the spins, to each of these values of S_z there must correspond an equal value of the energy. Similarly the total angular momentum M is a constant of the motion and it may be proved that to each component M_z of M there is related an equal value of the energy. It can also be proved that: (1) The eigenvalues of M^2 are $L(L+1)$ where L is an integer. (2) To each eigenvalue of M^2 there correspond $2L+1$ independent wave functions which can be chosen.

The various groups into which the fifteen values of (S_z, M_z) of Fig. 22 fall are shown in

FIG. 22. The S_z-M_z diagram.

Table 3. In assigning a name to each of the three groups we have followed the language of spectroscopy in which a multiplet is denoted by S, P, D,... according as $M = 0, 1, 2,...$, the multiplicity $2S+1$

TABLE 3

M	S	Values of (S_z, M_z)	Name of group	Energy
0	0	(0, 0)	^1S multiplet	w_1
1	1	$(-1, -1)$, $(-1, 0)$, $(-1, 1)$ $(0, -1)$, $(0, 0)$, $(0, 1)$ $(1, -1)$, $(1, 0)$, $(1, 1)$	^3P multiplet	w_2
2	0	$(0, -2)$, $(0, -1)$, $(0, 0)$ $(0, 1)$, $(0, 2)$	^1D multiplet	w_3

due to the spin being written on the top left-hand side. Thus for $M = 0$, $S = 0$ we write ^1S, etc. From this table it will be observed

that the values $S_z = 0$, $M_z = 0$ are common to the ^1S, ^3P, ^1D multiplets
and $S_z = 0$, $M_z = \pm 1$ are common to ^3P, ^1D. The table also shows
that there are actually only three distinct values of the energy which
we have denoted by w_1, w_2, w_3, or, which is the same thing, that there are
only three distinct roots of the determinantal equation (66), one being
a simple root corresponding to the ^1S multiplet, another a ninefold root
for the ^3P, and the remaining one a fivefold root for the ^1D.

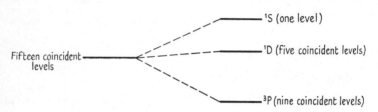

Fig. 23. The lower energy levels of the carbon atom.

So far we have made no approximation beyond assuming that the
energies of the mutual interactions of the spins and the interaction of
the spins with the space coordinates are of a lower order of magnitude
than the energies being considered here. In considering the determinantal equation (Fig. 21), however, we introduce certain approximations
by rejecting some of the elements. The determinant on the left-hand side
of the equation is made up of a chain of squares grouped together along
the diagonal and other elements lying outside these squares. As a first
approximation we assume that these elements are so small that they
may be neglected. The equation (Fig. 21) then splits up into two or more
equations, one of which is
$$|A_0| = 0.$$

Now since the values $S_z = 0$, $M_z = 0$ are common to the ^1S, ^3P, ^1D
multiplets, it follows that the three-by-three matrix in (65) leads to a
factor of the form
$$(W-w_1)(W-w_2)(W-w_3) = 0, \tag{67}$$
and the two-by-two matrices lead to factors
$$(W-w_2)(W-w_3) = 0,$$
and the complete determinantal equation is
$$(W-w_1)(W-w_2)^5(W-w_3)^9 = 0.$$
It follows that two of the roots of the equation can be found by a direct
calculation based on the wave functions of the original six-electron

system. It is not necessary to calculate the wave functions of the atom itself, since these roots can be derived from a formula of the type (26).

To determine the third root we make use of the fact that if we write the three-by-three factor of the equation $|A_0| = 0$ in the form

$$\begin{vmatrix} -W+u_{11} & u_{12} & u_{13} \\ u_{21} & -W+u_{22} & u_{23} \\ u_{31} & u_{32} & u_{33}-W \end{vmatrix} = 0,$$

it must be equivalent to equation (67). Equating the coefficients of W^2 in these two equations we obtain the relation

$$w_1+w_2+w_3 = u_{11}+u_{22}+u_{33}$$

for the determination of w_3 once w_1 and w_2 are known. Thus it is only necessary to calculate the *diagonal* elements of A_0 to determine all three roots w_1, w_2, w_3.

The method of Lennard-Jones and Slater sketched briefly above may be used to determine the energy levels of a complex atom in all cases in which the multiplets differ in type. If, on the other hand, there are two or more multiplets of the same type, say, ^3P multiplets, the above method yields only the sum of the energies of these multiplets. To evaluate the individual energies it is necessary to find those combinations of wave functions which make the appropriate square of the determinant diagonal.

In conclusion, we summarize the main steps in the determination of the energy levels of complex atoms by the perturbation method; they are:

(i) determining the wave functions of the electrons separately in a spherically symmetrical field $\sum_{j=1}^{Z} V_j'$;

(ii) deducing the approximate wave functions of the many-electron system in determinantal form;

(iii) calculating the diagonal matrix elements of $V - \sum_{j=1}^{Z} V_j'$ with respect to these approximate wave functions.

We indicated above that in many problems of physical interest elements of the infinite determinant lying outside the chain of squares strung along the leading diagonal are so small that they may be neglected. In the preceding analysis they were taken to be zero, but it is possible to obtain better approximations by taking them into account. Methods of doing so have been considered by Lennard-Jones.[†]

† J. E. Lennard-Jones, *Proc. Roy. Soc.* A, **129**, 598–615 (1930).

30. The statistical method of Thomas and Fermi

A semi-classical method of finding the density of electrons in a heavy atom has been formulated by Thomas[†] and Fermi.[‡] This forms a fair approximation for heavy atoms only. The method is as follows: as in the method of Hartree, the electrons are pictured as moving in an electrostatic potential Φ due to the nucleus and to the charge cloud of the electrons themselves. Electrons are supposed, much as in the theory of metals, to have all energies up to a maximum $-e\Phi_0$. The maximum kinetic energy is then, at any point (x, y, z), equal to $e(\Phi-\Phi_0)$, and hence the maximum momentum of any electron at the point (x, y, z) is

$$p_{\max} = \sqrt{\{2me(\Phi-\Phi_g)\}}. \qquad (68)$$

We now assume that a volume δV can be chosen at any point containing a large number of wave-lengths (h/p) but such that $\Phi-\Phi_0$ is virtually constant within it. With this assumption, assuming that all electrons are in their lowest state and that they obey the Pauli exclusion principle, it follows that if $n(x, y, z)\,\delta V$ is the number of electrons in the volume element

$$n(x, y, z) = \frac{8\pi}{3}\left(\frac{p_{\max}}{h}\right)^3.$$

The 2 has its origin in the fact that two electrons are to be found in each quantized state.

Substituting for $p_{\max}$ from equation (68) we have

$$n(x, y, z) = \frac{8\pi}{3h^3}\{2me(\Phi-\Phi_0)\}^{\frac{3}{2}}. \qquad (69)$$

The potential function Φ is now determined by the Poisson equation

$$\nabla^2\Phi = -4\pi\rho,$$

and $\rho = -ne$, n being given by equation (69). Thus finally we obtain for Φ the non-linear equation

$$\nabla^2\Phi = \alpha(\Phi-\Phi_0)^{\frac{3}{2}}, \qquad (70)$$

where
$$\alpha = \frac{32\pi^2 e}{3h^3}(2me)^{\frac{3}{2}}. \qquad (71)$$

The boundary conditions to be satisfied by the potential function Φ are readily determined. If the atom or ion is of atomic number Z, then for small values of r, Φ is very nearly equal to Ze/r; thus the boundary condition

$$\lim_{r\to 0} r\Phi = Ze \qquad (72)$$

is valid.

[†] L. H. Thomas, *Proc. Camb. Phil. Soc.* **23**, 542 (1927).
[‡] E. Fermi, *Zeits. f. Physik*, **48**, 73; **49**, 550 (1928). See also L. Brillouin, *L'Atome de Thomas–Fermi et la méthode du champ 'self-consistent'* (Paris, 1934).

On the other hand, if the total number of electrons in the atom is N, then

$$\int n(x,y,z)\,d\tau = N, \tag{73}$$

where the integral is taken over all space; in the case of a neutral atom $N = Z$.

Assuming radial symmetry and introducing new variables

$$\xi = (Ze)^{\frac{1}{3}}\alpha^{\frac{2}{3}}r, \qquad \phi = \frac{\xi(\Phi-\Phi_0)}{\alpha^{\frac{2}{3}}(Ze)^{\frac{2}{3}}}, \tag{74}$$

we may write equation (70) in the simplified form

$$\frac{d^2\phi}{d\xi^2} = \phi^{\frac{3}{2}}\xi^{-\frac{1}{2}} \quad (\xi > 0). \tag{75}$$

The boundary condition (72) is now replaced by

$$\lim_{\xi \to 0} \phi(\xi) = 1. \tag{76}$$

Now the number of electrons in the volume between $r = 0$ and r is

$$z(r) = \int_0^r 4\pi r^2 n(r)\,dr,$$

and, by Poisson's equation, we can replace n by $\nabla^2\Phi/4\pi e$ so that

$$z(r) = \frac{1}{e}\int_0^r \nabla^2\Phi r^2\,dr = Z\int_0^\xi \frac{\partial^2\phi}{\partial\xi^2}\xi\,d\xi.$$

Integrating by parts and introducing the boundary condition (76), we have

$$z(r) = Z\left(1+\xi\frac{\partial\phi}{\partial\xi} - \phi\right), \tag{77}$$

whence

$$1-\frac{z(r)}{Z} = \phi-\xi\frac{\partial\phi}{\partial\xi}. \tag{78}$$

This equation gives a simple method of determining $z(r)$ graphically from the ϕ–ξ curve determined by the differential equation (75), the boundary condition (76), and a further boundary condition of the type

$$\lim_{\xi \to 0}\frac{d\phi}{d\xi} = -m. \tag{79}$$

Suppose that APP' is a curve determined in this way (cf. Fig. 24); A is the point $(0, 1)$, P is (ξ, ϕ). If we draw the tangent to the curve at P and produce it to cut the ϕ-axis at B, then it is easily seen that the distance OB is equal to $\phi-\xi\partial\phi/\partial\xi$ and hence by equation (78) to $1-z(r)/Z$. Since $OA = 1$ it follows that $AB = z(r)/Z$; we thus have a simple graphical method of determining the number of electrons within a sphere of radius r centred at the nucleus of the atom.

The solution of equation (75) presents some difficulty; it is non-linear and involves a singularity at $\xi = 0$. Furthermore, the boundary conditions cannot be satisfied directly since one must be satisfied at

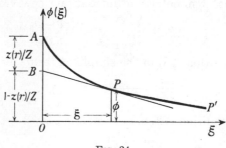

FIG. 24.

the singular point $\xi = 0$ and the other at infinity. Since ϕ'' is infinite at $\xi = 0$ it is not possible to use a Taylor expansion in the neighbourhood of the origin; instead we use an expansion of the form

$$\phi = 1 - m\xi + a\xi^{\frac{3}{2}} + b\xi^2 + c\xi^{\frac{5}{2}} + d\xi^3 + \dots.$$

With this form for the function ϕ we have

$$\phi'' = \tfrac{3}{4}a\xi^{-\frac{1}{2}} + 2b + \tfrac{15}{4}c\xi^{\frac{1}{2}} + 6d\xi + O(\xi^{\frac{3}{2}})$$

and

$$\phi^{\frac{3}{2}}\xi^{-\frac{1}{2}} = \xi^{-\frac{1}{2}} - \tfrac{3}{2}m\xi^{\frac{1}{2}} + \tfrac{3}{2}a\xi + O(\xi^{\frac{3}{2}}),$$

so that equating the two expressions we obtain

$$a = \tfrac{4}{3}, \qquad b = 0, \qquad c = -\tfrac{2}{5}m, \qquad d = \tfrac{1}{4}a = \tfrac{1}{3}.$$

The coefficients of higher powers in the expansion have been determined by Baker;[†] he finds that for small values of ξ, ϕ is given approximately by

$$\phi = 1 - m\xi + \tfrac{4}{3}\xi^{\frac{3}{2}} - \tfrac{2}{5}m\xi^{\frac{5}{2}} + \tfrac{1}{3}\xi^3 + \tfrac{3}{70}m^2\xi^{\frac{7}{2}} - \tfrac{2}{15}m\xi^4 + \tfrac{4}{63}(\tfrac{2}{3} + \tfrac{1}{16}m^3)\xi^{\frac{9}{2}} + O(\xi^5).$$

$$(80)$$

Numerical solutions of equations (75) for larger values of ξ have been obtained by Baker, and also by Bush and Caldwell,[‡] making use of the differential analyser. It is found that there is only one solution of equation (75) which tends uniformly to zero as $\xi \to \infty$, the one corresponding to a value

$$m_1 = 1 \cdot 58856$$

in equation (79). When m exceeds the critical value m_1 the curve cuts

† E. B. Baker, *Phys. Rev.* **36**, 630 (1930).
‡ V. Bush and S. H. Caldwell, *Phys. Rev.* **38**, 1898 (1931).

the ξ-axis at a point ξ_0 (cf. Fig. 25); and when $m < m_1$ the curve decreases steadily to a minimum point (ξ_m, ϕ_m), then increases steadily to infinity as ξ approaches a certain value a, and finally decreases to zero as $\xi \to 0$. Curves relating ϕ_m to ξ_m are given in the paper by Baker.

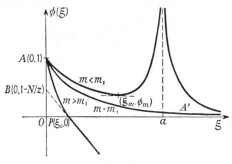

FIG. 25.

Asymptotic formulae for these solutions have been derived by Sommerfeld;[†] for $m = m_1$ he obtains for large values of ξ

$$\phi \sim \left\{ \frac{1}{1+(\xi/12^{\frac{2}{3}})^{0.772}} \right\}^{3.886} \sim \frac{144}{\xi^3}.$$

For large values of ξ this reduces to

$$\phi \sim 144\xi^{-3},$$

a solution which may be obtained by substituting

$$\phi = A\xi^{-n}$$

into equation (75) and equating powers of ξ on both sides of the equation. Similarly when $m < m_1$ it can be shown that

$$\phi \sim \frac{400a}{(\xi-a)^4} \quad (\xi \to a).$$

For neutral atoms we have

$$\lim_{r\to\infty} z(r) = N = Z;$$

in other words, the curve $\phi(\xi)$ tends to infinity in such a way that the tangent to it passes through the origin, since

$$\lim_{\xi\to\infty} OB = 1 - \frac{1}{Z}\lim_{r\to\infty} z(r) = 0.$$

The only curve which satisfies this condition is the curve AA' for which

† A. Sommerfeld, *Zeits. f. Physik*, **78**, 283 (1932); **80**, 415 (1933).

$d\phi/d\xi = -m_1$ when $\xi = 0$. The curve is asymptotic to $\phi(\xi) = 0$, i.e.
$\Phi - \Phi_0 = 0$, so that if Φ is taken to be zero at infinity, Φ_0 must also be
zero, which means that the maximum energy $-e\Phi_0$ of an electron in
a neutral atom is zero.

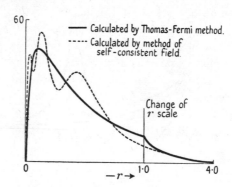

FIG. 26. Radial distribution of charge for Rb+.

For positive ions the number of electrons N is less than the atomic
number Z, so that

$$\lim_{\xi \to \infty} OB = 1 - \frac{N}{Z} > 0.$$

In this case we choose a curve with $m > m_1$ such that the tangent to
the curve at the point $P(\xi_0, 0)$ where it cuts the axis $\phi = 0$ passes
through the point $B(0, 1 - N/Z)$. The equation of the line BP is

$$\phi(\xi) = \left(1 - \frac{N}{Z}\right)\left(1 - \frac{\xi}{\xi_0}\right),$$

which in the old coordinate system reduces to

$$\Phi - \Phi_0 = e(Z - N)\left(\frac{1}{r} - \frac{1}{r_0}\right),$$

and so represents the Coulomb field outside the ion. It follows at once
that

$$E_0 = -e\Phi_0 < 0,$$

showing that the maximum energy of the electrons in the ion is
negative; the electrons cannot therefore escape from the ion.

As an example[†] of the kind of results obtained by the Fermi–Thomas
method, Fig. 26 shows the density of electrons in the heavy ion,
rubidium+. The electron density is readily calculated from equation
(69) once the wave function ϕ defined by equation (74) has been found
by numerical integration of the non-linear differential equation (75).

† D. R. Hartree, *Proc. Camb. Phil. Soc.* **24**, 121 (1928).

The full curve shows the radial charge density calculated in this way and the dotted curve that calculated by the method of the self-consistent field (§ 28.2 above). It will be noted from this curve that the Thomas–Fermi method gives a good smoothed-out approximation to the distribution of charge constituting the self-consistent field. For this reason it is often useful to use the Thomas–Fermi method to obtain a first approximation to the field in the Hartree method.

It would also appear that if the *details* of the field or charge distribution are not considered to be important the Thomas–Fermi field or charge distribution may be sufficiently accurate. It should, however, be remembered that in this method the radial charge density for small r is proportional to $r^{\frac{1}{2}}$, while in the wave-mechanical treatment it is proportional to r^2.

VII

INTERATOMIC FORCES

31. Introduction

ALL treatments based on quantum mechanics of the forces between atoms and molecules make use of a theorem due originally to Born and Oppenheimer.† This states that any problem in which atoms or molecules interact can be treated in the following way:

First one supposes that the nuclei of the atoms concerned are at rest at points $\mathbf{R}_1$, $\mathbf{R}_2$,..., $\mathbf{R}_N$, N being the total number of nuclei in the system under consideration. One then obtains solutions of the Schrödinger equation for the electrons of the system moving in the field of these nuclei. These solutions will be written $\psi_n(\mathbf{R}; q)$, where q are the coordinates, including spin, of the electrons, and $W_n(\mathbf{R})$ are the corresponding energy values. One then treats the motion of the nuclei by means of a second Schrödinger equation, in which $W_n(\mathbf{R})$, together with the Coulomb interaction between the nuclei, plays the part of the potential energy function. If $\Psi(\mathbf{R})$ is a solution of this equation, the wave function of the whole system is taken to be

$$\Psi(\mathbf{R})\psi_n(\mathbf{R}, q). \tag{1}$$

This approximation is used in almost any problem involving interatomic forces, such as

(a) The vibration and rotation of a molecule.

(b) The (gas-kinetic) collision between molecules.

(c) Calculations of the lattice energy or elastic constants of solids.

The use of the wave function (1) is of course an approximation only; the neglected term in the wave function is of order $(m/M)^{\frac{1}{4}}$, where m is the electronic mass and M the nuclear mass. For a proof, the reader is referred to the original paper.

31.1. *Rotation and vibration of diatomic molecules in their lowest electronic states*

The problem of calculating the energy levels has already been treated briefly in Chapter V. We start by assuming that the electronic problem is solved, and that the energy of the electronic system in its ground state is known for all separations R of the nuclei. Let $U(R)$ denote the sum of this energy and the Coulomb interaction of the nuclei.

† M. Born and J. R. Oppenheimer, *Ann. der Physik*, **84**, 457 (1927).

Then the Schrödinger equation for nuclear motion is, according to the approximation introduced above,

$$\frac{\hbar^2}{2M_1}\nabla_1^2\psi + \frac{\hbar^2}{2M_2}\nabla_2^2\psi + \{W - U(R)\}\psi = 0.$$

As already shown (§ 23.2), if the centre of gravity is at rest, this equation reduces to

$$\frac{\hbar^2}{2M}\nabla^2\psi + \{W - U(R)\}\psi = 0,$$

where ψ is a function of $\mathbf{R}$, the (vector) distance between the nuclei and $M = M_1 M_2/(M_1 + M_2)$. Taking spherical polar coordinates, ψ takes the form

$$\psi = \Theta_{k,n}(\theta, \phi)f(R)/R,$$

where f is the solution vanishing at the origin of

$$f'' + \frac{2M}{\hbar^2}\left\{W - U(R) - \frac{k(k+1)}{R^2}\right\}f = 0. \tag{2}$$

The function $U(R)$ will depend on the electronic ground state of the molecule under consideration, and will not in general be expressible in terms of simple functions. For stable molecules the energies of the lower states can usually be found by writing

$$U(R) = U_0 + \tfrac{1}{2}K(R - R_e)^2,$$

which is a good approximation near the minimum of the energy curve. This method was adopted in Chapter VI.

Another method is to make use of the function introduced by Morse;[†] this is

$$U(R) = F\{1 - e^{-a(R-R_0)}\}^2.$$

The form of this function is qualitatively of the type that we expect for the force between atoms, except that it does not tend to infinity when R tends to zero; this is unlikely to be of importance. For the Morse function an exact solution of the Schrödinger equation has been given for $k = 0$ and an approximate one for $k \neq 0$. The energy values are (if the minimum of the curve is taken to be zero)

$$h\nu(n+\tfrac{1}{2}) - x\nu^2(n+\tfrac{1}{2})^2 + Bk(k+1) + Dk^2(k+1)^2 - \alpha(n+\tfrac{1}{2})k(k+1),$$

where

$$\nu = \frac{a}{2\pi}\Big/\sqrt{\left(\frac{2F}{M}\right)}, \qquad x = \frac{h^2c}{4F}, \qquad B = \frac{h^2}{8\pi^2 I},$$

$$D = \frac{h^5}{128\pi^6 M^3 \nu^2 c r_0^6}, \qquad \alpha = \frac{3h^2\nu}{16\pi^2 M r_0^2 D}\left(\frac{1}{ar_0} - \frac{1}{a^2 r_0^2}\right).$$

It will be seen how, in this formula, the term $h\nu(n+\tfrac{1}{2})$ represents the

† P. M. Morse, *Phys. Rev.* **34,** 57 (1929); C. L. Pekeris, ibid. **45,** 98 (1934). See also Pauling and Wilson, *Introduction to Quantum Mechanics*, p. 272.

vibrational levels, $Bk(k+1)$ the rotational levels, and that the other terms are of smaller order of magnitude for small n, k.

31.2. *Review of types of interatomic force*

We must now give an outline of types of force between atoms and ions which give rise to the formation of molecules and solid bodies. Among these the simplest are the purely polar forces between ions. Thus a very satisfactory theory of the properties of crystalline alkali-halides (e.g. NaCl) has been built up on the assumption that these materials are formed from positively charged metal ions and negatively charged halide ions, which attract each other according to the inverse square law. An account of this theory is given in Chapter VIII. The introduction of quantum mechanics does not affect the calculation of electrostatic attraction between ions; it does, however, affect our ideas of the extent to which the forces other than the electrostatic attraction affect the cohesion.

Secondly there are the so-called van der Waals forces between two neutral atoms or molecules. The van der Waals force may be defined as the force between two atoms or molecules when they are so far apart that their wave functions do not overlap. In general the potential energy of two molecules at a distance R apart, where R is great compared with molecular dimensions, can be expressed in the form

$$-A/R^6,$$

where A is a constant.

All other forces between atoms or molecules which are neither charged nor carry a permanent dipole arise only when they approach closely enough for there to be an appreciable overlap between the space covered by their respective wave functions. These 'overlap' forces are of three main kinds:

(a) The repulsive forces which arise mainly between closed shells, such as rare gases and ions like Na^+, Cl^-, Ag^+;

(b) The homopolar forces responsible for the bonds such as those between hydrogen atoms in H_2 or between carbon in diamond, graphite, or the molecules of organic chemistry;

(c) Metallic forces; by these are meant the forces between the atoms of a metal or alloy in the solid or liquid state.

32. Van der Waals' forces

32.1. *Calculation of van der Waals' forces by classical methods*

We have seen in the previous chapters that an atom may be thought of as consisting of a small positively charged nucleus surrounded by an electron cloud. For atoms which have spherical symmetry the centre of this electron distribution coincides with the nucleus. If, however, the atom is placed in a uniform electric field, the electron cloud is distorted in such a way that its centre is displaced away from the nucleus causing the atom to have an electric moment. The atom is then said to be polarized. It can be shown in a classical way that the van der Waals forces between neutral atoms can be interpreted in terms of these polarizations. We shall discuss this method before proceeding to the more accurate quantum mechanical calculations.

If the strength F of the electric field is not too great we expect the dipole induced in the atom to be proportional to F. Denoting the magnitude of the dipole by p we may then write

$$p = \alpha F, \qquad (3)$$

where the constant α is called the coefficient of polarizability. The energy W_p of the dipole p in a constant field F is given by

$$W_p = -\int_0^F p \, dF = -\tfrac{1}{2}\alpha F^2. \qquad (4)$$

If the field F is fluctuating about the value zero the mean of the polarization energy W_p remains finite,

$$\overline{W_p} = -\tfrac{1}{2}\alpha\overline{F^2}, \qquad (5)$$

since the mean of the square of the field $\overline{F^2}$ will not be zero.

Let us now consider the field F due to n dipoles of strengths μ_n placed at a great distance r from the atom and inclined at angles θ_n to the vector $\mathbf{r}$. Then if r is sufficiently great the field will be uniform, and have components

$$F_r = \sum_n \frac{2\mu_n \cos\theta_n}{r^3}, \qquad F_\theta = \sum_n \frac{\mu_n \sin\theta_n}{r^3}.$$

A neutral atom in which electrons move in the field of a nucleus may be represented by an ensemble of fluctuating dipoles of this type; we may thus write

$$\mu_n = es_n,$$

where s_n is the distance of the nth electron from the nucleus. For such an arrangement we have

$$\overline{F^2} = \frac{e^2}{r^6}\left[4\overline{\left(\sum_n s_n \cos\theta_n\right)^2} + \overline{\left(\sum_n s_n \sin\theta_n\right)^2}\right] = \frac{2\beta}{r^6},$$

β being interpreted as a kind of mean square of the dipole moment of an atom. Substituting from equation (6) into equation (5) we find that the effect of this atom on another distant atom is to change the energy by an amount W_p given by

$$W_p = -\alpha\beta/r^6. \tag{7}$$

The interaction energy of two atoms with atomic polarizabilities α_1, α_2 and mean square dipole moments β_1, β_2 is thus

$$W = -\frac{\alpha_1\beta_2 + \alpha_2\beta_1}{r^6}, \tag{8}$$

it being assumed that the effects are additive.

This classical method of calculation shows the characteristic features of van der Waals' forces. The negative sign in the expression (8) for the interaction energy implies that the two atoms attract one another. The force between the two atoms varies as the inverse seventh power of the distance; we shall see that this conclusion is confirmed by the use of the methods of wave mechanics. It is found, however, that the multiplicative constant $\alpha_1\beta_2 + \alpha_2\beta_1$ given by the classical theory is about five times too great if the value of β is deduced from measurements of the magnetic susceptibility.[†]

32.2. *Polarizability of an atom in an electric field*

The considerations of the last section show that in order to obtain the van der Waals attraction between atoms it is necessary to calculate the dipole induced on an atom placed in a static electric field, and thus the polarizability of the atom.

The calculation will first be carried through for an atom with one electron in a Coulomb field. The coordinates of the electron are denoted by (x, y, z). Then if an electric field F is introduced along the z-axis the perturbing term introduced into the Hamiltonian, in other words the potential energy of the electron in this field, is

$$H' = -Fez. \tag{9}$$

The Schrödinger equation then becomes

$$\nabla^2\psi + \frac{2m}{\hbar^2}\left(W + \frac{e^2}{r} - eFr\cos\theta\right)\psi = 0. \tag{10}$$

If we take $\psi_0 = e^{-r/a}, \qquad W_0 = -e^2/2a,$
and write $\psi = \psi_0 - \phi = \psi_0\{1 - F\cos\theta . R(r)\}, \tag{11}$

then W will differ from W_0 by a term of order F^2. Thus substituting from (11) into (10), making use of the equation

$$\nabla^2\psi_0 + \frac{2m}{\hbar^2}\left(W_0 + \frac{e^2}{r}\right)\psi_0 = 0, \tag{12a}$$

† P. Debye, *Phys. Zeits.* **21**, 178 (1920); **22**, 302 (1921).

and neglecting terms of order F^2 we obtain

$$\nabla^2\phi + \frac{2m}{\hbar^2}\left(W_0 + \frac{e^2}{r}\right)\phi + \frac{2m}{\hbar^2}eFr\cos\theta\,\psi_0 = 0. \tag{12b}$$

The ordinary differential equation for $R(r)$ then becomes

$$\frac{d^2R}{dr^2} + 2\left(\frac{1}{r} - \frac{1}{a}\right)\frac{dR}{dr} - \frac{2R}{r^2} = -\frac{2r}{ea}, \tag{13}$$

which has the particular integral

$$R = \frac{a^2}{e}\left\{\frac{r}{a} + \frac{1}{2}\left(\frac{r}{a}\right)^2\right\}. \tag{14}$$

To determine the complementary function we let

$$R(r) = \sum_{n=0}^{\infty} a_n r^{\rho+n}$$

and equate powers of $\rho-2$ to obtain the indicial equation

$$(\rho-1)(\rho+2) = 0.$$

The root $\rho = -2$ must be rejected since it would not lead to a function R which tends to zero with r. Putting $\rho = 1$ and equating coefficients of r^{n-1} we obtain the recurrence relation

$$\frac{a_n}{a_{n-1}} = \frac{2}{a}\frac{n+1}{n(n+2)},$$

which shows that, as $n \to \infty$,

$$\frac{a_n}{a_{n-1}} \sim \frac{2}{an},$$

so that, for large values of r,

$$R(r) \sim e^{2r/a}.$$

Any wave function ϕ containing this complementary function violates the boundary conditions; ϕ is therefore given by equations (11), (14). Hence to the first order we have

$$\psi = e^{-r/a}\left\{1 - \frac{Fa^2}{e}\cos\theta\left(\frac{r}{a} + \frac{r^2}{2a^2}\right)\right\}. \tag{15}$$

Making use of the form (11) for the wave function ψ, and of the equations (12a) and (12b) we have

$$H\psi = W_0(\psi_0 - \phi) - eFr\phi\cos\theta$$

as far as powers of order F^2. Thus neglecting powers of order F^3 we
have

$$W = W_0 - \frac{eF \int \psi_0^* \phi r \cos\theta \, d\tau}{\int \psi_0^* \psi_0 \, d\tau}$$

$$= W_0 - \tfrac{1}{2}F^2 a^3 \int\limits_0^\pi \cos^2\theta \sin\theta \, d\theta \int\limits_0^\infty e^{-2r/a}\left(\frac{r}{a} + \frac{r^2}{2a^2}\right)\frac{r^3 \, dr}{a^4} \Big/ \int\limits_0^\infty e^{-2r/a}\frac{r^2 \, dr}{a^3}.$$

The integrations are elementary and give finally

$$W = W_0 - \frac{9F^2 a^3}{4}.$$

But in terms of the polarizability α we have

$$W = W_0 - \tfrac{1}{2}\alpha F^2,$$

so that, since the two formulae are equivalent,

$$\alpha = \tfrac{9}{2}a^3. \tag{16}$$

This corresponds to a value $0\cdot677.10^{-24}$ cm.^{3} for the polarizability of
the normal hydrogen atom.

An alternative treatment of the polarizability, valid for any field,
is as follows: the considerations of Chapter III show that the perturbed
wave function is

$$\psi_0 + eF \sum_n \frac{Z_{0n}\psi_n}{W_n - W_0},$$

where $\psi_0(x, y, z)$ is the wave function of the ground state, $\psi_n(x, y, z)$ of
any excited state, and

$$Z_{0n} = \int \psi_n^* z \psi_0 \, d\tau. \tag{17}$$

The charge density in the perturbed atom, neglecting terms of order
F^2, is thus

$$\rho(x, y, z) = e|\psi_0|^2 + e^2 F \sum_n \left\{\frac{Z_{0n}}{W_n - W_0}\psi_n \psi_0^* + \text{complex conjugate}\right\}. \tag{18}$$

The second term is not in general spherically symmetrical and will thus
give rise to a dipole moment. Thus, for instance, if ψ_0 corresponds to
an s-state and ψ_n to a p-state, the product $\psi_n^* \psi_0$ will be of the form
$zf(r)$, and will be as illustrated in curve (3) in Fig. 27. The change in
the charge density of the atom is also illustrated.

The dipole moment of the atom is equal to

$$\int z\rho(x, y, z) \, d\tau,$$

which, on substituting from (18) gives for the polarizability (dipole divided by field)

$$\alpha = 2e^2 \sum_n \frac{|Z_{0n}|^2}{W_n - W_0}. \qquad (19)$$

The quantities $|Z_{0n}|^2$, here introduced for the first time, have considerable importance for the theory. It is convenient to introduce the dimensionless quantity f_n defined by

$$f_n = \frac{2m}{\hbar^2}(W_n - W_0)|Z_{0n}|^2.$$

The quantity f_n is called the 'oscillator strength' of the transition $0 \to n$ of the atom or molecule concerned. The reason for this is obvious. If we write $\nu_n = (W_n - W_0)/h$ and substitute in (19), we find for the polarizability α,

$$\alpha = \frac{e^2}{4\pi^2 m} \sum_n \frac{f_n}{\nu_n^2}. \qquad (20)$$

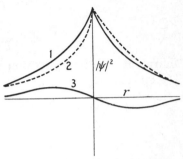

Fig. 27. Charge density in an atom. (1) —— unperturbed; (2) .... perturbed; (3) $\psi_n^* \psi_0$.

Now a 'classical' electron bound to a fixed point with a restoring force such that it would vibrate with frequency ν would give a polarizability $e^2/4\pi^2 m\nu^2$. The real atom, therefore, behaves as though it were a collection of oscillators of frequency ν_n and strength f_n.

In Chapter X it will be shown that the quantities f_n determine the intensities of the corresponding absorption lines.

In the next section it will be shown that

$$\sum_n f_n = 1$$

for a one-electron atom, or for a series of transitions in which only one electron takes part. Thus if, as is frequently the case, one absorption line ν is much stronger than all the others, the polarizability α is given approximately by

$$\alpha \sim \frac{e^2}{4\pi^2 m\nu^2}$$

as on the classical theory.

The proof that for the hydrogen atom formulae (16) and (19) are equivalent is left to the reader.

32.3. *The f-sum rule*

We have in this section to prove that

$$\sum_n f_n = 1.$$

As a preliminary we show that

$$\int \psi_n^* \frac{\partial \psi_0}{\partial z} d\tau = \frac{m}{\hbar^2}(W_n - W_0) \int \psi_n^* z \psi_0 \, d\tau. \tag{21}$$

This may be proved in an elementary way from Schrödinger's equation. Thus

$$\nabla^2 \psi_0 + \frac{2m}{\hbar^2}(W_0 - V)\psi_0 = 0,$$

and

$$\nabla^2 \psi_n^* + \frac{2m}{\hbar^2}(W_n - V)\psi_n^* = 0.$$

Multiplying the first equation by $\psi_n^* z$, the second by $\psi_0 z$, integrating over all space and subtracting, we obtain

$$\int (\psi_n^* z \nabla^2 \psi_0 - \psi_0 z \nabla^2 \psi_n^*) \, d\tau = \frac{2m}{\hbar^2}(W_n - W_0) \int \psi_n^* z \psi_0 \, d\tau.$$

Since

$$\psi_n^* z \nabla^2 \psi_0 = \psi_n^* \nabla^2(z\psi_0) - z\psi_n^* \frac{\partial \psi_0}{\partial z},$$

we have, making use of Green's theorem, the required result (21).

It follows that

$$\sum_n f_n = -2 \sum_n \int \psi_n^* z \psi_0 \, d\tau \int \psi_n \frac{\partial \psi_0}{\partial z} d\tau,$$

and, by the argument given on p. 95, the right-hand side is

$$-2 \int \psi_0^* z \frac{\partial \psi_0}{\partial z} d\tau.$$

It follows from partial integration that this is equal to $\int \psi_0^* \psi_0 \, d\tau$ and thus to unity.

32.4. *Calculation of van der Waals force based on wave mechanics*

As already stated, the term van der Waals' force is used in this book to describe the force between two atoms or molecules which are far enough apart for the overlap between the wave functions to be neglected.

We shall calculate the attraction between two hydrogen or one-electron atoms, a and b, at a distance R from each other. The atoms are not necessarily of the same type; we denote by $u_0(r)$, $u_n(r)$ the wave functions of an electron in the normal and excited states in atom a, and by $v_0(r)$, $v_n(r)$ the wave functions for an electron in atom b. Since the overlap is neglected, it is not necessary to use antisymmetrical wave functions; we may locate electron 1 in atom a and electron 2 in atom b, and take for the zero-order wave function of the system

$$u_0(r_1)v_0(r_2).$$

The interaction energy $V(\mathbf{r}_1, \mathbf{r}_2)$ between the two atoms is then

$$V = e^2\left[\frac{1}{R} - \frac{1}{|\mathbf{r}_a - \mathbf{r}_2|} - \frac{1}{|\mathbf{r}_b - \mathbf{r}_1|} + \frac{1}{|\mathbf{r}_1 - \mathbf{r}_2|}\right],$$

where $\mathbf{r}_a$, $\mathbf{r}_b$ denote the positions of the nuclei of the two atoms.

If we use the perturbation theory of Chapter III to work out the change of the energy of the system of the two atoms due to V, the answer will obviously be zero; the integral

$$\int V(\mathbf{r}_1, \mathbf{r}_2)|u_0(r_1)|^2\, d\tau_1$$

is the electrostatic potential of an electron r_2 *outside* the unperturbed atom a. This will be zero since the unperturbed atom is spherically symmetrical. We have to carry the perturbation theory to a higher order of accuracy and calculate the energy using perturbed wave functions.

By equation (10) of Chapter III the perturbed wave function is

$$u_0(r_1)v_0(r_2) + \sideset{}{'}\sum_{n,n'} \frac{(n, n'|V|0, 0)}{W_n + W'_{n'} - W_0 - W'_0} u_n(r_1)v_{n'}(r_2). \tag{22}$$

Here W_0, W_n and W'_0, W'_n denote the energies of the normal and excited states of the two atoms and

$$(n, n'|V|0, 0) = \iint u_n^*(r_1)v_{n'}^*(r_2)V(\mathbf{r}_1, \mathbf{r}_2)u_0(r_1)v_0(r_2)\, d\tau_1\, d\tau_2.$$

This means that owing to the interaction energy either atom may be perturbed and carry a dipole; but the position of the electron in one atom depends on the position of the electron in the other. The average dipole moment of either atom is zero, although the average interaction energy of the dipoles on each is not.

If we use (22) to calculate the mean value of the interaction energy we obtain

$$\sideset{}{'}\sum_{n,n'} \frac{|(n, n'|V|0, 0)|^2}{W_n + W'_{n'} - W_0 - W'_0}.$$

To calculate $(n, n'|V|0, 0)$, we note that it simply represents the electrostatic potential energy of two electrostatic charge densities

$$eu_n^*u_0 \quad \text{and} \quad ev_n^*v_0$$

in one another's field. If these have dipole moments, the energy is, so long as R is great compared with the atomic diameter,

$$-\frac{e^2}{R^3}\{2z_{0n}z'_{0n'} + x_{0n}x'_{0n'} + y_{0n}y'_{0n'}\}.$$

z is here taken to be along the line joining the two nuclei, and

$$z_{0n} = \int u_n^* z u_0 \, d\tau, \qquad z'_{0n'} = \int v_n^* z v_0 \, d\tau.$$

It is possible to choose the states n so that only one of z_{0n}, x_{0n}, y_{0n} does not vanish for a given state. Thus the interaction energy is

$$\frac{e^4}{R^6} \sum_{n,n'} \frac{4z_{0n}^2 z'^2_{0n'} + x_{0n}^2 x'^2_{0n'} + y_{0n}^2 y'^2_{0n'}}{W_0 + W'_0 - W_n - W'_{n'}},$$

and by symmetry this can be written

$$\frac{6e^4}{R^6} \sum_{n,n'} \frac{z_{0n}^2 z'^2_{0n'}}{W_0 + W'_0 - W_n - W'_{n'}}. \tag{23}$$

As in the last section, if for each of the atoms considered one transition, of frequency ν, ν' respectively, has an 'oscillator strength' large compared with the others, the interaction energy between the two atoms may be written

$$-\tfrac{3}{2}h\left(\frac{e^2}{4\pi^2 m}\right)^2 \frac{1}{\nu\nu'(\nu+\nu')} \frac{1}{R^6}. \tag{24}$$

This term, therefore, will give the interaction energy between two molecules or atoms having *strong* absorption lines of frequencies ν, ν', all other lines being weak.

The theory given here of the van der Waals attraction between molecules is due originally to F. London and R. Eisenschitz.† When the summations are carried out it is found that the van der Waals interaction energy between two hydrogen atoms is

$$-6\cdot48\frac{e^2}{a}\left(\frac{a}{R}\right)^6 = -\frac{175}{(R/a)^6} \text{ volts}, \tag{25}$$

where a is the atomic unit of length ($0\cdot53$ A).

The same result has been arrived at by Lennard-Jones‡ by the use of his generalized form of the Schrödinger perturbation theory. Denoting the two electrons by 1 and 2 and their distances from one nucleus by r and those from the other by p, the Hamiltonian of the perturbation term is

$$H_1 = -e^2\left(\frac{1}{p_1} + \frac{1}{r_2} - \frac{1}{r_{12}} - \frac{1}{R}\right). \tag{26}$$

If the distance between the two nuclei, R, is large and it is assumed that the electrons are never very far from their respective nuclei so

† F. London and R. Eisenschitz, *Zeits. f. Physik*, **60**, 491 (1930). See also the account given by H. Bethe, *Handb. d. Physik*, **241**/1, 547 (1933).

‡ J. E. Lennard-Jones, *Proc. Roy. Soc.* A, **129**, 598 (1929). (§ 18.4 above.)

that r_1, p_2 are small in comparison with r_2, p_1, and R, then by expanding the expression (26) for H_1 in the form

$$H_1 = -\frac{e^2 r_1 p_2}{R^3}\{3\cos(\mathbf{r}_1, \mathbf{R})\cos(\mathbf{p}_2, \mathbf{R}) - \cos(\mathbf{r}_1, \mathbf{p}_2)\} + O\left(\frac{1}{R^4}\right),$$

and applying his perturbation theory Lennard-Jones derived the formula (25).

Although the calculation of the long-range forces between hydrogen atoms is of great theoretical interest it is of little practical importance. The practically important case of helium atoms has been considered by Baber and Hassé[†] by a method involving various refinements of the London–Eisenschitz method. Calculations on the van der Waals interaction between heavier atoms have been performed[‡] and are found to lead to results in reasonably close agreement with the experimental observations.

The calculation of the van der Waals force between two hydrogen molecules has been carried out by Massey and Buckingham[§] using a variational method. Particular interest is attached to this calculation because of the fact that the hydrogen molecule being axially symmetrical possesses a permanent quadripole electric moment. Part of the force between two hydrogen molecules is therefore made up of the static interaction between these quadripole moments. It is found that the interaction energy in this case is

$$V = \frac{G(\alpha, \beta, \theta)}{R^5} - \frac{F(\alpha, \beta, \theta)}{R^6}, \qquad (27)$$

where the angles α, β, θ determine the fixed orientations of the two symmetric diatomic molecules. Of the two terms the second is the dynamical dipole-dipole interaction of the type which gives rise to the van der Waals force between two hydrogen atoms in s-states, and the first the quadripole interaction referred to above. It is found that whereas the average of F over all orientations is finite, that of G vanishes, so that the static force is not of predominant importance in gas-kinetic phenomena.

The interaction of the dipole system of one atom with the quadripole system of another has been considered by various authors.[||] It is found

† T. D. H. Baber and H. R. Hassé, *Proc. Camb. Phil. Soc.* **33**, 253 (1937).

‡ J. G. Kirkwood, *Phys. Zeits.* **33**, 57 (1932); H. Hellmann, *Acta Physicochim. USSR.* **2**, 273 (1935); R. A. Buckingham, *Proc. Roy. Soc.* A, **160**, 94 (1937).

§ H. S. W. Massey and R. A. Buckingham, *Proc. Roy. Irish Acad.* **45**, 31 (1938).

|| H. Margenau, *Phys. Rev.* **38**, 747 (1931); R. A. Buckingham, loc. cit.; J. E. Mayer, *J. Chem. Phys.* **1**, 270 (1933).

that this interaction gives rise to a term proportional to r^{-8} which is appreciable for moderate distances; for instance, Mayer calculates that the dipole-quadripole interaction amounts to 20 per cent. of the dipole-dipole interaction in the energy of certain crystals (NaCl, KCl, KI).

32.5. *The calculation of the van der Waals constants from observed polarizabilities*

In the investigations of Kirkwood, Hellmann, and Buckingham, cited above, on the van der Waals interaction between heavy atoms, a great deal of attention was devoted to attempts to relate the constant c of the van der Waals energy $(-c/r^6)$ to the coefficient of polarizability. The previous calculations were improved by Buckingham,† who made use of wave functions calculated by the method of self-consistent fields, and included the effect of electron exchange.

For an atom with N electrons in a single shell, Buckingham found that the polarizability of the atom can be written in the form

$$\alpha = \frac{4}{9N}(\overline{R^2})^2 a^3, \tag{28}$$

where a is the radius of the first Bohr orbit and $\overline{R^2}$ is a certain mean of the square of the radius of the outer orbits measured in atomic units. Introducing a mean radius of the outer orbits in centimetres by means of the equation

$$\sigma^2 = \overline{R}^2 a^2/N,$$

we can write equation (28) in the form

$$\alpha = \frac{4}{9}\frac{N\sigma^4}{a}. \tag{29}$$

The constant, c, of the van der Waals field between two unequal atoms (N_1 and N_2) is found by Buckingham to be related to the σ, thus defined, by the equation

$$c = \frac{4}{9}\left(\frac{N_1 N_2 e^2}{a}\right)\frac{\sigma_1^4 \sigma_2^4}{\sigma_1^2 + \sigma_2^2}, \tag{30}$$

or, in terms of polarizabilities

$$c = \tfrac{3}{2}a^{\frac12}e^2\frac{\alpha_1 \alpha_2}{\sqrt{(\alpha_1/N_1)} + \sqrt{(\alpha_2/N_2)}}. \tag{31}$$

The formula (31) is readily generalized in the case in which there are several shells each with a characteristic size and polarizability of the

† R. A. Buckingham, loc. cit.

(n_1, l_1) sub-group of electrons in the atom 1 by $\alpha(n_1, l_1)$ and the number of atoms in it by $\nu(n_1, l_1)$, then formula (31) is replaced by

$$c = \tfrac{3}{2}a^{\frac{1}{2}}e^2 \sum \frac{\alpha(n_1, l_1)\alpha(n_2, l_2)}{\sqrt{\{\alpha(n_1, l_1)/\nu(n_1, l_1)\}} + \sqrt{\{\alpha(n_2, l_2)/\nu(n_2, l_2)\}}}, \tag{32}$$

where the summation extends over all pairs of sub-groups.

By means of this formula the van der Waals force constants can be calculated from observed polarizabilities. A series of values of c was calculated by Buckingham and is shown in Table 4 below.

TABLE 4

Interaction	c $(10^{-60} ergs\, cm.^6)$	Interaction	c $(10^{-60} ergs\, cm.^6)$	Interaction	c $(10^{-60} ergs\, cm.^6)$
He—He	1·63	A—A	63·5	Na$^+$—Na$^+$	3·70
He—Ne	3·48	A—Kr	92·7	Na$^+$—K$^+$	10·4
He—A	9·89	A—Xe	135·5	Na$^+$—Rb$^+$	15·1
He—Kr	14·4	..	..	Na$^+$—Cs$^+$	21·6
He—Xe	20·7	Xe—Xe	293	..	..
..	..	..	..	K$^+$—K$^+$	33·3
Ne—Ne	7·48	Li$^+$—Li$^+$	0·097	K$^+$—Rb$^+$	48·4
Ne—A	20·5	Li$^+$—Na$^+$	0·584	K$^+$—Cs$^+$	71·3
Ne—Kr	30·0	Li$^+$—K$^+$	1·51	..	..
Ne—Xe	42·6	Li$^+$—Rb$^+$	2·21	Rb$^+$—Rb$^+$	70·5
..	..	Li$^+$—Cs$^+$	3·14	Rb$^+$—Cs$^+$	104
Kr—Kr	136	..	..	..	..
Kr—Xe	199	..	..	Cs$^+$—Cs$^+$	155

33. Overlap forces

In the last sections we have considered the van der Waals forces between atoms, which arise when the overlap between the wave functions is negligible. All other forces that occur between neutral atoms may be classed 'overlap forces' and arise only when the wave function of one atom overlaps that of the other. Among overlap forces can be included:

(a) The valence forces of chemistry.

(b) The forces of repulsion which always set in when atoms or ions with a closed shell configuration approach closely.

Both types of force may be calculated by the same methods; two methods, in particular, are available. These are:

(i) The method of London–Heitler.

(ii) The method of molecular orbitals.

Neither method will, of course, give an exact answer, but both can be treated as approximate methods from which a start can be made to build up more accurate wave functions.

In either method, the Hamiltonian H of the electrons in the molecule must first be written down; an approximate wave-function Ψ must then be found, and the energy of the molecule calculated from the formula

$$W = \int \Psi^* H \Psi \, d\tau. \tag{33}$$

The methods differ in the form taken by the approximate wave functions.

The difference can be seen most simply in the case of a diatomic molecule, and the hydrogen molecule H_2 will be considered first. In the method of Heitler and London wave functions are set up for an electron in one atom in the absence of the other atom. Thus in hydrogen let $\psi_a(\mathbf{r})$ denote the wave function for an electron in one of the atoms of the molecule in the absence of the other, and $\psi_b(\mathbf{r})$ the wave function of an electron in the other. In the original paper by Heitler and London[†] on the hydrogen molecule H_2, ψ_a and ψ_b were taken to be wave functions for electrons in the ground states; thus if the two nuclei are located at points R_a, R_b and r_a denotes the vector $r - R_a$ and r_b the vector $r - R_b$, then

$$\psi_a(\mathbf{r}) = ce^{-r_a/a_H}, \qquad \psi_b(\mathbf{r}) = ce^{-r_b/a_H},$$

where c is the normalizing constant. In other cases, in particular in considering the carbon bonds, the wave functions will not necessarily refer to the normal state, since a lower value of W, and hence a better approximation, can be obtained otherwise.

We then set up our approximate wave-function Ψ; it must have the required antisymmetry in the coordinates of the two electrons, and will thus have one of the two forms (according to the arguments of Chap. V)

$$\Psi = A[\psi_a(\mathbf{r}_1)\psi_b(\mathbf{r}_2) + \psi_a(\mathbf{r}_2)\psi_b(\mathbf{r}_1)]\chi_A(s_1, s_2), \tag{34a}$$

$$\Psi = B[\psi_a(\mathbf{r}_1)\psi_b(\mathbf{r}_2) - \psi_a(\mathbf{r}_2)\psi_b(\mathbf{r}_1)]\chi_s(s_1, s_2). \tag{34b}$$

Here $\chi_A(s_1, s_2)$ is an antisymmetrical wave function in the coordinates of the two spins, giving therefore a singlet for each set of orbital wave-functions ψ_a, ψ_b when the energy W is calculated from (33); $\chi_s(s_1, s_2)$ is symmetrical and gives a triplet series of terms. A, B are normalizing factors.

If the energy W of the molecule is now calculated according to (33) using the wave functions (34a), (34b) respectively, we find

$$W = A^2\{Q + J\} \quad \text{in case (34a)}$$
$$= B^2\{Q - J\} \quad \text{in case (34b)},$$

† W. Heitler and F. London, *Zeits. f. Physik*, **44**, 455 (1927).

where $$Q = \int\!\!\int \psi_a(\mathbf{r}_1)\psi_b(\mathbf{r}_2)H\psi_a(\mathbf{r}_1)\psi_b(\mathbf{r}_2)\, d\tau_1\, d\tau_2$$

and $$J = \int\!\!\int \psi_a(\mathbf{r}_1)\psi_b(\mathbf{r}_2)H\psi_a(\mathbf{r}_2)\psi_b(\mathbf{r}_1)\, d\tau_1\, d\tau_2.$$

The integral J is called the 'exchange integral'; for hydrogen it is negative, and varies with distance more rapidly than Q. It thus leads to attraction and to the formation of a stable molecule for the singlet state ($34\,a$) but not for the triplet states ($34\,b$).

In the method of molecular orbitals,† one starts with wave functions for the individual electron in which each electron is supposed to be shared equally between the two atoms. Wave functions can thus be set up
$$\psi_\alpha(\mathbf{r}) = \psi_a(\mathbf{r}) + \psi_b(\mathbf{r}) \tag{35}$$
or
$$\psi_\beta(\mathbf{r}) = \psi_a(\mathbf{r}) - \psi_b(\mathbf{r}), \tag{36}$$
where ψ_a and ψ_b are as defined above. Alternatively wave functions may be obtained which are a better approximation to the problem of an electron moving in some sort of self-consistent field for the whole molecule. One then builds up the molecule, putting not more than two electrons into each state corresponding to the wave-functions ψ_α, ψ_β, etc.

The method of molecular orbitals is in general very suitable for handling the excited states of molecules and for the discussion of complex molecules; for the discussion of metals it is at present the only practicable method, the London–Heitler approximation proving too difficult for the mathematical methods now available (cf. Chap. VIII). It is probably not so suitable as the starting-point of detailed numerical work.

The reason for this may be seen by setting up the wave functions for the lowest singlet and triplet states in hydrogen; these are, using the method of orbitals,
$$\psi_\alpha(\mathbf{r}_1)\psi_\alpha(\mathbf{r}_2)\chi_A(s_1, s_2) \tag{37}$$
and
$$[\psi_\alpha(\mathbf{r}_1)\psi_\beta(\mathbf{r}_2) - \psi_\alpha(\mathbf{r}_2)\psi_\beta(\mathbf{r}_1)]\chi_S(s_1, s_2). \tag{38}$$
The product $\psi_\alpha(\mathbf{r}_1)\psi_\alpha(\mathbf{r}_2)$ may be written
$$\psi_a(\mathbf{r}_1)\psi_a(\mathbf{r}_2) + \psi_b(\mathbf{r}_1)\psi_b(\mathbf{r}_2) + \psi_a(\mathbf{r}_1)\psi_b(\mathbf{r}_2) + \psi_a(\mathbf{r}_2)\psi_b(\mathbf{r}_1).$$
This differs from the wave function ($34\,a$) in including the terms $\psi_a(\mathbf{r}_1)\psi_a(\mathbf{r}_2)$, $\psi_b(\mathbf{r}_1)\psi_b(\mathbf{r}_2)$ which represent both electrons in the same atom. The method of molecular orbitals thus allows electrons with

† The name is due to J. E. Lennard-Jones (*Trans. Faraday Soc.* **25**, 668 (1929)); he and F. Hund (*Zeits. f. Physik*, **51**, 759 (1928), ibid. **63**, 719 (1930)) first introduced it. It has been extensively developed by R. A. Milliken (*Rev. Mod. Phys.* **4**, 19 (1932)) and by Coulson (refs. pp. 189, 192).

opposite spins to come into the same atom, and when the energy is calculated a large term will arise from the interaction between them. This term is certainly greatly over-estimated in the orbital method; the best approximation to the wave function would be of the type

$$k\{\psi_a(\mathbf{r}_1)\psi_a(\mathbf{r}_2)+\psi_b(\mathbf{r}_1)\psi_b(\mathbf{r}_2)\}+\psi_a(\mathbf{r}_1)\psi_b(\mathbf{r}_2)+\psi_a(\mathbf{r}_2)\psi_b(\mathbf{r}_1), \qquad (38\,a)$$

with k between zero and unity.

On the other hand, the wave function (38) for the triplet states reduces exactly to the same form as in the London–Heitler approximation (34 b). In the orbital model, then, the symmetry of the wave function prevents two electrons with the same spin from coming into the same atom.

33.1. *Detailed discussion of the hydrogen molecule by the London–Heitler method*†

In this section a discussion is given of the hydrogen molecule in its lowest electronic state treated according to the approximation of Heitler and London. The discussion of the last paragraph shows that in its lowest state the spins of the two electrons have a symmetrical wave function and must therefore be antiparallel, that the ground state is therefore a singlet (spin moment zero), and that the energy of the molecule is given by formula (33). In this section we have, therefore, only to set down the Hamiltonian and work out the normalizing factors A, B and the integrals Q, J.

The normalizing factor will be discussed first. The wave functions $\psi_a(r)$, $\psi_b(r)$ will be taken as normalized to unity. Then it is easily seen that

$$A^2 = 1/(2+2\Delta^2), \quad B^2 = 1/(2-2\Delta^2),$$

where

$$\Delta = \int \psi_a(r)\psi_b(r)\,d\tau. \qquad (39)$$

We have thus to calculate Q, J, and Δ.

The Hamiltonian for the system is

$$-\frac{\hbar^2}{2m}(\nabla_1^2+\nabla_2^2) - \frac{e^2}{r_{a1}} - \frac{e^2}{r_{b1}} - \frac{e^2}{r_{a2}} - \frac{e^2}{r_{b2}} + \frac{e^2}{r_{12}} + \frac{e^2}{R_{ab}}. \qquad (40)$$

Here r_{a1} denotes the distance between the nucleus a and the electron with coordinate r_1; r_{12} is the distance between the two electrons, and R_{ab} the distance between the nuclei. The term in e^2/R_{ab} ensures that W will give the total energy of the molecule, including the repulsion between the nuclei.

† For further details see, for example, *Handbuch der Physik*, vol. **24**/1, 535 (1933); Pauling and Wilson, *Introduction to Quantum Mechanics*, p. 340 (Cambridge, Mass., 1935).

The simplest form to take for the wave-functions $\psi_a(r)$, $\psi_b(r)$ is that of the unperturbed hydrogen atom; this was the course adopted in the original paper of London and Heitler. With these wave functions the integral can be evaluated to give for the energies W_S, W_A of the symmetrical and antisymmetrical states

$$W_S = 2W_H + \frac{e^2}{R_{ab}} + \frac{W_{11}+W_{12}}{1+\Delta^2}, \quad (41)$$

$$W_A = 2W_H + \frac{e^2}{R_{ab}} + \frac{W_{11}-W_{12}}{1-\Delta^2}, \quad (42)$$

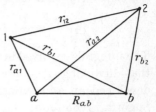

FIG. 28. Coordinates used for the hydrogen molecule.

where W_H is the energy $(-me^4/2\hbar^2)$ of the ground state of the hydrogen atom, Δ is defined by equation (39) and hence is

$$\Delta = \frac{1}{\pi a^3} \int e^{-(r_{a1}+r_{b1})/a}\, d\tau_1, \quad (43)$$

and W_{11} and W_{12} denote the integrals

$$W_{11} = e^2 \int\int \psi^2(r_{a1})\psi^2(r_{b2})\left(\frac{1}{r_{12}} - \frac{1}{r_{a2}} - \frac{1}{r_{b1}}\right) d\tau_1 d\tau_2$$

$$= \frac{e^2}{\pi a^3} \int\int e^{-2(r_{a1}+r_{b2})/a}\left(\frac{1}{r_{12}} - \frac{1}{r_{a2}} - \frac{1}{r_{b1}}\right) d\tau_1 d\tau_2, \quad (44)$$

$$W_{12} = \tfrac{1}{2}e^2 \int\int \psi(r_{a1})\psi(r_{a2})\psi(r_{b1})\psi(r_{b2})\left\{\frac{2}{r_{12}} - \frac{1}{r_{a1}} - \frac{1}{r_{a2}} - \frac{1}{r_{b1}} - \frac{1}{r_{b2}}\right\} d\tau_1 d\tau_2$$

$$= \frac{e^2}{2\pi a^3} \int\int e^{-(r_{a1}+r_{a2}+r_{b1}+r_{b2})/a}\left\{\frac{2}{r_{12}} - \frac{1}{r_{a1}} - \frac{1}{r_{a2}} - \frac{1}{r_{b1}} - \frac{1}{r_{b2}}\right\} d\tau_1 d\tau_2. \quad (45)$$

The problem is thus reduced to the evaluation of the integrals Δ, W_{11}, W_{12}.

To evaluate the integral Δ we introduce confocal elliptic coordinates ξ, η defined by the relations

$$\xi = \frac{r_a+r_b}{R_{ab}}, \qquad \eta = \frac{r_a-r_b}{R_{ab}} \quad (46)$$

and the azimuthal angle ϕ. The variables ξ, η so defined lie in the ranges $1 \leqslant \xi \leqslant \infty$, $-1 \leqslant \eta \leqslant 1$ and the volume element becomes

$$d\tau = \tfrac{1}{8}R_{ab}^3(\xi^2-\eta^2)\, d\xi d\eta d\phi. \quad (47)$$

Substituting from equations (46) and (47) into (43) we obtain

$$\Delta = \frac{R_{ab}^3}{4a^3} \int_1^\infty e^{-R_{ab}\xi/a}\, d\xi \int_{-1}^1 (\xi^2-\eta^2)\, d\eta = \left(1 + \frac{R_{ab}}{a} + \frac{R_{ab}^2}{3a^2}\right)e^{-R_{ab}/a}. \quad (48)$$

In the expression (44) for the integral W_{11} the first term may be evaluated by the use of the elliptic coordinates ξ and η, the second and third directly. The final result is

$$W_{11} = -\frac{e^2}{R_{ab}} + \frac{e^2}{a}e^{-2R_{ab}/a}\left\{\frac{a}{R_{ab}} + \frac{5}{8} - \frac{3}{4}\frac{R_{ab}}{a} - \frac{1}{6}\frac{R_{ab}^2}{a^2}\right\}. \quad (49)$$

The integrals involved in the evaluation of W_{12} are cumbersome; indeed, that involving $1/r_{12}$ presents some difficulty. Heitler and London developed an approximation for W_{12}; its value was later derived by Sugiura,† who found the expression

$$W_{12} = -\frac{e^2}{a}e^{-2R_{ab}/a}\left\{\frac{21}{8} + \frac{103}{20}\frac{R_{ab}}{a} + \frac{59}{15}\frac{R_{ab}^2}{a^2} + \frac{11}{15}\frac{R_{ab}^3}{a^3}\right\} +$$

$$+ \frac{6e^2}{5R_{ab}}\left\{\Delta^2\left(\gamma + \log\frac{R_{ab}}{a}\right) + \Delta'^2\mathrm{Ei}\left(-\frac{4R_{ab}}{a}\right) - 2\Delta\Delta'\mathrm{Ei}\left(-\frac{2R_{ab}}{a}\right)\right\}, \quad (50)$$

where Δ is given by equation (48), Δ' by the equation

$$\Delta' = \left(1 - \frac{R_{ab}}{a} + \frac{R_{ab}^2}{3a^2}\right)e^{R_{ab}/a},$$

γ is Euler's constant, and Ei denotes the integral logarithm

$$\mathrm{Ei}(Z) = \int_{-\infty}^{Z}\frac{e^t}{t}\,dt \quad (Z < 0).$$

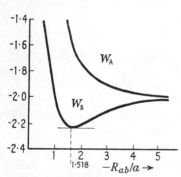

FIG. 29. Energies of the symmetrical and antisymmetrical states of H_2 as a function of the distance between the atoms.

Substituting from equations (48), (49), and (50) into equations (41) and (42) we obtain expressions for the energies W_S and W_A as functions of R_{ab}. The variation of these functions with R_{ab} is shown in Fig. 29; the function W_A decreases monotonically while W_S has a minimum at $R_{ab}/a = 1.518$. W_A corresponds then to repulsion at all distances so that a stable molecule is not formed.

On the other hand, W_S corresponds to the attraction of the two hydrogen atoms with the formation of a stable molecule. The equilibrium value of the relative position of the nuclei is given by $$R_{ab} = 1.518a = 0.80 \text{ A},$$

which is in excess of the known experimental value 0.7395 A. The corresponding theoretical value of the heat of dissociation is 3.14 eV

† Y. Sugiura, *Zeits. f. Physik*, **45**, 484 (1927).

in contrast to the observed value 4·48 eV. The vibrational frequency of the nuclei, determined from the curvature of the function W_S in the neighbourhood of its minimum, comes out as 4,800 cm.$^{-1}$; the value obtained from observations of band spectra is 4,405·3 cm.$^{-1}$

33.2. *Improvements in the approximation of London and Heitler*

A simple improvement is to use for $\psi_a(r)$, $\psi_b(r)$ not the wave functions for an electron in an unperturbed hydrogen atom but the wave functions for an electron moving in the field of a charge z, which will then be chosen to minimize the energy for each value of R_{ab}. This was first done by Wang,† who found a value of z, at the interatomic spacing giving minimum energy, given by $z = 1·166$.

The addition to the London–Heitler wave functions of polar wave functions corresponding to electron configurations H^+H^- and H^-H^+ has also been considered by Weinbaum.‡ Weinbaum takes a wave function of the type (38 a) discussed above, with $\psi(r)$ as before the $1s$ wave function for an electron moving in a charge ze. He finds $z = 1·193$ and $k = 0·256$ for the values of the parameters giving minimum energy. The fact that k is less than $\frac{1}{2}$ shows that the London–Heitler is a better approximation than that of molecular orbitals, which gives $k = 1$, for the hydrogen molecule.

Other improvements in the wave functions are:

(a) That of Rosen,§ who takes for $\psi(r)$ a mixture of s and p functions of the type
$$\psi_{1s}(r) + \sigma\psi_{2p}(\mathbf{r}).$$
He finds $\sigma = 0·10$.

(b) Further work by Weinbaum (loc. cit.), who combines this refinement with that of polar states. He finds
$$z' = 1·19, \qquad \sigma = 0·07, \qquad k = 0·176.$$

TABLE 5

	Heat of dissociation (eV.)	R_{ab} (A)	Vibrational frequency (cm.$^{-1}$)
Heitler–London	3·14	0·80	4800
Wang.	3·76	0·76	4900
Weinbaum (ionic terms) . . .	4·00	0·77	4750
Rosen (addition of p terms) . .	4·02	0·77	4260
Weinbaum (ionic terms and p terms) .	4·10	. .	. .
James and Coolidge	4·722	0·74	. .
Experiment	4·477	0·7395	4405·3

† S. C. Wang, *Phys. Rev.* **31**, 579 (1928).
‡ S. Weinbaum, *J. Chem. Phys.* **1**, 593 (1933).
§ N. Rosen, *Phys. Rev.* **38**, 2099 (1931).

(c) A much more complicated wave function set up by James and Coolidge,† in which terms in r_{12} are included.

The results of these calculations are given in Table 5.‡

For further details the reader is referred to the original papers, or the accounts by Pauling and Wilson (loc. cit.).

33.3. Some other applications of the London–Heitler method

Repulsive forces between atoms and ions with the closed shell configuration. Only for helium and neon have detailed calculations of the interaction energy between two atoms with the closed shell configuration been made. The overlap energy is found to be repulsive at all distances. The reason for this may be seen qualitatively as follows: each electron in one helium atom will interact with two electrons in the other, one of which has spin parallel to its own and one which has spin antiparallel. As regards the interaction between the electrons with parallel spins, we know that the spin wave function must be symmetrical and the orbital function therefore antisymmetrical. The contribution to the energy of the molecule is thus of the form

$$Q+J.$$

As regards the interaction between electrons with antiparallel spins, the spin wave function is as likely to be symmetrical as antisymmetrical, and the contribution to the energy of the molecule is thus of the form

$$\tfrac{1}{2}(Q+J)+\tfrac{1}{2}(Q-J)=Q.$$

The total energy of the pair of interacting atoms is thus

$$2Q+J.$$

The exchange integral J being negative, repulsion between the molecules results at all distances.

Detailed computations of the interaction between two helium atoms along these lines have been made by Gentile§ and Slater.‖ Slater obtains a complicated expression for the interaction energy that can be approximated closely by

$$7{\cdot}7\times10^{-10}e^{-2{\cdot}43R/a_0}, \qquad a_0=\frac{\hbar^2}{me^2}=0{\cdot}529\text{ A}.$$

This expression, added to a term giving van der Waals' attraction, has

---

† H. M. James and A. S. Coolidge, *J. Chem. Phys.* **1**, 825 (1933).
‡ From Pauling and Wilson, *The Structure of Band Spectra*.
§ G. Gentile, *Zeits. f. Physik*, **63**, 795 (1930).
‖ J. C. Slater, *Phys. Rev.* **32**, 349 (1928).

been extensively used for the calculation of the equation of state of helium gas.† An expression for the complete interaction energy given by Slater and Kirkwood is

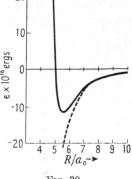

$$\left\{7 \cdot 7 e^{-2 \cdot 43 R/a_0} - \frac{0 \cdot 68}{(R/a_0)^6}\right\} 10^{-10} \text{ ergs.}$$

This curve gives a shallow minimum of depth 10^{-15} ergs (6×10^{-4} eV) at $R \simeq 2 \cdot 9$ A. It is not certain whether the 'potential hole' is deep and wide enough to permit the formation of a stable molecule.

Computations have also been carried out for neon‡ using the same method. For the repulsive potential is found

$$1 \cdot 18 \times 10^4 \, e^{-R/0 \cdot 395} \text{ eV,}$$

where R is the distance between the atoms in atomic units.

Fig. 30.

33.4. *The hydrogen molecule by the method of molecular orbitals*

The elements of the method of molecular orbitals have been discussed above; the wave functions of the individual electrons are taken to be the solutions of some Schrödinger equation

$$\nabla^2 \psi_\alpha + \frac{2m}{\hbar^2} (W - V) \psi_\alpha = 0,$$

where V is some field which is the same for all the electrons. The essential points about the approximation are thus:

(a) that each electron is thought of as being shared between all the atoms of the molecule, its position being uncorrelated with the positions of the others (at any rate those of opposite spin);

(b) the wave functions for the individual electrons are orthogonal to each other.

To illustrate the method we shall consider the ground state of the hydrogen molecule.§ Suppose we denote by $\phi(1)$ the molecular orbit for electron 1 in the field of the two nuclei A and B, then in the molecular orbital treatment we write for the wave function of the hydrogen molecule

$$\psi = \phi(1)\phi(2)\chi_A(s_1, s_2), \tag{51}$$

---

† Cf. W. H. Keesom, *Helium* (Amsterdam, 1942); J. de Boer and A. Michels, *Physica*, **6**, 409 (1939); H. S. W. Massey and R. A. Buckingham, *Proc. Roy. Soc.* A **168**, 378 (1938); E. Beth and G. E. Uhlenbeck, *Physica*, **4**, 915 (1937); J. C. Slater and J. G. Kirkwood, *Phys. Rev.* **37**, 682 (1931).

‡ W. E. Bleick and J. Mayer, *J. Chem. Phys.* **2**, 252 (1934).

§ C. A. Coulson, *Trans. Faraday Soc.* **33**, 1479 (1937).

where $\chi_A(s_1, s_2)$ denotes the spin wave function which is usually omitted since it makes no further contribution either to the wave function or to the energy. The figures 1 and 2 stand for $\mathbf{r}_1$ and $\mathbf{r}_2$.

The molecular orbital method therefore depends on the solution of the wave equation for a single electron moving in the field of two fixed protons. The solution of the problem of the hydrogen molecular ion (H_2^+) is thus fundamental to the discussion of molecular structure by the method of molecular orbitals and must be investigated first.

The Hamiltonian of the system may be written

$$H = -\frac{\hbar^2}{2m}\nabla^2 - \frac{e^2}{r_a} - \frac{e^2}{r_b} + \frac{e^2}{R_{ab}}.$$

To solve the Schrödinger equation

$$H\phi = W\phi \tag{52}$$

we transform to the elliptic coordinates ξ, η, by equations (46) with azimuthal angle χ. In these coordinates

$$\frac{1}{r_a} + \frac{1}{r_b} = \frac{4}{R_{ab}}\frac{\xi}{\xi^2 - \eta^2}.$$

Introducing the radius a_0 of the lowest orbit of the Bohr atom $(a_0 = \hbar^2/me^2)$, transforming the Laplacian to these coordinates, and writing

$$W = \frac{e^2}{R_{ab}}(1+w),$$

we find that equation (52) reduces to

$$\frac{\partial}{\partial\xi}\left\{(\xi^2-1)\frac{\partial\phi}{\partial\xi}\right\} + \frac{\partial}{\partial\eta}\left\{(1-\eta^2)\frac{\partial\phi}{\partial\eta}\right\} + \left\{\frac{1}{\xi^2-1} + \frac{1}{1-\eta^2}\right\}\frac{\partial^2\phi}{\partial\chi^2} +$$

$$+ 2\left(\frac{R_{ab}}{a_0}\right)\{\tfrac{1}{4}w(\xi^2-\eta^2)+\xi\}\phi = 0.$$

This equation is separable; writing

$$\phi = X(\xi)Y(\eta)\Phi(\chi),$$

we find that the functions X, Y, and Φ satisfy the ordinary differential equations

$$\frac{d^2\Phi}{d\chi^2} + \lambda^2\Phi = 0$$

$$\frac{d}{d\xi}\left\{(\xi^2-1)\frac{dX}{d\xi}\right\} - \left\{\frac{\lambda^2}{\xi^2-1} - f(\xi)\right\}X = 0$$

$$\frac{d}{d\eta}\left\{(1-\eta^2)\frac{dY}{d\eta}\right\} - \left\{\frac{\lambda^2}{1-\eta^2} + g(\eta)\right\}Y = 0,$$

where λ, μ are constants introduced when the equations are separated and the functions f, g are defined by

$$f(\xi) = \frac{2R_{ab}}{a_0}(\tfrac{1}{4}w\xi^2+\xi)+\mu, \qquad g(\eta) = \frac{R_{ab}w}{2a_0}\eta^2+\mu.$$

In the lowest possible electronic state $\lambda = 0$, so that writing

$$F = -\frac{1}{X}\frac{dX}{d\xi}, \qquad G = -\frac{1}{Y}\frac{dY}{d\eta}, \tag{53}$$

we have

$$\frac{dF}{d\xi} = F^2+\frac{f(\xi)-2\xi F}{\xi^2-1}, \qquad \frac{dG}{d\eta} = G^2-\frac{g(\eta)+2\eta G}{\eta^2-1}. \tag{54}$$

The equations (54) have been integrated numerically by Burrau.† The range of the variables is $1 \leqslant \xi \leqslant \infty$, $-1 \leqslant \eta \leqslant +1$; by assigning a value to the ratio R_{ab}/a_0 the solution of the equations can be expanded in a power series for $0 \leqslant \eta \leqslant \tfrac{1}{2}$ and in another series for $\tfrac{1}{2} \leqslant \eta \leqslant 1$. The two series have the same sum at $\eta = \tfrac{1}{2}$ only if w has a certain value. In this way w (and hence W) is determined for each value of the internuclear distance R_{ab}; the results obtained by Burrau are shown in the table below. The accuracy of Burrau's calculations

R_{ab}/a_0	0	1·0	1·3	1·6	1·8	2·0	2·2	2·4	2·95	∞
a_0W/e^2	+00	−0·896	−1·110	−1·186	−1·198	−1·204	−1·200	−1·192	−1·158	−1·000

has been improved upon by Hylleraas‡ who assumed a solution of the form

$$Y(\eta) = \sum_{n=|\lambda|}^{\infty} c_n P_n^{|\lambda|}(\eta),$$

and also by Steensholt.§ These treatments correct Burrau's values by very small amounts; all three give $R_{ab} = 2\cdot00a_0$ for the equilibrium value. This corresponds to a value $R_{ab} = 1\cdot06$ A in agreement with Richardson's spectroscopic estimate‖ of the distance between the protons in the ion.

A method such as that of Hylleraas is necessary to obtain accurate forms for the wave function ϕ for the H_2^+ problem; it is found, however, that by taking ϕ to be a linear combination of atomic orbitals it is possible to construct a wave function which is sufficiently accurate for molecular calculations. If ψ_a, ψ_b denote the wave functions of the electron treated in atoms A and B, supposed normalized to unity, then one may take

$$\phi = A\psi_a(r_a)+B\psi_b(r_b).$$

† O. Burrau, *Kgl. Danske Vid. Selskab.* **7**, 14 (1927).
‡ E. A. Hylleraas, *Zeits. f. Physik*, **71**, 739 (1931).
§ G. Steensholt, ibid. **100**, 547 (1936); *Norske Vid.-Akad. Avh.* No. 4, 1936.
‖ O. W. Richardson, *Trans. Faraday Soc.* **25**, 686 (1929).

The constants A and B are found by minimizing the energy

$$W = \int \phi^* H \phi \, d\tau \Big/ \int \phi^* \phi \, d\tau; \tag{55}$$

in this way we find $A = \pm B = (2 \pm 2\Delta)^{-\frac{1}{2}}$,

giving for the wave functions

$$\phi = \frac{1}{\sqrt{(2+2\Delta)}} (\psi_a + \psi_b) \tag{56}$$

and $$\phi = \frac{1}{\sqrt{(2-2\Delta)}} (\psi_a - \psi_b). \tag{57}$$

The form of these two wave functions is shown in Fig. 31.

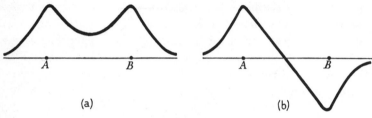

(a)   (b)

Fig. 31.

For the wave function ψ_a we shall assume the form

$$\psi(r_a) = \left(\frac{c^3}{\pi a_0^3}\right)^{\frac{1}{2}} e^{-cr_a/a_0} \tag{58}$$

differing from the wave function of the ground state of the hydrogen atom by the inclusion of a 'screening constant', c, which will be a function of the nuclear separation R_{ab}. Substituting from (58) into equation (56) and inserting in equation (55), we obtain for the energy W,

$$W = \frac{e^2}{a_0}\left(Fc^2 - Gc + \frac{a_0}{R_{ab}}\right), \tag{59}$$

where $F(\rho)$, $G(\rho)$ are known functions of the variable $\rho = cR_{ab}/a_0$; the expressions for F, G are rather cumbersome but may be evaluated in the same way as the integrals in § 33.1. For a given nuclear separation R_{ab} the best value of c is given by the equation

$$\left(\frac{\partial W}{\partial c}\right)_{R_{ab}} = 0,$$

the suffix R_{ab} denoting that R_{ab} is assumed constant during the differentiation. It follows immediately from (59) that c is a root of the equation

$$c\left(2F + c\rho \frac{dF}{d\rho}\right) = G + \rho \frac{dG}{d\rho}. \tag{60}$$

The values of c determined from this equation are shown in Fig. 32, and the corresponding curves for W as a function of R_{ab} are given in

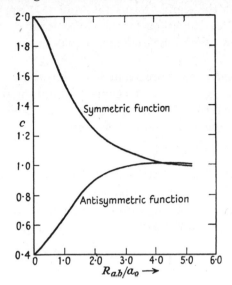

FIG. 32. Variation of c with R_{ab}/a_0.

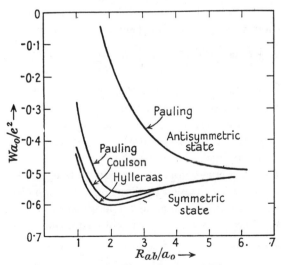

FIG. 33. Energy curves of H_2^+.

Fig. 33. Also shown on the same diagram are Pauling's curves obtained by taking $c = 1$ in equation (58) and inserting this wave function in (55) with the combinations (56) and (57), and the curves obtained by

Hylleraas and Steensholt from the accurate forms of ϕ in spheroidal coordinates.

It appears that the simple forms (56) and (57) approximate quite well to the exact wave functions for the molecular hydrogen ion derived from the solution of the Schrödinger equation in confocal elliptic coordinates.

Let us now consider the hydrogen molecule for which the Hamiltonian is (40), (cf. Fig. 28). In the molecular orbital method the wave-function ψ is of the form (51). Dropping the spin factor and substituting for $\phi(1)$ and $\phi(2)$ from equation (56) we have

$$\psi = K_1\{\psi(r_{a1})+\psi(r_{b1})\}\{\psi(r_{a2})+\psi(r_{b2})\}$$
$$= K_1\{\psi(r_{a1})\psi(r_{a2})+\psi(r_{b1})\psi(r_{a2})+\psi(r_{a1})\psi(r_{b2})+\psi(r_{b1})\psi(r_{b2})\}, \quad (61)$$

where K_1 denotes a normalization factor.

Using the wave function (61) with $\psi(r_{a1})$ defined by (58) we find that the energy can be put in the form

$$W = \frac{e^2}{a_0}\left(2Fc^2-2Gc+Jc+\frac{a_0}{R_{ab}}\right), \quad (62)$$

where F and G are the same functions of ρ as in the case of the molecular hydrogen atom, and J is another function of the same type arising from the presence of the term $1/r_{12}$ in the Hamiltonian (40). Applying the variation method as before we find that c is a root of the equation

$$2c\left(2F+\rho\frac{dF}{d\rho}\right) = \left(2G+2\rho\frac{dG}{d\rho}-J-\rho\frac{dJ}{d\rho}\right).$$

Calculating the explicit forms of F, G, J we can draw a curve of the type Fig. 34 which gives c as a function of R_{ab}/a_0. The values for the ion H_2^+ are also shown on the same scale. It will be seen from this diagram that the repulsion between the two electrons in the neutral molecule tends to diminish the value of c.

The corresponding curve for the energy (62) is shown in Fig. 35 together with the curve obtained by Coulson using the Heitler–London method with the variation principle. The constants of the hydrogen molecule obtained by these methods of approximation are shown below.

	R_{ab}/a_0	Binding energy (volts)	c
Molecular orbital . .	0·732	3·470	1·197
Heitler–London . .	0·743	3·761	1·166
Observed . . .	0·741	4·477	..

It would seem that in the simple case of the hydrogen molecule the molecular-orbital and the electron-pair treatments are almost equally good. It is found, however, that in more complicated polar molecules

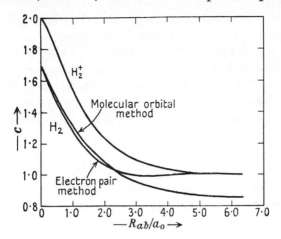

FIG. 34. c as a function of R_{ab} for H_2 and H_2^+.

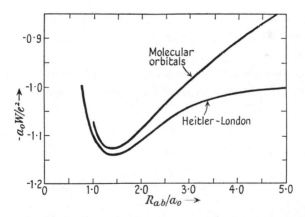

FIG. 35. H_2 molecular energy curves.

the molecular-orbital method is superior to the electron-pair (or Heitler–London) method. The method of molecular orbitals has been applied to a few molecules.†

† See, for example, C. A. Coulson, *Trans. Faraday Soc.* **33**, 388 (1937) (CH_4); *Proc. Camb. Phil. Soc.* **31**, 244 (1935) (He_3^+); *Proc. Roy. Soc.* **169**, 413 (1939) (polyenes and aromatic molecules); J. K. Knipp, *J. Chem. Physics*, **4**, 300 (1936) (LiH^+); H. M. James, *J. Chem. Physics*, **3**, 9 (1935) (Li_2^+); C. A. Coulson and G. S. Rushbrooke, *Proc. Camb. Phil. Soc.* **36**, 193 (1940) (unsaturated hydrocarbons); J. E. Lennard-Jones and C. A. Coulson, *Trans. Faraday Soc.* **35**, 811 (1939) (polynuclear hydrocarbon molecules).

34. Distribution of momentum in the hydrogen molecular ion

A great deal of theoretical work has recently been done on momentum distributions in molecules.† In addition to its intrinsic interest the determination of the momentum distribution of the electrons in a molecule is of importance since it determines

(i) the shape of the Compton line when X-rays are scattered from the molecule;‡

(ii) the distribution of the fast inelastically scattered electrons from the molecule.§

Since these quantities can now be determined experimentally with a fair degree of accuracy it is important to attempt some kind of theoretical treatment of the distribution of momentum in molecular systems. Although Coulson and Duncanson have discussed the momentum distribution in several molecules we shall confine our attention to that in the molecular hydrogen ion H_2^+.

According to transformation theory, the momentum wave function $\chi(p)$ of the molecular hydrogen ion is obtained from its space wave function $\phi(\mathbf{r})$ by means of the Fourier integral

$$\chi(\mathbf{p}) = \frac{1}{h^{\frac{3}{2}}} \int e^{-i(\mathbf{p}.\mathbf{r})/\hbar} \phi(\mathbf{r}) \, d\tau, \tag{63}$$

where for the symmetrical wave function we may assume ϕ is given by equation (56) with the ψ's given by equation (58). If we use atomic units (Chap. VI above) and denote the position vectors of the nuclei by $\mathbf{r}_a$, $\mathbf{r}_b$, then (63) assumes the form

$$\chi(\mathbf{p}) = \frac{e^{-i(\mathbf{p}.\mathbf{r}_a)} + e^{-i(\mathbf{p}.\mathbf{r}_b)}}{\sqrt{(2+2\Delta)}} A(p), \tag{64}$$

where $$A(p) = \frac{1}{(2\pi)^{\frac{3}{2}}} \int e^{-i(\mathbf{p}.\mathbf{r}-\mathbf{r}_a)} \psi(\mathbf{r}) \, d\tau = \frac{2^{\frac{3}{2}}c^{\frac{5}{2}}}{\pi(p^2+c^2)^2}. \tag{65}$$

The density function is then

$$\chi(\mathbf{p})\chi^*(\mathbf{p}) = \frac{1+\cos(\mathbf{p}.\mathbf{R}_{ab})}{1+\Delta} A(p)A^*(p). \tag{66}$$

Now the function $A(p)$ is simply the momentum distribution of the atomic orbital (58), so that the density (66) is the same as it would be

---

† B. Hicks, *Phys. Rev.* **52**, 436 (1937); C. A. Coulson, *Proc. Camb. Phil. Soc.* **37**, 55, 74 (1941); W. E. Duncanson, ibid. **37**, 397 (1941); C. A. Coulson and W. E. Duncanson, ibid. **37**, 67, 406 (1940), ibid. **38**, 100 (1942).

‡ J. W. M. Du Mond and H. A. Kirkpatrick, *Phys. Rev.* **52**, 419 (1937).

§ A. L. Hughes and M. M. Mann, ibid. **53**, 50 (1938).

if the electron were confined to one of the nuclei, except for the factor

$$\frac{1+\cos(\mathbf{p}.\mathbf{R}_{ab})}{1+\Delta},$$

which gives rise to a kind of diffraction effect and is consequently called the diffraction factor.

The density function $\chi(\mathbf{p})\chi^*(\mathbf{p})$ given by equation (66) has symmetry around the internuclear axis, so it is desirable to draw the contours of equal momentum density in a plane through this axis. The result is shown in Fig. 36, from which it will be observed that the contours

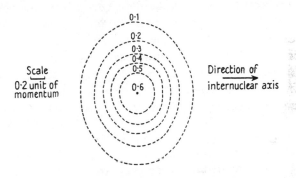

FIG. 36. Contours of constant momentum density for H_2^+.
(From Coulson, *Proc. Camb. Phil. Soc.* **37**, 62 (1941).)

are approximately ellipses with major axes perpendicular to the direction of the internuclear axis; there is thus greater probability in directions perpendicular to the bond than along it.

The probability $I_x(p_z)\,dp_x$ that the component of the momentum along the internuclear axis has a value between p_x and p_x+dp_x is determined by the equation

$$I_x(p_x) = \int_{-\infty}^{\infty}\int_{-\infty}^{\infty} \chi(\mathbf{p})\chi^*(\mathbf{p})\,dp_y\,dp_z = \frac{8c^5}{3\pi(1+\Delta)}\frac{1+\cos R_{ab}p_x}{(p_x^2+c^2)^3}. \quad (67)$$

In the case of a hydrogen atom $R_{ab}=0$, $c=1$, $\Delta=1$, so that

$$I_x(p_x) = \frac{8}{3\pi(p_x^2+1)^3}. \quad (68)$$

The variation of the functions (67) and (68) with p_x is shown graphically in Fig. 37, from which it is evident that in the molecular ion there are fewer large values of p_x than in the atom; if we calculated the probability functions $I_y(p_y)$, $I_z(p_z)$, perpendicular to the internuclear axis we should obtain precisely the opposite effect.

For the application of these principles to more complex molecules the reader is referred to the papers by Coulson and Duncanson cited above.

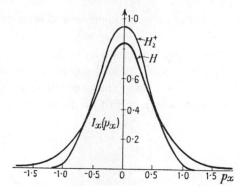

FIG. 37. Distribution of component of momentum along the internuclear axis.

35. Qualitative results for more complex molecules†

35.1. *The principle of maximum overlapping*

The mathematical difficulties encountered in the calculation of the energies of molecular orbits, other than those of H_2 and H_2^+, are so formidable that problems of molecular structure are usually discussed with the aid of a new assumption known as the *principle of maximum overlapping*. It is assumed as a first approximation that the exchange energy is due to the overlapping of the electron clouds surrounding the nuclei and that the energy of a molecular orbit is lowest (i.e. the binding energy is greatest) when the atomic orbits which it resembles overlap as much as possible.

In applying this principle we require a knowledge of the probability distribution functions for atomic orbitals. We saw in the case of the hydrogen atom that a $1s$ wave function is of the form

$$\psi(1s) = f_1(r),$$

so that the angular dependence of the wave function for an atomic orbital is of the type shown in Fig. 38 a. The angular dependence of the wave function

$$\psi(2p_x) = \frac{x}{r} f_2(r)$$

for a $2p_x$-atomic orbital is shown in Fig. 38 b. The squares of these functions give the angular dependence of the probability distribution

† See L. Pauling, *The Nature of the Chemical Bond*, chap. iii (Cornell Univ.); C. A. Coulson, *Proc. Roy. Soc. Edin.* A, **61**, 115–39 (1941–2).

functions. The $2p_y$, $2p_z$ orbitals are of the same form as the $2p_x$ one except that the axis of symmetry is Oy, Oz respectively in place of Ox. In the s-orbit the electron is practically confined within a sphere whereas an electron in a $2p$-orbit is most likely to be found around or within a region with the dumb-bell shape of Fig. 38.

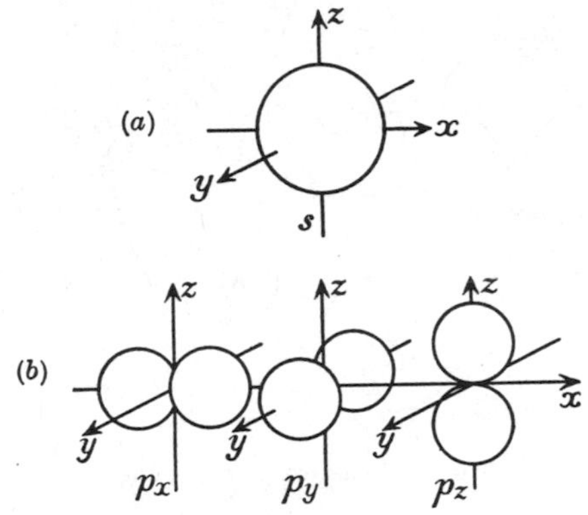

FIG. 38. Polar representation of absolute values of the angular wave function for $1s$-orbital and $2p$-orbitals.

The use of the principle of maximum overlapping is most simply illustrated with reference to the water molecule H_2O. Each hydrogen atom is in a $1s$-state. The oxygen atom has the electronic structure

$$(1s)^2(2s)^2(2p)^4,$$

the two inner K-electrons keep close to the nucleus and do not affect the binding, while those filling the $2s$ atomic orbital form a closed sub-group round the nucleus. Of the four remaining electrons two fill the $2p_z$-orbital and do not take part in the formation of molecules (since they are paired together); finally, there is one electron in the $2p_x$ orbit and one in the $2p_y$ orbit. They alone take part in molecule building. We assume further that the $2s$ and $2p$ wave functions do not mix. If this is so, then by the principle of maximum overlapping the greatest binding energy is obtained by placing one hydrogen atom along the x-axis and the other along the y-axis, as shown on the left in Fig. 39, which is taken from Coulson's paper.† We see immediately that the angle between the bonds, HOH, should be about 90°; this derivation, however, ignores the mixing of the $2p$ and the $2s$ wave functions and the repulsion between the two hydrogen atoms. These corrections have

† C. A. Coulson, loc. cit., Fig. 6.

the effect of increasing the bond angle. The observed bond angles for water-type molecules (oxygen family) are:[†]

$$H_2O \quad . \quad . \quad . \quad 105°$$
$$F_2O \quad . \quad . \quad . \quad 100°$$
$$Cl_2O \quad . \quad . \quad . \quad 115°$$
$$H_2S \quad . \quad . \quad . \quad 92°$$

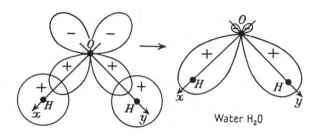

Water H_2O

FIG. 39. The water molecule.

35.2. Carbon molecules: hybridization of wave functions

In the carbon atom two of the six electrons are in K-shell orbits and take no part in chemical binding. The other four electrons are L-shell electrons whose orbits are chosen from $2s$, $2p_x$, $2p_y$, $2p_z$. The nature of the bonds that carbon forms in any particular molecule determines the way in which these four orbits are formed. In carbon, since the energy of the $2s$ is nearly equal to that of the $2p$-orbits, we may form compound, or hybrid, orbitals by taking linear combinations of the $2s$, $2p$ wave functions. Denote the latter wave functions by $\psi(2s)$, $\psi(2p_x)$, $\psi(2p_y)$, $\psi(2p_z)$ and assume they are orthogonal and normalized. From them form four new wave functions ψ_r ($r = 1, 2, 3, 4$) defined by the equations

$$\psi_r = a_r\psi(2s) + b_r\psi(2p_x) + c_r\psi(2p_y) + d_r\psi(2p_z) \tag{69}$$

($r = 1, 2, 3, 4$), where the a's, b's, c's, and d's are constant. The energy of the orbits corresponding to these wave functions is that of the nearly equal $2s$ and $2p$ states. If we denote the direction cosines of a certain direction by $\mathbf{r}_i = (l_i, m_i, n_i)$, then the wave function

$$\psi(2p_i) = l_i\psi(2p_x) + m_i\psi(2p_y) + n_i\psi(2p_z) \tag{70}$$

is of the type $\psi(2p)$ and has its maxima along the directions (l_i, m_i, n_i) and $(-l_i, -m_i, -n_i)$. With this notation we may write equations (69) in the form

$$\psi_i = a_i\psi(2s) + b_i\psi(2p_i) \tag{71}$$

[†] A. F. Wells, *Structural Inorganic Chemistry* (Oxford, 1944).

$(i = 1, 2, 3, 4)$, and note that the maxima of this function are also along the direction $\mathbf{r}_i$. For the wave functions (71) we have

$$\int \psi_i \psi_j \, d\tau = a_i a_j + b_i b_j \int \psi(2p_i)\psi(2p_j) \, d\tau$$

and

$$\int \psi(2p_i)\psi(2p_j) \, d\tau = l_i l_j + m_i m_j + n_i n_j = \cos\theta_{ij},$$

so that the orthogonality and normalization relations yield the ten equations

$$a_i a_j + b_i b_j \cos\theta_{ij} = \delta_{ij} \tag{72}$$

$(i, j = 1, 2, 3, 4)$ for the determination of the eight constants a_i, b_i. In this equation θ_{ij} denotes the angle between the directions $\mathbf{r}_j$ and $\mathbf{r}_i$; $\cos\theta_{ii}$ is taken to be unity.

CASE (i). *Tetrahedral bonds.* If we take the directions $\mathbf{r}_1$, $\mathbf{r}_2$, $\mathbf{r}_3$, $\mathbf{r}_4$ to be normal to the faces of a regular tetrahedron then, for $i \neq j$,

$$\cos\theta_{ij} = -\tfrac{1}{3},$$

and equations (72) reduce to

$$a^2 + b^2 = 1, \qquad a^2 - \tfrac{1}{3}b^2 = 0,$$

where $a = a_1 = a_2 = a_3 = a_4$, $b = b_1 = b_2 = b_3 = b_4$. We thus have

$$a = \tfrac{1}{2}, \qquad b = \tfrac{1}{2}\sqrt{3},$$

so that the wave functions are

$$\psi_i = \tfrac{1}{2}\psi(2s) + \tfrac{1}{2}\sqrt{3}\,\psi(2p_i). \tag{73}$$

If we take as axes the lines joining the mid-points of the edges of the regular tetrahedron the vertices have coordinates of the type $(1, 1, 1)$, $(1, -1, -1)$, $(-1, 1, -1)$, $(-1, -1, 1)$, and the wave functions (73) become

$$\left.\begin{aligned}
\psi_1 &= \tfrac{1}{2}\{\psi(2s) + \psi(2p_x) + \psi(2p_y) + \psi(2p_z)\} \\
\psi_2 &= \tfrac{1}{2}\{\psi(2s) + \psi(2p_x) - \psi(2p_y) - \psi(2p_z)\} \\
\psi_3 &= \tfrac{1}{2}\{\psi(2s) - \psi(2p_x) + \psi(2p_y) - \psi(2p_z)\} \\
\psi_4 &= \tfrac{1}{2}\{\psi(2s) - \psi(2p_x) - \psi(2p_y) + \psi(2p_z)\}
\end{aligned}\right\} \tag{74}$$

Functions of this type are called *tetrahedral orbitals*; in each of them the electron is concentrated in a particular direction about which the wave pattern is symmetrical. The wave functions of this type have a form resembling that of Fig. 40.

If, when it is ready to form a molecule, the carbon atom has its four unpaired electrons each in one of these tetrahedral orbitals, the principle of maximum overlapping shows that it can form four equivalent bonds directed to the four corners of a regular tetrahedron whose centroid coincides with the carbon nucleus. The four bonds thus make angles of 109° 28′ with each other. In this way we can account for the characteristic tetravalency of carbon—cf. the methane molecule CH_4 (Fig. 41). When the four radicals which are bonded to the carbon atom are not

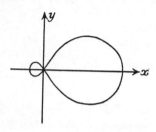

FIG. 40. Single tetrahedral orbital.

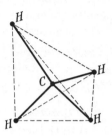

FIG. 41. The methane molecule.

all identical, it can be shown that their mutual repulsions and different electron affinities do not affect the tetrahedral angles by more than two or three degrees. The tetrahedral bond can also be shown to be very stable.

CASE (ii). *Trigonal bonds.* If we take the directions r_1, r_2, r_3 to lie in a plane making angles $2\pi/3$ with each other and take r_4 to be normal to this plane, then

$$\cos\theta_{12} = \cos\theta_{23} = \cos\theta_{31} = -\tfrac{1}{2},$$
$$\cos\theta_{14} = \cos\theta_{24} = \cos\theta_{34} = 0,$$

and so from equations (72) we have

$$a_1 = a_2 = a_3 = 1/\sqrt{3},$$
$$b_1 = b_2 = b_3 = \sqrt{\tfrac{2}{3}},$$
$$a_4 = b_4 = 0.$$

Choosing r_4 to lie along the z-axis and r_1 to lie along the x-axis we then find

$$\psi_{\mathrm{I}} = \{\psi(2s) + \sqrt{2}\,\psi(2p_x)\}/\sqrt{3}$$
$$\psi_{\mathrm{II}} = \{\sqrt{2}\,\psi(2s) - \psi(2p_x) + \sqrt{3}\,\psi(2p_y)\}/\sqrt{6}$$
$$\psi_{\mathrm{III}} = \{\sqrt{2}\,\psi(2s) - \psi(2p_x) - \sqrt{3}\,\psi(2p_y)\}/\sqrt{6}$$
$$\psi_{\mathrm{IV}} = \psi(2p_z).$$

These orbitals are called *trigonal orbitals.* They resemble the tetragonal orbitals in the sense that the first three (which are shown in Fig. 42) possess a marked directional property. The principal directions lie in one plane and are separated by angles of 120°; the fourth orbital is an undisturbed 'dumb-bell' with its axis normal to the plane containing the other three. There is one electron in each of the trigonal orbits when a carbon atom is about to form an unsaturated molecule, such as ethylene (C_2H_4), in which the bond angles are 120°.

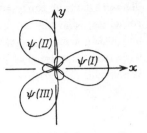

Fig. 42. The three co-planar trigonal orbitals.

35.3. *The ethylene double-streamers*

As an illustration of the occurrence of trigonal wave functions we shall now consider the structure of an unsaturated molecule, ethylene:

$$\begin{array}{ccc} H & & H \\ & \diagdown C = C \diagup & \\ H & & H \end{array}$$

in which there is a double bond. The two carbon atoms are in the trigonal state so that we can form five 'sausage' bonds each of two electrons, such that there are three bonds from each carbon atom. Normal to the plane of these orbitals there is a dumb-bell orbital corresponding to a mobile electron which is unpaired and not engaged in the formation of a bond as yet. The criterion of maximum overlapping demands that the bonds in the CH_2 plane are at angles of 120° with each other; the best we can do with the mobile electrons from the two carbon atoms is to pair these together somehow. If the two CH_2 planes of the molecule coincide the two dumb-bells are in parallel directions so that they overlap most in this direction. These $2p_z$ electrons will then form themselves into molecular orbitals of the type shown in Fig. 44, in which the probability function has the form of two streamers one on each side of the C_2H_4 plane. For such a molecular orbital the wave function will be approximately

$$\psi = \psi_a(2p_z) + \psi_b(2p_z).$$

Both electrons have, of course, the same 'double-streamer' wave function; it should be noted that it is not a case of the upper streamer representing one electron and the lower streamer the other. The two streamers are inseparable, constituting the additional factor which converts a single bond into a double bond.

A characteristic feature of the double bond is its high reactivity. Since the streamer electrons are not so tightly bound as the other electrons—the atomic orbitals from which they are built do not overlap as much—it is easier to form new molecules by disengaging them from one another and linking them with other atoms.

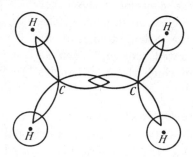

FIG. 43. Overlapping of atomic orbitals in ethylene.

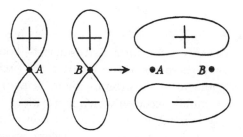

FIG. 44. Mobile electrons in ethylene.

Similarly, the triple bond is formed by the addition of a further pair of streamer electrons in a plane normal to that of the other pair of streamers.

35.4. *The benzene molecule* (C_6H_6)

A molecule of some importance in organic chemistry is the benzene molecule and it is one of the classic problems of chemistry to determine the distribution of electrons in this molecule. Now a number of sources indicate that all the carbon and hydrogen atoms lie in one plane. We see then that for this to be possible each of the carbon atoms must be in a trigonal state. The atomic orbitals (Fig. 45) then form twelve 'sausage' bonds and the molecule forms a plane ring containing six carbon atoms. There are then six mobile electrons left unpaired; their orbitals are dumb-bells whose axes pass through the carbon nuclei and are normal to the hexagon formed by the carbon nuclei (Fig. 46). These electrons will, however, interact and will be free to move about from one carbon nucleus to another, forming molecular orbitals of the type shown in Fig. 46. The streamer bonds which we encountered in ethylene are now spread out over a wider space—we have two streamers going right round the molecule one on either side of the carbon hexagon.

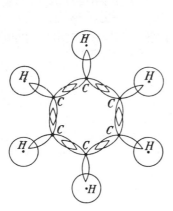

FIG. 45. Overlapping of atomic orbitals in benzene.

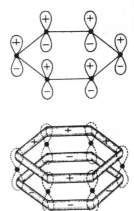

FIG. 46. Mobile electrons in benzene.

If we write ψ_1, ψ_2,..., ψ_6 for the dumb-bell orbitals the molecular orbitals streaming round the molecule will, by an analogy with the case of H_2, be of the form

$$\psi = \sum_{r=1}^{6} c_r \psi_r.$$

The constants c_r have to be chosen (by a minimum energy method) so that this function is as good a solution of the wave equation as possible. It can be shown that there are six possible molecular orbitals of the required character each with different values for the c_r and each having a different value for the energy. If E_0 is the energy of an isolated $2p_z$ atomic orbit and β is a certain constant, of negative value, whose magnitude is known from comparison measurements on ethane and ethylene, these molecular energies are

$$E_0+2\beta, \quad E_0+\beta, \quad E_0+\beta, \quad E_0-\beta, \quad E_0-\beta, \quad E_0-2\beta.$$

The energies of the first three orbitals are thus less than that of an isolated $2p_z$ atomic orbit; these levels are called *bonding orbits*. There will be two electrons in each of these bonding orbits in the normal state of benzene so that their energy is $6E_0+8\beta$. If we had supposed that the molecule had a configuration 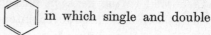 in which single and double

bonds alternate, the energy would have been $6E_0+6\beta$. The extra energy 2β gained by removing the restriction to localization has been called the *resonance energy*. The value 2β is about 30 k.cals. which agrees quite well with the experimental value (37 k.cals.).

Similar calculations to those we have outlined briefly for benzene have been carried out for other molecules of this type and have been found to explain many of the well-known facts of organic chemistry. For example, it has been shown that the characteristic colour of many of the organic dyes may be attributed to the excitation of a mobile electron from a bonding orbit to an unoccupied orbit with energy exceeding E_0. The results of calculations of the resonance energies of a few unsaturated molecules are embodied in the table below.† It will be observed that the agreement with the experimental values for the resonance energies is reasonably good when we consider the nature of the approximations involved.

TABLE 6

| Molecule | Resonance energy (k.cals.) | |
	Calculated	Experimental
Butadiene	5	5
Hexatriene	11	..
Octatetraene	17	..
Benzene	30	37
Diphenyl	65	87
Naphthalene	63	75

† C. A. Coulson, op. cit., p. 130.

VIII

THEORY OF SOLIDS

36. Cohesive forces in ionic crystals

THE theory of the cohesive forces in ionic crystals developed by Max Born† and his collaborators was one of the first successful applications of atomic physics to the theory of solids. Though not strictly an application of quantum mechanics, it forms the basis of subsequent developments, and it will be necessary to give an account of it here.

The aim of Born's work is to account for the lattice energy, lattice constant, crystal structure, and elastic properties of ionic crystals in terms of an atomic model. The theory has been applied most successfully to alkali halides, and will be explained here with reference to them. Alkali halides have the simple cubic structure; this is shown in Fig. 47.

The theory worked out by Born rests on the following assumptions:

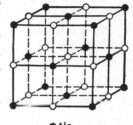

● Na
○ Cl

FIG. 47. Sodium chloride structure.

(a) The crystal is built up of positively and negatively charged ions, carrying charges $\pm e$ respectively. Ions of unlike sign therefore attract each other and ions of like sign repel, the force in each case being equal to e^2/r^2.

(b) Any two ions repel one another with an additional force that is practically equal to zero until their separations fall below a certain value, when the repulsion increases rapidly. We shall denote the potential energy due to this repulsion by $w(r)$ and call it the overlap energy, because it only comes into play when the electronic clouds of the ions overlap. The total potential energy of a pair of ions of unlike sign is thus

$$w(r)-e^2/r,$$

where r is the distance between them.

The form of the function $w(r)$ could in principle be calculated for any given pair of ions by the methods of quantum mechanics, but this has not actually been done (cf. Chap. VII); in the theory as developed

---

† For a survey see the following: N. F. Mott and R. W. Gurney, *Electronic Processes in Ionic Crystals* (Oxford, 1940); F. Seitz, *Modern Theory of Solids* (New York, 1942); M. Born, article in the *Handbuch der Physik*, **24/2** (Berlin 1933).

at present it has been usual to take an empirical form for the interaction energy $w(r)$, either

$$w(r) = \lambda r^{-s} \quad \text{with} \quad s \sim 9 \tag{1}$$

or
$$w(r) = Ae^{-r/\rho}, \tag{2}$$

a form which is suggested by quantum mechanical calculations of the
force between rare gas atoms.†

The ions adhere to form a stable crystal because of the electrostatic
attraction between unlike ions, which outweighs the repulsion between
like ions. They keep apart because, when two ions overlap, the strong
repulsive force with energy $w(r)$ comes into play. On this basis we have
to calculate the energy required to separate the crystal into its
constituent ions. This may be done as follows:

Let ϕ denote the electrostatic potential at any lattice point of the
crystal due to all the ions except the one occupying that point. This
quantity has been worked out for a number of structures; for the rock-
salt structure at a point normally occupied by a positive ion it is

$$\phi = -e\alpha_M/r,$$

where r is the shortest distance between ions of unlike sign and α_M is
a numerical constant known as the Madelung constant. For the rock-
salt (simple cubic) structure it has the value

$$\alpha_M = 1\cdot7476....$$

The electrostatic energy per ion pair is thus

$$-\alpha_M e^2/r.$$

In calculating the energy due to the overlap forces, the simplest
assumption is that the forces fall off so rapidly with distance that only
ions which are nearest neighbours need be taken into account. Since
each ion has six nearest neighbours, the overlap energy per ion pair
is then
$$6w(r),$$

and the total energy per ion pair is thus

$$U(r) = -\frac{e^2\alpha_M}{r} + 6w(r). \tag{3}$$

To determine the two unknown constants in the function $w(r)$ we
make use of experimental values of the lattice parameter and the compressibility (χ). The condition that the crystal is in equilibrium under
zero pressure, namely,
$$dU(r)/dr = 0, \tag{4}$$

† Cf. § 33.3.

gives one relation between these quantities, and for the compressibility χ a short calculation gives

$$\frac{1}{\chi} = \frac{1}{18r}\frac{d^2 U(r)}{dr^2}. \tag{5}$$

If we use the expression (1) for $w(r)$, equations (4) and (5) give

$$\frac{\alpha_M e^2}{6\lambda s} = \frac{1}{r^{s-1}}$$

and

$$\chi = \frac{18r^4}{\alpha_M e^2 (s-1)}.$$

The second of these equations gives s and the first λ, all in terms of measurable quantities. Estimates of the repulsive energy $w(r)$ can thus be made.

The theory has been refined by including in the energy the van der Waals attraction between the ions, the repulsion between ions which are not nearest neighbours, the zero-point vibrational energy, and so on. By comparison of theoretical formulae with observed lattice constants and compressibilities, values of $w(r)$ have been deduced for the interaction energy of halide ions with alkali, silver, thallium, and cuprous ions.[†]

For the alkali-halides a particularly convenient form of interaction energy is given by Mayer;[‡] this is (in ergs)

$$w(r) = 4 \times 10^{-12} e^{-(r-r_1-r_2)/\rho},$$

where $\rho = 0 \cdot 345 \times 10^{-8}$ cm. and r_1, r_2 are ionic radii shown in the table.

TABLE 7. *Basic radii r_1 and $r_2 \times 10^8$ cm.*

Li$^+$	.	. 0·475	F$^-$	.	.	1·110
Na$^+$	.	. 0·875	Cl$^-$	.	.	1·475
K$^+$	.	. 1·185	Br$^-$	.	.	1·600
Rb$^+$	.	. 1·320	I$^-$	.	.	1·785
Cs$^+$	.	. 1·455				

The energy per ion pair required to separate the crystal into its constituent ions is, on the simple treatment given above, easily seen to be given by

$$|U| = \frac{\alpha_M e^2}{r}\left(1 - \frac{1}{s}\right). \tag{6}$$

This has a value of the order 5–6 eV. per ion pair, or 120 k.cals. As $s \sim 9$, the greater part of (6) is due to the electrostatic forces. $|U|$ is

† For references cf. Mott and Gurney, loc. cit., chap. i.
‡ J. E. Mayer, *J. Chem. Phys.* **1**, 270 (1933).

connected with the energy U_A per ion pair necessary to dissociate the crystal into neutral atoms by the formula

$$|U| = U_A - E + I,$$

where I is the ionization potential of the metal atom and E the electron affinity of halogen ion. From calculated values of U (deduced from formula (6)), using known values of r, χ and experimental values of U_A, I, one can thus deduce theoretical values of the electron affinities E, which are not in general known in any other way. The success of the theory lies in the agreement between the values of E deduced from different compounds; this is shown below.

TABLE 8. *Electron affinities of the halogens in k.cals.*

Metal with which combined	F	Cl	Br	I
Li	95·0	85·7	81·2	75·8
Na	96·5	86·5	80·9	73·9
K	95·5	87·1	81·2	73·2
Rb	95·8	85·7	82·0	73·8
Cs	93·8	87·3	82·0	74·2
(Sutton and Mayer†) .	..	..	..	72·4

It seems that the theory built up along these lines gives a satisfactory account of cohesion in alkali and silver halides. For oxides and sulphides and in general for crystals where the ions carry two or more charges, no recent comparison between theory and experiment has been made.‡ The difficulties in doing so are due to the following facts:

(a) The van der Waals forces between oxide ions are large and difficult to estimate.

(b) It is possible that some 'homopolar' forces exist between the ions as well as the electrostatic attraction; in other words, the overlap force is not wholly repulsive in character.

(c) The oxide ion O^{--} is not stable in free space.

37. Crystals in thermal equilibrium

37.1. *Lattice vibrations*

In a crystal in thermal equilibrium at a temperature T, we must consider three types of deviation from the perfect lattice:

(a) The lattice vibrations of the atoms.

(b) The existence of vacant lattice points.

(c) The existence of interstitial atoms or ions.

† P. P. Sutton and J. E. Mayer, *J. Chem. Phys.* **3**, 20 (1935).
‡ See an early attempt by J. Sherman, *Chem. Rev.* **11**, 93 (1932).

The theory of the lattice vibrations will not be considered in detail here.[†] We may remind the reader of the rather crude (Einstein) model, in which each atom of a monatomic solid is supposed to vibrate independently of all the other atoms with frequency v; the mean energy of each atom is thus

$$3\left\{\tfrac{1}{2}hv + \frac{hv}{e^{hv/kT}-1}\right\}. \tag{7}$$

The temperature hv/k is known as the characteristic temperature and denoted by Θ. For temperatures large in comparison with Θ, (7) reduces to $3kT$, giving a specific heat of $3Nk$, where N is the number of atoms per gramme. If $\overline{x^2}$ is the mean amplitude of the thermal vibrations

$$\overline{x^2} = \hbar^2 T/Mk\Theta^2, \tag{8}$$

where M is the mass of an atom.

In an exact theory of the lattice vibrations and of the contribution of the specific heat due to them,[‡] it is necessary to analyse the vibrations of the lattice into its normal modes, and denote by $n(v)\,dv$ the number of normal modes with frequency between v and $v+dv$; the total number of modes for a solid of N atoms is $3N$, so that

$$\int n(v)\,dv = 3N.$$

The total integral energy is thus

$$\int n(v)\left\{\tfrac{1}{2}hv + \frac{hv}{e^{hv/kT}-1}\right\}dv.$$

The calculation of $n(v)$ for any real solid is a very difficult problem. Debye showed that for small v

$$n(v) = \text{const. } v^3$$

and showed how to calculate the constant in terms of the elastic constants of the solid.[§]

37.2. *Vacant lattice points and interstitial ions*

In addition to the thermal vibrations, a crystal in thermodynamical equilibrium differs from a perfect crystal through the presence of

(a) Interstitial atoms or ions.

(b) Vacant lattice points.

The case of a monatomic solid (metal) will be treated first.

It will be possible for atoms from the surface layer to diffuse into the body of the crystal, where they will be found in the so-called

---

† See, for example, R. H. Fowler, *Statistical Mechanics*, 2nd ed. (Cambridge, 1937) or F. Seitz, loc. cit.

‡ For most materials this is much the most important contribution.

§ For recent calculations of $n(v)$ cf. M. Blackman, *Proc. Roy. Soc.* A, **148**, 384 (1935), **159**, 46 (1937); *Proc. Camb. Phil. Soc.* **33**, 94 (1937). Also see Seitz, loc. cit., p. 103.

'interstitial positions', as illustrated in Fig. 48 a. We may denote by W_i the energy necessary for the formation of an interstitial atom. W_i will tend to be large for close-packed structures, for which the space available in an interstitial position is small and the distortion of the surroundings necessary to make room for an interstitial atom large.

(a)   (b)

FIG. 48. Showing formation of interstitial ions (a) and vacant lattice points (b).

In any case an elementary calculation† gives for the number of interstitial ions per unit volume

$$n_i = N_i e^{-W_i/kT},$$

where N_i is the number of interstitial positions per unit volume.

In the same way, vacant lattice points (holes) can be formed at the surface by diffusion inwards, as shown in Fig. 48 b. Let W_h be the energy necessary to form a hole; then in equilibrium the concentration of holes is

$$n_h = Ne^{-W_h/kT},$$

where N is the number of lattice points per unit volume.

For close-packed metals it is probable that W_h is less than W_i, so that the holes will greatly outnumber the interstitial ions; for copper, theoretical calculations‡ indicate that this is in fact the case. According to these workers, self-diffusion in metals takes place through the motion of holes. It is suggested that an atom will not move from one lattice point to another unless there is a hole next to it.§

In ionic crystals, in principle it is possible to have vacant lattice points and interstitial ions of both signs; in general, however, the energy required to put the large negative ion into an interstitial position is

† The number of ways that the n_i ions can be distributed is

$$P = N_i!/n_i!(N_i-n_i)!,$$

and the free energy is therefore

$$n_i W_i - kT \log P.$$

Making this a minimum with respect to charges in n_i, and remembering that $n_i \ll N_i$, the given equation is obtained.

‡ H. Huntingdon and F. Seitz, *Phys. Rev.* **61**, 315 (1942).

§ For a discussion of the mechanism, cf. R. P. Johnson, *Phys. Rev.* **56**, 814 (1939); G. Wyllie, *Proc. Phys. Soc.* **59**, 694 (1947).

so large that the concentration is negligible. Also any large volume of the crystal must be electrically neutral; otherwise large fields will be set up by the space charge.

It is thus convenient to consider two types of defect, both of which are electrically neutral.

(a) An interstitial ion (usually positive) and some distance from it a vacant lattice point from which the ion may be supposed to have come. This is called a Frenkel defect.† It will be noted that a Frenkel defect can be formed in the body of the crystal. If W_f is the energy necessary, the concentration of Frenkel defects is given by‡

$$n = \sqrt{(N_i N)} e^{-\frac{1}{2}W_f/kT}.$$

(b) Two vacant lattice points, one of each sign, wandering about independently of each other. This is called a Schottky defect. If W_s is the energy necessary to form a Schottky defect, the concentration will be

$$n = N e^{-\frac{1}{2}W_s/kT}.$$

The formulae are valid only if W_s, W_f differ considerably, so that only one type of defect is actually formed in appreciable quantities.

It is believed that Schottky defects are formed in alkali halides somewhat above room temperature,§ while Frenkel defects are formed at a concentration of about 10^{-10} per atom in silver halides at room temperature.

The ionic conductivity that all solid ionic crystals show at high enough temperatures is probably due to defects of one or other of these types, and either to the motion of interstitial ions, or to the motion of holes, or both.

A direct proof of the importance of holes (vacant lattice points) is given by the well-known experiments of Koch and Wagner;‖ crystals of silver halide were prepared containing small quantities of $CdCl_2$ or $CdBr_2$ in solid solution. In these crystals each Cd^{++} ion replaces two Ag^+ ions in the lattice; the crystal must thus contain at least as many holes as there are Cd^{++} ions. The number of holes is thus greatly increased and the conductivity, especially at comparatively low temperatures, is greatly increased also.

38. Electronic motion in crystals

For the understanding of the motion of electrons in both metals and non-metals it is essential to study the motion of an electron in a field

---

† J. Frenkel, *Zeits. f. Physik*, **35**, 652 (1926).

‡ Mott and Gurney, loc. cit., chap. ii.

§ F. Seitz, *Rev. Mod. Phys.* **18**, 384 (1946).

‖ E. Koch and C. Wagner, *Zeits. f. phys. Chem.* B, **38**, 295 (1937).

which is periodic in space with the period of a crystal lattice. The necessity for this may be seen most easily by considering a crystal such as sodium chloride into which an *extra* electron has been introduced. (In practice this can be done by photo-electric excitation, cf. Mott and Gurney, loc. cit., Chap. IV.) One can imagine the electron located on one of the metal ions and thus forming a metal atom. But if the electron transfers its position to the next atom, there is no change of energy; and the potential barrier between the two positions can easily be penetrated by tunnel effect. The electron is thus free to move through the crystal. The wave functions describing its motion will be wave packets or plane waves, like those describing the motion of an electron in free space, and can extend right through the crystal.

Similar wave functions are used to describe the free electrons in metals. Their use depends on the assumption that, so far as its effect on a given electron is concerned, the field of all the other electrons can be averaged in the sense of the Hartree approximation (Chaps. V, VI). This will be discussed further in the section devoted to metals.

In either case, therefore, it is necessary to study the motion of an electron in a field which is periodic with the period of the crystal lattice.

38.1. *Motion in a periodic field*

In order to understand the properties of an electron in a periodic field we shall consider first the one-dimensional case; we consider, then, the solutions of the Schrödinger equation

$$\frac{d^2\psi}{dx^2} + \frac{2m}{\hbar^2}\{W - V(x)\}\psi = 0, \tag{9}$$

where V is a periodic function of x with period a.

For a solution ψ to represent a possible state of the electron in an infinite metal, ψ must be bounded for all x. We shall show that the values of the energy W for which such solutions are possible fall into a series of *bands*, as shown in Fig. 49. All such solutions can be written in the form

$$e^{ikx}u(x) \quad (-\pi/a < k < \pi/a),$$

where $u(x)$ is periodic with period a.

For each allowed band of energy values, k varies continuously from $-\pi/a$ to π/a, so that a series of allowed energy bands can be defined, $W_1(k)$, $W_2(k)$, and so on.

Various proofs have been given, and we shall refer to one due to Kramers.† Kramers first points out that, if $\psi_1(x)$ and $\psi_2(x)$ are inde-

---

† H. A. Kramers, *Physica*, **2**, 483 (1935); see also F. Seitz, loc. cit., p. 278.

pendent solutions of the Schrödinger equation, then since $\psi_1(x+a)$ is also a solution, it follows that

$$\psi_1(x+a) = A\psi_1(x)+B\psi_2(x).$$

It is then easy to show that two linear combinations of ψ_1, ψ_2 may be chosen, ϕ_1, ϕ_2, with the property

$$\phi_1(x+a) = \lambda_1\phi_1(x),$$
$$\phi_2(x+a) = \lambda_2\phi_2(x).$$

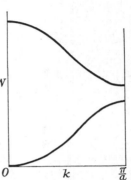

From these equations we have, differentiating each equation and multiplying by the other,

$$(\phi_1'\phi_2-\phi_1\phi_2')_{x+a} = \lambda_1\lambda_2(\phi_1'\phi_2-\phi_1\phi_2')_x. \tag{10}$$

For any Schrödinger equation, however, if ϕ_1, ϕ_2 are any two independent solutions corresponding to the same energy,

$$\phi_1''\phi_2-\phi_1\phi_2'' = 0,$$

so that $\phi_1'\phi_2-\phi_1\phi_2' = \text{const.}$

FIG. 49. Allowed values of the energy W as a function of wave-number k.

It follows from (10) that $\lambda_1\lambda_2 = 1.$

Now if ψ is bounded, it is clear that both λ_1 and λ_2 must be real or imaginary quantities with modulus unity. For if this were not the case, then $|\psi|$ would increase either with increasing or decreasing x, and would not be a bounded function. Thus we may write

$$\lambda_1 = e^{ik}, \qquad \lambda_2 = e^{-ik}.$$

It follows that the two solutions ϕ_1, ϕ_2 have the forms

$$e^{\pm ikx}u_k(x), \tag{11}$$

where $u_k(x)$ is periodic in x with period a.

It follows that the lowest state of each band of energy values is periodic, and that the higher states consist of plane waves modulated by the periodic field.†

Wigner and Seitz‡ have given the following method for determining the wave function in the lowest state in one of the energy bands in close-packed metals, which is of particular importance. They point out that if planes are drawn bisecting the lines which join nearest neighbours in the crystal, a polyhedron is formed surrounding each

† For an evaluation of the wave functions in a particularly simple type of periodic field, cf. R. Kronig and W. G. Penney, *Proc. Roy. Soc.* A, **130**, 499 (1931).

‡ E. Wigner and F. Seitz, *Phys. Rev.* **44**, 804 (1933); cf. also Mott and Jones, loc. cit., chap. iv.

atom. Supposing we now look for a periodic wave-function $u(x, y, z)$ which has the symmetry of an s wave function (spherical symmetry) in the neighbourhood of each atom. Then clearly $\partial u/\partial n$ must vanish on the boundary of the polyhedron. In order to calculate u, the poly-

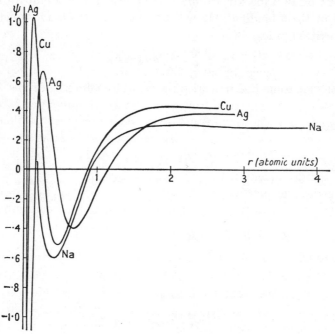

Fig. 50. Wave functions for metallic sodium, copper, and silver.

hedron is replaced by a sphere of equal volume, radius r_0. Then the Schrödinger equation

$$\frac{1}{r^2}\frac{d}{dr}\left(r^2\frac{du}{dr}\right) + \frac{2m}{\hbar^2}(W - V)u = 0$$

has to be integrated subject to the boundary condition

$$\frac{du}{dr} = 0 \quad \text{for} \quad r = r_0.$$

It is clear that a whole series of energy values will exist, for which u vanishes on 0, 1, 2,... spheres round each nucleus. For sodium with configuration $(1s)^2(2s)^2(2p)^6(3s)^1$, the states with respectively zero and one node will correspond to the X-ray K and L levels, and the wave functions will not differ much from those for the free atoms. The case corresponding to the valence electrons of various metals is shown in Fig. 50. For sodium states with more than two nodes correspond to high *positive* energies W. Each of these wave functions and energy values corresponds to the lowest state of a band of energies. These bands will be referred to as s-bands or s-zones.

The variation of energy with $\mathbf{k}$ within an s-band can be investigated by means of an approximate method known in the literature as 'the method of tight binding'. It will be seen that the wave-function $\psi_{\mathbf{k}}$ can be written in the form

$$\psi_{\mathbf{k}} = \sum_l e^{i(\mathbf{k}\mathbf{r}_l)}\phi_k(\mathbf{r}-\mathbf{r}_l), \tag{12}$$

where $\phi_{\mathbf{k}}(\mathbf{r})$ is some function with the requisite number of zeros tending to zero at a few atomic radii from $r = 0$, and the summation is over all lattice points $\mathbf{r}_l$. The wave function of Wigner–Seitz type illustrated in Fig. 50 could, for instance, be so represented. Let us assume this done; and make the following approximations:

(a) ϕ is independent of $\mathbf{k}$;

(b) overlap is negligible between the wave-functions $\phi(\mathbf{r}-\mathbf{r}_l)$, $\phi(\mathbf{r}-\mathbf{r}_{l'})$ unless the lattice-points $\mathbf{r}_l$, $\mathbf{r}_{l'}$ are nearest neighbours.

Then, denoting by H the Hamiltonian operator,

$$H = -\frac{\hbar^2}{2m}\nabla^2 + V,$$

the energy $W_{\mathbf{k}}$ of the state $\mathbf{k}$ will be given by

$$W_{\mathbf{k}} = \int \psi_{\mathbf{k}}^* H \psi_{\mathbf{k}}\, d\tau \Big/ \int \psi_{\mathbf{k}}^* \psi_{\mathbf{k}}\, d\tau.$$

With the approximations given above, this reduces to

$$W_k = \frac{A - B\sum e^{i(\mathbf{k}\rho_l)}}{A' - B'\sum e^{i(\mathbf{k}\rho_l)}}. \tag{13}$$

Here ρ_l is the vector joining an atom to its nearest neighbours, and the summation is over all the neighbours of any one atom; also

$$A = \int \phi^* H \phi\, d\tau,$$

$$A' = \int \phi^* \phi\, d\tau,$$

$$B = \int \phi^*(\mathbf{r}) H \phi(\mathbf{r}-\rho)\, d\tau,$$

$$B' = \int \phi^*(\mathbf{r}) \phi(\mathbf{r}-\rho)\, d\tau.$$

For a simple cubic lattice of lattice constant a for example,

$$\sum e^{i(\mathbf{k}\rho_l)} = 2\{\cos k_x a + \cos k_y a + \cos k_z a\}.$$

From this formula, we see that all values of **k** within the cube

$$-\pi/a < k_x < \pi/a$$
$$-\pi/a < k_y < \pi/a$$
$$-\pi/a < k_z < \pi/a$$

correspond to independent wave functions with energies in the s-band. The corresponding cube in k-space (Fig. 51) is called a 'Brillouin zone'.

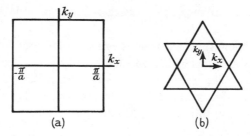

(a)   (b)

FIG. 51. Zone in k-space for s-states in (a) a simple cubic lattice, and (b) in a hexagonal close-packed lattice (two dimensions).

It is clear that for a crystal of N atoms the number of electronic states in the zone is $2N$, since two spin directions are allowed for each wave-function ψ_k. This is the case for any crystal structure. For the simple cubic it is instructive to verify this result by quantizing **k** by laying down the condition that ψ must be periodic in x, y, z with period na where n is a large integer. This is a conventional quantizing condition; it would be appropriate for a wire bent round into a circle, for a coordinate measured along the circumference of the wire. We deduce from this condition that

$$k_x = 2\pi n'/na \quad (n' = -\tfrac{1}{2}n,...,0,...,+\tfrac{1}{2}n),$$

which gives the required number of values.

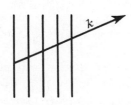

FIG. 52. Showing Bragg reflection from crystal planes.

To find the limits of the zone for structures other than simple cubic, we must draw in k-space the lines for which first-order Bragg reflections occur. This will enclose the required zone. This may be seen as follows: Fig. 52 shows a series of crystal planes, and it is supposed that a wave-vector **k** in the direction shown is reflected by them. Then, by the Bragg condition for reflection, in the wave function (12) the sign of the coefficient of the wave function ϕ_k will change in going from one atom to the next. It is clear that this represents the extreme form of the wave function, in the sense that a larger numerical value of **k** in the same direction would lead to a repetition of wave functions already described by smaller values.

We shall illustrate this principle by considering the s Brillouin zone for close-packed atoms in a plane (Fig. 51 b). There are then three sets of planes, at angles of 120° to each other, and spaced $\sqrt{3}a/2$ apart. The first Brillouin zone is thus a hexagon of side $1/\sqrt{3}a$ and volume $\sqrt{3}/2a^2$. Since the number of atoms per unit area is $\sqrt{3}/2a^2$, it will be seen that we have in the zone a number of states equal to the number of atoms.

For $\sum e^{i(\mathbf{k}\mathbf{\rho}_l)}$ we obtain

$$\sum e^{i(\mathbf{k}\mathbf{\rho}_l)} = 2\cos k_x a + 4\cos \tfrac{1}{2}k_x a \cos \tfrac{1}{2}\sqrt{3}\, k_y a.$$

It will be seen from formulae (13) that near the bottom of any zone

$$W = \text{const.} + \alpha \mathbf{k}^2.$$

We may write $\qquad\qquad \alpha = \hbar^2/2m^*;$

m^* will then be called the 'effective mass' of an electron moving in the crystal lattice. For energies near the bottom of a band, an electron moving in a periodic lattice will behave exactly as a particle in free space† with charge e and mass m^*. The approximation is often made of replacing m^* by m.

Fig. 53. p wave function of lowest energy for metallic lithium; the dots represent adjacent atoms.

In addition to the s-zones already described, p- or d-zones can be formed by a similar process. They will not be discussed in any detail here. Fig. 53 shows the general appearance of the lowest p wave function for lithium. The symmetry of such a wave function is such that it will be described by $k_x = \pi/a$ rather than $k = 0$.

Although the energy corresponding to this wave function will in general be higher than that of the state ($k_x = \pi/a$, $k_y = k_z = 0$) in the s-zone, it will not necessarily be higher than *all* states in the s-zone. Thus the energy band of the s-zone may overlap the energy band of the p-zone. If one plots against energy W the number $N(W)\,dW$ of states in the energy range dW one gets a curve such as that of Fig. 54 a.

† It is assumed that the lattice is rigid, i.e. that the atoms are not vibrating. Under these conditions the mean free path is infinite. In practice an electron will move with a finite free path, as shown in § 40.7.

39. Conductors and insulators

In metals and also non-metals such as diamond one can treat each electron as moving in the field of the positive ions and the field of all the other electrons, averaged in the sense of the Hartree or Fock approximation (Chaps. V, VI). This field is, of course, periodic, so that the wave functions are of the type described in the last section.

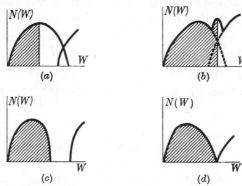

FIG. 54. Density of states in solids; $N(W)dW$ gives the number of states with energies between W and $W+dW$. (a) Monovalent metal; (b) divalent metal; (c) insulator; (d) graphite.

Only two electrons are allowed to be in each state specified by a quantized value of $\mathbf{k}$. We have seen that each s-zone contains $2N$ states. Therefore, for monovalent metals (sodium, silver, etc.), the first zone will be half full. This is shown in Fig. 54, where curves plotting $N(W)$ against W are shown.

If a zone is half full, it is clearly possible for the solid to carry a current, because within the zone a state can exist in which there are more electrons moving in one direction than the other. It is clear, therefore, why atoms such as Cu, Ag, Au, Na, K, etc., form metallic, conducting lattices.

On the other hand, if a zone is fully occupied, the electrons of the zone cannot contribute to the current because exactly as many are in states with wave-vector $\mathbf{k}$ in one direction as in the other. Insulators, therefore, are materials in which each zone is either full or empty (Fig. 54 c). An important intermediate case (graphite)† is sketched in Fig. 54 d.

The fact that atoms with two electrons in the outer ring form conducting lattices (except helium) shows that for these materials the s-zone must overlap the p-zone, as shown in Fig. 54 b.

† P. R. Wallace, *Phys. Rev.* **71**, 622 (1947).

It must be emphasized that the model used here, in which each electron is supposed to move in the averaged field of all the other electrons, is of course an approximation. What is assumed is that, if an antisymmetrical determinant of the type of Chapter VI, equation (11) is set up, in which the orbital wave functions are of the form $e^{i(\mathbf{kr})}u_k(\mathbf{r})$, then this will be a useful approximation of zero order to the true wave function. It is very difficult to give convincing reasons why this should be the case for metals.

For further discussions of the validity of the collective electron model, and for attempts to improve it, cf. papers by Schubin and Wonsowski,† and by Bethe.‡

40. Applications of the collective electron model to metals

In this section an outline only can be given of some of the applications of the collective electron method to the properties of metals:

40.1. *Emission and absorption of soft X-rays*

If any metal is used as an anticathode in an X-ray tube, part of the emitted radiation will correspond to transitions from the conduction band (the occupied states) into a lower X-ray level. If the mean energy

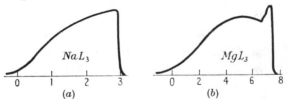

FIG. 55. L_3 emission bands of sodium and magnesium.

$h\nu$ of the emitted radiation is not too great compared with the width of the band of energies of the occupied states, the form of the emitted band can be determined experimentally. Fig. 55 shows the form of the L_3 band for sodium and magnesium.§ From the theoretical point of view, we expect the emitted intensity to be proportional to

$$N(W)p(W), \tag{14}$$

where $p(W)$ is the transition probability from a state of energy W into the X-ray level. The form of the band shown in Fig. 55b has the characteristics that we expect for a divalent metal, namely two overlapping zones and a sharp cut-off for high energies.

† S. Schubin and S. Wonsowski, *Proc. Roy. Soc.* A, **145**, 159 (1934).

‡ H. Bethe, *Zeits. f. Physik*, **71**, 205 (1931).

§ From H. W. B. Skinner, *Rep. Progress in Physics*, **5**, 271 (1938); see also H. M. O'Bryan and H. W. B. Skinner, *Proc. Roy. Soc.* A, **176**, 229 (1940).

In the same way the absorption intensity may be expected to be given by (14), where $N(W)$ refers to the empty levels.

For a review of the emission and absorption of soft X-rays, and their interpretation in terms of theory, cf. Skinner, loc. cit.

40.2. *Specific heats*

The electrons in a metal are subject to the Fermi–Dirac distribution law. According to this law, the probability that at temperature T a state with energy W is occupied is

$$f(W) = \frac{1}{e^{(W-\zeta)/kT}+1}. \tag{15}$$

It means that if W is much less than ζ, i.e. if $\zeta - W \gg kT$, the probability is practically unity; while, if $W - \zeta \gg kT$, the probability is approximately

$$e^{-(W-\zeta)/kT}.$$

The parameter ζ is given by the equation

$$\int_0^\infty N(W)f(W)\,dW = \text{total number of electrons.}$$

ζ differs only slightly from the energy of the highest occupied state at the absolute zero. $f(W)$ is illustrated in Fig. 56.

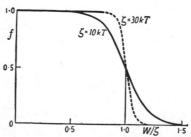

Fig. 56. Fermi distribution law for electrons in a metal.

The energy of the electrons at temperature T is

$$\int N(W)f(W)W\,dW.$$

This differs from the value at absolute zero by a term of order $N(\zeta)(kT)^2$, since the number of excited electrons will be of order $N(\zeta)kT$ and they will each have energy of order kT. The contribution of the electrons to the specific heat is thus linear in the temperature. A calculation of its magnitude gives†

$$\tfrac{2}{3}\pi^2 k^2 T N(\zeta).$$

If the calculations refer to a gramme-atom, $N(\zeta)$ is of order

$$N(\zeta) \sim N/\zeta,$$

where N is the number of free electrons per gramme-atom. Assuming this to be of the same order as the number of atoms, we see that the specific heat is of order

$$3Nk\left(\frac{2kT}{\zeta}\right).$$

Since ζ is equal to several electron volts, the electronic specific heat at room temperature will be of the order of 1 per cent. of that due to the vibrations of the atoms.

At low temperatures, however, where the contribution of the lattice vibrations varies as T^3, the contribution of the electrons is the predominant term, and at the temperatures of liquid helium has been observed for a number of metals. Expressing the linear term per gramme-atom as γRT, γ has the following values ($\times 10^{-4}$):

Cu‡	Al§	Ni‖	Fe††	Pd‡‡	Pt‡
0·888	1·742	8·742	6·0	16	8·0

The value for aluminium holds only down to the transition point to the superconductive state, $1 \cdot 13°$ K.

The high values for the transition metals will be noted. These are associated with a partly filled band formed from the d-states of the free atom.§§

40.3. *Paramagnetism*

As for the specific heat, one can argue that the number of free electrons (free to change their spins without infringing the exclusion principle) is $kTN(\zeta)$ and that each of these contributes μ^2/kT to the susceptibility ($\mu = e\hbar/2mc$). An exact calculation gives for the susceptibility

$$2\mu^2 N(\zeta).$$

† Cf. N. F. Mott and H. Jones, *Theory of the Properties of Metals and Alloys*, p. 178 (Oxford, 1936).

‡ J. A. Kok and W. H. Keesom, *Physica*, **3**, 1035 (1936).

§ Ibid. **4**, 835 (1937).

‖ W. H. Keesom and C. W. Clark, ibid. **2**, 513 (1935).

†† W. H. Keesom and B. Kurrelmeyer, ibid. **6**, 364 (1939).

‡‡ G. L. Pickard, *Nature*, **138**, 123 (1936).

§§ Mott and Jones, loc. cit., chap. vi.

One therefore expects a correlation between the electronic specific heat and the susceptibility. As shown above, the paramagnetic metals Pd and Pt do in fact have large electronic specific heats; but the values of $N(\zeta)$ determined from the specific heats are 2–4 times smaller than those from the paramagnetism. It is known that for ferromagnetic materials an interaction between the electrons exists which leads them to set themselves with their spins parallel; for Pd and Pt a force of this type probably exists also, not strong enough to lead to ferromagnetism but enough to increase the paramagnetism.

40.4. *Thermionic emission*

An equation for the current emitted from a metal surface at temperature T under fields strong enough to give saturation can be derived as follows, it being assumed that the effect of Bragg reflection (i.e. of the zone structure) of the electrons in the metal can be neglected.

Within the metal, the number of electrons with moments between p_x, p_x+dp_x, etc., and in the volume element dx, dy, dz is given by the Fermi–Dirac law

$$\frac{2}{h^3}\frac{dxdydz\,dp_x\,dp_y\,dp_z}{e^{(W-\zeta)/kT}+1}\quad\left(W=\frac{\mathbf{p}^2}{2m}\right). \tag{16}$$

For electrons with energy great enough to leave the metal, this becomes

$$\frac{2}{h^3}dxdydz\,dp_x\,dp_y\,dp_z\,e^{(\zeta-W)/kT}.$$

Let the surface of the metal be the yz-plane. Then we have to consider only the motion perpendicular to this plane. Since

$$\int_{-\infty}^{\infty}e^{-p^2/2mkT}\,dp=\sqrt{(2\pi mkT)},$$

it follows that the number of electrons per unit area of surface in a layer of thickness dx and with p_x in the range dp_x is

$$\frac{4\pi mkT}{h^3}e^{\zeta/kT}e^{-\frac{1}{2}p_x^2/mkT}\,dp_x\,dx.$$

Let $\zeta+\phi$ be the minimum energy that an electron must have in order to leave the metal, and let r be the reflection coefficient for an electron with momentum p_x. Then the number leaving the surface per unit area per unit time is

$$\frac{4\pi mkT}{h^3}e^{\zeta/kT}\int_{\zeta+\phi}^{\infty}(1-r)\frac{p_x}{m}e^{-\frac{1}{2}p_x^2/mkT}\,dp_x.$$

On the assumption that $r \sim 0$ (probable in view of the existence of the image force) this gives for the current per cm.^{2}

$$AT^2e^{-\phi/kT},$$

where $A = 4\pi mk^2e/h^3 \sim 120$ amp./cm.^{2}

For a discussion of the value of A for different models for the surface, cf. R. H. Fowler, *Statistical Mechanics*, 2nd ed. (Cambridge, 1936), p. 349, and for a discussion of the validity of the formula, cf. F. Seitz, *Theory of Solids*, p. 165.

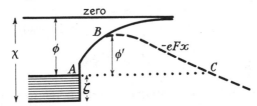

FIG. 57. Showing potential energy of an electron at the boundary of a metal.
————— In the absence of a field.
– – – – With a field.

In fairly strong fields the work function is reduced; this effect is known as Schottky† emission. This is because the field on an electron outside the metal at a distance x from the surface is that due to the image force $-e/4x^2$. Outside the surface, then, the potential energy of an electron is $-e^2/4x$. When the field F is introduced an additional term $-eFx$ is added to the potential energy. The function

$$-eFx-e^2/4x$$

has its maximum at $x = \frac{1}{2}\sqrt{(e/F)}$, and has there the value $-e^{\frac{3}{2}}F^{\frac{1}{2}}$. Thus the effective work function ϕ' is

$$\phi' = \phi-e^{\frac{3}{2}}F^{\frac{1}{2}}.$$

This is shown in Fig. 57.

The current I_F for a field F should thus satisfy the relation

$$\frac{T(\log I_F-\log I_0)}{F^{\frac{1}{2}}} = \frac{e^{\frac{3}{2}}}{k}.$$

This relation has been shown to be valid over a remarkably wide range of temperatures and for fields up to 10^6 volt/cm. by de Bruyne.‡

40.5. *Cold emission*

For very strong fields (of the order 10^7 volt/cm.) emission from an electrode into a vacuum will take place by tunnel effect *through* the

† W. Schottky, *Zeits. f. Physik*, **18**, 63 (1923).
‡ N. A. de Bruyne, *Proc. Roy. Soc.* A, **120**, 423 (1928).

potential barrier ABC of Fig. 57. A current is thus obtained which is independent of temperature.

The theory of the effect is as follows. Let us denote by $D(p_x)$ the probability that an electron with momentum p_x in the x-direction will pass through the barrier. Then the number of electrons leaving unit area per unit time is

$$\frac{2}{h^3} \int \frac{p_x}{m} D(p_x)\, dp_x\, dp_y\, dp_z,$$

where the integration is over all values of $\mathbf{p}$ such that

$$p_x^2 + p_y^2 + p_z^2 \leqslant 2m\zeta.$$

Setting $2m\zeta = p^2$, and writing $p_x = p - \theta$, it is easily seen that this gives

$$\frac{4\pi p^2}{mh^3} \int\limits_0^\infty D(p - \theta)\theta\, d\theta,$$

where the upper limit of the integral may be taken to be infinity, since D decreases rapidly with increasing θ.

The transparency factor D will be of the form $Ae^{-\beta}$, where A is a factor of the order unity, and β may be obtained from the WKB approximation (Chap. I, § 3.3) as follows:

$$\beta = 2\kappa \int \sqrt{(V - W)}\, dx \quad (\kappa = 2m/\hbar^2)$$

$$= 2\kappa \int\limits_0^{(\chi - \xi)/eF} \sqrt{(eF_x)}\, dx \quad (2m\xi = p_x^2)$$

$$= \tfrac{4}{3}\kappa(\chi - \xi)^{\frac{3}{2}}/F.$$

For values of p_x in the neighbourhood of p we have

$$\beta = \tfrac{4}{3}\kappa\phi^{\frac{3}{2}}\left(1 + \frac{3}{2}\frac{\theta p}{m\phi} + \dots\right).$$

Putting $A = 1$, this gives for the number of electrons emitted per unit area per unit time

$$\frac{e^2 F^2}{2\pi h\phi} e^{-\frac{4}{3}\kappa\phi^{\frac{3}{2}}/F}.$$

If the approximation $A = 1$ is not made, a result is obtained which does not differ from this appreciably† if $\phi \sim \zeta$.

40.6. *Metallic cohesion*

No detailed account will be given in this book of the theory of metallic cohesion. In the treatments given up till now the energy of the metal has been divided up into the following parts:

(a) The interaction of the conduction electrons with each other and with the metallic ions, and the electrostatic interaction of the latter with each other.

† Cf. R. H. Fowler, loc. cit.

(*b*) The repulsion which comes into play when the ions overlap.

In copper or silver (*b*) is important; the ions appear to be in contact, so that the force between them is the determining factor for the compressibility; for the alkali metals, on the other hand, the ions do not overlap. For metals such as tungsten it may not be possible to make a distinction between ions and conduction electrons.

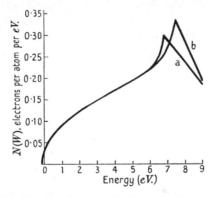

Fig. 58. Density of electronic states, (*a*) face-centred, (*b*) body-centred cubic.

In considering the force (*a*), it is of importance that the 'atomic sphere' surrounding each atom is electrically neutral; thus in calculating the potential energy of the system one has only to consider the interaction of the electrons within each sphere with each other and with the ion. This interaction is mainly responsible for the cohesion of the metal.

For metals with more than one electron per atom the kinetic energy of the electrons will be much more sensitive to the crystal structure than for metals with one electron. This is because of the zone structure explained in an earlier section. Fig. 58 shows the density of states. $N(W)dW$ is the number of electrons with energies between W and $W+dW$ for the conduction electrons in the s-zone in a metal with body- and face-centred cubic structures, and the same atomic volume; the calculations are due to H. Jones.† It will be seen that for metals with only one electron per atom there is little difference between the energies, but for larger numbers the body-centred structure has the lower total energy. On the basis of these ideas Jones has shown why in alloys of CuZn, CuAl, CuSn, etc., transitions from the face- to the body-centred structure and other similar transitions occur at a nearly constant ratio

† H. Jones, *Proc. Phys. Soc.* **49**, 243 (1937).

of free electrons to atoms (Hume–Rothery rule). For these two particular structures it is not difficult to see why this should be so. For the
face-centred structure reflection occurs first for the (111) set of planes,
and thus for a wave-number k equal to $\sqrt{3}d/\pi$. For the body-centred
cubic, on the other hand, where the longest wave-length for the Bragg
reflection is given by the (110) lines, k is $\sqrt{2}d/\pi$. In these formulae d is
the lattice parameter in either case. If a^3 is the atomic volume, then
since the two structures contain 4 and 2 atoms respectively in the unit
cube, these wave numbers are in the ratio

$$\sqrt{3}a/2^{\frac{1}{3}} \quad \text{and} \quad \sqrt{2}a,$$

i.e. $1{\cdot}37a$ and $1{\cdot}41a$.

40.7. *Electrical conductivity*

The wave mechanical theory of electrical conduction in metals is
based on the following deductions from the theory:

(α) Free electrons will go through a *perfect* crystal lattice for an
infinite distance without being scattered.

(β) Scattering, giving a finite mean free path, can be due to impurities or foreign atoms in solid solution, thermal vibrations,
crystal boundaries, or any other disturbance to the periodicity
of the lattice.

(γ) In the scattering process an electron gains or loses an energy of
the order kT and thus small compared with ζ (the Fermi energy);
the only electrons which can make collisions are those with kinetic
energy approximately equal to ζ.

Calculations of the conductivity due to heat motion at low temperatures ($T < \Theta$, where Θ is the Debye temperature) will not be
considered here; if $T > \Theta$ for pure metals, and also for the resistance
due to impurities, it is possible to express the conductivity of a metal
in the following way (Mott and Jones, loc. cit., p. 258 et seq.):

The conductivity σ is given by

$$\sigma = ne^2\tau/m,$$

where n is the number of free electrons per unit volume and τ, the time
of relaxation, is given by

$$1/\tau = vNA,$$

where N is the number of atoms per unit volume, v the maximum
velocity of the Fermi distribution, and A an effective collision area
given by

$$A = \int (1 - \cos\theta)I(\theta)\,d\omega,$$

where $I(\theta)$ is the cross-section for scattering into the solid angle $d\omega$ by each atom† (in an alloy the mean probability).

From this formula we can deduce that for $T > \Theta$ the resistance of a pure metal is proportional to T; for if x is the displacement of any one atom from its mean position, it is clear that the scattered amplitude is proportional to x, and hence that $I(\theta)$ is proportional to x^2. The mean value of x^2, however, is proportional to potential energy of all the vibrating atoms and thus to half the total heat content. This in its turn is proportional to T.

We may deduce also an instructive formula due to Nordheim‡ on the resistance of alloy systems such as AgAu which form a continuous range of solid solutions. Suppose that the two types of atom are denoted by A and B and that $V_A(r)$, $V_B(r)$ denote the potential energies of an electron in an atom of either type. If the number of atoms of the two types in the alloy are in the ratio c to $1-c$, then the mean potential energy in all atoms is

$$cV_A(r) + (1-c)V_B(r).$$

In A atoms the potential differs from this by

$$(1-c)(V_B - V_A)$$

and in B atoms by $$c(V_A - V_B).$$

The intensities of the waves scattered from atoms of the two types are thus proportional to

$$(1-c)^2, \qquad c^2,$$

and hence the total scattering (resistance) is proportional to

$$c(1-c)^2 + (1-c)c^2,$$

which reduces to $$c(1-c). \tag{17}$$

Equation (17), therefore, shows the way in which the residual resistance of an alloy varies with composition. Good agreement with experiment is obtained for alloys such as PdPt, AgAu.

41. Electronic motion in non-metals

In this section a summary will be given of the electronic behaviour, from the theoretical viewpoint, of ionic and other crystals which are insulators at low temperatures and if not exposed to light which they absorb.

Such crystals have a full zone of energy levels separated by a finite energy gap from an empty zone (the 'conduction band'). If an *extra*

---

† Cf. chap. ix.
‡ L. Nordheim, *Ann. der Physik*, **9**, 607 (1931).

electron is introduced into the conduction band, it will move freely through the lattice. Also if an electron is removed from a full band, the resulting vacancy, called a 'positive hole', can carry current. A 'positive hole' behaves like an electron of positive charge; the analogy with Dirac's theory of the positive electron will be noted.

Materials which conduct through the motions of electrons in a normally full band give a Hall coefficient† of sign opposite to that obtained in materials where the current is due to positive holes; this is the most important way of distinguishing them.

If a material contains per unit volume n electrons (or positive holes) of effective mass m, its conductivity is

$$\sigma = \frac{ne^2}{m}\tau,$$

where τ is the time of relaxation. Calculations of τ for ionic crystals have been made;‡ since in ionic crystals electrons will have energies of the order kT (0·025 eV.) instead of about 5 eV. as for metals, the changes in the potential due to atomic vibrations will no longer be small compared with the kinetic energy of the electron. It is rather doubtful therefore whether the perturbation theory on which these calculations are based is a good approximation. In any case one expects a mean free path of the order of a few multiples of the interatomic distance, except perhaps at low temperatures. Thus with $v \sim 10^7$ cm./sec., $\tau \sim 10^{-14}$ sec.

Electrons can be introduced into the conduction band in the following ways:

(a) Excitation from the full band, either through the absorption of a quantum of radiation (photo-conductivity) or through the passage of a fast charged particle.

(b) Excitation by thermal energy of an electron in an 'impurity centre' (see below). This occurs in semi-conductors.

(c) An electron can enter at the boundary of a crystal, e.g. from a metal electrode.

41.1. Semi-conductors

In most semi-conductors the conductivity would be low for a pure crystal. The conductivity has its origin in the presence of a number

---

† The phenomenon known as the Hall effect is the following: If a current j flows in a conductor perpendicular to a magnetic field H, an e.m.f. E is observed perpendicular to j and H. The Hall constant is defined as E/jH. It is easy to see that $eH\bar{v}/c = eE$, where $\bar{v}$, the velocity of drift in the direction of the current, is j/en, n is the number of carriers per cm.³ Thus $E/jH = 1/enc$.

‡ H. Fröhlich and N. F. Mott, Proc. Roy. Soc. A, 171, 496 (1939).

of 'impurity centres'; for these the energy Q required to remove an electron into the conduction band is low enough, at the temperature considered, for a sufficient number of electrons to be free to give a significant contribution to the conductivity.

According to the theory originally given by A. H. Wilson,† if N is the number of impurity centres per unit volume, the number of free electrons (in the conduction band) is, per unit volume, about

$$3 \times 10^9 N^{\frac{1}{2}} e^{-\frac{1}{2}Q/kT}.$$

Various types of impurity centres are believed to exist, as follows:

(a) In materials such as zinc oxide a small excess (say, one part in 10^4) of zinc can exist. The zinc *ion* can be lodged interstitially in the lattice. Round such an ion the force on an electron in the conduction band is $e^2/\kappa r^2$, where κ is the dielectric constant. It can thus be shown that there will exist, just below the level of the conduction band, a series of stationary states leading up to a series limit, just as for a free atom; but that, for the p-states, at any rate for which the field near the centre does not matter much, the order of magnitude of the energies, measured from the bottom of the conduction band as zero, is

$$-me^4/2\hbar^2\kappa^2 n^2, \tag{18}$$

or smaller by a factor κ^2 than for a free atom. Also the radial extent of the wave function is of order

$$n^2\hbar^2\kappa/me^2.$$

These results will apply, as regards order of magnitude, for the ground state ($n = 1$), provided that the free atom is too large to go into the interstitial space. Since $\kappa \sim 10$ for most semi-conductors, it will be seen:

(i) that the energies required to release an electron may well be as small as $0 \cdot 1$ eV.;

(ii) that the radial extent of the dissolved atom may be of the order 10–30 A, and interaction between the centres may be expected at quite low concentrations. This may account for the known fact that Q often depends on concentration.

(b) Excess metal may also be taken up in an ionic lattice through the presence of points in the lattice from which a negative ion is missing. The field round such a point will be again of the form $e^2/\kappa r^2$, an electron can be trapped there, and the same arguments about small energy and

† A. H. Wilson, ibid. A, **133**, 458 (1931); *Theory of Metals*, p. 65 (Cambridge, 1936); *Semi-conductors and Metals* (Cambridge, 1939).

large radius will apply. The 'F-centres' or colour centres which can be introduced into alkali halides by heating in metal vapour are of this type.

(c) If an oxide contains excess oxygen, this will be taken up through the presence of lattice points from which a metal ion is missing, the oxygen ion being too big for an interstitial position. To keep the substance neutral, an equal number of positive holes must be present, which will be trapped in the neighbourhood of these points. As the temperature is raised, some will become free, and conduction becomes possible through the motion of positive holes. This is the mechanism responsible for conduction in Cu_2O with excess oxygen.

(d) In Se, Si, SiC the mechanism is not understood in detail. One can, however, say that the presence of atoms with an electronic structure which is *not* a closed shell in numbers greater than that demanded by the crystal structure should give electronic (excess) conduction, and the presence of vacant lattice points should give defect conduction (conduction by positive holes). The higher the dielectric constant, the lower will be Q, other things being equal.

41.2. *Optical properties of impure crystals*

Any dissolved atom (i.e. electron trapped in the field of an interstitial ion or place where a negative ion is missing) should have in principle a *line* absorption spectrum leading up to a series limit. This is because the electron moves in a Coulomb field superimposed on the periodic field of the lattice. In practice these absorption lines will be greatly broadened by the vibration of the crystal.

The well-known F-band which accounts for the colour of alkali halides with excess metal is probably an $s–p$ transition of the trapped electron.

Absorption of light in the band due to an impurity, therefore, will not lead directly to photo-conduction; nevertheless photo-conductivity is often observed, for instance, in alkali and silver halides. This is probably because the energy interval between the excited state of the centre and the bottom of the conduction band is so small that heat motion enables the electron to escape before it falls back to the ground state, except at very low temperatures.

41.3. *Photo-conductivity*

One must distinguish between photo-conductivity of a semi-conductor, where the absorption of light merely increases the conductivity already present, and the primary photo-current in insulators (alkali halides with F-centres, silver halides at low temperatures, etc.). The latter has been investigated by R. W. Pohl and his school.† In this work a crystal is placed between electrodes, given a short illumination, and the quantity nex measured, where n is the number of electrons released (usually equal to the number of quanta absorbed) and x the

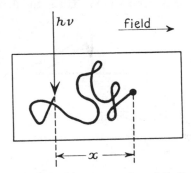

FIG. 59. Path of an electron released by light in an alkali halide crystal.

distance drifted by each electron before it is 'trapped'. This trapping is a marked feature of insulating crystals; an electron in the conduction band survives only a certain time before being trapped. The energy necessary to release an electron from a trap is, of course, less than from one of the original impurity centres. x, the distance drifted, will be proportional to the field F and inversely to the number of traps.

Other examples of trapping are:

(a) In zinc sulphide phosphors, where illumination at low temperatures gives rise to trapped electrons which return to their original centres with emission of radiation only after warming up.

(b) The action of light on photographic emulsion, where the first process appears to be the release by light of an electron which is trapped at a point where the latent image will be formed.

41.4. *Optical properties of pure crystals; the exciton*

In this section we discuss the optical absorption of a pure non-metallic crystal, that is to say, the absorption spectrum due to the atom or ions that form the crystal lattice. It should be emphasized that any allowed transitions of this type will lead to a very strong absorption coefficient, of the order 10^6 cm.$^{-1}$

† R. W. Pohl, *Proc. Phys. Soc.* **49** (extra part), 3 (1937); F. Seitz, *Rev. Mod. Phys.* **18**, 384 (1946); N. F. Mott and R. W. Gurney, *Electronic Processes in Ionic Crystals*, chap. iv (Oxford, 1940).

In Fig. 60, if a quantum of frequency $h\nu_0$ is absorbed, a free electron and a positive hole are produced; both can move in the lattice independently, giving (in theory) photo-conduction. The frequency $h\nu_0$ is not, however, the lowest that can be absorbed, because it is possible for the electron and positive hole to exist in a series of states in which they are bound in one another's field. If r is the distance between them

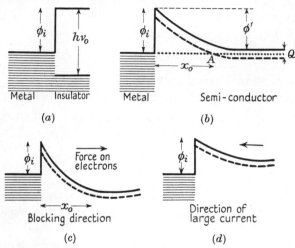

Fig. 60. Potential energy of electron at metal/non-metal interface: (a) insulator; (b) semi-conductor in equilibrium; (c) field in blocking direction; (d) field in opposite direction.

and $\mathbf{R}$ the coordinate of the centre of gravity, we shall expect these bound states to be of the form

$$e^{i(\mathbf{kR})}\psi_n(r),$$

where $\psi_n(r)$ are wave functions similar to those for a hydrogen atom. An electron and positive hole bound together in this way has been termed by Frenkel† an exciton; the formulation given here is due to Wannier.‡

If an exciton is formed by the absorption of a quantum of light, it will be formed in a state for which $\mathbf{k} = 0$; therefore, owing to the Coulomb field between a positive hole and an electron, we expect the absorption spectrum to consist of a series of lines leading up to a series limit. In practice the lines will be broadened by heat motion.

Attempts have been made to account for the absorption spectrum of alkali halides along these lines.

† J. Frenkel, *Phys. Rev.* **37**, 17 (1931).
‡ G. H. Wannier, ibid. **52**, 191 (1937).

An alternative description of the exciton may be given, which corresponds more closely to that of Frenkel's original paper. In this we consider a crystalline array of atoms, numbered 1, 2,..., r,..., n. Let $\psi_r(x)$ denote the wave function of an electron in the ground state of the atom r, and $\psi'_r(x)$ the corresponding wave function for some given excited state. Let $\Psi_r(x_1,...,x_n)$ be the wave function describing the whole system of n atoms when all the atoms are in the ground state except atom r; this can be formed by setting up an antisymmetrical determinant from functions of the type

$$\psi_1(x_1)\psi_2(x_2)...\psi'_r(x_r)...\psi_n(x_n).$$

Then it can be shown that Ψ_r is not a *stationary* state of the system, but that the stationary states are of the form

$$\sum_r e^{i(\mathbf{kR}_r)}\Psi_r(x_1,...,x_n),$$

where $\mathbf{R}_r$ is the position of the rth atom. A wave function of this type represents the place where the atom is excited, moving about the lattice with wave-number $\mathbf{k}$. In other words, an excited atom hands over its energy to a neighbour, the process is repeated, and so on. The place where the excitation is at any moment is called the exciton.

41.5. *Contact between a metal and an insulator*

If a metal is in contact with an insulator, we may introduce a 'work function' ϕ_i which represents the work necessary to take an electron from the metal into the conduction band of the insulator (Fig. 60). ϕ_i will not, of course, be equal to the work function ϕ which is defined as the work necessary to remove an electron from the metal to vacuum across a clean surface. Experimental evidence indicates that usually ϕ_i is less than ϕ. From the theoretical point of view the image force is $\frac{1}{4}e^2/\kappa r^2$ instead of $\frac{1}{4}e^2/r^2$, so the contribution from that term to the work function will be very much smaller.

Given two metals of work functions ϕ, ϕ' against a vacuum and ϕ_i, ϕ'_i against a given insulator, it is tempting to assume that

$$\phi-\phi' = \phi_i-\phi'_i,$$

but it is doubtful if it is a good approximation, and arguments can be given to suggest that $\phi_i-\phi'_i$ has the same sign as $\phi-\phi'$, but is considerably smaller. The field at the boundary of a metal will be changed if another solid is brought into contact with it.

It will be assumed that ϕ_i is always positive.

A non-metal with no electrons normally in the conduction band will act as an insulator in contact with a metal under the following conditions:

(a) ϕ_i is too big for thermionic emission.

(b) The applied field is not great enough for strong field emission.

It is possible that another factor in the action of insulators is the presence of 'traps', so that any electrons which get into the conduction band set up a space charge which repels other electrons.

41.6. *Contact between a metal and a semi-conductor*

If the non-metal considered above has impurity centres (e.g. dissolved atoms) which can lose electrons to the conduction band for the expenditure of energy Q less than ϕ_i, it is clear that the centres near to the metal will lose electrons to it.

A positive space charge is thus set up in the semi-conductor, and an equal negative charge induced on the metal. The potential energy $V(x)$ of an electron in the semi-conductor is thus as shown in Fig. 60 (b). It is shown in Mott and Gurney, op. cit. Chap. VI, that ϕ', the contact potential between metal and semi-conductor, is equal to $\phi_i - \frac{1}{2}Q$ at low temperatures.

The shape of the barrier may easily be calculated in the practically important case where $Q \ll \phi_i$. In that case we may assume that all centres are empty up to the point A in Fig. 60 (b); thus if N is the number of centres per unit volume, $V(x)$ satisfies Poisson's equation

$$\frac{d^2V(x)}{dx^2} = 4\pi Ne^2.$$

At the point A, we may assume, since $Q \ll \phi_i$, that $dV/dx = 0$. Thus if A is a distance x_0 from the metal, $V(x)$ is given by

$$V(x) = 2\pi Ne^2(x^2 - 2xx_0). \tag{19}$$

Putting $x = x_0$ in this equation and neglecting the difference between ϕ_i, ϕ' we find
$$\phi_i = 2\pi Ne^2x_0^2,$$
which gives the width of the barrier layer. In practical cases $x_0 \sim 10^{-6}$ cm.

The barrier between a metal and semi-conductor may be expected to have strong rectifying properties, *if* the resistance is an appreciable part of the resistance of the whole circuit. The theory indicates that the direction of high resistance is for motion of electrons from metal to semi-conductor (it will be the opposite for defect conductors). The reason is made clear in Figs. 60 (c) and (d). Electrons are supposed to go over the barrier with the help of heat motion (no tunnel effect); a potential difference equal to ϕ_i will remove the barrier preventing the motion of electrons from semi-conductor to metal, but does not affect the height of the barrier opposing motion in the opposite direction.

The theory of the effect is as follows:

Figs. 60 (c) and (d) show that, if a potential V_0/e is placed across the barrier, $V(x)$ is still given by (19) with

$$\phi_i + V_0 = 2\pi N e^2 x_0^2.$$

The equation governing the current j crossing unit area of the barrier per unit time is

$$j = -vn(x)\frac{dV(x)}{dx} - eD\frac{dn(x)}{dx}.$$

Here $n(x)$ is the density of electrons at a distance x from the metal, v and D are the mobility and diffusion coefficient of an electron. Since

$$D/v = kT/e,$$

this may be written

$$j = -vkT\left[\frac{n}{kT}\frac{dV}{dx} + \frac{dn}{dx}\right].$$

This can be integrated by multiplying both sides by $e^{V/kT}$; we obtain

$$j\int_0^x e^{V(x)/kT}\,dx = vkT[n(0) - n(x)]e^{V(x)/kT}.$$

We now take a value (x_1) of x beyond the barrier; we find

$$j = \int_0^{x_1} e^{V(x)/kT}\,dx = vkT(n_0 - n_1)e^{-(V_0+\phi')/kT},$$

where n_1 is the density of electrons far from the barrier.

We note:

(a) $n_1 v = \sigma$, the conductivity of the semi-conductor.

(b) Substituting from (19) for $V(x)$, we find

$$\int_0^{x_1} e^{V(x)/kT}\,dx \simeq \int_0^\infty e^{-4\pi N e^2 x x_0/kT}\,dx$$

$$= kT/4\pi N e^2 x_0.$$

(c) At points where $V_0 = 0$, $j = 0$. Hence $n_0 = n_1 e^{-\phi'/kT}$.

Hence, finally,

$$j = 2\sigma\sqrt{\{2\pi N e^2(V_0+\phi)\}}e^{-\phi'/kT}\{1 - e^{-V_0/kT}\}.$$

A barrier of this type seems first to have been described by Schottky.[†] For such barriers tunnel effect is probably unimportant, though for high voltages in the blocking direction there may be some field emission from the metal to the semi-conductor.

When thin ($\sim 10^{-7}$ cm.) insulating layers exist on the surface of a semi-conductor (as, for instance, oxide layers on silicon and SiC crystals), tunnel effect may play an important part in rectification.[‡]

[†] W. Schottky, *Zeits. f. Physik*, **113**, 367 (1939); ibid. **117**, 574 (1941); see also review by J. Joffe, *Electrical Communication*, **22**, 217 (1945).

[‡] C. Dilworth, *Proc. Phys. Soc.* **60**, 315 (1948).

IX

COLLISION PROBLEMS

42. Introduction

THE problems to be considered in this chapter are of the following type:†
a beam of particles, for example, electrons, is incident on an atom or
atomic nucleus or other scattering centre; it is required to find the
number of particles that are scattered out
of the beam in a definite direction. For this
purpose we define the scattering cross-section
$I(\theta)$ as follows: if the beam is such that ν
particles cross unit area per unit time, then
the number of particles scattered per unit
time through an angle θ into a solid angle
$d\omega$ is $\nu I(\theta) d\omega$. It will be noticed that $I(\theta)$
has the dimensions of an area; the scattering

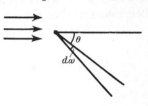

FIG. 61. Showing scattering
of particles through an angle θ
into a solid angle $d\omega$.

is the same as it would be if the particles had to hit an area $I(\theta) d\omega$
in order to be scattered into the solid angle $d\omega$.

$$\text{The quantity} \qquad \int I(\theta)\, d\omega = \int_0^\pi I(\theta) 2\pi \sin\theta\, d\theta$$

is called the total cross-section for scattering.

It will easily be seen that if the particles are moving through a
medium containing N scattering centres per unit volume, the probability per unit length of path that a particle will be scattered into the
solid angle $d\omega$ is
$$N I(\theta)\, d\omega.$$

In the case of electrons incident on atoms, if their energy is greater
than the first excitation potential, they may be scattered either
elastically or after losing energy. In such a case we introduce the
quantity $I_0(\theta)$ to refer to elastic scattering and $I_n(\theta)$ to refer to scattering after excitation of the atom to the state n; the quantity $N I_n(\theta)\, d\omega$
thus gives the number of particles scattered per unit time into the solid
angle $d\omega$ after raising the atom to the nth excited state.

† General references for the subject-matter of this chapter are: N. F. Mott and H. S. W.
Massey, *The Theory of Atomic Collisions* (Oxford, 1933); J. H. McMillen, 'Elastic
Electron Scattering in Gases', *Rev. Mod. Phys.* **11**, 84 (1939)—a review both of theory
and experiment on the subject; *Handbuch der Physik*, **24**/1 (Berlin, 1933), article by
H. Bethe, especially for discussion of stopping power.

43. Scattering by a centre of force

The simplest collision problem is that of a stream of particles incident on a centre of force; by this is meant a region of space in which the potential energy of a particle is not zero but some function $V(r)$ which tends to zero as r tends to infinity. If, for example, $V(r)$ is equal to $ZZ'e^2/r$, then the problem is that of a beam of particles each with charge $Z'e$ incident on an atomic nucleus with charge Ze. To a good approximation the scattering of a beam of fast electrons by an atom can be treated by taking for the field of the atom a screened Coulomb field, such as that for which

$$V(r) = \frac{Ze^2}{r}\exp(-qr).$$

The Schrödinger equation for a particle in such a field is

$$\nabla^2\psi + \frac{2m}{\hbar^2}\{W - V(r)\}\psi = 0, \tag{1}$$

where W is positive, being equal to the kinetic energy of an electron at a point remote from the atom. Writing

$$k^2 = 2mW/\hbar^2, \qquad U(r) = 2mV(r)/\hbar^2,$$

this takes the form $\qquad \nabla^2\psi + \{k^2 - U(r)\}\psi = 0. \tag{1.1}$

To describe the scattering it is necessary to find a solution that will have the form of an incident wave and a scattered wave. Thus a solution must be sought which, for points distant from the scattering centre, has the asymptotic form

$$\psi \sim e^{ikz} + r^{-1}e^{ikr}f(\theta) + \text{terms of order } 1/r^2. \tag{2}$$

If this is multiplied by the appropriate time factor $e^{-2\pi i\nu t}$, it is seen that the first term represents a plane wave advancing from left to right along the z-axis. This wave describes a beam in which there is one particle per unit volume so that the number of particles crossing unit area per unit time is $v\ (= \hbar k/m)$. The second term represents an outgoing wave; in this $|f(\theta)|^2/r^2$ is equal to the number of particles per unit volume at a distance r from the origin, and thus the number per unit time incident on an area A is

$$v|f(\theta)|^2A/r^2.$$

It follows that the number scattered into the solid angle $d\omega$ is $v|f(\theta)|^2\,d\omega$ and hence that

$$I(\theta) = |f(\theta)|^2. \tag{3}$$

The scattering is thus completely determined if $f(\theta)$ is known.

43.1. *Exact solution of the wave equation representing an incident and a scattered wave*

In this section we shall show how a solution of equation (1) of type (2) can be obtained. We require first an expansion of the plane wave

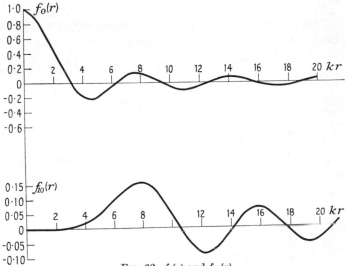

FIG. 62. $f_0(r)$ and $f_{10}(r)$.

e^{ikz} in a series of spherical harmonics. The required expansion is, writing $z = r\cos\theta$,

$$e^{ikr\cos\theta} = \sum_{l=0}^{\infty}(2l+1)i^l P_l(\cos\theta)f_l(r), \tag{4}$$

where

$$f_l(r) = \left(\frac{\pi}{2kr}\right)^{\frac{1}{2}}J_{l+\frac{1}{2}}(kr) \tag{4.1}$$

and $J_{l+\frac{1}{2}}$ is the Bessel function of order $l+\frac{1}{2}$. For the first of these functions

$$f_0(r) = (kr)^{-1}\sin kr.$$

The asymptotic form of $f_l(r)$ is, for large r,

$$f_l(r) \sim (kr)^{-1}\sin(kr-\tfrac{1}{2}l\pi). \tag{5}$$

Plots of $f_0(r)$ and $f_{10}(r)$ are given in Fig. 62 for $k = 1$.

A proof of these propositions is given in any text-book on Bessel functions.† A proof of enough of them for the purposes of this chapter may be obtained as follows: equation (4) may be regarded as an expansion of the left-hand side in a series of Legendre functions $P_l(\cos\theta)$

† For example, G. N. Watson, *Bessel Functions.*

with the functions $f_l(r)$ unknown; then multiplying both sides of (4) by $P_l(\cos\theta)\sin\theta$ and integrating with respect to θ from 0 to π, we obtain, writing $\cos\theta = t$,

$$f_l(r) = \frac{1}{2i^l}\int_{-1}^{+1} e^{ikrt}P_l(t)\,dt. \tag{6}$$

This equation defines $f_l(r)$; it also enables an asymptotic expression to be obtained; integrating by parts, equation (6) gives

$$f_l(r) = \frac{i^{-l}}{2ikr}[e^{ikrt}P_l(t)]_{t=-1}^{t=+1} + \text{terms of order } \frac{1}{r^2}.$$

Thus, since $P_l(1) = 1$ and $P_l(-1) = (-1)^l$, we find

$$f_l(r) = (kr)^{-1}\sin(kr - \tfrac{1}{2}l\pi), \tag{7}$$

which is identical with equation (5).

Turning now to the equation (1) for a particle in a central field, we see that the general solution of this equation with axial symmetry must be of the form
$$\sum_l A_l P_l(\cos\theta)F_l(r), \tag{8}$$

where the A_l are arbitrary constants and the function F_l is the bounded solution of

$$\frac{1}{r^2}\frac{d}{dr}\left(r^2\frac{dF}{dr}\right) + \left\{k^2 - U(r) - \frac{l(l+1)}{r^2}\right\}F = 0.$$

This may be written

$$\frac{d^2}{dr^2}(rF) + \left\{k^2 - U(r) - \frac{l(l+1)}{r^2}\right\}rF = 0. \tag{9}$$

It follows that if $U(r)$ tends to zero sufficiently rapidly as r tends to infinity, then the bounded solution *must* have the form at infinity

$$F_l \sim (kr)^{-1}\sin(kr - \tfrac{1}{2}l\pi + \eta_l). \tag{10}$$

The phase η_l can in general only be determined by numerical integration of equation (9), though approximate methods of evaluating them are given on p. 238; the term $\tfrac{1}{2}l\pi$ is added so that η_l shall vanish if $U(r)$ is zero.

The constants A_l in (8) must now be chosen so that it shall have the asymptotic form (2); in other words, they must be chosen so that

$$\sum A_l P_l(\cos\theta)F_l(r) - e^{ikz} \tag{11}$$

shall represent an outgoing wave only. Substituting from (4) for e^{ikz} we obtain for (11)

$$\sum P_l(\cos\theta)\{A_l F_l(r) - (2l+1)i^l f_l(r)\}.$$

Substituting the asymptotic forms of F_l, f_l, we have for the term in the curly brackets

$$(kr)^{-1}\{A_l\sin(kr-\tfrac{1}{2}l\pi+\eta_l)-(2l+1)i^l\sin(kr-\tfrac{1}{2}l\pi)\}.$$

This may be written

$$\frac{1}{2ikr}[\{A_l e^{i\eta_l}-(2l+1)i^l\}e^{ikr-\frac{1}{2}l\pi i}-\{A_l e^{-i\eta_l}-(2l+1)i^l\}e^{-ikr+\frac{1}{2}l\pi i}].$$

In order that this may represent an outgoing wave only the second term must vanish; we set therefore

$$A_l = (2l+1)i^l e^{i\eta_l},$$

and the scattered wave takes the form $r^{-1}e^{ikr}f(\theta)$ with

$$f(\theta) = \frac{1}{2ik}\sum_{l=0}^{\infty}(2l+1)(e^{2i\eta_l}-1)P_l(\cos\theta). \tag{12}$$

This formula for the scattered amplitude was first given by Faxen and Holtsmark.† Further details are given by Mott and Massey, op. cit., Chap. II.

Certain theorems of importance about the phases η_l will now be proved.

(a) The expression (12) for the intensity of the scattered wave does not depend on the assumption of a static field of force, but can be deduced generally from the conservation of particles if there is no inelastic scattering. The proof is fairly obvious and will not be given here.

(b) For slow particles, of wave-length $(\hbar/mv)$ large compared with the radial extension of $V(r)$, the scattering is spherically symmetrical so that only η_0 needs to be considered.

(c) As v tends to zero, η_0 in general tends to zero in such a way that the scattered cross-section remains finite. In one particular case, that of an attractive field in which the incident particle is capable of being held by the scattering field in a bound stationary state of exactly zero energy, η_0 remains finite as v tends to zero. Therefore the scattered cross-section given by (12) tends to infinity.

The proof is as follows: if a bound state of zero energy exists in the field of potential $V(r)$, this means that

$$d(rF)/dr = 0$$

at the boundary of the field. But it follows from this that, as k tends to zero, η_0 tends to $\tfrac{1}{2}\pi$.

† H. Faxen and J. Holtsmark, *Zeits. f. Physik*, **45**, 307 (1927).

(d) Various approximate expressions may be found for the phases η_l. In the first place let us write

$$g_l(r) = krf_l(r), \qquad G_l(r) = krF_l(r).$$

Thus, from equation (9), it follows that

$$G_l \frac{d^2 g_l}{dr^2} - g_l \frac{d^2 G_l}{dr^2} = G_l U(r) g_l.$$

Integrating from zero to r, we find

$$G_l(r) \frac{dg_l}{dr} - g_l(r) \frac{dG_l}{dr} = \int_0^r G_l(r') U(r') g_l(r') \, dr'.$$

We assume that $U(r)$ tends to zero faster than $1/r$, so that the integral on the right converges. Then, inserting the asymptotic forms (7) and (10) for G_l and g_l, we see that

$$\sin \eta_l = -\frac{1}{k} \int_0^\infty G_l(r) g_l(r) U(r) \, dr. \tag{13}$$

This formula is exact. An approximation valid when l is large is to replace G_l by g_l so that

$$\sin \eta_l \simeq -\frac{1}{k} \int_0^\infty [g_l(r)]^2 U(r) \, dr$$

$$= -\frac{\pi m}{\hbar^2} \int_0^\infty V(r) [J_{l+\frac{1}{2}}(kr)]^2 r \, dr.$$

If this approximation is used for all l, and $\sin \eta_l$ is put equal to η_l, we obtain for $f(\theta)$

$$f(\theta) = -\frac{2m}{\hbar^2} \int_0^\infty \frac{\sin Kr}{Kr} V(r) r^2 \, dr, \tag{14}$$

where

$$K = 2k \sin \tfrac{1}{2}\theta.$$

This follows from the expansion†

$$\frac{\sin Kr}{Kr} = \sum_{l=0}^\infty (2l+1) P_l(\cos \theta) \{f_l(r)\}^2.$$

Equation (14) is known as the 'Born approximation' to the scattered amplitude; in practice it is seldom a sufficient approximation. Born's original derivation is given in the next section.

† G. N. Watson, loc. cit., p. 363.

An alternative and improved approximate method of determining the phases has been given by Pais,† as follows. A suitable solution of equation (9) when there is no interaction is

$$g_l(r) = (\tfrac{1}{2}\pi kr)^{\frac{1}{2}} J_{l+\frac{1}{2}}(kr).$$

Pais takes the effect of the interaction into account by using a solution of the type
$$G_l(r) = (\tfrac{1}{2}\pi kr)^{\frac{1}{2}} J_{l+\lambda+\frac{1}{2}}(kr),$$

where λ is to be determined from equation (9) by a variation method. He is then able to show that

$$\frac{2l+\lambda+1}{2l+2\lambda+1}\lambda = \frac{2m}{\hbar^2}\int_0^\infty V(r)\{J_{l+\lambda+\frac{1}{2}}(kr)\}^2 r\,dr.$$

If this equation is solved graphically or by a method of successive approximations, then the phase is given by

$$\eta_l = -\tfrac{1}{2}\pi\lambda.$$

Hulthen‡ has used a variational method to obtain η_l; if

$$L = \int_0^\infty \psi^*\left\{\frac{d^2}{dr^2} + k^2 - \frac{l(l+1)}{r^2} - U(r)\right\}\psi\,dr,$$

and ψ is a function containing undetermined parameters c, then optimum values will be given by the condition $\partial L/\partial c = 0$. Hulthen takes for ψ
$$\psi(r) = \cos\eta\sin kr + (1-e^{-\lambda r})(1+he^{-\lambda r})\sin\eta\cos kr,$$

with h as an adjustable parameter, in finding the phase η_0 with a field of the type $V(r) = -br^{-1}e^{-\lambda r}$ used in Meson theory.

Other methods of obtaining phase shifts will be described in the second edition of Mott and Massey, op. cit. (to appear shortly).

Massey and Buckingham§ have worked out the scattering to be expected from a large number of fields which occur in nuclear theory.

44. Born's approximation for the scattering of particles by a centre of force: alternative treatment

For the scattering of particles by a centre of force, it is possible, as shown in the last section, to obtain an exact solution of the wave equation. An important approximate method was first introduced by Born,‖ in which the field $V(r)$ is treated as a perturbation. This is known in the literature as the Born approximation.

---

† A. Pais, *Proc. Camb. Phil. Soc.* **42**, 45 (1946).

‡ L. Hulthen, *Fysiogr. Sallsk. Lund. Forhandl.* **14**, 21 (1944).

§ H. S. W. Massey and R. A. Buckingham, *Proc. Roy. Soc.* A, **163**, 281 (1937).

‖ M. Born, *Zeits. f. Physik*, **37**, 863 (1926) and **38**, 803 (1926). The former paper is the first in which the probability interpretation of ψ was introduced, and is the first discussion of a collision problem in wave mechanics.

We make use of the fact that a solution of the inhomogeneous equation

$$\nabla^2\psi + k^2\psi = F(x,y,z),$$

where $F(x,y,z)$ is a known function, is

$$\psi = -\frac{1}{4\pi}\int \frac{e^{ik|\mathbf{r}-\mathbf{r}'|}}{|\mathbf{r}-\mathbf{r}'|} F(x',y',z')\,d\tau'.$$

For a proof see, for example, Mott and Massey, op. cit., Chap. VI, or any text-book on electromagnetic theory.

If we write the wave equation in the form (1.1), namely

$$\nabla^2\psi + \{k^2 - U(r)\}\psi = 0,$$

and treat $U(r)$ as small, then we may set

$$\psi = e^{ikz} + \psi_1$$

and neglect the product $U\psi_1$. Substituting for ψ we obtain therefore

$$\nabla^2\psi_1 + k^2\psi_1 = U(r)e^{ikz},$$

of which a solution is

$$\psi_1 = -\frac{1}{4\pi}\int \frac{e^{ik|\mathbf{r}-\mathbf{r}'|}}{|\mathbf{r}-\mathbf{r}'|} U(r')e^{ikz'}\,d\tau'.$$

It is easily seen that this solution behaves at infinity like an outgoing wave; the asymptotic form is in fact

$$\psi_1 \sim \frac{e^{ikr}}{r}f(\theta),$$

where

$$f(\theta) = -\frac{1}{4\pi}\int e^{-ik(\mathbf{n}\mathbf{r})+ikz}U(r)\,d\tau$$

with $\mathbf{n} = \mathbf{r}/r$.

A convenient way of writing this is

$$f(\theta) = -\frac{2\pi m}{h^2}\int e^{i(\mathbf{k}_0-\mathbf{k}.\mathbf{r})}V(r)\,d\tau, \tag{15}$$

where $\mathbf{k}_0$, $\mathbf{k}$ are vectors of magnitude k in the directions of motion of the particle before and after scattering.

It will be noticed that the same formula can be obtained by the methods of Chapter X for the probability per unit time that a particle makes a transition from the initial state with momentum $\mathbf{k}_0$ and wave function e^{ikz} to a final state with momentum $\mathbf{k}$.

Formula (15) may be simplified (when $V(r)$ is spherically symmetrical) by taking polar coordinates with axes in the direction of the vector $\mathbf{k}_0-\mathbf{k}$; we thus obtain

$$f(\theta) = \frac{2\pi m}{h^2}\iint e^{iKr\cos\theta'}V(r)2\pi\sin\theta'\,d\theta'\,r^2\,dr,$$

where $K = |\mathbf{k_0}-\mathbf{k}| = 2k\sin\frac{1}{2}\theta$. On integration with respect to θ' this gives

$$f(\theta) = -\frac{2m}{\hbar^2} \int\limits_0^\infty \frac{\sin Kr}{Kr} V(r)r^2\,dr$$

as in formula (14).

For example, if $V(r) = \frac{Ze^2}{r}\exp(-qr)$ (screened Coulomb field), this gives

$$f(\theta) = \frac{Ze^2}{2mv^2}\operatorname{cosec}^2\tfrac{1}{2}\theta\,\frac{1}{1+(q/2k\sin\frac{1}{2}\theta)^2}.$$

If q/k is small, the scattered intensity tends to

$$I(\theta) = \left(\frac{Ze^2}{2mv^2}\right)^2\operatorname{cosec}^4\tfrac{1}{2}\theta,$$

which, as seen in the next section, is the classical expression for the scattered intensity.

44.1. Scattering by a Coulomb field

If a beam of charged particles, each carrying a charge $Z'e$, and such that one particle crosses unit area per unit time, falls on a single nucleus of infinite mass and charge Ze, then according to Newtonian mechanics the number of particles $I(\theta)\,d\omega$ scattered per unit time through an angle θ into a solid angle $d\omega$ is given by

$$I(\theta) = \left(\frac{ZZ'e^2}{2mv^2}\right)^2\operatorname{cosec}^4\tfrac{1}{2}\theta.$$

The proof of this, the Rutherford scattering formula, is given in any text-book on nuclear physics.

The same formula is exactly valid in (non-relativistic) wave mechanics, provided

(a) the Coulomb law of interaction, $V(r) = ZZ'e^2/r$, is assumed to hold down to all distances;

(b) the velocity of the particles is small compared with c, the velocity of light.

Classical results are also valid for the collision between two charged particles of finite mass, *except* when both particles are identical (two α-particles or two electrons, cf. Chapter V).

For details of the proof of this the reader is referred to the original papers or to Mott and Massey, op. cit., Chap. III. One has to obtain a solution of the equation

$$\nabla^2\psi+\left\{k^2-\frac{2me^2ZZ'}{\hbar^2}\frac{1}{r}\right\}\psi = 0$$

representing an incident and scattered wave. The solution may be shown to be

$$\psi = F(-i\alpha;\ 1;\ ik(r-z)),$$

where F is the hypergeometric function defined by

$$F(a;\ b;\ x) = 1 + \frac{a}{b.1}x + \frac{a(a+1)}{b(b+1)1.2}x^2 + \dots$$

and

$$\alpha = ZZ'e^2/\hbar v.$$

The asymptotic form is $\psi = I + Sf(\theta),$

where I represents an incident wave and is given by

$$I = e^{ikz + i\alpha \log k(r-z)}$$

and S, the scattered wave, is given by

$$S = r^{-1}e^{ikr - i\alpha \log kr},$$

and $$f(\theta) = \frac{ZZ'e^2}{2mv^2}\operatorname{cosec}^2 \tfrac{1}{2}\theta\, e^{i\alpha \log(1-\cos\theta) + i\pi + 2i\eta_0},$$

where $$e^{2i\eta_0} = \Gamma(1+i\alpha)/\Gamma(1-i\alpha).$$

It will be seen that neither the incident nor the scattered waves have the normal form; this is due to the slow convergence of the Coulomb field.

On forming the scattered intensity $I(\theta) = |f(\theta)|^2$ we see that the classical formula of Rutherford is obtained. Planck's constant only arises in the *phase* of f, which is not observable (except in the collision between identical particles; cf. Chapter V).

44.2. *Collisions between electrons and atoms*

Up to this point we have considered only the scattering of electrons by a centre of force. We have now to outline a theory of the scattering of a beam of electrons by an atom, in which the interaction between an incident electron and the electrons in the atom is taken into account. In the subsequent analysis we shall discuss the scattering of a beam of electrons by a hydrogen atom; the extension to a many-electron atom is straightforward.

We denote the Schrödinger equation for the hydrogen atom by

$$\{H(p,r) - W\}\psi(\mathbf{r}) = 0,$$

where H is the usual Hamiltonian operator and r the coordinate of the electron. Let W_n, ψ_n be the characteristic energies and corresponding wave function. Then the Schrödinger equation for an additional electron interacting with the atom is

$$\left\{ -\frac{\hbar^2}{2m}\nabla_1^2 + H(\mathbf{p}_2, \mathbf{r}_2) + V(\mathbf{r}_1, \mathbf{r}_2) - W \right\}\Psi(\mathbf{r}_1, \mathbf{r}_2) = 0. \tag{16}$$

Here r_1, r_2 are the coordinates of the two electrons and

$$V(\mathbf{r}_1, \mathbf{r}_2) = -\frac{e^2}{r_1} + \frac{e^2}{|\mathbf{r}_1 - \mathbf{r}_2|}.$$

The Hamiltonian is, of course, symmetrical in the coordinates of the two electrons.

To obtain an approximate solution, we expand $\Psi(\mathbf{r}_1, \mathbf{r}_2)$ in a series of characteristic functions $\psi_n(\mathbf{r}_2)$,

$$\Psi(\mathbf{r}_1, \mathbf{r}_2) = \sum_n F_n(\mathbf{r}_1)\psi_n(\mathbf{r}_2).$$

Equation (16) then becomes

$$\sum_n \left\{ -\frac{\hbar^2}{2m}\nabla_1^2 + V(\mathbf{r}_1, \mathbf{r}_2) + W_n - W \right\} F_n(\mathbf{r}_1)\psi_n(\mathbf{r}_2) = 0.$$

Multiplying by $\psi_n^*(\mathbf{r}_2)$ and integrating over all r_2

$$\left\{ \frac{\hbar^2}{2m}\nabla^2 + W - W_n \right\} F_n(\mathbf{r}_1) = \int \psi_n^*(\mathbf{r}_2) V(\mathbf{r}_1, \mathbf{r}_2)\Psi(\mathbf{r}_1, \mathbf{r}_2)\, d\tau_2. \qquad (17)$$

If we denote the function on the right by $G_n(\mathbf{r}_1)$, a solution for F_n behaving at infinity like an outgoing wave can be obtained, so long as $W - W_n$ is positive; for if we set

$$k_n^2 = 2m(W - W_n)/\hbar^2,$$

the solution is

$$F_n = -\frac{1}{4\pi} \int \frac{e^{ik_n|\mathbf{r}_1 - \mathbf{r}_2|}}{|\mathbf{r}_1 - \mathbf{r}_2|} G_n(\mathbf{r}_2)\, d\tau_2,$$

which, as shown in the last section, behaves in the required way.

To obtain explicit expressions for F_n, we must make some approximation for $\Psi(\mathbf{r}_1, \mathbf{r}_2)$ in the right-hand side of (17). We require that $\Psi(\mathbf{r}_1, \mathbf{r}_2)$ should represent an incident wave falling on an atom in the ground state; the wave function representing this will be

$$e^{ik_0 z_1}\psi_0(\mathbf{r}_2). \qquad (18)$$

Owing to the interaction term scattered waves will also be formed. The simplest approximation will be to substitute (18) for $\Psi(\mathbf{r}_1, \mathbf{r}_2)$ in the right-hand side of (17); this procedure is known as Born's approximation.

Equation (17) thus becomes

$$\{\nabla^2 + k_n^2\} F_n(\mathbf{r}) = \frac{2m}{\hbar^2} V_{0n}(\mathbf{r})e^{ik_0 z},$$

where

$$V_{0n}(\mathbf{r}) = \int \psi_n^*(\mathbf{r}_2) V(\mathbf{r}_1, \mathbf{r}_2)\psi_0(\mathbf{r}_2)\, d\tau_2.$$

This equation is solved just as in the last section, and an asymptotic expression obtained; we find

$$F_n(\mathbf{r}) \sim r^{-1}e^{ik_n r}f_n(\theta, \phi),$$

where
$$f_n(\theta, \phi) = -\frac{1}{4\pi}\frac{2m}{\hbar^2}\int e^{i(\mathbf{k}_0-\mathbf{k}_n\cdot\mathbf{r})}V_{0n}(\mathbf{r})\,d\tau.$$

Here $\mathbf{k}_0$ is the wave number of the electron before the collision and $\mathbf{k}_n$ afterwards.

The obvious interpretation would be that

$$I_n = \frac{k_n}{k_0}|f_n(\theta, \phi)|^2,$$

$I_n\,d\omega$ being the cross-section for scattering into the solid angle $d\omega$ after exciting the atom to the nth state. This interpretation would, how-ever, neglect the possibility of a 'rearrangement collision', i.e. a collision in which the incident electron is captured by the atom and ejects another one in its place. To account for these we can expand $\Psi'(\mathbf{r}_1, \mathbf{r}_2)$ alternatively in the form

$$\Psi'(\mathbf{r}_1, \mathbf{r}_2) = \sum G_n(\mathbf{r}_2)\psi_n(\mathbf{r}_1)$$

and obtain
$$\{\nabla^2+k_n^2\}G_n(\mathbf{r}_2) = \frac{2m}{\hbar^2}\psi_0(\mathbf{r}_2)\int e^{ikz_1}V(\mathbf{r}_1, \mathbf{r}_2)\psi_n^*(\mathbf{r}_1)\,d\tau_1,$$

whence an expression for G_n representing an outgoing wave can be obtained as before; then if

$$G_n \sim r^{-1}e^{ik_n r}g_n(\theta, \phi)$$

we might suppose that $d\omega\,k_n|g_n|^2/k_0$ was the partial cross-section for a rearrangement collision. Actually, however, this interpretation is only valid if the two electrons have opposite spins, and so are distin-guishable; if the spins are parallel a wave function antisymmetrical in the space coordinates must be used, of the form

$$\Psi'(\mathbf{r}_1, \mathbf{r}_2)-\Psi'(\mathbf{r}_2, \mathbf{r}_1).$$

It may be shown† that the cross-section for scattering is then given by

$$I_n = \frac{k_n}{k_0}\{\tfrac{3}{4}|f-g|^2+\tfrac{1}{4}|f+g|^2\}.$$

Among the many applications of these formulae, we mention only some work on elastic collisions. Neglecting the term g representing

† The formula was first given by J. R. Oppenheimer, *Phys. Rev.* **32**, 361 (1928); see also Mott and Massey, op. cit., p. 113. An analogous formula for the simpler case of the collisions of one free particle with another is given in Chapter V of this book.

rearrangement collisions, it will be seen that the field $V_{00}(r)$ responsible for elastic scattering is just the electrostatic field due to the charged nucleus and a uniform negative charge distribution $-e|\psi_0(r)|^2$.

For hydrogen this may be evaluated to give

$$V_{00}(r) = -e^2\left(\frac{1}{r}+\frac{1}{a_0}\right)e^{-2r/a_0},$$

where $a_0 = \hbar^2/me^2 = 0 \cdot 54 \times 10^{-8}$ cm. For other atoms the best available approximation is to use the potential given by the method of the self-consistent field (Hartree field).†

For atomic hydrogen an analytic expression for the elastic scattering may be obtained; this is

$$I(\theta) = \frac{4(8+a_0^2\,K^2)^2}{a_0^2(4+a_0^2\,K^2)^4},$$

where $$K = |\mathbf{k_1}-\mathbf{k_0}| = 2k\sin\tfrac{1}{2}\theta.$$

It will easily be seen that an improved approximation to the elastic scattering is obtained by finding the exact solution of

$$\nabla^2\psi+\left\{k^2-\frac{2m}{\hbar^2}V_{00}(r)\right\}\psi = 0$$

instead of using Born's approximation; this amounts to inserting $F_0(\mathbf{r_1})\psi_0(\mathbf{r_2})$ instead of $e^{ik_0z_1}\psi_0(\mathbf{r_2})$ in the right-hand side of (17). This method is the one which has actually been most used in calculating electron scattering in gases.

For references to the many papers on the subject up to 1938, see the second general reference at the beginning of this chapter. Among more recent work Massey‡ and his co-workers have estimated a self-consistent field for methane by averaging the proton distribution over all directions, and have used this field to calculate the scattering of slow electrons; the results are in quite good agreement with experiment.

44.3. *Relative intensities of elastically and inelastically scattered particles*

The following considerations show that it is impossible to obtain inelastic scattering from an atom (or nucleus) unless there is some elastic scattering present too. We shall confine ourselves to the case where the dimensions of the nucleus are small compared with the wavelength, so that the scattering is spherically symmetrical.

† Cf. Chapters V, VI; an analytic expression for the field of helium is given by E. A. Hylleraas, *Zeits. f. Physik*, **54**, 347 (1929).

‡ R. A. Buckingham, H. S. W. Massey, and S. R. Tibbs, *Proc. Roy. Soc. A*, **178**, 119 (1941).

A spherically symmetrical solution of the wave equation of the system must then have the asymptotic form

$$\Psi(r, q) = r^{-1}[e^{-ikr}\psi_0(q) + Ae^{ikr}\psi_0(q) + Be^{ik'r}\psi_e(q)]. \tag{19}$$

Here $\psi_0(q)$, $\psi_e(q)$ represent the wave functions of the atom (nucleus) in its normal and excited states, k, k' the wave numbers of the elastically and inelastically scattered particles. The wave function representing an incident plane wave and scattered wave is

$$\left\{e^{ikz} - \frac{\sin kr}{kr}\right\}\psi_0(q) + a\Psi(r, q),$$

where a, chosen to make terms in e^{-ikr} vanish, must be $-1/2ik$. Thus the elastically scattered intensity is

$$I_0 = \frac{1}{4k^2}(1+A)^2$$

and the inelastically scattered intensity

$$I_e = \frac{1}{4k^2}\frac{k'}{k}|B|^2.$$

Since, however, the conservation of charge applied to equation (19) gives

$$1 = |A|^2 + \frac{k'}{k}|B|^2,$$

we see that I_0 cannot vanish unless $A = -1$ and I_e vanishes too; and if I_e has the largest possible value ($A = 0$, $I_e = 1/4k^2$), then

$$I_0 = 1/4k^2.$$

Such a formula would, for instance, apply to the scattering of slow neutrons by a nucleus of very strong absorbing power.

X

INTERACTION OF RADIATION WITH MATTER

45. Introduction

IN this section we shall show how to solve problems of the following type. An atom, or molecule, or any other system, is initially known to be in a given stationary state, denoted by the suffix zero, so the energy of the state is W_0. It is then acted on by a variable external field for a certain time, say by the field of a passing α-particle or gas molecule, or by a light wave. At the end of that time it *may* have made a transition to any other state, with energy W_n. We require to calculate the probability P_{0n} that the transition has occurred.

The physical principles by means of which the calculation is made are as follows: The wave equation for the unperturbed system (atom or molecule) is

$$i\hbar \frac{\partial \Psi}{\partial t} = H_0 \Psi,$$

where H_0 is the Hamiltonian operator of the unperturbed system. The solutions of this equation are

$$\Psi_n = \Psi_n(q) e^{-iW_n t/\hbar},$$

and the system is supposed initially, at time $t = 0$, to be in the state with wave-function Ψ_0. In the presence of the perturbing field let the wave equation be

$$i\hbar \frac{\partial \Psi}{\partial t} = (H_0 + U)\Psi. \tag{1}$$

The quantity U is the addition to the Hamiltonian due to the perturbing field, and will be a function of q, $\partial/\partial q$, and of the time. For instance, if we are dealing with the perturbation of a hydrogen atom by the field of a passing α-particle, U is the potential energy of an electron in the field of the α-particle.

The equation (1), being of the first order in t, enables us to determine Ψ at any subsequent time t. Suppose at time t we expand $\Psi(q, t)$ as a series

$$\Psi(q, t) = \sum_n a_n(t)\Psi_n(q, t). \tag{2}$$

Then, by the usual interpretation of wave mechanics, the quantity P_n given by

$$P_n = |a_n(t)|^2$$

is the probability that at time t the system is in the state n.

To obtain the coefficients $a_n(t)$, we substitute (2) into (1); we obtain

$$i\hbar \sum_n \frac{da_n}{dt} \Psi_n(q,t) = U\Psi(q,t).$$

Multiplying both sides by $\Psi_n^*(q,t)$ and integrating over all q, this equation reduces to

$$i\hbar \frac{da_n}{dt} = \int \Psi_n^*(q,t) U\Psi(q,t)\, dq. \tag{3}$$

To obtain an explicit solution we must in general assume that the perturbation is small, i.e. that during the perturbation the change in $\Psi(q,t)$ is not large. With this assumption we replace $\Psi(q,t)$ in the right-hand side of (3) by its original form $\Psi_0(q,t)$; we thus obtain

$$i\hbar \frac{da_n}{dt} = \int \Psi_n^*(q,t) U\Psi_0(q,t)\, dq.$$

Writing
$$\int \Psi_n^*(q) U\Psi_0(q)\, dq = (n|U|0),$$

we see that
$$a_n(t) = \frac{1}{i\hbar} \int_0^t (n|U|0) e^{i(W_0 - W_n)t/\hbar}\, dt. \tag{4}$$

We note that in this expression $(n|U|0)$ is in general a function of t.

Certain generalizations can be made at once from the expression (4):

(a) If the perturbing field varies slowly with time, so that many oscillations of the exponential function in (4) occur while U remains sensibly constant, the transition probability will be small.

(b) If U is periodic in the time with period ν (as, for instance, if U is the perturbing energy due to a light wave), then $a_n(t)$ will not *increase* with the time unless $h\nu = W_0 - W_n$. We see therefore that for the excitation of atoms or molecules by light the Bohr frequency condition can be deduced from the theory, and that if U is independent of the time, transitions to states of equal energy only occur.

45.1. *Excitation of atoms by a passing α-particle*

In this section we shall show how to calculate the probability that an atom is excited by an α-particle which passes a long way from it. Actually the first attempt† to calculate the stopping power of matter for α-particles was made in this way; but the method used in Chapter IX, in which the motion of the α-particle as well as that of the electrons is treated through a wave function, is much more convenient. The

---

† J. A. Gaunt, *Proc. Camb. Phil. Soc.* **23**, 732 (1927).

calculation is included here as being the simplest and most instructive example of the calculation of transition probabilities, not for its practical value.

The α-particle is supposed to move with constant velocity v past a hydrogen atom at the origin of coordinates, passing it at a distance p. If we take $t = 0$ to be the moment when the α-particle is nearest to the atom, then the perturbing energy U at any other time is, for an electron at the point (x, y, z)

$$U = \frac{-Ze^2}{\sqrt{\{(X-x)^2+(Y-y)^2+(Z-z)^2\}}}.$$

Here Ze is the charge on the α-particle, and X, Y, Z are the coordinates of its position at time t, given by

$$X = vt,$$
$$Y = p,$$
$$Z = 0.$$

Expanding U for small values of x, y, z we have

$$U = -\frac{Ze^2}{R}\left[1+\frac{xX+yY}{R^2}\right].$$

Since we have assumed that p is large compared with the radius of the atom, only the first terms in the expansion need be taken.

The quantity $a_n(t)$ is thus given, after the α-particle has passed $(t \to \infty)$, by

$$a_n = Ze^2 \int_{-\infty}^{\infty} \frac{x_{0n}vt+y_{0n}p}{(p^2+v^2t^2)^{\frac{3}{2}}} e^{2\pi i \nu_{0n}t} dt.$$

For the evaluation of these integrals, the reader is referred to the paper by Gaunt already quoted.

45.2. *Transitions to unquantized states*

A perturbing field (e.g. the field of a passing charged particle, or a light wave) may ionize an atom or molecule; in other words, transitions may be caused to states with unquantized energy. To calculate the appropriate transition probabilities, the simplest procedure will be to introduce fictitious quantization by enclosing the whole system in a large box, of side L, say. For instance, suppose the final state of the particle is represented by the wave function of a free particle

$$\Psi_k'(\mathbf{r}) = e^{i(\mathbf{k}\mathbf{r})}.$$

Then if we introduce our box of side L, together with the boundary condition that Ψ_k shall be periodic with period L, the normalized wave function is

$$\sqrt{\frac{1}{L^3}}\, e^{i(\mathbf{k}\mathbf{r})} \quad (\mathbf{k} = 2\pi\mathbf{n}/L;\ \mathbf{n} = (n_1, n_2, n_3)).$$

If we write $\qquad (n|U|0) = \dfrac{1}{L^{\frac{3}{2}}} \displaystyle\int e^{-i(\mathbf{k}\mathbf{r})} U\Psi_0(\mathbf{r})\, d\tau,$

then the transition probability to the state n is given by $|a_n(t)|^2$ with $a_n(t)$ given by (4). For values of $\mathbf{k}$ lying in the limits between k_1 and k_1+dk_1, k_2 and k_2+dk_2, k_3 and k_3+dk_3, the number of states is

$$L^3\, dk_1\, dk_2\, dk_3/(2\pi)^3. \tag{5}$$

Thus if $\qquad (k|U'|0) = \displaystyle\int e^{-i(\mathbf{k}\mathbf{r})} U\Psi_0(r)\, d\tau,$

the chance that the electron is ejected into a state with wave numbers in these limits is

$$\left.\begin{array}{c}\dfrac{dk_1\, dk_2\, dk_3}{(2\pi)^3}\, |a'(t)|^2, \\[2mm] a'(t) = \dfrac{1}{i\hbar} \displaystyle\int_0^t (K|U'|0) e^{i(W_0-W_k)t/\hbar}\, dt \end{array}\right\} . \tag{6}$$

where

45.3. *Transitions due to a perturbation periodic in the time*

This case is of great importance because of its application to the action of light waves on atoms and molecules.

We suppose that the perturbing term which has to be added to the Hamiltonian of the system is of the form

$$U = a \cos(2\pi\nu t + \epsilon),$$

where a, ϵ are functions of p and q but do not contain the time. It is convenient to write this in the form

$$U = Fe^{2\pi i\nu t} + F^* e^{-2\pi i\nu t},$$

where F is a complex function of p and q and F^* is its complex conjugate. Formula (4) then gives for the probability P_n that at time t a transition has been made to the state n of energy W_n

$$P_n = |a_n(t)|^2,$$

where

$$a_n = \frac{1}{i\hbar}\left[(n|F|0) \int_0^t \exp\left\{i\left(2\pi\nu - \frac{W_0-W_n}{\hbar}\right)t\right\} dt + \right.$$

$$\left. + (n|F^*|0) \int_0^t \exp\left\{i\left(-2\pi\nu - \frac{W_0-W_n}{\hbar}\right)t\right\} dt\right]. \tag{7}$$

Here $\qquad (n|F|0) = \int \Psi_n^*(q) F(p, q) \Psi_0(q)\, dq,$

which is not a function of time.

Unless $\qquad |W_n - W_0| = 2\pi\hbar\nu,$ $\qquad\qquad$ (8)

the integrals in (7) do not increase with the time. The sudden imposition of the field will cause transitions, but after a time equal to $1/\nu$ the probability that a transition has taken place does not grow any greater. Only values of the frequency for which (8) is satisfied need therefore be considered.

If we write $\qquad \nu_{0n} = (W_0 - W_n)/2\pi\hbar$

and suppose that ν lies in the neighbourhood of ν_{0n}, then only one of the two terms of (7) will be significant. Carrying out the integration with respect to t we find

$$a_n(t) \simeq \frac{1}{i\hbar}(n|F|0)\frac{\exp\{2\pi i(\nu - \nu_{0n})t\} - 1}{2\pi i(\nu - \nu_{0n})},$$

and hence $\qquad P_n(t) = \frac{1}{\hbar^2}|(n|F|0)|^2\frac{2\{1 - \cos 2\pi(\nu - \nu_{0n})t\}}{\{2\pi(\nu - \nu_{0n})\}^2}.$ $\qquad$ (9)

If ν is equal to ν_{0n}, the probability $P_n(t)$ that a transition has occurred increases as the *square* of the time, instead of linearly with the time as one would expect. However, this apparent contradiction can be resolved as follows:

If the final state is quantized, we shall have to consider perturbation by radiation with a band of frequencies extending over the natural width of the absorption line. This is done in § 46 and it is shown that a transition probability proportional to t is obtained. In this section we suppose that the final state is unquantized—in other words, that the calculation refers to the ionization of an atom by a light wave or other periodic disturbance. The fictitious quantization of § 45.2 may be introduced, the atom being enclosed in a 'box' of side L. Then

$$|(n|F|0)|^2 = \frac{1}{L^3}\left|\int e^{-i(\mathbf{kr})}F\Psi_0'(\mathbf{r})\, d\tau\right|^2,$$

and the number of states for which the particle is moving with its momentum in the solid angle $d\Omega$ about the vector $\mathbf{k}$, and with energy in the range dW, is by (5)

$$L^3\, d\Omega\, m^{\frac{3}{2}}h^{-3}(2W)^{\frac{1}{2}}\, dW = \rho(W)\, dW, \quad \text{say.}$$

To obtain the probability that, after time t, the particle is ejected in a direction lying in the solid angle $d\Omega$, we have to sum over the transition probabilities to all these states; this gives, making L tend to infinity so that the summation is replaced by an integral,

$$d\Omega \int P_n(t)\rho(W_n)\,dW_n.$$

Now the quantity $P_n(t)$ has a very strong maximum when W_n passes through the value for which $\nu - \nu_{0n}$ vanishes, and for large t practically all the value of the integral comes from here. Thus in all terms in $\rho(W_n)P_n(t)$ except the term involving the time factor, we may set W_n equal to this value, i.e.

$$W_n = W_0 + 2\pi\hbar\nu.$$

The time factor gives

$$\int \frac{2\{1 - \cos 2\pi(\nu - \nu_{0n})t\}}{\{2\pi(\nu - \nu_{0n})\}^2}\,dW,$$

or with $2\pi(\nu - \nu_{0n}) = x$,

$$\int \frac{2(1 - \cos xt)}{x^2}\,dx.$$

When t is large the limits of integration may be replaced by $\pm\infty$ and we obtain

$$\hbar t \int \frac{2(1 - \cos y)}{y^2}\,dy.$$

The integral is equal to 2π; thus, finally, the probability that a transition will have taken place after time t is

$$(t/\hbar)|(n|F|0)|^2\rho(W_n),\tag{10}$$

which increases linearly with t as it should.

The probability per unit time that the electron is ejected with its momentum in the solid angle $d\Omega$ is

$$d\Omega \frac{mv}{4\pi^2\hbar^2}\left|\int e^{-i(\mathbf{kr})}F\Psi_0(r)\,d\tau\right|^2.$$

45.4. *Transitions caused by a perturbing term independent of the time*

This is a special case of the problem considered in the last section, the frequency ν being taken to be zero.

Formula (9) remains valid. Since U is now independent of t, it may be written

$$P_n(t) = \frac{1}{\hbar^2}|(n|U|0)|^2 \frac{2\{1 - \cos 2\pi\nu_{0n}t\}}{(2\pi\nu_{0n})^2}.$$

Here U is the perturbing potential and the matrix element $(n|U|0)$ is formed with normalized wave functions. When t is large the function on the right has a strong maximum for ν_{0n} equal to zero, i.e. for transitions in which energy is conserved.

If, as before, we introduce the function $\rho(W)\,dW$ to denote the number of states with energy between W and dW (and if necessary subject also to other conditions, such as having the direction of momentum in a given solid angle), then the probability after time t that a transition has occurred is

$$\int P_n(t)\rho(W)\,dW.$$

As t tends to infinity, this gives as before

$$t|(n|U|0)|^2\rho(W)/\hbar \tag{11}$$

for transitions in which energy is conserved. For other transitions it does not increase with t.

The following is an example: A beam of electrons is incident on a centre of force in which the potential energy of an electron is $V(r)$. If we normalize $\Psi_0'(r)$ to represent a beam such that one electron crosses unit area per unit time, then

$$\Psi_0'(r) = v^{-\frac{1}{2}}e^{i(\mathbf{k}_0 \cdot \mathbf{r})}.$$

Equation (10) then gives for the number of particles scattered into the solid angle $d\omega$ per unit time

$$\left|\frac{m}{2\pi\hbar^2}\int e^{i(\mathbf{k}_0-\mathbf{k})\cdot\mathbf{r}}V(r)\,d\tau\right|^2 d\omega,$$

which agrees with the formula found by another method in Chapter IX, equation (15).

46. Emission and absorption of radiation

The correct description of the intensities of spectral lines according to the quantum theory was first given by Einstein.[†] Corresponding to the transition between any two states n and m of an atomic system, he introduced three probability coefficients A_{nm}, B_{nm}, and B_{mn}. The state n is supposed to be the state of highest energy, and the coefficient A_{nm} is defined as follows: $A_{nm}\,dt$ is the probability that an atom, initially in the state n, will make a spontaneous transition in the time interval dt to the state m. This probability was supposed to be independent of the past history of the atom or of the process by which it had been brought to the state n.

The coefficients B_{nm} and B_{mn} are defined as follows: suppose the atom is in the presence of radiation, unpolarized and incident equally in all directions, such that the energy density with frequency between ν and $\nu+d\nu$ is $I(\nu)\,d\nu$. Let ν_{nm} be the frequency corresponding to the transition between the states n, m. Then if the atom is in the state m

† A. Einstein, *Phys. Zeits.* **18**, 121 (1917).

(the lower state), the chance in a time interval dt that it will make a transition to the state n with the absorption of a quantum of radiation is $B_{mn} I(\nu_{nm}) dt$. Also, if it is in the upper state n, the chance that in the presence of the radiation it will make a transition to the ground state is

$$\{A_{nm} + B_{nm} I(\nu_{nm})\} dt.$$

Einstein was able to prove the following relationships:

$$B_{nm} = B_{mn}, \qquad A = \frac{8\pi h \nu^3}{c^3} B. \tag{12}$$

The proof is as follows: Suppose a number of the atoms concerned are in thermal equilibrium in an enclosed space at temperature T, together with the (black body) radiation in equilibrium at that temperature. Then as many atoms must make the transition upwards as make the transition downwards. Hence

$$N_n[A_{nm} + B_{nm} I(\nu_{nm})] = B_{mn} I(\nu_{nm}) N_m,$$

where N_n, N_m are the numbers of atoms in the two states. Now in thermal equilibrium, by Boltzmann's laws,

$$\frac{N_n}{N_m} = e^{-(W_n - W_m)/kT},$$

which by the Bohr frequency condition gives

$$\frac{N_n}{N_m} = e^{-h\nu_{nm}/kT}.$$

Thus
$$I(\nu_{nm}) = \frac{A_{nm}}{B_{mn} e^{h\nu_{nm}/kT} - B_{nm}}.$$

Comparing this with the well-known formula for the intensity of black body radiation,

$$I(\nu) = \frac{8\pi h \nu^3 \, d\nu}{c^3} \frac{1}{e^{h\nu/kT} - 1},$$

we see that equations (12) are satisfied.

In attempting a quantal theory of the emission and absorption of radiation we are faced with the following position: The theory of absorption and stimulated emission is relatively elementary; the light wave can be treated as an electromagnetic field periodic in the time, and the probability that the atom will make a transition from one state to another under its influence can be calculated by the methods of the last section. As we have seen, the Bohr frequency condition can be deduced from the theory, and the values of the Einstein B coefficients obtained. The A coefficient can then be deduced from equation (12). But this elementary theory does not *by itself* predict spontaneous emission; in the absence of a field one cannot see why transitions should occur at all. To account for spontaneous transitions one must introduce a more complete theory in which atom and radiation are both considered as one system, and the radiation itself is quantized.

The elementary theory will be given in the next section; the more complete theory in § 47 and the following sections.

46.1. *Elementary theory of absorption*

As explained in the last section, in this section we shall treat the action of a light wave on an atom as that of a perturbing electromagnetic field. Such a theory will account for absorption, but not for emission.

A plane polarized light wave moving along the z-axis can be written in the form

$$H_y = E_x = b \sin 2\pi\nu\left(\frac{z}{c} - t\right),$$
$$H_x = E_y = 0.$$

(13)

It is convenient to describe this by a vector potential $\mathbf{A}$ and scalar potential ϕ, from which $\mathbf{E}$ and $\mathbf{H}$ can be deduced from the equations

$$\mathbf{E} = -\frac{1}{c}\frac{\partial \mathbf{A}}{\partial t} - \operatorname{grad}\phi,$$

$$\mathbf{H} = \operatorname{curl}\mathbf{A}.$$

If we set

$$A_x = a \cos 2\pi\nu\left(\frac{z}{c} - t\right) \quad (a = bc/2\pi\nu),$$
$$A_y = A_z = 0,$$

it is easily verified that (13) is satisfied. The energy density I in the wave is given by

$$I = \frac{\overline{\mathbf{E}^2 + \mathbf{H}^2}}{8\pi} = \frac{\pi a^2 \nu^2}{2c^2}.$$

By equation (46) of Chapter I, the perturbing term introduced by a vector potential $\mathbf{A}$ for which $\operatorname{div}\mathbf{A} = 0$ is

$$\frac{e\hbar}{imc}(\mathbf{A}\,\operatorname{grad}).$$

In our case this gives

$$\frac{e\hbar a}{2imc}\left\{e^{2\pi i\nu(z/c - t)}\frac{\partial}{\partial x} + \text{complex conjugate}\right\}.$$

Thus the probability that after time t the atom has made a transition from a state with wave-function ψ_0 to a state with wave-function ψ_n is given by (9) with

$$|(n|F|0)|^2 = \left(\frac{e\hbar a}{2mc}\right)^2 Q_n,$$

where

$$Q_n = \left|\int \Psi_n^* e^{2\pi i v z/c} \frac{\partial \Psi_0}{\partial x} d\tau\right|^2.$$

Substituting in terms of the energy density we find for the probability $P_n(t)$

$$P_n(t) = \frac{e^2}{m^2 v^2} I(v) Q_n \frac{2\{1 - \cos 2\pi(v - v_{0n})t\}}{\{2\pi(v - v_{0n})\}^2}.$$

As in the previous section, if we set v equal to v_{0n} we find that $P_n(t)$ increases as the *square* of the time. We have therefore to consider that the atom is irradiated by a band of frequencies, with energy density $I(v) dv$ in the range dv. Since

$$\int_{-\infty}^{\infty} \frac{2\{1 - \cos 2\pi(v - v_{0n})t\}}{\{2\pi(v - v_{0n})t\}^2} dv = t, \tag{14}$$

we see that the probability per unit time that the atom makes a transition from the state 0 to the state n is

$$\frac{1}{2\pi} I(v_{0n}) \left|\frac{e}{mv} \int \Psi_n^* e^{2\pi i v z/c} \frac{\partial \Psi_0}{\partial x} d\tau\right|^2.$$

It will be noted that the z-axis is the direction of propagation of the wave, the x-axis the direction of polarization.

The Einstein B-coefficient will be obtained by averaging over all directions of incidence and polarization.

The integral

$$\int \Psi_n^* e^{2\pi i v z/c} \frac{\partial \Psi_0}{\partial x} d\tau \tag{15}$$

thus determines the absorption and emission intensities. This quantity can be simplified, making use of the fact that for light absorbed in the line spectrum of an atom, the wave-length c/v of the light is large compared with the diameter of the atom. We may thus expand

$$e^{2\pi i v z/c} = 1 + \frac{2\pi i v z}{c} + \dots.$$

To a first order of approximation, therefore, the integral (15) reduces to

$$\int \Psi_n^* \frac{\partial \Psi_0}{\partial x} d\tau.$$

By equation (21) of Chapter VII this may be written

$$\frac{2\pi m}{\hbar} v_{0n} \int \Psi_n^* x \Psi_0 d\tau.$$

Thus the probability of absorption takes the form

$$2\pi e^2 |x_{0n}|^2 I(\nu_{0n})/\hbar^2.$$

Averaging over all directions of polarization we obtain for the B-coefficient

$$B = \frac{2\pi e^2}{3\hbar^2}(|x_{0n}|^2 + |y_{0n}|^2 + |z_{0n}|^2),$$

and by (11) for the A-coefficient

$$A = \frac{32\pi^3 e^2 \nu^3}{3\hbar c}(|x_{0n}|^2 + |y_{0n}|^2 + |z_{0n}|^2).$$

It is convenient to express these quantities in terms of oscillator strengths f_n (Chap. VII, p. 169); we obtain

$$B = e^2 f_n / 6\hbar m\nu, \qquad A = 8\pi^2 e^2 \nu^2 f_n / 3mc^2. \tag{16}$$

This form is convenient because f_n is dimensionless, and because

$$\sum f_n = 1,$$

where the summation is over all transitions which start from a given state.

46.2. Selection rules

Suppose that the state 0 has orbital quantum numbers l, u; in other words, that the part of the wave function involving θ, ϕ is

$$P_l^u(\cos\theta)e^{iu\phi}.$$

Suppose also that the state n has quantum numbers l', u'. Then the matrix elements x_{0n}, y_{0n}, z_{0n} will contain integrals of the type

$$\iint P_{l'}^{u'}(\cos\theta)e^{-iu'\phi} \begin{array}{c} \cos\theta \\ \sin\theta\cos\phi \\ \sin\theta\sin\phi \end{array} P_l^u(\cos\theta)e^{iu\phi}\sin\theta\,d\theta d\phi.$$

It is obvious that this integral vanishes unless

$$u - u' = \pm 1 \quad \text{or} \quad 0. \tag{17}$$

The integral also vanishes unless

$$l - l' = \pm 1. \tag{18}$$

This is shown in the appendix to this book; it is easily verified in the simple case where $l = 0$.

Equations (15) and (16) give the well-known *selection rules* for optical transition. If they are not satisfied the 'dipole moments' z_{0n}, etc., vanish, and to obtain the transition probability we must then take the second term in the expansion (14); the integral (15) becomes

$$\frac{2\pi\nu}{c}\int \Psi_n^* z \frac{\partial\Psi_0}{\partial x}\,d\tau.$$

Transitions for which this quantity does not vanish are said to possess a 'quadripole' moment. It will be seen that for transitions with a quadripole moment the transition probabilities are smaller by a factor of order (radius of atoms/wave-length of light)^2 than for those with a dipole moment.

It is worth remarking that there is one type of transition for which the transition probability vanishes exactly; this is for transitions from one s-state to another, so that both Ψ_0 and Ψ_n are spherically symmetrical.

46.3. *Alternative treatment of emission*

For certain purposes, especially some of the applications of relativistic quantum theory in Chapter XI, it is very useful to have an expression for the electromagnetic field radiated by an atom. The treatment given in this section is semi-classical, and can only be justified on the basis of quantum electrodynamics; it is none the less very useful.

Suppose that in an atom there exists a charge density given by and a current j

$$\left.\begin{array}{l} \rho = \rho_0(x,y,z)e^{-2\pi i\nu t}+\text{c.c.} \\ \mathbf{j} = \mathbf{j}_0(x,y,z)e^{-2\pi i\nu t}+\text{c.c.} \end{array}\right\} \tag{19}$$

Then the electromagnetic field radiated by this charge and current are given by the equations

$$\nabla^2 A_0 - \frac{1}{c^2}\frac{\partial^2 A_0}{\partial t^2} = -4\pi\rho,$$

$$\nabla^2 \mathbf{A} - \frac{1}{c^2}\frac{\partial^2 \mathbf{A}}{\partial t^2} = -\frac{4\pi}{c}\mathbf{j}.$$

Here A_0, $\mathbf{A}$ are the scalar and vector potentials. If we consider retarded potentials only, obtaining thus a solution representing an outgoing wave, the solution is

$$A_0 = e^{-2\pi i\nu t}\int \frac{e^{2\pi i\nu|\mathbf{r}'-\mathbf{r}|/c}}{|\mathbf{r}-\mathbf{r}'|}\rho_0(x',y',z')\,d\tau'+\text{c.c.}$$

with a similar expression for $\mathbf{A}$. For large r this becomes

$$A_0 = \frac{e^{2\pi i\nu(r/c-t)}}{r}\int e^{-2\pi i\nu(\mathbf{n}\mathbf{r}')/c}\rho_0(x',y',z')\,d\tau'. \tag{20}$$

Here $\mathbf{n}$ denotes the vector $\mathbf{r}/r$.

Suppose now that an atom is in an excited state 0, and that we wish to know the field that will be radiated into transitions to lower states. We shall make the following new assumption: that corresponding to any lower state n, the field radiated initially is that which would be given classically by a charge density ρ_{0n} and current density j_{0n} given by (19) with

$$\rho_0 = e\Psi_n \Psi_0^*,$$

$$\mathbf{j}_0 = \frac{e\hbar}{2i}(\Psi_n \operatorname{grad} \Psi_0^* - \Psi_0^* \operatorname{grad} \Psi_n),$$

$$h\nu = W_0 - W_n.$$

For the corresponding expressions using Dirac's relativistic equation cf. p. 309.

It may easily be verified, using Schrödinger's equations, that the continuity equation is satisfied:

$$\operatorname{div} j + \frac{\partial \rho}{\partial t} = 0.$$

The field radiated is then given by (20).

It may be verified, by obtaining the energy radiated per unit time and dividing by $h\nu$, that equation (16) for the A-coefficient is obtained.

47. Proper treatment of the radiation problem : quantization of the field

We have seen that an elementary theory, in which the electromagnetic field is treated as a perturbation acting on an atom, can account for the absorption but not for spontaneous emission. To account for this, it is necessary to quantize the electromagnetic field and to treat the whole assembly, atom and radiation, as one dynamical system.

The theory, due originally to Dirac,[†] is based on the following idea: The radiation is thought of as shut up in a box; there will thus be a series of normal modes each with its discrete frequency ν. We know from the experimental evidence reviewed in Chapter I that the energy of light of frequency ν can change only by multiples of $h\nu$; and thus it involves no great step forward to treat each normal mode as a vibrating system, with wave functions appropriate to a simple harmonic oscillator. A transition in which an atom emits or absorbs radiation is thus treated as a transition of the whole system in which the appropriate normal mode of the radiation changes its quantum number by unity. The perturbing energy (not a function of the time) is the interaction between the atom and the radiation.

We have first to set up the Hamiltonian of the radiation field in the

† P. A. M. Dirac, *Proc. Roy. Soc.* A, **114**, 243 (1927).

absence of any charged particle. This field is conveniently described by a vector potential $\mathbf{A}$ chosen so that the scalar potential vanishes everywhere. The electric and magnetic vectors are then given by

$$\mathbf{E} = -\dot{\mathbf{A}}/c, \qquad \mathbf{H} = \operatorname{curl}\mathbf{A}.$$

A typical standing wave, representing radiation shut up in a box, may be written

$$\mathbf{A} = \beta\mathbf{e}\sin(\mathbf{\varkappa r})\cos\kappa ct. \tag{21}$$

Here $\mathbf{e}$ is a unit vector, β an arbitrary constant, and $1/\kappa$ any length. In a volume V the number of normal modes with given polarization, frequencies between ν and $\nu+d\nu$, and direction $\mathbf{\varkappa}$ of propagation in the solid angle $d\Omega$ is†

$$V\rho_\nu d\nu d\Omega = V\nu^2 d\Omega d\nu/c^3. \tag{22}$$

The function $\rho_\nu = \nu^2/c^3$ will be called the density function of the radiation.

We now write instead of (21)

$$\mathbf{A} = \sqrt{(8\pi c^2)}\mathbf{e}\sin(\mathbf{\varkappa r})q(t). \tag{23}$$

The quantity $q(t)$ is the dynamical variable which specifies the state of the vibrating normal mode. We shall treat it exactly as the dynamical variable of an oscillator according to quantum mechanics. For this we need the Hamiltonian and hence the wave equation of the radiation field. The purpose of the normalizing factor $\sqrt{(8\pi c^2)}$ will appear below.

The electric and magnetic vectors $\mathbf{E}$ and $\mathbf{H}$ derived from the vector potential $\mathbf{A}$ (23) are

$$\left.\begin{aligned}\mathbf{E} &= -\sqrt{(8\pi)}\mathbf{e}\sin(\mathbf{\varkappa r})\dot{q}(t) \\ \mathbf{H} &= \sqrt{(8\pi c^2)}(\mathbf{\varkappa}\times\mathbf{e})\cos(\mathbf{\varkappa r})q(t)\end{aligned}\right\}. \tag{24}$$

Now since $\mathbf{\varkappa}$ and $\mathbf{e}$ are perpendicular vectors and $\mathbf{e}$ is a unit vector we have

$$(\mathbf{\varkappa}\times\mathbf{e})^2 = \kappa^2.$$

Making use of this result and of the fact that the mean values of $\sin^2(\mathbf{\varkappa r})$ and $\cos^2(\mathbf{\varkappa r})$ are $\frac{1}{2}$, we find that the energy of this wave is

$$W = \frac{1}{8\pi}\int (\mathbf{E}^2+\mathbf{H}^2)\,d\tau = \tfrac{1}{2}(\dot{q}^2+c^2\kappa^2 q^2). \tag{25}$$

The momentum conjugate to the coordinate q in the Hamiltonian formalism is

$$p = \frac{\partial W}{\partial\dot{q}} = \dot{q};$$

so that, putting

$$c^2\kappa^2 = 4\pi^2\nu^2, \tag{26}$$

† Cf. J. H. Jeans, *Dynamical Theory of Gases*, 4th ed., chap. xvi (Cambridge, 1925).

we have for the Hamiltonian of this vibration

$$W = \tfrac{1}{2}(p^2 + 4\pi^2\nu^2 q^2). \tag{27}$$

It follows that, with the normalizing factor as chosen, the vibrating normal mode behaves like a simple harmonic oscillator of mass unity. This is true either in classical or wave mechanics.

In wave mechanics we may set up the usual Schrödinger equation

$$\frac{\partial^2\phi}{\partial q^2} + \frac{1}{\hbar^2}\{W - 4\pi^2\nu^2 q^2\}\phi = 0. \tag{28}$$

The possible values of the energy will be

$$W_n = (n + \tfrac{1}{2})h\nu, \tag{29}$$

where n is an integer, and the wave functions are the Hermitian polynomials discussed in Chapter II and the Appendix.

The pure radiation field may then be described by the superposition of fundamental vibrations of the type (23) with a range of frequencies

$$\nu_1, \nu_2, \nu_3, ..., \nu_s.$$

The number of frequencies lying in any given range is determined by the formula (22), but the vectors $\mathbf{e}_s$, $\varkappa_s$ are considered to be distributed at random. The Hamiltonian of the radiation field is obtained by taking the sum of all the contributions W_s of the type (27); thus it is†

$$W = \sum_s W_s = \sum_s \tfrac{1}{2}(p_s^2 + 4\pi^2\nu_s^2 q_s^2). \tag{30}$$

In the quantum theory of radiation it is often more convenient to replace the cosine and sine waves representing the radiation field by their complex exponential forms, which represent waves moving in definite directions instead of standing waves. In this representation we write for the vector potential

$$\mathbf{A} = \sum_s \mathbf{A}_s = \sum_s \{\mathbf{a}_s q_s(t) + \mathbf{a}_s^* q_s^*(t)\}, \tag{31}$$

where the field coordinate $q_s(t)$ is now complex and

$$\mathbf{a}_s = \sqrt{(4\pi c^2)}\mathbf{e}_s \exp i(\varkappa_s \mathbf{r}). \tag{32}$$

The Hamiltonian of the radiation field can be calculated as in the case of real wave functions; it comes out to be

$$W = \sum_s (\dot{q}_s \dot{q}_s^* + 4\pi^2\nu_s^2 q_s q_s^*) = \sum_s (p_s p_s^* + 4\pi^2\nu_s^2 q_s q_s^*). \tag{33}$$

---

† It can easily be shown that the sum on the right-hand side of (30) representing the sum of the energies of all the oscillators is equal to the energy of the radiation field. It should also be observed that only the radiation field can be represented by a superposition of stationary waves in this fashion; such a representation is not possible for radiation in the presence of an external electromagnetic field.

Now since q_s is a solution of the harmonic equation

$$\ddot{q}_s + 4\pi^2 \nu_s^2 q_s = 0,$$

it follows that $\dot{q}_s \dot{q}_s^* = 4\pi^2 \nu_s^2 q_s q_s^*;$

we may thus write the Hamiltonian (33) in the form

$$W = 8\pi^2 \sum_s \nu_s^2 q_s q_s^*.$$

This may be reduced to the form for the real variable

$$W = \tfrac{1}{2} \sum_s (\bar{p}_s^2 + 4\pi^2 \nu_s^2 \bar{q}_s^2)$$

by the substitutions

$$q_s = \frac{1}{2}\left(\bar{q}_s + \frac{i}{2\pi\nu_s}\bar{p}_s\right), \qquad q_s^* = \frac{1}{2}\left(\bar{q}_s - \frac{i}{2\pi\nu_s}\bar{p}_s\right).$$

47.1. *Hamiltonian of the complete system*

We have now to determine the Hamiltonian of the atom and the radiation field considered as a single mechanical system. The non-relativistic motion of an electron in an electromagnetic field described by a vector potential $\mathbf{A}$ and a scalar potential ϕ is uniquely determined by the Hamiltonian $\mathfrak{H} = e\phi/c + (\mathbf{P} - e\mathbf{A}/c)^2/2m,$

where $\mathbf{P}$ denotes the momentum of the electron, m its mass. Writing V for ϕ/c, expanding the scalar product $(\mathbf{P} - e\mathbf{A}/c)^2$, and retaining only terms of order $1/c$, we have

$$\mathfrak{H} = \mathbf{P}^2/2m + eV - e(\mathbf{P} . \mathbf{A})/mc. \tag{34}$$

The Hamiltonian of the complete system comprising the atom and the radiation field is obtained by adding to (34) the Hamiltonian of the radiation field, equation (30) or (33) above, and by substituting for the vector potential $\mathbf{A}$ the corresponding expression (23) or (31). Substituting from equations (31) and (33) into equation (34) we obtain for the Hamiltonian of the coupled system

$$\mathfrak{H} = \mathfrak{H}_0 + \mathfrak{H}_1, \tag{35}$$

where $$\mathfrak{H}_0 = \frac{1}{2m}\mathbf{P}^2 + eV + \sum_s \tfrac{1}{2}(p_s^2 + 4\pi^2\nu_s^2 q_s^2) \tag{36}$$

is the sum of the Hamiltonians of the pure radiation field and of a particle moving in a field free from radiation, and

$$\mathfrak{H}_1 = -\frac{2e\sqrt{\pi}}{m} \sum_s \{q_s e^{i(\kappa_s . \mathbf{r})} + q_s^* e^{-i(\kappa_s . \mathbf{r})}\}(\mathbf{e}_s . \mathbf{P}) \tag{37}$$

is the energy of interaction between the electron and the radiation field.

The transition probability for a transition in which the electron jumps from one state to another, emitting or absorbing a quantum, can now be written down at once from formula (11). Suppose that the direction of propagation of the light wave lies in a solid angle $d\Omega$ about the direction $\varkappa$. Let this wave have N quanta before the process, N' after, and let the suffix 0 denote the initial state of the atom and the suffix n the final state. Then, substituting $\mathfrak{H}_1$ for U in the formula (11), the probability per unit time that the transition occurs is

$$\frac{1}{\hbar}|(N', n|\mathfrak{H}_1|N, 0)|^2\rho(W),\tag{38}$$

where $\Psi'_{N',n}$ and $\Psi'_{N,0}$ are solutions of the unperturbed wave equation

$$\mathfrak{H}_0\,\Psi = W\Psi,\tag{39}$$

and in this case

$$\mathfrak{H}_1 = -\frac{2\sqrt{\pi}e}{m}\{qe^{i(\varkappa \mathbf{r})}+q^*e^{-i(\varkappa \mathbf{r})}\}(\mathbf{e}.\mathbf{P}).\tag{40}$$

47.2. *Calculation of the matrix elements*

In the last section we showed that, in order to obtain the transition probability of a process involving the emission or absorption of radiation, we have to consider the solutions of the wave equation (39) of the unperturbed system. Suppose that Ψ'_n is an eigenfunction and W_n the corresponding energy value of the Schrödinger equation

$$\left(\frac{1}{2m}\mathbf{P}^2+eV\right)\Psi'_n = \left(-\frac{\hbar^2}{2m}\nabla^2+eV\right)\Psi'_n = W_n\,\Psi'_n,$$

and that ϕ_N is an eigenfunction and W_N a corresponding energy value of the wave equation

$$(p^2+4\pi^2\nu^2q^2)\phi_N = W_N\phi_N.$$

Then the function $\qquad\Psi'_{N,n} = \Psi'_n\phi_N\tag{41}$

is an eigenfunction of the Schrödinger equation (39) corresponding to the eigenvalue $\qquad W_{N,n} = W_N+W_n.\tag{42}$

Substituting from (40) and (41) into the equation defining the matrix element $(N', n|\mathfrak{H}_1|N, 0)$, we obtain the equation

$(N', n|\mathfrak{H}_1|N, 0)$

$$= -\frac{2\sqrt{\pi}e}{m}\left\{(n|P_s|0)\int \phi_{N'}^*\, q\phi_N\, dq+(n|P_s^*|0)\int \phi_{N'}^*\, q^*\phi_N\, dq\right\},\tag{43}$$

where the matrix elements $(n|P_s|0)$ and $(n|P_s^*|0)$ are defined by the formulae

$$\left.\begin{aligned}(n|P_s|0) &= \int \Psi_n^* e^{i(\kappa r)}(\mathbf{e}.\mathbf{P})\Psi_0 d\tau \\ (n|P_s^*|0) &= \int \Psi_n^* e^{-i(\kappa r)}(\mathbf{e}.\mathbf{P})\Psi_0 d\tau\end{aligned}\right\}. \tag{44}$$

Since the functions ϕ_N are the eigenfunctions of the wave equation for a linear oscillator, it follows that the integral

$$\int \phi_{N'}^* q\phi_N dq$$

vanishes unless $|N-N'| = 1$ and also that

$$\int \phi_N^* q\phi_{N+1} dq = \left\{\frac{h(N+1)}{4\pi\nu}\right\}^{\frac{1}{2}}. \tag{45}$$

The energy corresponding to the eigenfunction ϕ_N is

$$W = h\nu(N+\tfrac{1}{2}). \tag{46}$$

Substituting from equation (45) into equation (43) we see that the matrix element $(N', n|\mathfrak{H}_1|N, 0)$ is different from zero only if $N' = N\pm 1$. We thus obtain for the two non-vanishing matrix elements

$$\left.\begin{aligned}(N+1, n|\mathfrak{H}_1|N, 0) &= -\frac{e}{m}\left\{\frac{h(N+1)}{\nu}\right\}^{\frac{1}{2}} \int \Psi_n^* e^{i(\kappa r)}p_e\Psi_0 d\tau \\ (N-1, n|\mathfrak{H}_1|N, 0) &= -\frac{e}{m}\left\{\frac{hN}{\nu}\right\}^{\frac{1}{2}} \int \Psi_n^* e^{-i(\kappa r)}p_e\Psi_0 d\tau\end{aligned}\right\}, \tag{47}$$

where $$p_e = (\mathbf{Pe})$$

denotes the component of the vector $\mathbf{P}$ in the direction of the polarization.

For a process in which a quantum is emitted, N is zero, and for the absorption of a quantum $N = 1$. Thus the transition probability for a transition in which an electron jumps from one state (0) to another (n) with the *emission* of a quantum of frequency ν is

$$\frac{e^2\nu}{m^2c^3\hbar}\left|\int \Psi_n^* e^{i(\kappa r)}p_e\Psi_0 d\tau\right|^2, \tag{48}$$

and the transition probability for a similar process in which a quantum is *absorbed* is

$$\frac{e^2\nu}{m^2c^3\hbar}\left|\int \Psi_n^* e^{-i(\kappa r)}p_e\Psi_0 d\tau\right|^2. \tag{49}$$

If the final state of the electron belongs to the continuous spectrum

$$\rho_W dW = mcp\, dW d\Omega/h^3c^3,$$

where p is the momentum of the electron. In that case (38) becomes

$$\frac{2\pi p e^2 \, d\Omega}{h^3 m c^2}\left(\int \Psi_n^* e^{-i(\kappa r)} p_e \Psi_0 \, d\tau\right)^2. \tag{49 a}$$

48. First-order radiation processes

48.1. *The emission of radiation*

As a first example of the application of the general theory developed in the preceding sections we consider the emission of light by a hydrogen atom. Suppose that initially the electron is in an excited state in which its wave function is Ψ_n, and that it falls to the ground state with the emission of a quantum of radiation of frequency ν. The wave function of the electron in the ground state is Ψ_0, say. Then the roles of the suffixes n and 0 are interchanged in equation (48). It follows from equation (8) that the transition probability is negligible unless the frequency of the emitted radiation is

$$\nu = (W_n - W_0)/h,$$

which is the value given by Bohr's frequency relation.

The square of the matrix element occurring in the expression (48) can be reduced easily to a familiar form. In general the wave-length of the radiation emitted is large in comparison with the dimensions of the atom so that the function $\exp i(\kappa r)$ ($\kappa = 2\pi\nu/c$) will be practically constant over that part of the space in which the wave functions of the electron differ appreciably from zero. We may therefore write

$$\int \Psi_0^* e^{i(\kappa r)} p_e \Psi_n \, d\tau = e^{i(\kappa r)} \int \Psi_0^* p_e \Psi_n \, d\tau.$$

If, now, we write $\qquad \mathbf{P} = m\mathbf{v}$

and denote by Θ the angle between the velocity vector $\mathbf{v}$ and the direction of polarization, we obtain

$$\int \Psi_0^* p_e \Psi_n \, d\tau = m \cos\Theta \int \Psi_0^* \mathbf{v} \Psi_n \, d\tau,$$

so that $\qquad \left|\int \Psi_0^* p_e \Psi_n \, d\tau\right|^2 = m^2 \cos^2\Theta \left|\int \Psi_0^* \mathbf{v} \Psi_n \, d\tau\right|^2.$

Now $\qquad \int \Psi_0^* v_x \Psi_n \, d\tau = 2\pi i\nu \int \Psi_0^* x \Psi_n \, d\tau = 2\pi i\nu(0|x|n)$

and similarly for the y- and z-components of the velocity $\mathbf{v}$. Thus

$$\left|\int \Psi_0^* p_e \Psi_n \, d\tau\right|^2 = 4\pi^2 \nu^2 m^2 \cos^2\Theta |(0|\mathbf{r}|n)|^2 \tag{50}$$

where $|(0|\mathbf{r}|n)|^2$ denotes the sum

$$(0|x|n)^2 + (0|y|n)^2 + (0|z|n)^2. \tag{51}$$

Equation (48) then gives for the chance per unit time that a quantum is emitted into the solid angle $d\Omega$

$$\frac{8\pi^3\nu^3e^2}{hc^3}\cos^2\Theta|(0|\mathbf{r}|n)|^2\,d\Omega. \tag{52}$$

Multiplying this expression by $h\nu$ and integrating over all angles we obtain an expression for the total intensity of the radiation emitted by the atom in unit time. The summation over the directions of polarization replaces $\cos^2\Theta$ by $\sin^2\theta$, where θ is the angle between the direction of propagation $\varkappa$ and the position vector $\mathbf{r}$ of the electron; making this substitution in (52) and integrating over all possible values of the angles, we find that the total intensity radiated per unit time is

$$S = \frac{64\pi^4e^2\nu^4}{3c^3}|(0|\mathbf{r}|n)|^2. \tag{53}$$

This is the same formula as that given on p. 257.

In the classical theory, if we take as a model of the light source a single electron bound elastically to a massive charge and moving with simple harmonic motion of frequency ν in a straight line with amplitude $\mathbf{r}$, we find that the energy emitted per unit time is

$$S = \frac{32\pi^4e^2\nu^4}{3c^3}\bar{\mathbf{r}}^2. \tag{54}$$

We see therefore that the radiation is the same as that which would be given out by a classical dipole of amplitude $\mathbf{r}$ given by

$$\bar{\mathbf{r}}^2 = 2|(0|\mathbf{r}|n)|^2.$$

48.2. The photoelectric effect

We saw in the last section that when light is emitted by an atom its frequency ν is given by the equation

$$\nu = (W_m - W_n)/h, \tag{55}$$

where W_m, W_n are two energy levels of the atom. In a similar way it can be shown that light of frequency ν can be absorbed by an atom only if ν satisfies a relation of the type (55). Another process is possible, however, for light of such a frequency that $h\nu$ exceeds the ionization potential, I. It may then happen that the electron absorbs a quantum of radiation of sufficient energy to cause it to leave the atom with kinetic energy $h\nu - I$. We can easily calculate the transition probability for a process of this type, if we assume that the kinetic energy of the ejected electron is very much greater than the ionization potential I and if we employ non-relativistic wave mechanics throughout. This last assumption is equivalent to assuming that the kinetic energy of the electron in the continuous spectrum is small in comparison with the rest-energy mc^2 of the electron.

We shall carry out the calculation for an electron in a $(1s)$ state and thus for the K-electron of an atom.

In the integral occurring in the expression (49) for the transition probability, Ψ_0° is thus the wave function

$$\Psi_0^{\circ} = (\pi a^3)^{-\frac{1}{2}} e^{-r/a} \quad (a = a_0/Z)$$

of the electron in the K-shell, and, if the energy of the ejected electron is very much greater than the ionization potential, Ψ_n is the wave function corresponding to an electron in the continuous spectrum with momentum $\mathbf{p}$, i.e. the plane wave

$$\Psi_n^{\circ} = e^{i(\mathbf{p}\mathbf{r})/\hbar c}.$$

If we write $\mathbf{q} = \mathbf{p} - \mathbf{\varkappa}/\hbar c,$

then $\mathbf{q}$ is the momentum transferred to the atom and we have

$$\int \Psi_n^* p_e e^{-i(\mathbf{\varkappa}\mathbf{r})} \Psi_0^{\circ} d\tau = p_e(\pi a^3)^{-\frac{1}{2}} \int e^{-\alpha r/\hbar c + i(\mathbf{q}\mathbf{r})/\hbar c} d\tau,$$

where we have written $a = \hbar c/\alpha$. Using the result

$$\int e^{-\gamma r + i(\mathbf{\beta}\mathbf{r})} d\tau = \frac{8\pi\gamma}{(\beta^2 + \gamma^2)^2},$$

we then obtain

$$\int \Psi_n^* p_e e^{-i(\mathbf{\varkappa}\mathbf{r})} \Psi_0^{\circ} d\tau = p_e \left(\frac{\alpha^3}{\pi \hbar^3 c^3}\right)^{\frac{1}{2}} \frac{8\pi\alpha(\hbar c)^3}{(\alpha^2 + q^2)^2}. \tag{56}$$

Substituting this value of the integral into the expression (49 a) for the transition probability and dividing by the intensity of the primary beam per cm.² (i.e. by c for a single quantum), we obtain the quantity

$$d\phi = \frac{32e^2}{m\pi v} p p_e^2 \frac{\alpha^5}{(\alpha^2 + q^2)^4} d\Omega, \tag{57}$$

which has the dimensions of an area and is called the differential cross-section, or the effective area that has to be hit by a quantum to eject an electron in the solid angle $d\Omega$.

To obtain the total cross-section for the ejection of photo-electrons in any direction we integrate (57) over all angles. Since the K-shell contains two electrons we multiply by 2 to obtain the cross-section ϕ_κ for the photo-effect of the K-shell; the result of the integration is†

$$\phi_\kappa = 64\phi_0 \left(\frac{137}{Z}\right)^2 \left(\frac{I}{h\nu}\right)^{\frac{7}{2}}, \tag{58}$$

† W. Heitler, loc. cit., pp. 122–3.

where
$$\phi_0 = \frac{8\pi}{3}\left(\frac{e^2}{mc^2}\right)^2. \tag{59}$$

If $h\nu$ is nearly equal to I the exact wave functions of the continuous spectrum are used for Ψ_n in the evaluation of the matrix element. The formula (58) is then replaced by†

$$\phi_\kappa = 128\pi \frac{\exp(-4\rho \cot^{-1}\rho)}{1-e^{-2\pi\rho}} \frac{137^3}{Z^2}\left(\frac{I}{h\nu}\right)^4, \tag{60}$$

where ρ is defined by
$$\rho^2 = \frac{I}{h\nu - I},$$

i.e. ρ^2 is the ratio of the ionization energy to the kinetic energy of the ejected photo-electron.

48.3. *The breadth of spectral lines*

The theory developed in § 48.1 accounts for the emission of radiation from an atom and is based on the supposition that energy is conserved in the process. Such an assumption leads to a formula for the intensity of a *sharp* spectral line emitted by an atom. We know from spectroscopic observations, however, that the lines of an atomic spectrum are not sharp but possess a certain characteristic breadth. That this natural line breadth does not follow from the analysis of § 48.1 is due to the fact that in solving the equation

$$\mathfrak{H}\Psi = i\hbar\frac{\partial\Psi}{\partial t}, \tag{61}$$

where $\mathfrak{H}$ is given by equations (35)–(37), we employed an approximate method whose use is only justifiable for small values of the time t. An improved method of solution of equation (61) valid for higher values of t has been developed by Weisskopf and Wigner‡ and has been found to lead to a simple formula for the breadth of a spectral line.

We shall consider only the case in which the atom has two states, an excited state described by the wave-function Ψ_n and possessing energy W_n and a ground state of energy W_0 whose wave function is Ψ_0. The extension of the analysis to atoms with several states presents no essentially new features. We assume that initially the atom is in the excited state in the absence of radiation and that it falls to the ground state with the emission of a quantum of radiation $h\nu_s$ whose frequency ν_s is *approximately* equal to the fundamental frequency

$$\nu_0 = (W_n - W_0)/h, \tag{62}$$

given uniquely by the energy difference between the two states.

† M. Stobbe, *Ann. der Physik*, **7**, 661 (1930).
‡ V. Weisskopf and E. Wigner, *Zeits. f. Physik*, **63**, 54 (1930); **65**, 18 (1930).

The solution of equation (61) can readily be obtained if the solutions Ψ_n, and the eigenvalues W_n of the Schrödinger equation (39) are known. If we write

$$\Psi = \sum_k b_k(t)\Psi_k\, e^{iW_k t/\hbar} \tag{63}$$

and substitute this wave function in equation (61), we obtain the equation

$$\sum_k b_k(t)e^{iW_k t/\hbar}\mathfrak{H}_1\Psi_k + i\hbar \sum_k \dot{b}_k(t)e^{iW_k t/\hbar}\Psi_k = 0.$$

Multiplying both sides of this equation by the conjugate wave function Ψ_n^* and integrating over the space of *all* the coordinates—those describing the radiation field as well as those defining the position of the electron—we obtain the system of differential equations

$$\dot{b}_n(t) = \frac{i}{\hbar}\sum_{k=0}^{\infty} (n|\mathfrak{H}_1|k)e^{i(W_k-W_n)t/\hbar}b_k(t). \tag{64}$$

It follows from equation (63) that the quantity $|b_n(t)|^2$ is the probability of finding the system in a state of energy W_n at time t.

Denoting by $(n, 0)$ the state in which no radiation is present and the electron is in state Ψ_n, and by $(0, 1_s)$ the state in which the electron is the ground state and a quantum $h\nu_s$ is the only radiation present, equations (64) reduce to

$$\left.\begin{aligned}
\dot{b}_{n,0}(t) &= \frac{i}{\hbar}\sum_s (n, 0|\mathfrak{H}_1|0, 1_s)b_{0,1_s}(t)e^{-2\pi i(\nu_0-\nu_s)t} \\
\dot{b}_{0,1_s}(t) &= \frac{i}{\hbar}(0, 1_s|\mathfrak{H}_1|n, 0)b_{n\,0}(t)e^{2\pi i(\nu_0-\nu_s)t}
\end{aligned}\right\}. \tag{65}$$

Initially, at time $t = 0$,

$$b_{n,0}(0) = 1, \qquad b_{0,1_s}(0) = 0. \tag{66}$$

If we now make the substitution

$$b_{n,0}(t) = e^{-\gamma t} \tag{67 a}$$

in equations (65), we obtain immediately by a simple integration

$$b_{0,1_s}(t) = \frac{i}{\hbar}(0, 1_s|\mathfrak{H}_1|n, 0)\frac{e^{[2\pi i(\nu_0-\nu_s)-\gamma]t}-1}{2\pi i(\nu_0-\nu_s)-\gamma}. \tag{67 b}$$

As $t \to \infty$ the exponential factor decreases rapidly to zero so that

$$b_{0,1_s}(t) \to -\frac{i}{\hbar}\frac{(0, 1_s|\mathfrak{H}_1|n, 0)}{2\pi i(\nu_0-\nu_s)-\gamma}.$$

The probability that, after a time t, long in comparison with the lifetime $1/2\gamma$ of the excited state of the atom, a quantum of radiation $h\nu_s$ has been emitted is therefore

$$\frac{(0, 1_s|\mathfrak{H}_1|n, 0)^2}{\hbar^2\{4\pi^2(\nu_0-\nu_s)^2+\gamma^2\}}.$$

Multiplying by $h\nu_0$ and the density function ρ_ν, integrating over all directions of propagation and summing over both directions of polarization we obtain for the intensity distribution

$$I(\nu)\,d\nu = \frac{h\nu_0\,d\nu}{\hbar^2\{4\pi^2(\nu_0-\nu)^2+\gamma^2\}} \int \rho_\nu(n, 0|\mathfrak{H}_1|0, 1_s)^2\,d\Omega.$$

Now the total probability of a spontaneous transition per unit time is

$$w = \frac{2\pi}{\hbar} \int \rho_W(n, 0|\mathfrak{H}_1|0, 1_s)^2\,d\Omega, \tag{68}$$

so that

$$I(\nu) = \frac{w}{2\pi}\frac{I_0}{4\pi^2(\nu-\nu_0)^2+\gamma^2} \tag{69}$$

where we have written I_0 for $h\nu_0$.

We have yet to determine the constant γ. Substituting from equation (67 a) into the first equation of the set (65), we obtain the relation

$$\gamma = \frac{1}{\hbar^2} \sum_s \frac{(n, 0|\mathfrak{H}_1|0, 1_s)^2}{2\pi i(\nu_0-\nu_s)-\gamma}[1-e^{[2\pi i(\nu_s-\nu_0)+\gamma]t}].$$

We now replace the summation with respect to s by an integral over ν_s, first multiplying the integrand by $\rho_W\,dw d\Omega$. We then have to evaluate an integral of the type

$$\int f(\nu_s)\frac{1-\exp\{2\pi i(\nu_s-\nu_0)+\gamma\}t}{2\pi i(\nu_0-\nu_s)-\gamma}\,d\nu_s,$$

which reduces to $\frac{1}{2}f(\nu_0)$. It then follows immediately that

$$\gamma = \tfrac{1}{2}w,$$

where w is given by equation (68). The formula (69) then reduces to

$$I(\nu) = \frac{w}{2\pi}\frac{I_0}{4\pi^2(\nu-\nu_0)^2+w^2/4}. \tag{70}$$

The form of the distribution function $I(\nu)$ is shown in Fig. 63. $I(\nu)$ has its maximum at $\nu = \nu_0$ when its value is

$$I(\nu_0) = 2I_0/\pi w.$$

It should also be observed that

$$I\left(\nu_0 \pm \frac{w}{4\pi}\right) = \tfrac{1}{2}I(\nu_0).$$

The formula (70) is identical with that deduced in the classical theory for exponentially damped harmonic oscillators; in the classical result the formula (68) for w is replaced by

$$w = 8\pi^2 e^2 \nu_0^2 / 3mc^3.$$

Although the intensity of the line is measured by the total area under the curve, a reasonably accurate estimate of the intensity is given by

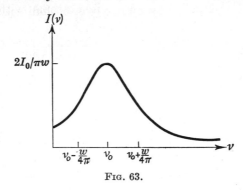

FIG. 63.

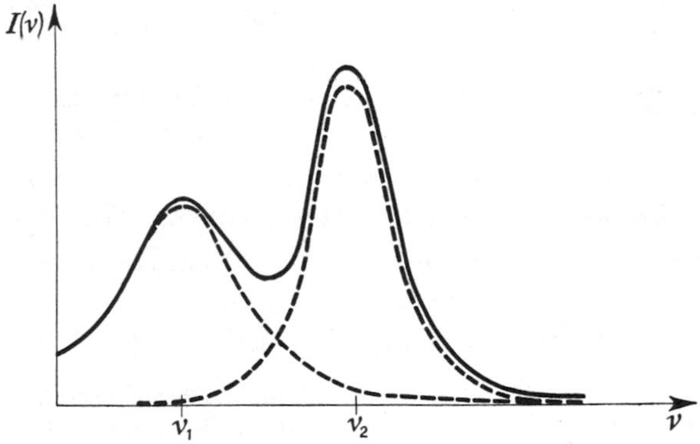

FIG. 64.

the height of the peak. In actual practice it usually happens that there are several components of different intensities very close to each other. If the half-widths of the lines are comparable with the separation we get a distorted curve, in which it is difficult to distinguish the individual components; for example, Fig. 64 shows the intensity curve of the H_α-line as measured by Hansen.† In this instance the experimental curve is composed of three component curves of which the central is almost completely overlapped by the other two.

We have only considered the broadening of spectral lines caused by

† G. Hansen, *Ann. der Physik*, **78**, 558 (1925).

the damping due to the emission of the radiation itself. In addition to this there are several other causes contributing to the broadening of a line:

(a) The Doppler effect due to the fact that the radiating atoms are not at rest.†

(b) The effect of collisions of excited atoms with neighbouring atoms.‡

(c) Interactions of excited atoms with neighbouring atoms leading to a shift or splitting of the excited states.§

We shall not consider these effects here; for accounts of them the reader is referred to the papers cited.

49. Radiation processes of higher order

In the radiation processes considered above it has been possible to obtain the transition probabilities by calculating the matrix element $(n|\mathfrak{H}_1|m)$ for the transition from an initial state m to a final state n. $\mathfrak{H}_1$ denotes the interaction between the electron and the radiation field, and Ψ_n, Ψ_m are eigenfunctions of the wave equation (39). In these problems it so happened that these matrix elements did not all vanish. In many problems the matrix elements vanish for direct transitions from the initial to the final state. When this is the case it is necessary to improve the method of approximation. As in the case of second-order perturbation theory (Chap. III above), we have to repeat the calculations, retaining terms of a higher order. The inclusion of these higher order terms is equivalent to assuming the existence of 'intermediate' states n' such that $(n|\mathfrak{H}_1|n')$ and $(n'|\mathfrak{H}_1|m)$ do not vanish although $(n|\mathfrak{H}_1|m)$ does.

Thus in the case of scattering by an atom when a quantum $\mathbf{k}_0$ is absorbed and a secondary quantum $\mathbf{k}$ is emitted we have two such intermediate states. In the first $\mathbf{k}_0$ has been absorbed and $\mathbf{k}$ is not yet emitted; in the second $\mathbf{k}$ has been emitted and $\mathbf{k}_0$ is not yet absorbed.

In the general case, let us denote the initial state by n_0, the final state by n, and the intermediate states by n'. Then assuming a solution of the wave equation (61), in a series of the form (63), we have initially

$$b_{n_0}(0) = 1,$$

and all the other b's zero.

† M. N. Saha and B. N. Srivastava, *A Treatise on Heat*, 2nd ed., Appendix 4 (Allahabad, 1935).

‡ J. H. Van Vleck and V. F. Weisskopf, *Rev. Mod. Phys.* **17**, 227 (1945); H. Fröhlich, *Nature* (1946).

§ V. Weisskopf, *Phys. Zeits.* **34**, 1 (1933); *Observatory*, No. 713 (1933).

Thus, as a first approximation, we may take b_{n_0} to be unity on the right-hand side of equation (64), and all the $b_m(t)$ zero except the $b_{n'}$. In this way we obtain the system of differential equations:

$$\dot{b}_{n'}(t) = \frac{i}{\hbar}(n'|\mathfrak{H}_1|n_0)e^{i(W_{n_0}-W_{n'})t/\hbar}, \tag{71}$$

$$\dot{b}_n(t) = \frac{i}{\hbar}\sum_{n'}(n|\mathfrak{H}_1|n')b_{n'}(t)e^{i(W_{n'}-W_n)t/\hbar}. \tag{72}$$

Integrating equation (71) we obtain

$$b_{n'}(t) = (n'|\mathfrak{H}_1|n_0)\frac{e^{i(W_{n_0}-W_{n'})t/\hbar}-1}{W_{n_0}-W_{n'}}, \tag{73}$$

the condition $b_{n'}(0) = 0$ being satisfied. Substituting from (73) into (72) we derive the differential equation

$$\dot{b}_n(t) = \frac{i}{\hbar}\sum_{n'}\frac{(n|\mathfrak{H}_1|n')(n'|\mathfrak{H}_1|n_0)}{W_{n_0}-W_{n'}}\{e^{i(W_{n_0}-W_n)t/\hbar}-e^{i(W_{n'}-W_n)t/\hbar}\}$$

for the determination of b_n. Integrating this equation we obtain

$$b_n(t) = \sum_{n'}\frac{(n|\mathfrak{H}_1|n')(n'|\mathfrak{H}_1|n_0)}{W_{n_0}-W_{n'}}\left\{\frac{e^{i(W_{n_0}-W_n)t/\hbar}-1}{W_{n_0}-W_n}-\frac{e^{i(W_{n'}-W_n)t/\hbar}-1}{W_{n'}-W_n}\right\},$$

which may be written in the form

$$b_n(t) = \mathfrak{H}_1\frac{e^{i(W_{n_0}-W_n)t/\hbar}-1}{W_{n_0}-W_n}+\sum_{n'}\frac{(n|\mathfrak{H}_1|n')(n'|\mathfrak{H}_1|n_0)}{(W_n-W_{n'})(W_{n_0}-W_{n'})}\{e^{i(W_{n'}-W_n)t/\hbar}-1\},$$

with

$$\mathfrak{H}_1 = \sum_{n'}\frac{(n|\mathfrak{H}_1|n')(n'|\mathfrak{H}_1|n_0)}{W_n-W_{n'}}. \tag{74}$$

If we form $|b_n(t)|^2$ and neglect terms containing $W_n-W_{n'}$ since they play no role in this case, we obtain

$$|b_n(t)|^2 = \frac{2|\mathfrak{H}_1|^2}{(W_{n_0}-W_n)^2}\left\{1-\cos\frac{(W_{n_0}-W_n)t}{\hbar}\right\}. \tag{75}$$

If, as before, we assume that in the neighbourhood of the final state there is a large number of states with energy between W and $W+dW$, then by means of equation (75) we obtain for the transition probability per unit time

$$w = \frac{2\pi}{\hbar}\rho_{W_0}|\mathfrak{H}_1|^2. \tag{76}$$

For radiation processes for which both the matrix element $(n_0|\mathfrak{H}_1|n)$ and the sum $\sum_{n'}(n|\mathfrak{H}_1|n')(n'|\mathfrak{H}_1|n_0)/(W_n-W_{n'})$ vanish, it is necessary to assume that two successive intermediate states n' and n'' exist for which $(n_0|\mathfrak{H}_1|n')$, $(n'|\mathfrak{H}_1|n'')$, and $(n''|\mathfrak{H}_1|n)$ are different from zero. The transition probability is again given by equation (76) except that now $\mathfrak{H}_1$ is defined by the equation

$$\mathfrak{H}_1 = \sum_{n'} \sum_{n''} \frac{(n_0|\mathfrak{H}_1|n')(n'|\mathfrak{H}_1|n'')(n''|\mathfrak{H}_1|n)}{(W_{n_0}-W_{n'})(W_{n_0}-W_{n''})}. \tag{77}$$

The transition probability per unit time for the simple types of radiation problem considered in § 48 is, of course, also given by equation (76), but now

$$\overline{\mathfrak{H}}_1 = (n_0|\mathfrak{H}_1|n). \tag{78}$$

Thus we may classify radiation processes according to the type of formula used for the calculation of the quantity H_1 occurring in the formula (76). The radiation process is said to be *of the first order* if H_1 is given by equation (78), *of the second order* if it is given by equation (74), *of the third order* if it is given by (77), and so on for higher orders. Furthermore, it is evident from equation (78) that $\mathfrak{H}_1$, and consequently the matrix element $(n_0|\mathfrak{H}_1|n)$, is of the first order in e, so that for a radiation process of the first order, the transition probability per unit time, w, is of order e^2. Similarly for radiation processes of the second order w is of order e^4, and for those of the third order w is of order e^6.

Examples of radiation processes of the first order have already been considered above (§ 48). As an example of a radiation process of the second order we may cite the Compton effect. In this case the initial state consists of a quantum with momentum $\mathbf{k}_0$ ($|\mathbf{k}_0| = h\nu_0/c$) and a free electron at rest with energy $W_0 = mc^2$; in the final state we have a quantum of momentum $\mathbf{k}$ and an electron with momentum $\mathbf{k}_0-\mathbf{k}$ and energy $W_0+h(\nu_0-\nu)$. The only possible intermediate states are:

(a) One in which the electron has momentum $\mathbf{k}_0$ and there is no light quantum present. The quantum of light has been absorbed by the electron; in the transition to the final state the electron emits a quantum of momentum $\mathbf{k}$.

(b) Another in which the electron has momentum $-\mathbf{k}$ and there are two light quanta with momenta $\mathbf{k}_0$ and $\mathbf{k}$ present. The electron has emitted a quantum of momentum $\mathbf{k}$; in the transition to the final state it absorbs the quantum with momentum $\mathbf{k}_0$.

It is possible to calculate the matrix elements corresponding to each of the transitions and from them to calculate the differential cross-section for the scattering process.† Other examples of radiation processes of the second order are:

(i) The coherent scattering of light.

† W. Heitler, *The Quantum Theory of Radiation*, 2nd ed. § 16. Cf. Chap. XI.

(ii) The Raman effect.

(iii) Resonance fluorescence.

(iv) 'Two quanta' annihilation of positrons.

Among processes of the third order the most important is 'Bremsstrahlung'—the emission of radiation by an electron passing through the field of a nucleus; others include double scattering and the creation of positron-electron pairs in the field of a nucleus.

It can be shown that the application of the quantum theory of radiation to all of these problems† leads to reasonable results if the interaction, $\mathfrak{H}_1$, between the radiation field and an electron is considered as small and the solution only worked out to the first non-vanishing approximation in $\mathfrak{H}_1$. If, however, the higher approximations in $\mathfrak{H}_1$ are considered the result always diverges, so that the higher approximations have no physical meaning; thus it is found that the second approximation of the interaction energy between an electron and the radiation field diverges even if there are no light quanta present in the field. This energy is known as the *transverse self-energy* of the electron. The theory we have developed cannot therefore be regarded as exact. Recently, however, Heitler and Peng‡ have shown how the theory may be formulated to eliminate divergencies of this type.

50. Radiation damping

Introduction. It is well known that in considering the motion of an electron in classical electrodynamics it is necessary to consider the *reaction* of its field on its motion. The case of electromagnetic radiation in interaction with an electron is of interest in many applications, but the discovery of the meson in cosmic-ray experiments and the formulation of meson theories of nuclear forces has emphasized anew the importance of considering 'damping' effects in radiation processes.

50.1. *Classical theory of radiation damping*

The effect of radiation damping in the classical theory of radiating electrons was first considered by Lorentz, who used as a model for the electron a small sphere charged with electricity and hence possessing mass on account of the energy of the electric field surrounding it. Lorentz showed that the retardation of the electromagnetic field inside an electron produces a force which is equal to

$$\tfrac{2}{3}e^2\dddot{v}/c^3. \tag{79}$$

This expression is only a first approximation to the correct result for

† See p. 287 below.   ‡ See p. 281 below.

an electron of finite radius, being the first term of an expansion in ascending powers of $r_0 \nu/c$, where ν is the frequency and r_0 the radius of the classical electron. The form of the higher terms of the series depends upon the nature of the structure of the electron—i.e. on the nature of the forces that hold the charge on the electron—and therefore cannot be treated in the classical theory. The main reason for retaining the Lorentz model of the electron was that it gave rise to the concept that all mass is of electromagnetic origin. However, the discovery of the neutron has proved that an elementary particle can have mass which is not of electromagnetic origin and thus removed the main reason for retaining the finite radius of the electron in the Lorentz model.

The main difficulty in returning to a model of the electron as a point charge is that, if we apply Maxwell's theory, the field in the immediate neighbourhood of the point electron has an infinite energy. This difficulty may be resolved in either of two ways. It might be possible to devise a scheme of electrodynamics in which the field of a point charge is modified for distances smaller than a certain critical radius in such a way that the energy of the field becomes finite; the field strength calculated from the modified theory would then be less than the classical value for distances smaller than the critical radius. A modification of the classical Maxwell equations of this type is the non-linear field theory of Born and Infeld;† because of the non-linearity the equations of this theory are not easily handled and can be carried over into quantum mechanics only with great difficulty.

Another way out of the difficulty is to consider that the classical value of the field strength as measured by the force on other particles is valid for all distances, but the particle's own field does not contribute to its rest mass. This is the basis of Dirac's classical theory of radiating electrons.‡ Dirac retains Maxwell's theory to describe the field right up to the point-singularity which represents the electron, and by subtracting the infinite self-energy of the point-electron from the total energy of the system in an invariant way obtains a relativistic expression for the force of retardation of the electromagnetic field inside an electron which reduces to the Lorentz expression (79) in the non-relativistic approximation.

Furthermore, Dirac brings forward evidence for believing that this

---

† M. Born, *Proc. Roy. Soc.* A, **143**, 410 (1934); M. Born and L. Infeld, ibid. **144**, 425 (1934); **147**, 522 (1934); **150**, 141 (1935).

‡ P. A. M. Dirac, ibid. **167**, 148 (1938).

expression is exact within the limits of the classical theory. The self-consistent scheme of equations set up by Dirac for the calculation of effects due to the interaction of electrons with radiation is identical with the set due to Lorentz. The two theories differ, however, in their interpretation of the finite size of the electron; in Dirac's theory the finite size reappears in a new sense, the interior of the electron being a region of failure, not of the equations of the electromagnetic field, but of some of the elementary properties of space-time.

For instance, let us consider the case of an electron initially at rest being set in motion by the passage over it of a pulse of radiation of infinitely short duration. If the pulse is moving along the y-axis but is polarized in the x-direction the electric force may be represented by

$$\mathbf{E} = (k\,\delta(t-y), 0, 0),$$

where k is a constant and δ denotes the Dirac delta function.† If k is so small that the electron acquires a velocity small in comparison with that of light we may use the non-relativistic equation of motion

$$m\dot{\mathbf{v}} - \frac{2}{3}\frac{e^2}{c^3}\ddot{\mathbf{v}} = \mathbf{F}, \tag{80}$$

which reduces in this case to

$$\ddot{x}/\tau - \dddot{x} = \kappa\,\delta(t), \tag{81}$$

where $\qquad \tau = 2e^2/3mc^3, \qquad \kappa = 3c^3k/2e^2.$

The solution of equation (81) is readily found to be

$$\dot{x} = \begin{cases} ke^{t/\tau}/m & (t < 0) \\ k/m & (t > 0). \end{cases}$$

Thus for positive values of t the electron is moving with constant velocity k/m, as we would expect. There is, however, a departure from the ordinary ideas of causality; although the pulse does not act on the electron until the time $t = 0$ the electron acquires an acceleration *before* that time. It would appear that the electron knew in advance that the pulse was coming and acquired an acceleration just sufficient to balance the effect of the pulse when it does act. We can surmount this difficulty by assuming that the electron has a finite radius of order

$$c\tau = 2e^2/3mc^2$$

† The Dirac delta function is defined to be zero when the argument is not zero and to be infinite when the argument is zero in such a way that the function and the axis enclose unit area, i.e.

$$\delta(x) = 0 \quad (x \neq 0), \qquad \delta(x) = \infty \quad (x = 0)$$

$$\int_{-\infty}^{\infty} \delta(x)\,dx = 1.$$

since the electron begins to acquire an acceleration when the pulse is distant from the centre of the electron by this amount.

Suppose now that electromagnetic waves are being radiated from a point A and detected at a point B a distance $x+y$ away; and that there is an electron at a point E on the line AB distant x from A. Then if a pulse is emitted by A at $t = 0$, the electron will start radiating at a time

$$x/c - \tau$$

and a signal will be detected at B at time

$$(x+y)/c - \tau.$$

If we denote by c' the equivalent velocity of light in the interior of the electron and by b the radius of the electron, we then have

$$\frac{x-b}{c} + \frac{y-b}{c} + \frac{2b}{c'} = \frac{x+y}{c} - \tau,$$

whence we obtain $c' = c(1 - c\tau/2b)^{-1}.$

Now b is of order $c\tau$ so that c' is of order $2c$; that is, it is possible for a signal to be transmitted through the interior of an electron with a velocity exceeding that of light—in contradiction to our ideas of the nature of space and time.

The theory proposed by Dirac thus violates the postulates of the theory of relativity; for all that, the theory is constructed in such a way as to be invariant under Lorentz transformations.

The difficulty that the electromagnetic energy becomes infinite in the neighbourhood of a point charge has been removed by Pryce[†] by the introduction into the energy integral of an additive vector field, which depends on the variables of the charge alone, so as to make the integral finite at the point charge. This additional field may be regarded as a negatively infinite energy having its origin in the charge itself. The procedures adopted by Dirac and Pryce are different, but both consist in adding terms to the usual expression for the field energy which make the total field energy of a point charge finite. That this procedure is physically sensible and not merely a mathematical device was suggested by Bhabha and Corben,[‡] who extended the method to give the complete classical theory of a spinning particle moving in an electromagnetic field.

[†] M. H. L. Pryce, *Proc. Roy. Soc.* A, **168**, 389 (1938); see also G. Wentzel, *Zeits. f. Physik*, **86**, 479, 635 (1933); **87**, 726 (1934).

[‡] H. J. Bhabha and H. C. Corben, *Proc. Roy. Soc.* A, **178**, 273 (1941).

Dirac's theory leads to the non-relativistic equations of motion

$$m\dot{\mathbf{v}} - \frac{2e^2}{3c^3}\ddot{\mathbf{v}} = \mathbf{F},\qquad(82)$$

where $\mathbf{F}$ denotes the external force and dots denote differentiation with respect to t. These equations differ from the usual Newtonian equations of motion

$$m\dot{\mathbf{v}} = \mathbf{F}$$

in that they involve differential coefficients of the third order. To solve the system of equations completely for the space coordinates (x, y, z), we need to know their initial values and those of $\dot{\mathbf{v}}$ and $\ddot{\mathbf{v}}$, thus introducing more arbitrary constants into the solution than are necessary to fix the actual motion. The solutions of the equations of motion fall into two types—physical and non-physical solutions—which must be distinguished. In solving particular problems the procedure is to write down all the solutions of the equations (82) and then determine which of them are physically possible. For example, in the case of an electron moving in the absence of an external field, there are two solutions† of the relativistic equations, one in which the velocity of the electron tends to that of light and a second in which the electron moves with uniform velocity; the former solution is non-physical, the latter physical. The solutions corresponding to the motion of the electron of the hydrogen atom have been discussed by Eliezer,‡ who shows that there is no solution in which the electron falls into the nucleus. Eliezer has also considered the effect of radiation damping on the motion in a plane of an electron in a uniform magnetic field§; the physical motion is one in which the electron spirals round inwards until it comes to rest, but there is also a non-physical solution in which the electron spirals outwards with increasing velocity.

As an example of the use of equations (82) we shall consider the effect of radiation damping on the scattering of light by a free electron. A light wave with the frequency ν and the field strength

$$\mathbf{E} = \mathbf{E}_0\, e^{2\pi i \nu t}$$

may fall upon a free electron which is initially at rest. The equation of motion (82) then becomes

$$m\ddot{\mathbf{x}} - \gamma\dddot{\mathbf{x}} = e\mathbf{E}_0\, e^{2\pi i \nu t},\qquad(83)$$

where, for convenience, we have written

$$\gamma = 2e^2/3c^3.\qquad(84)$$

---

† P. A. M. Dirac, loc. cit., p. 156.
‡ C. J. Eliezer, *Proc. Camb. Phil. Soc.* **39**, 173 (1943).   § Ibid. **42**, 40 (1946).

Equation (83) has the periodic solution

$$\mathbf{x} = \mathbf{x}_0 e^{2\pi i \nu t},$$

where

$$-m(2\pi\nu)^2\mathbf{x}_0 + i(2\pi\nu)^3\gamma\mathbf{x}_0 = e\mathbf{E}_0,$$

so that

$$\mathbf{x}_0 = -\frac{e\mathbf{E}_0}{4\pi^2\nu^2(m-2i\pi\nu\gamma)}.$$

The total energy radiated per second is now

$$s = \frac{2}{3}\frac{|\dot{\mathbf{v}}|^2}{c^3} = \frac{2e^2}{3c^3}|\mathbf{E}_0|^2\frac{1}{m^2(1+\kappa^2)},$$

where

$$\kappa = \frac{2\pi\gamma\nu}{m} = \frac{4\pi e^2\nu}{3mc^3}$$

and the total cross-section[†] for scattering is thus

$$\phi = \frac{8\pi}{3}\left(\frac{e^2}{mc^2}\right)^2\frac{1}{1+\kappa^2}. \tag{85}$$

50.2. Quantum theory of radiation damping

The incorporation into the quantum theory of the classical methods of Lorentz and Dirac has recently been discussed by several authors. The first quantum treatment of the effect of radiation damping on the scattering of light by free electrons was given by Waller,[‡] but it was only by ignoring the initial conditions which the solutions of the perturbation equations must satisfy that he was able to derive a solution of the equations. Waller's theory was developed further by Gora,[§] who overcame the difficulty arising from the initial conditions by assuming that the interaction, H_1, between an electron and the radiation field, is switched on adiabatically. Thus we assume that $H_1 = 0$ initially and is switched on over a time period large compared with the period of the light wave. Gora's results are also incorrect because of the omission of some of the terms in Waller's equations. The correct equations to include the effect of radiation damping for the special case of scattering were derived simultaneously by Heitler[||] and Wilson[††] by entirely independent methods; Heitler adopted Gora's assumption of adiabatic switching on of the perturbation energy, and Wilson employed a limiting process to eliminate the terms which make the solution of the problem difficult. A divergence-free quantum theory of radiation including the effects of radiation damping was formulated

† Cf. H. Casimir, *Zeits. f. Physik*, **81**, 496 (1933).
‡ I. Waller, ibid. **88**, 436 (1934).
§ E. Gora, *Acta Phys. Polonica*, **7**, 159, 374 (1938–9).
|| W. Heitler, *Proc. Camb. Phil. Soc.* **37**, 291 (1941).
†† A. H. Wilson, ibid. **37**, 301 (1941).

subsequently by Heitler and Peng.† The theory proposed by these authors is frankly heuristic; they arrive at a divergence-free formation by simply omitting the divergent integrals from the original theory. This formalism is then shown to be Lorentz invariant. A general procedure for this omission has so far only been formulated for one class of problems, the calculation of transition probabilities. Despite the heuristic basis of the Heitler–Peng theory its authors claim that, in view of its close agreement with experimental results, it will form a correct part of future quantum electrodynamics or a good approximation, having perhaps a similar relation to future quantum theory as the Bohr theory had to wave mechanics.

Independently of these investigations Dirac‡ made an attempt to produce a new method of field quantization which would remove the divergence difficulties from quantum electrodynamics. By introducing the idea of quanta of negative energy and making use of a certain limiting process, Dirac showed that in his theory the integrals corresponding to the divergent integrals of the previous theories are convergent. Dirac's theory has certain features in common with the Heitler–Peng theory; in the limit of quanta of low energy both theories reduce to the classical theory of radiating electrons due to Dirac.§ The relation between the two theories has been discussed by Gormley and Heitler,‖ who find that, contrary to expectation, the Heitler–Peng theory is not a consequence of Dirac's quantum electrodynamics. It is found that for processes involving the scattering of high-energy quanta the two theories give rise to very different results, and that, in certain cases, Dirac's theory has no solution at all whereas the Heitler–Peng theory has. This last difficulty arises from the quanta of negative energy, and it would seem that this part, at least, of Dirac's theory has to be abandoned.

No completely satisfactory basis for the subtraction process employed by Heitler and Peng has yet been found, but numerous applications have led to results in agreement with experiment. As this theory is discussed at some length in the last chapter of Heitler's book†† we shall, in the following sections, mainly follow the method of treating radiation damping developed by Wilson. The connexion of this method with the

---

† W. Heitler and H. W. Peng, ibid. **38**, 296 (1942).

‡ P. A. M. Dirac, *Proc. Roy. Soc.* A, **180**, 1 (1942); *Comm. Dublin Inst. Adv. Studies*, A, No. 1 (1943). Cf. W. Pauli, *Rev. Mod. Phys.* **15**, 175 (1943).

§ Cf. last section.

‖ P. G. Gormley and W. Heitler, *Proc. Roy. Irish Acad.* **50**, A, 29 (1944).

†† W. Heitler, *The Quantum Theory of Radiation*, 2nd ed. (Oxford, 1942).

physical concept of 'damping' is not immediately obvious; it would seem that Wilson's method consists merely of a more accurate solution of the wave equation for a Hamiltonian involving the electron and the radiation field. The relation of this process to radiation damping is purely formal—the mathematical analysis corresponding closely to the subtraction method of Dirac for the classical theory.

50.3. Solution of the radiation equations for direct transitions

We first of all consider the case in which the transition between the initial and final states takes place directly, and not through intermediate states. Let n_0 denote the initial state of the system, and n one of the possible final states of the system in which a quantum of radiation of any frequency, polarization, and direction of propagation has been emitted, such that the energy of the complete system is approximately conserved. As in § 48.3 we have to solve the wave equation

$$(\mathfrak{H}_0 + \mathfrak{H}_1)\Psi = i\hbar \frac{\partial \Psi}{\partial t}$$

of the coupled system where $\mathfrak{H}_0$ is the sum of the Hamiltonians of the pure radiation field and of an electron moving in a field free from radiation and $\mathfrak{H}_1$ is the energy of interaction between the electron and the radiation field. We assume again a solution of the form (63) where the Ψ_k, W_k are the eigenfunctions and eigenvalues of the Schrödinger equation

$$\mathfrak{H}_0 \Psi_k = W_k \Psi_k.$$

It follows immediately from equation (64) that the perturbation equations for the probability amplitudes $b_{n_0}(t)$, $b_n(t)$ are

$$\dot{b}_{n_0}(t) = \frac{i}{\hbar} \sum_n (n_0|\mathfrak{H}_1|n) b_n(t) e^{i(W_n - W_{n_0})t/\hbar}, \tag{86}$$

$$\dot{b}_n(t) = \frac{i}{\hbar}\{(n|\mathfrak{H}_1|n_0) b_{n_0}(t) e^{i(W_{n_0} - W_n)t/\hbar} + \sum_{n'} (n|\mathfrak{H}_1|n') b_{n'}(t) e^{i(W_{n'} - W_n)t/\hbar)}\}. \tag{87}$$

The initial conditions satisfied by the probability amplitudes are

$$b_{n_0}(0) = 1, \qquad b_n(0) = 0. \tag{88}$$

If we write the solutions of equations (86) and (87) in the form

$$b_{n_0}(t) = e^{-\gamma t}, \quad b_n(t) = U_n \frac{e^{-\gamma t + i(W_{n_0} - W_n)t/\hbar} - 1}{W_{n_0} - W_n + i\hbar\gamma}, \tag{88a}$$

we see that the initial conditions (88) are automatically satisfied. The function U_n is a function of the variables defining the final state; it is assumed to be a slowly varying function of W_n which is neither infinite nor zero when $W_n = W_{n_0}$. If we substitute for b_{n_0}, $b_{n'}$ in equation (87) we obtain immediately

$$\dot{b}_n(t) = \frac{i}{\hbar}\bigg[(n|\mathfrak{H}_1|n_0)e^{i(W_{n_0}-W_n)t/\hbar-\gamma t}+$$
$$+ \sum_{n'} (n|\mathfrak{H}_1|n')U_{n'}\frac{e^{-\gamma t+i(W_{n_0}-W_{n'})t/\hbar}-1}{W_{n_0}-W_{n'}+i\hbar\gamma}e^{i(W_{n'}-W_n)t/\hbar}\bigg]. \quad (89)$$

As before we replace the summation by an integral over W_n. Denoting by $\rho_{W_n}d\omega_n dW_n$ the number of states with energy between W_n and W_n+dW_n for which the quantum of radiation is scattered into the solid angle $d\omega_n$, the sum is then replaced by

$$e^{-\gamma t+i(W_{n_0}-W_n)t/\hbar}\int \frac{1-e^{-\gamma t+i(W_{n'}-W_n)t/\hbar}}{W_{n_0}-W_{n'}+i\hbar\gamma}U_n(n|\mathfrak{H}_1|n')\rho_{W_{n'}}d\omega_{n'}dW_{n'}$$
$$= i\pi e^{-\gamma t+i(W_{n_0}-W_n)t/\hbar}\bigg[\int (n|\mathfrak{H}_1|n')U_{n'}\rho_{W_{n'}}d\omega_n'\bigg]_{W_{n'}=W_{n_0}}.$$

Substituting for the sum in (89) and for $b_n(t)$ by its value (88 a) we obtain finally

$$U_n = (n|\mathfrak{H}_1|n_0)+i\pi\bigg[\int (n|\mathfrak{H}_1|n')U_{n'}\rho_{W_{n'}}d\omega_{n'}\bigg]_{W_{n'}-W_{n_0}}. \quad (90)$$

Equation (90) is an integral equation for the determination of the function U_n.

We have next to determine the parameter γ. Substituting from equation (88 a) into equation (86) we obtain

$$\gamma = -\frac{i}{\hbar}\sum_n (n_0|\mathfrak{H}_1|n)U_n\frac{1-e^{\gamma t+i(W_n-W_{n_0})t/\hbar}}{W_{n_0}-W_n+i\hbar\gamma}.$$

Replacing the sum by an integral as before we have

$$\gamma = \frac{\pi}{\hbar}\int (n_0|\mathfrak{H}_1|n)U_n\rho_{W_n}d\omega_n. \quad (91)$$

As an example of the solution of equation (90) we consider the scattering of light by free electrons. If we denote by n_0 the initial state of the whole system (i.e. electron+quantum) and its final state by n, then the matrix element $(n_0|\mathfrak{H}_1|n)$ is given by equation (49 a). Substituting the Schrödinger wave functions for a free electron into (49 a) we obtain

$$(n_0|\mathfrak{H}_1|n) = \frac{\hbar e^2}{m\nu}(\mathbf{e}_0\,\mathbf{e}),$$

where, as before, $\mathbf{e}_0$ and $\mathbf{e}$ denote unit vectors in the initial and final directions of the polarization respectively. As a trial solution we put

$$U_n = U(\mathbf{e}_0\,\mathbf{e}),$$

then
$$U = \frac{\hbar e^2}{m\nu} = \frac{1}{1-i\kappa},$$

where
$$\kappa = \frac{e^2\nu}{2mc^3} \frac{\int (\mathbf{e}_0\,\mathbf{e}')(\mathbf{e}'\mathbf{e})\,d\omega'}{(\mathbf{e}_0\,\mathbf{e})}.$$

Now it is readily shown that

$$\int (\mathbf{e}_0\,\mathbf{e}')(\mathbf{e}'\,\mathbf{e})\,d\omega' = \frac{8\pi}{3}(\mathbf{e}_0\,\mathbf{e}),$$

so that $\kappa = 4\pi e^2\nu/3mc^3$. Integrating over all directions of the emitted quantum and summing over the two polarizations we obtain the formula

$$\phi = \frac{8\pi}{3}\left(\frac{e^2}{mc^2}\right)^2 \frac{1}{1+\kappa^2} \qquad (85\,a)$$

for the total cross-section of scattering, in agreement with the classical equation (85).

50.4. *Transitions through intermediate states*

If in considering the scattering of light by free electrons we use Dirac's relativistic equation for the motion of an electron, we find that the transition between the initial and final states cannot take place directly but must take place through intermediate states. We shall now derive the integral equations corresponding to equation (90) for transitions of this type. As before, let us denote the initial and final states by n_0 and n; and let us denote an intermediate state attainable from the ground state of the atom by the absorption of a light quantum with a given frequency, polarization, and direction by m. The perturbation equations then take the form

$$-i\hbar\dot{b}_{n_0}(t) = \sum_m (n_0|\mathfrak{H}_1|m)b_m(t)e^{i(W_m - W_{n_0})t/\hbar}, \qquad (92)$$

$$-i\hbar\dot{b}_m(t) = (m|\mathfrak{H}_1|n_0)b_{n_0}(t)e^{i(W_{n_0}-W_m)t/\hbar} + \sum_n (m|\mathfrak{H}_1|n)b_n(t)e^{i(W_n - W_m)t/\hbar}, \quad (93)$$

$$-i\hbar\dot{b}_n(t) = \sum_m (n|\mathfrak{H}_1|m)b_m(t)e^{i(W_m - W_n)t/\hbar}. \qquad (94)$$

In these equations W_{n_0} and W_n are approximately equal, but may be very different from W_m, the energy of the intermediate state; the intermediate states are such that momentum is approximately conserved. The probability amplitudes $b_{n_0}(t)$, $b_n(t)$ again satisfy the initial conditions (88) and in addition $b_m(0) = 0$. Substituting from equations (88 a), the solution of (93) satisfying this initial condition is found to be

$$b_m(t) = \left\{(m|\mathfrak{H}_1|n_0) + i\pi\left[\int (m|\mathfrak{H}_1|n)U_n\rho_{W_n}\,d\omega_n\right]_{W_n = W_{n_0}}\right\}\frac{e^{-\gamma t + i(W_{n_0}-W_m)t/\hbar} - 1}{W_{n_0} - W_m + i\hbar\gamma}.$$

$$(95)$$

Substituting from (88 a) and (95) in (94) we obtain

$$U_n \, e^{-\gamma t + i(W_{n_0} - W_n)t/\hbar}$$

$$= \sum_m (n|\mathfrak{H}_1|m) \Big\{ (m|\mathfrak{H}_1|n_0) + i\pi \Big[\int (m|\mathfrak{H}_1|n') U_{n'} \, \rho_{W_{n'}} \, d\omega_{n'} \Big]_{W_{n'} = W_{n_0}} \Big\} \times$$

$$\times \frac{e^{-\gamma t + i(W_{n_0} - W_n)t/\hbar} - e^{i(W_m - W_n)t/\hbar}}{W_{n_0} - W_m + i\hbar\gamma}. \quad (96)$$

Let us now consider in particular the scattering of light by a free electron. If a free electron absorbs a quantum the resulting intermediate state m_0 is sharply defined by the law of conservation of momentum and the sum with respect to m reduces to a single term—that with m replaced by m_0. The resulting equation has no solution since there is no term on the left which we can equate to the term with factor $e^{i(W_m - W_n)t/\hbar}$ on the right. Instead of considering the electron to be free we consider it to be bound, the binding energy of the electron being small in comparison with the energy of the quantum of radiation. There is then a continuum of intermediate states and it is possible to make the corresponding terms involving $e^{i(W_m - W_n)t/\hbar}$ on the right of equation (96) give a zero contribution to the final result. To demonstrate this we have merely to observe that the matrix elements $(n_0|\mathfrak{H}|m)$ are not delta functions—although $(n_0|\mathfrak{H}_1|m_0)$ is—so that the summation with respect to m gives zero for sufficiently large values of t, since $e^{i(W_m - W_n)t/\hbar}$ is a rapidly varying quantity and the denominator does not vanish at any point where the matrix elements are not zero. In this way we can equate the coefficients of $e^{-\gamma t + i(W_{n_0} - W_n)t/\hbar}$ and then pass to the limit of a free electron by replacing the sum by a single term. In this way we obtain the equation

$$U_n = \frac{(n|\mathfrak{H}_1|m_0)(m_0|\mathfrak{H}_1|n_0)}{W_{n_0} - W_{m_0} + i\hbar\gamma} + i\pi \frac{(n|\mathfrak{H}_1|m_0)\Big[\int (m_0|\mathfrak{H}_1|n') U_{n'} \, \rho_{W_{n'}} \, d\omega_{n'} \Big]_{W_{n'} = W_{n_0}}}{W_{n_0} - W_{m_0} + i\hbar\gamma}$$

$$(97)$$

for the determination of the unknown function U_n.

This procedure gives us the formulae for the scattering of radiation by a free electron initially at rest; by applying a Lorentz transformation we obtain the results for the case in which the electron is in motion originally. The method outlined above seems at first sight rather artificial, but, as remarked by Wilson, it is in fact closely analogous to the procedure by which the scattering of an electron by a Coulomb field is derived from Born's scattering formula by calculating the scattering produced by a screened nucleus and then proceeding to the limit of zero screening.

To determine the parameter γ of equation (97) we substitute from equations (88a) and (95) into equation (92) to obtain

$$i\hbar\gamma e^{-\gamma t} = \sum_m \left\{ (m|\mathfrak{H}_1|n_0) + i\pi \left[\int (m|\mathfrak{H}_1|n) U_n \rho_{W_n} d\omega_n \right] \right\} (n_0|\mathfrak{H}_1|m) \times$$
$$\times \frac{e^{-\gamma t} - e^{i(W_m - W_{n_0})t/\hbar}}{W_{n_0} - W_m + i\hbar\gamma}.$$

Eliminating the terms involving the factor $e^{i(W_m - W_{n_0})t/\hbar}$ and proceeding to the limit of zero binding we obtain

$$i\hbar\gamma$$
$$= \frac{(m_0|\mathfrak{H}_1|n_0)(n_0|\mathfrak{H}_1|m_0)}{W_{n_0} - W_{m_0} + i\hbar\gamma} + i\pi \frac{(n_0|\mathfrak{H}_1|m_0)\left[\int (m_0|\mathfrak{H}_1|n') U_{n'} \rho_{W_{n'}} d\omega_{n'} \right]_{W_{n'} = W_{n_0}}}{W_{n_0} - W_{m_0} + i\hbar\gamma}.$$

If there is more than one intermediate state in the case of zero binding the analysis proceeds along similar lines.

The γ's in the denominators of equation (97) can usually be neglected and we obtain an integral equation of the type

$$U_n = U_n^0 + i\pi \int K(n, n') U_{n'} \rho_{W_{n'}} d\omega_{n'}, \tag{98}$$

where

$$U_n^0 = \sum_m \frac{(n|\mathfrak{H}_1|m)(m|\mathfrak{H}_1|n_0)}{W_{n_0} - W_m} \tag{99}$$

and

$$K(n, n') = \sum_m \frac{(n|\mathfrak{H}_1|m)(m|\mathfrak{H}_1|n')}{W_{n_0} - W_m}. \tag{100}$$

It is possible to investigate the influence of radiation damping on scattering processes by a more conventional method, namely, the stationary method of the perturbation theory. Ma and Hsüeh have shown† that this method gives rise to the integral equations derived by Heitler and Wilson for two-stage transitions when the effect of radiation damping is included in the analysis.

50.5. *Solutions of the integral equations*

Because of the complicated nature of the kernel of the integral equation it seems hopeless to attempt to derive a general solution. Some progress has, however, been made with the solution of the integral equations for certain special problems. The influence of radiation damping on the formula for the scattering of radiation by free electrons has been investigated by Wilson,‡ using Dirac's relativistic wave equation for the electron. Wilson considers the scattering in the frame of reference in which the total linear momentum of the system is zero;

† S. T. Ma and C. F. Hsüeh, *Proc. Camb. Phil. Soc.* **40**, 168 (1944). See also W. Pauli, *Meson Theory of Nuclear Forces*, chapter iv (New York, 1946).
‡ A. H. Wilson, loc. cit., p. 307.

the kernel does not then depend too strongly on the angle of scattering and we can replace it by an average value. Thus equation (98) is replaced by the equation

$$U_n[1+4\pi^2 i \overline{U_n^0 \rho_{W_n}}] = U_n^0,$$

where the bar denotes a mean value of the nature of a root mean square. Hence

$$|U_n|^2 = \frac{|U_n^0|^2}{1+16\pi^2 |\overline{U_n^0}|^2 \rho_{W_n}^2}.$$

With this approximation Wilson obtains the general formula

$$d\phi = \frac{d\phi_0}{1+\pi\phi_0 p^2/h^2} \tag{101}$$

for the differential cross-section, $d\phi$, in terms of the differential cross-section for zero-damping, $d\phi_0$; the initial momenta of the light quantum and the electron are $\mathbf{p}$ and $-\mathbf{p}$. This formula is not exact; the second term in the denominator should be multiplied by a numerical factor of order unity to improve the approximate method of averaging.

By means of this formula Wilson shows that the damping is given correctly by the classical theory for low frequencies; however, at high frequencies ($h\nu > 137mc^2$) he finds that, contrary to classical expectation, the influence of damping on the cross-section is always negligible.[†] Since all applications of radiation theory to high-energy problems of the type arising in the theory of cosmic rays depend on the smallness of the damping effect, this result is of considerable importance. Because of this, and the fact that Wilson's procedure of averaging under the integral sign may not lead to correct results, the problem has been re-examined recently by Power;[‡] expanding the solution of the integral equation in ascending powers of e^2, Power shows that the extra term, due to damping, in the Klein–Nishina formula is small in comparison with the main term, thus confirming Wilson's result.

Approximate solutions of equations (90) and (97) have also been discussed by Hsüeh and Ma[§], by means of a variational method. Separating the summation over the directions of polarization from the other integration they write equation (90) in the form

$$U_n = (n|\mathfrak{H}_1|n_0)+i\pi\sum_{p_{n'}}\int (n|\mathfrak{H}_1|n')U_{n'}\rho_{W_{n'}}d\omega_{n'},$$

[†] The formula (Klein–Nishina) for the cross-section without damping is discussed on p. 316.
[‡] S. C. Power, *Proc. Roy. Irish Acad.* **50**, A, 139 (1945).
[§] C. F. Hsüeh and S. T. Ma, *Phys. Rev.* **67**, 303 (1945).

and note that it is equivalent to the equation

$$\sum_{p_{n_0}} \sum_{p_n} \int \delta U_n^* \Big[U_n - (n|\mathfrak{H}_1|n_0) - i\pi \sum_{p_{n'}} \int (n|\mathfrak{H}_1|n') U_{n'} \rho_{W_{n'}} d\omega_{n'} \Big] \rho_{W_n} d\omega_n = 0,$$

where δU_n^* denotes an arbitrary variation of the complex conjugate of U_n. Substituting

$$U_n = \alpha(n|\mathfrak{H}_1|n_0),$$

where α is a parameter independent of n and n_0 and varying U_n^*, we have

$$\delta\alpha^* \sum_{p_{n_0}} \sum_{p_n} \int (n_0|\mathfrak{H}_1|n) \times$$

$$\times \Big[(n|\mathfrak{H}_1|n_0)(\alpha-1) - i\pi\alpha \sum_{p_{n'}} \int (n|\mathfrak{H}_1|n')(n'|\mathfrak{H}_1|n_0)\rho_{W_{n'}} d\omega_{n'} \Big] \rho_{W_n} d\omega_n = 0.$$

Solving this equation for α we obtain

$$\alpha = \frac{1}{1-i\kappa},$$

where

$$\kappa = \frac{\pi \sum_{p_{n_0}} \sum_{p_n} \sum_{p_{n'}} \iint (n_0|\mathfrak{H}_1|n)(n|\mathfrak{H}_1|n')(n'|\mathfrak{H}_1|n_0)\rho_{W_n}\rho_{W_{n'}} d\omega_n d\omega_{n'}}{\sum_{p_{n_0}} \sum_{p_n} \iint (n_0|\mathfrak{H}_1|n)(n|\mathfrak{H}_1|n_0)\rho_{W_n} d\omega_n}.$$

The formula for the cross-section is now

$$d\phi = |\alpha|^2 \, d\phi_0 = \frac{d\phi_0}{1+\kappa^2}. \tag{102}$$

This formula is of the same form as Wilson's result (101), but the damping factors in the two formulae are different. To test the validity of formula (102) it is of interest to use it to calculate the cross-section for the non-relativistic scattering of a quantum of radiation by an electron at rest and then to compare the result with the exact solution (85 a). Now from the equation

$$(n|\mathfrak{H}_1|n_0) = \frac{\hbar e^2}{m\nu}(\mathbf{e_0 \, e})$$

we have that

$$\kappa = \frac{\pi e^2 \hbar}{m\nu} \frac{\nu^2}{hc^3} \frac{\sum_{e_0} \sum_{e} \sum_{e'} \iint (\mathbf{e_0 \, e})(\mathbf{e e'})(\mathbf{e' \, e_0}) \, d\omega_n \, d\omega_{n'}}{\sum_{e_0} \sum_{e} \int (\mathbf{e_0 \, e})(\mathbf{e e_0}) \, d\omega_n},$$

and equation (102) then gives

$$U_n = \frac{e^2 \hbar}{m\nu} \frac{(\mathbf{e_0 \, e})}{1-i\kappa}$$

in agreement with the exact result (85 a).

We have seen that the effects of radiation damping are unimportant for processes involving free electrons. On the other hand, it was found by Heitler and Wilson that damping effects are appreciable in all processes involving mesons. Since then there have been various investigations of the effect of damping in problems on the motion of mesons. Relativistic formulae for the scattering of mesons by nuclear particles under the influence of radiation damping have been derived by Ma and Hsüeh.† The theory of radiation damping has also been applied to the creation of mesons by various processes. It was shown by Heitler and Peng‡ that in a collision between a fast nuclear particle and another nuclear particle at rest mesons are emitted with a very high probability; the production of mesons by light quanta has also been investigated.§ These papers form the basis of a theory†, ‡ which gives a satisfactory account of all the chief cosmic-ray phenomena associated with mesons, including their creation, their diffusion through the atmosphere, meson showers, and the transformation of charged mesons into neutral mesons; it is assumed that the mesons are produced by a primary radiation of protons. The agreement with the experimental results is sufficiently close to make it seem probable that the theory of cosmic-ray mesons based on the quantum theory of radiation damping is fundamentally correct.

† S. T. Ma, *Proc. Camb. Phil. Soc.* **39**, 168 (1943); S. T. Ma and C. F. Hsüeh, ibid. **40**, 167 (1944).

‡ W. Heitler and H. W. Peng, *Proc. Roy. Irish Acad.* **49**, A, 101 (1943); W. Heitler, ibid. **50**, A, 155 (1945); H. W. Peng, ibid. **49**, A, 245 (1944).

§ J. Hamilton and H. W. Peng, ibid. 197 (1944); J. Hamilton, W. Heitler, and H. W. Peng, *Phys. Rev.* **64**, 78 (1943).

XI
RELATIVISTIC QUANTUM MECHANICS

51. Introduction

THE theory of the spinning electron developed by Pauli and Darwin (Chap. IV) on the basis of the Schrödinger wave mechanics is incomplete in two important respects. Though it provides a suitable mathematical scheme for the description of many of the properties of the electron's spin deduced from spectroscopic observations, it gives no satisfactory account of its origin. Furthermore, no attempt was made to take account of the special theory of relativity, so that the theory cannot be applied to the discussion of problems involving electrons of high energy; and for many problems, such as the fine structure of the spectral lines of hydrogen, the corrections introduced by spin and by relativity are of the same order. Before the introduction of the concept of electron spin into wave mechanics various attempts† were made to establish a wave equation of the Schrödinger type invariant under Lorentz transformations. Unlike the non-relativistic Schrödinger equation, these equations were of the second order in the time-differential operator $\partial/\partial t$. Dirac solved both problems, that of constructing a relativistically invariant wave equation and that of explaining the origin of the electron spin, by observing that if the general interpretation of non-relativistic wave mechanics is to be preserved, the relativistic wave equation must be linear in $\partial/\partial t$. The beauty of Dirac's method lies in the fact that once a Lorentz-invariant wave equation, linear in the operator $\partial/\partial t$, has been constructed, the magnetic moment assumed in the model of the spinning electron proposed by Uhlenbeck and Goudsmit appears as the result of a simple calculation without the addition of a new physical assumption. Dirac's theory of the electron has met with conspicuous success in its application to the fine structure of atomic spectra, the scattering of fast electrons and of hard γ-rays, and the formation of pairs of electrons and positrons. The agreement with the observed experimental results is so good that it appears that Dirac's equation for a single electron is essentially correct. On the other hand, there is considerable doubt as to the validity of the extension of the theory to two electrons.

Before considering in detail the possible forms of the relativistic

---

† E. Schrödinger, *Ann. der Physik*, **81**, 109 (1926); O. Klein, *Zeits. f. Physik*, **37**, 895 (1926); V. Fock, ibid. **38**, 242 (1926); ibid. **39**, 226 (1926).

wave equation for an electron it will be of advantage to state the general conditions that we should expect such an equation to satisfy. The equation should satisfy the requirements of the special theory of relativity, that is to say, that it should be invariant under the group of Lorentz transformations. There is another kind of invariance which the equation must possess; this is 'gauge-invariance', the importance of which was realized first by Hermann Weyl.† In classical electrodynamics the field strengths $\mathbf{E}$ and $\mathbf{H}$ are related to the scalar and vector potentials ϕ and $\mathbf{A}$ by the formulae

$$\mathbf{H} = \operatorname{curl}\mathbf{A}, \qquad \mathbf{E} = -\operatorname{grad}\phi - \frac{1}{c}\frac{\partial\mathbf{A}}{\partial t},$$

$$\operatorname{div}\mathbf{A} + \frac{1}{c}\frac{\partial\phi}{\partial t} = 0.$$

The transformation

$$\phi = \phi' + \frac{1}{ec}\frac{\partial\Lambda}{\partial t}, \qquad \mathbf{A} = \mathbf{A}' - \frac{1}{e}\operatorname{grad}\Lambda,$$

where Λ is a solution of the wave equation

$$\nabla^2\Lambda = \frac{1}{c^2}\frac{\partial^2\Lambda}{\partial t^2},$$

leaves the form of the above equations unaltered and is called a gauge transformation.

We should also expect to be able to form a 4-vector representing current and charge density and to prove by means of the wave equation that the current satisfies a continuity equation both in the presence and in the absence of an external electromagnetic field. (The analogous case in the non-relativistic theory is given on p. 259.) Finally, we should be able to predict the existence of the spin and of the magnetic moment of the electron from the wave equation.

At first sight it would appear that it is necessary for the theory to give only positive values for the energy of the particle. We shall see that negative energy states of the electron arise in Dirac's theory but that it is possible to make use of them to account for observed properties of positrons (positively charged particles with the electronic charge and mass). Though Dirac's theory had this unexpected triumph of identifying the positron with a 'hole' in the aggregate of negative energy states, such a hypothesis, strictly speaking, removes from the theory its original basis as the theory of a *single* electron. Indeed, if

† H. Weyl, *Gruppentheorie und Quantenmechanik* (Leipzig, 1928).

we wish to obtain valid relativistic interpretations we cannot even properly formulate the problem of a single particle; we must instead study the many-particle problem from the beginning. In the many-particle problem in which the particles are considered to be moving at very high speeds the charge density $-eP$ need not be negative (in the algebraic sense) because of the possibility of the creation and annihilation of positrons. In other words, the probability function P need not always be positive in the many-electron problem.

52. Scalar relativistic wave equations

52.1. *The Hamiltonian for the relativistic motion of an electron*

In this section a derivation will be given of the Hamiltonian of a charged particle moving in an electromagnetic field. Consider the motion of an electron of rest mass m and charge $-e$ in an arbitrary electromagnetic field whose electric and magnetic vectors are denoted by $\mathbf{E}$ and $\mathbf{H}$ respectively. When the velocity of the electron is $\mathbf{v}$ its momentum is given by

$$\frac{m\mathbf{v}}{\sqrt{(1-v^2/c^2)}},$$

so that the equations of motion are

$$\frac{d}{dt}\left(\frac{m\mathbf{v}}{\sqrt{(1-v^2/c^2)}}\right) + e\mathbf{E} + \frac{e}{c}(\mathbf{v} \wedge \mathbf{H}) = 0. \tag{1}$$

Now if we denote the scalar and vector potentials of the field by ϕ and $\mathbf{A}$, then

$$\mathbf{E} = -\operatorname{grad}\phi - \frac{1}{c}\frac{\partial \mathbf{A}}{\partial t}, \qquad \mathbf{H} = \operatorname{curl}\mathbf{A},$$

and the vector equation of motion of the electron (1) reduces to

$$\frac{d}{dt}\left(\frac{m\mathbf{v}}{\sqrt{(1-v^2/c^2)}}\right) = e\operatorname{grad}\phi + \frac{e}{c}\frac{\partial \mathbf{A}}{\partial t} - \frac{e}{c}(\mathbf{v} \wedge \operatorname{curl}\mathbf{A}). \tag{2}$$

The equations of motion (2) may be written in the Lagrangian form

$$\frac{d}{dt}\left(\frac{\partial L}{\partial \dot{q}}\right) - \frac{\partial L}{\partial q} = 0 \quad (q = x, y, z)$$

if the Lagrangian function L is taken to be

$$L = -mc^2\sqrt{(1-v^2/c^2)} + e\phi - \frac{e}{c}(\mathbf{v}.\mathbf{A}). \tag{3}$$

This may easily be verified. The conjugate momenta are defined by the relations

$$p_i = \frac{\partial L}{\partial \dot{q}_i},$$

so that for the dynamical system described by the Lagrangian function (3) the momenta are p_x, p_y, p_z, where the vector $\mathbf{p}$ is given in terms of the vectors $\mathbf{v}$ and $\mathbf{A}$ by the equation

$$\mathbf{p} = \frac{m\mathbf{v}}{\sqrt{(1-v^2/c^2)}} - \frac{e}{c}\mathbf{A}. \tag{4}$$

The general expression $H = \sum_i \dot{q}_i p_i - L$

for the Hamiltonian of a system whose Lagrangian function is L, reduces for a single particle to the simple form

$$H = (\mathbf{p}.\mathbf{v}) - L. \tag{5}$$

Substituting from equations (3) and (4) into equation (5) we obtain

$$H = \frac{mc^2}{\sqrt{(1-v^2/c^2)}} - e\phi.$$

Solving equation (4) for $\mathbf{v}$ and substituting in this last equation we find that in terms of the momentum the Hamiltonian of a single particle moving at speeds comparable with that of light is

$$H = c\sqrt{\{m^2c^2 + (\mathbf{p} + e\mathbf{A}/c)^2\}} - e\phi. \tag{6}$$

For a conservative system the Hamiltonian, H, is equal to the energy of the system, which is denoted in this book by W. Writing $p_0 = W/c$, we see that equation (6) may be written in the symmetrical form

$$-\left(p_0 + \frac{e\phi}{c}\right)^2 + \left(\mathbf{p} + \frac{e\mathbf{A}}{c}\right)^2 + m^2c^2 = 0. \tag{7}$$

52.2. *Approximate relativistic equations*

The difficulty in setting up the relativistic Schrödinger equation directly from the Hamiltonian (6) arises from the interpretation of the square root. Approximate equations can, however, be derived by expanding the Hamiltonian H defined by equation (6) above in terms of v/c. In this way we obtain as a first approximation (cf. Chap. I, § 8)

$$H = mc^2 + \frac{1}{2m}\left(\mathbf{p} + \frac{e}{c}\mathbf{A}\right)^2 - e\phi. \tag{8}$$

In the second approximation we replace equation (8) by

$$H = mc^2 + \frac{1}{2m}\left(\mathbf{p} + \frac{e}{c}\mathbf{A}\right)^2 - \frac{1}{8m^3c^2}\left(\mathbf{p} + \frac{e}{c}\mathbf{A}\right)^4 - e\phi.$$

If in this equation we write $H = W' + mc^2$ and replace $(\mathbf{p} + e\mathbf{A}/c)^4/8m^3c^2$ by its first approximation $(W' + e\phi)^2/2mc^2$ given by equation (8), we find that to the order v^2/c^2

$$\frac{1}{2m}\left(\mathbf{p} + \frac{e\mathbf{A}}{c}\right)^2 - (W' + e\phi) - \frac{1}{2mc^2}(W' + e\phi)^2 = 0. \tag{9}$$

The Schrödinger equations corresponding to these Hamiltonians are obtained in the usual way by making the substitutions

$$H = -\frac{\hbar}{i}\frac{\partial}{\partial t}, \qquad \mathbf{p} = \frac{\hbar}{i}\left(\frac{\partial}{\partial x}, \frac{\partial}{\partial y}, \frac{\partial}{\partial z}\right) = \frac{\hbar}{i}\mathrm{grad} \tag{10}$$

in equations (8) and (9). This procedure applied to (8) yields the equation

$$\frac{1}{2m}\left\{\frac{\hbar}{i}\mathrm{grad}+\frac{e\mathbf{A}}{c}\right\}\left\{\frac{\hbar}{i}\mathrm{grad}+\frac{e\mathbf{A}}{c}\right\}\Psi + (mc^2-e\phi)\Psi+\frac{\hbar}{i}\frac{\partial\Psi}{\partial t} = 0,$$

which may be reduced to the form

$$\frac{\hbar^2}{2m}\nabla^2\Psi+\frac{ie\hbar}{mc}\{\mathbf{A}\,\mathrm{grad}\,\Psi+\tfrac{1}{2}\Psi\,\mathrm{div}\,\mathbf{A}\}+\left\{e\phi-\frac{e^2A^2}{2mc^2}\right\}\Psi$$
$$=\frac{\hbar}{i}\frac{\partial\Psi}{\partial t}+mc^2\Psi. \tag{11}$$

In this equation it should be noted that $\mathrm{div}\,\mathbf{A}$ does not vanish unless the scalar potential is constant with time, since ϕ and $\mathbf{A}$ are related by the equation

$$\mathrm{div}\,\mathbf{A}+\frac{1}{c}\frac{\partial\phi}{\partial t} = 0.$$

The equation (11) is correct only to the order v/c, where v is the velocity of the electron.

It will be noticed that equation (11) differs from the non-relativistic equation used in § 8 only in the small term in A^2, which can be neglected in most applications, and in the term $mc^2\Psi$, which can be removed by transforming to the new wave-function

$$\Psi' = e^{imc^2t/\hbar}\Psi.$$

If we multiply equation (11) by Ψ^*, and its complex conjugate by Ψ and subtract, we obtain an equation which may be written in the form of a continuity equation

$$\frac{\partial\rho}{\partial t}+\mathrm{div}\,\mathbf{j} = 0, \tag{12}$$

if ρ and $\mathbf{j}$ are taken to be defined by

$$\left.\begin{aligned}\rho &= -e\Psi\Psi^*\\ \mathbf{j} &= \frac{e\hbar}{2im}(\Psi^*\mathrm{grad}\,\Psi-\Psi\,\mathrm{grad}\,\Psi^*)-\frac{e^2}{mc}\mathbf{A}\Psi\Psi^*\end{aligned}\right\}. \tag{13}$$

Similar results may be obtained from equation (8) giving a better approximation.

52.3. *The Klein–Gordon Equation*

It was suggested by Gordon[†] that the exact relativistic wave equation should be established by making the substitutions (10), not in equation (6), but in the more symmetrical equation (7) and allowing the operator so formed to act on a wave-function Ψ. In this way we obtain the relativistic wave equation

$$\left\{\left(\frac{\hbar}{i}\mathrm{grad}+\frac{e\mathbf{A}}{c}\right)^2-\left(\frac{\hbar}{ic}\frac{\partial}{\partial t}-\frac{e\phi}{c}\right)^2+m^2c^2\right\}\Psi = 0. \tag{14}$$

This equation is known as the Klein–Gordon equation.

The Klein–Gordon equation involves us in serious difficulties in interpretation which arise because it is not linear in the time-differential operator $\partial/\partial t$. In non-relativistic quantum mechanics the Schrödinger equation

$$\left(H+\frac{\hbar}{i}\frac{\partial}{\partial t}\right)\Psi = 0$$

is linear in $\partial/\partial t$. It follows that if Ψ is known initially, the equation will determine it at all subsequent times. The results of any measurements on the position *and* momentum of a particle are used in forming the wave-function Ψ; the correct initial condition is thus that Ψ should be known, not Ψ and $\partial\Psi/\partial t$. With the Klein–Gordon equation, on the other hand, it would be necessary to know both Ψ and $\partial\Psi/\partial t$ in order to determine Ψ at all subsequent times.

The second difficulty arises when we attempt to find an expression for the current and charge density. Multiplying equation (14) by Ψ^*, the complex conjugate equation by Ψ, and subtracting we find that the resulting equation may be written in the form (12), where now

$$\left.\begin{aligned}\rho &= -eP = \frac{e\hbar}{2mc^2i}\left\{\Psi^*\frac{\partial\Psi}{\partial t}-\Psi\frac{\partial\Psi^*}{\partial t}\right\}-\frac{e^2}{mc^2}\phi\Psi\Psi^*\\[2mm]\mathbf{j} &= -\frac{e\hbar}{2mi}\{\Psi^*\mathrm{grad}\,\Psi-\Psi\,\mathrm{grad}\,\Psi^*\}-\frac{e^2}{mc}\mathbf{A}\Psi\Psi^*\end{aligned}\right\}. \tag{15}$$

These expressions for the charge density and the current density are due to Gordon and Klein.[‡] The difficulty arises from the interpretation of the quantity P defined by the first equation of (15). In the non-relativistic Schrödinger theory P would be the probability function for the position of an electron. Such a probability function satisfies two general conditions:

$$\text{(i)} \quad P \geqslant 0, \qquad \text{(ii)} \quad \frac{\partial}{\partial t}\int P\,d\tau = 0,$$

† W. Gordon, *Zeits. f. Physik*, **40**, 117 (1926).
‡ W. Gordon, ibid. **40**, 121 (1926); O. Klein, ibid. **41**, 414 (1927).

the integral being taken over all space. In a completely satisfactory relativistic theory we should expect P to satisfy both of these conditions together with the further condition that

$$\int P \, d\tau$$

is invariant under Lorentz transformations. We have already shown that the condition (ii) is satisfied by showing that ρ satisfies a continuity equation of the type (12). The third condition is satisfied automatically if it can be shown that ρ may be expressed as the fourth component of a 4-vector. This is readily done by considering the transformation properties of the set of four quantities

$$s_\mu = (\mathbf{j}_x, \mathbf{j}_y, \mathbf{j}_z, ic\rho). \tag{16}$$

The condition (i), however, is not satisfied, since

$$P = \frac{\hbar}{2mc^2 i}\left(\Psi \frac{\partial \Psi^*}{\partial t} - \Psi^* \frac{\partial \Psi}{\partial t}\right) + \frac{e\phi}{mc^2}\Psi\Psi^*,$$

and this can be made negative, both Ψ and $\partial\Psi/\partial t$ being arbitrary at the initial point in time. P is not therefore a satisfactory expression to replace the probability function $\Psi\Psi^*$ of the non-relativistic theory.

Although the expression for P given by equation (15) seems at first sight to be totally different from the non-relativistic formula $\Psi\Psi^*$, it can easily be seen that the formula derived from the Klein–Gordon equation reduces to that given by the Schrödinger equation when the kinetic energy of the particle is very much smaller than its rest energy. For if we substitute

$$\frac{\hbar}{i}\frac{\partial\Psi}{\partial t} = -W\Psi$$

in the first of equations (15), we obtain

$$P = \frac{\Psi\Psi^*}{mc^2}(e\phi + W). \tag{17}$$

From the fact that $W = W' + mc^2$ it follows immediately that

$$P = \Psi\Psi^*\left(1 + \frac{W' + e\phi}{mc^2}\right). \tag{18}$$

If now the kinetic energy is assumed to be small in comparison with the rest energy mc^2 we find that P is approximately equal to $\Psi\Psi^*$ as in the non-relativistic theory.

53. The Dirac wave equation for an electron

53.1. *The Dirac equation for an arbitrary field*

The considerations of the last section show that the correct relativistic wave equation must be linear in the differential operator $\partial/\partial t$; furthermore, in conformity with the special theory of relativity, the equation must be invariant under a Lorentz transformation. In the theory of relativity there is complete symmetry between the space coordinates x, y, z and the time coordinate ict, so that if our equation is linear in $\partial/\partial t$ it must also be linear in $\partial/\partial x$, $\partial/\partial y$, and $\partial/\partial z$. For this reason Dirac† took the relativistic wave equation to be of the form

$$0 = \left\{ \left(p_0 + \frac{e\phi}{c}\right) + \alpha_x\left(p_x + \frac{eA_x}{c}\right) + \alpha_y\left(p_y + \frac{eA_y}{c}\right) + \alpha_z\left(p_z + \frac{eA_z}{c}\right) + \beta \right\} \Psi,$$

(19)

where, as in the last section, ϕ denotes the scalar potential and (A_x, A_y, A_z) the vector potential; the operators p_x, p_y, p_z are defined by equation (10) and p_0 denotes the operator $(i\hbar/c)(\partial/\partial t)$. In equation (19) the quantities α_x, α_y, α_z, β are not ordinary numbers; their nature will be defined below. To determine the laws governing these quantities Dirac made the additional assumption that for an electron in the absence of a field the wave equation (19) would reduce to the Klein–Gordon equation (14). In the absence of an electromagnetic field both ϕ and $\mathbf{A}$ vanish and equation (19) reduces to

$$(p_0 + \alpha_x p_x + \alpha_y p_y + \alpha_z p_z + \beta)\Psi = 0.$$

Multiplying this equation by the operator

$$-p_0 + \alpha_x p_x + \alpha_y p_y + \alpha_z p_z + \beta,$$

we obtain the second-order wave equation

$$\left\{ -p_0^2 + \sum_{xyz} \alpha_x^2 p_x^2 + \sum_{xyz} (\alpha_x \alpha_y + \alpha_y \alpha_x) p_x p_y + \beta^2 + \sum_{xyz} (\alpha_x \beta + \beta \alpha_x) \right\} \Psi = 0.$$

This reduces to the Klein–Gordon equation for a free particle

$$(-p_0^2 + p_x^2 + p_y^2 + p_z^2 + m^2 c^2)\Psi = 0,$$

if the quantities α_x, α_y, α_z, β obey the relations

$$\left. \begin{array}{ll} \alpha_x^2 = \alpha_y^2 = \alpha_z^2 = 1, & \alpha_x \alpha_y + \alpha_y \alpha_x = 0, \text{ etc.,} \\ \beta^2 = m^2 c^2, & \alpha_x \beta + \beta \alpha_x = 0, \text{ etc.} \end{array} \right\}$$

(20)

Once the quantities α_x, α_y, α_z, and β have been determined from these equations, the wave equation for an electron in an arbitrary electromagnetic field can be taken to be (19). It should be noted that the wave-function Ψ appearing in this equation need not be a scalar; we shall see later that, because of the nature of the α's and β, the wave-function Ψ must, in fact, be assumed to have four components.

† P. A. M. Dirac, *Proc. Roy. Soc.* A, **117**, 610 (1928).

The Dirac equation (19) assumes a convenient form if we write

$$(x, y, z, ict) = (x_1, x_2, x_3, x_4),$$
$$(A_x, A_y, A_z, i\phi) = (A_1, A_2, A_3, A_4),$$
$$\left(\alpha_x, \alpha_y, \alpha_z, \frac{\beta}{mc}\right) = (\alpha_1, \alpha_2, \alpha_3, \alpha_4),$$

and put
$$\Pi_j = \frac{\hbar}{i} \frac{\partial}{\partial x_j} + \frac{eA_j}{c} \quad (j = 1, 2, 3, 4).$$

With this notation equation (19) may be written in the form

$$\left\{ \sum_{j=1}^{3} \alpha_j \Pi_j - i\Pi_4 + \alpha_4 mc \right\} \Psi = 0, \tag{21}$$

where now the quantities α_1, α_2, α_3, α_4 satisfy the relations

$$\alpha_\lambda \alpha_\nu + \alpha_\nu \alpha_\lambda = 2\delta_{\lambda\nu} \tag{22}$$

$(\lambda, \nu = 1, 2, 3, 4)$. If we write the three quantities $(\alpha_1, \alpha_2, \alpha_3)$ as a vector $\boldsymbol{\alpha}$ and introduce a vector operator $\boldsymbol{\Pi}$ in the same way, we may write equation (21) in the form

$$(\boldsymbol{\alpha} . \boldsymbol{\Pi} - i\Pi_4 + \alpha_4 mc)\Psi = 0.$$

It is sometimes more convenient to write the Dirac equation (21) in a more symmetrical form by introducing the operators

$$\beta_1 = i\alpha_4 \alpha_1, \qquad \beta_2 = i\alpha_4 \alpha_2, \qquad \beta_3 = i\alpha_4 \alpha_3, \qquad \beta_4 = \alpha_4. \tag{23}$$

Multiplying equation (21) on the left by $i\alpha_4$ and substituting from equation (23) we obtain the equation

$$\left(\sum_{j=1}^{4} \beta_j \Pi_j + imc \right) \Psi = 0. \tag{24}$$

The relations (23) give the operators β_j in terms of the operators α_j; the inverse relations can be readily shown to be

$$\alpha_1 = i\beta_1 \beta_4, \qquad \alpha_2 = i\beta_2 \beta_4, \qquad \alpha_3 = i\beta_3 \beta_4, \qquad \alpha_4 = \beta_4. \tag{25}$$

53.2. The Dirac matrices

So far the only information we possess about the quantities α_j $(j = 1, 2, 3, 4)$ is that they satisfy the equations (22). From these equations we now attempt to obtain a matrix representation of these quantities. The equations (22) are, of course, satisfied by the Pauli spin operators σ_x, σ_y, σ_z introduced on p. 97, but if we choose these operators as three of our α's we find it impossible to determine the fourth. If, however, we extend the Pauli matrices in a diagonal manner thus,

$$(\sigma_1, \sigma_2, \sigma_3) = \begin{pmatrix} \boldsymbol{\sigma} & 0 \\ 0 & \boldsymbol{\sigma} \end{pmatrix}, \tag{26}$$

where $\boldsymbol{\sigma}$ denotes the symbolic vector $(\sigma_x, \sigma_y, \sigma_z)$, and if we introduce the matrices

$$\rho_1 = \begin{pmatrix} 0 & 0 & 1 & 0 \\ 0 & 0 & 0 & 1 \\ 1 & 0 & 0 & 0 \\ 0 & 1 & 0 & 0 \end{pmatrix}, \qquad \rho_2 = \begin{pmatrix} 0 & 0 & -i & 0 \\ 0 & 0 & 0 & -i \\ i & 0 & 0 & 0 \\ 0 & i & 0 & 0 \end{pmatrix},$$

$$\rho_3 = \begin{pmatrix} 1 & 0 & 0 & 0 \\ 0 & 1 & 0 & 0 \\ 0 & 0 & -1 & 0 \\ 0 & 0 & 0 & -1 \end{pmatrix}, \tag{27}$$

we find that the σ's and ρ's satisfy the relations

$$\left. \begin{aligned} \sigma_r \sigma_s + \sigma_s \sigma_r = \rho_r \rho_s + \rho_s \rho_r = 2\delta_{rs} \\ \rho_r \sigma_t = \sigma_t \rho_r \end{aligned} \right\}. \tag{28}$$

If now we define a set of quantities α_ν by the equations

$$\alpha_1 = \rho_1 \sigma_1, \qquad \alpha_2 = \rho_1 \sigma_2, \qquad \alpha_3 = \rho_1 \sigma_3, \qquad \alpha_4 = \rho_3, \tag{29}$$

we find that all the conditions (22) are satisfied. Performing the matrix multiplications we obtain for the α's the four matrices $\alpha_4 = \rho_3$ and

$$\alpha_1 = \begin{pmatrix} 0 & 0 & 0 & 1 \\ 0 & 0 & 1 & 0 \\ 0 & 1 & 0 & 0 \\ 1 & 0 & 0 & 0 \end{pmatrix}, \qquad \alpha_2 = \begin{pmatrix} 0 & 0 & 0 & -i \\ 0 & 0 & i & 0 \\ 0 & -i & 0 & 0 \\ i & 0 & 0 & 0 \end{pmatrix},$$

$$\alpha_3 = \begin{pmatrix} 0 & 0 & 1 & 0 \\ 0 & 0 & 0 & -1 \\ 1 & 0 & 0 & 0 \\ 0 & -1 & 0 & 0 \end{pmatrix}. \tag{30}$$

From equation (23) we obtain for the β's the four matrices $\beta_4 = \alpha_4 = \rho_3$ and

$$\beta_1 = \begin{pmatrix} 0 & 0 & 0 & i \\ 0 & 0 & i & 0 \\ 0 & -i & 0 & 0 \\ -i & 0 & 0 & 0 \end{pmatrix}, \qquad \beta_2 = \begin{pmatrix} 0 & 0 & 0 & 1 \\ 0 & 0 & -1 & 0 \\ 0 & -1 & 0 & 0 \\ 1 & 0 & 0 & 0 \end{pmatrix},$$

$$\beta_3 = \begin{pmatrix} 0 & 0 & i & 0 \\ 0 & 0 & 0 & -i \\ -i & 0 & 0 & 0 \\ 0 & i & 0 & 0 \end{pmatrix}. \tag{31}$$

Furthermore, it can be proved that any four-rowed square matrix can be expressed as a linear combination of the sixteen matrices

$$\alpha_1, \quad \alpha_2, \quad \alpha_3, \quad \alpha_4, \quad \beta_1, \quad \beta_2, \quad \beta_3, \quad I$$

$$\alpha_1 \alpha_2, \quad \alpha_2 \alpha_3, \quad \alpha_3 \alpha_1, \quad \alpha_1 \alpha_2 \alpha_3, \quad \alpha_2 \alpha_3 \alpha_4, \quad \alpha_3 \alpha_1 \alpha_4, \quad \alpha_1 \alpha_2 \alpha_4, \quad \alpha_1 \alpha_2 \alpha_3 \alpha_4,$$

where I denotes the unit matrix

$$\begin{pmatrix} 1 & 0 & 0 & 0 \\ 0 & 1 & 0 & 0 \\ 0 & 0 & 1 & 0 \\ 0 & 0 & 0 & 1 \end{pmatrix}.$$

It should also be noted that all these matrices are unitary and Hermitian.†

The following properties of the σ and ρ matrices are of use in the application of the theory to the solution of special problems. The first set

$$\left.\begin{aligned} \rho_1\rho_2 &= -\rho_2\rho_1 = i\rho_3 \\ \sigma_1\sigma_2 &= -\sigma_2\sigma_1 = i\sigma_3 \end{aligned}\right\} \tag{32}$$

follows directly from the definitions of the quantities involved. Also if **B** is any vector commuting with **σ**, then by making use of equations (32) we can show that

$$(\boldsymbol{\sigma}.\mathbf{B})^2 = \mathbf{B}^2 + i\sum_{1,2,3} \sigma_3(B_1 B_2 - B_2 B_1). \tag{33}$$

Substituting $$\mathbf{B} = \mathbf{p} + \frac{e}{c}\mathbf{A} = \frac{\hbar}{i}\text{grad} + \frac{e}{c}\mathbf{A}$$

into this equation, we obtain the relation

$$\left(\boldsymbol{\sigma}.\mathbf{p} + \frac{e}{c}\mathbf{A}\right)^2 = \left(\mathbf{p} + \frac{e}{c}\mathbf{A}\right)^2 + \frac{\hbar e}{c}(\boldsymbol{\sigma}.\text{curl}\,\mathbf{A}). \tag{34}$$

53.3. *The relativistic invariance of the Dirac equations*

Since the quantities α and β may be represented by matrices of four rows and columns it follows that the wave-function Ψ upon which these quantities operate must itself be a column matrix with four elements; we shall write it in the form

$$\Psi = \begin{pmatrix} \Psi_1 \\ \Psi_2 \\ \Psi_3 \\ \Psi_4 \end{pmatrix}. \tag{35}$$

With this form of Ψ and the matrix representations of the β's given by the equations (31) we obtain by direct matrix multiplication

$$\beta_1\Psi = i\begin{pmatrix} \Psi_4 \\ \Psi_3 \\ -\Psi_2 \\ -\Psi_1 \end{pmatrix},\quad \beta_2\Psi = \begin{pmatrix} \Psi_4 \\ -\Psi_3 \\ -\Psi_2 \\ \Psi_1 \end{pmatrix},\quad \beta_3\Psi = i\begin{pmatrix} \Psi_3 \\ -\Psi_4 \\ -\Psi_1 \\ \Psi_2 \end{pmatrix},\quad \beta_4\Psi = \begin{pmatrix} \Psi_1 \\ \Psi_2 \\ -\Psi_3 \\ -\Psi_4 \end{pmatrix}.$$

† If A is a matrix, A' its transposed (obtained by interchanging its rows and columns), A^{-1} its inverse, and A^* the matrix whose elements are the complex conjugates of those of A, then if $A = A^{*\prime}$, A is said to be *Hermitian* and if $A = (A^{*\prime})^{-1}$, A is said to be *unitary*: see Turnbull and Aitken, *Canonical Matrices* (1932), p. 33.

Substituting these expressions into the left-hand side of equation (24) we obtain the Dirac equations in the following form:

$$\left.\begin{array}{l} \left(i\hbar\dfrac{\partial}{\partial t}-e\phi+mc^2\right)\Psi_1'+c\Pi_-\,\Psi_4'+c\Pi_3\,\Psi_3'=0 \\[2ex] \left(i\hbar\dfrac{\partial}{\partial t}-e\phi+mc^2\right)\Psi_2'+c\Pi_+\,\Psi_3'-c\Pi_3\,\Psi_4'=0 \\[2ex] \left(i\hbar\dfrac{\partial}{\partial t}-e\phi-mc^2\right)\Psi_3'+c\Pi_-\,\Psi_2'+c\Pi_3\,\Psi_1'=0 \\[2ex] \left(i\hbar\dfrac{\partial}{\partial t}-e\phi-mc^2\right)\Psi_4'+c\Pi_+\,\Psi_1'-c\Pi_3\,\Psi_2'=0 \end{array}\right\} . \tag{36}$$

(36) determines the four scalar wave-functions Ψ_1', Ψ_2', Ψ_3', and Ψ_4'. In these equations we have written Π_+, Π_- to denote the operators $\Pi_1\pm\Pi_2$.

In the form (36) the Dirac wave equations are unsymmetrical and so it is necessary to study their behaviour under a rotation of axes or under a Lorentz transformation. The proof of the invariance of the Dirac equations under a general transformation of the type indicated was due originally to Dirac;† an interesting proof based on the infinitesimal elements of the Lorentz group was given subsequently by Pauli.‡ The general formulae are complicated, but it is a simple matter to verify the invariance for certain special transformations.

We consider two observers moving with constant velocity relative to one another, one describing his observations of the behaviour of an electron in an electromagnetic field by a set of coordinates $(x_1, x_2, x_3, x_4 = ict)$ in a space of four dimensions, the other by a similar set of coordinates $(x_1', x_2', x_3', x_4' = ict')$. Then according to the special theory of relativity the two coordinate systems are related by the matrix equation

$$x = \omega x', \tag{37}$$

that is,

$$x_j = \sum_{j=1}^{4} \omega_{ij} x_i' \quad (j=1,2,3,4),$$

where the coefficients ω_{ij} are constants.

The first observer will represent his knowledge of the coordinates of the electron by a wave function of the type (35) satisfying the Dirac wave equation

$$\left(\sum_{j=1}^{4} \beta_j\, \Pi_j+imc\right)\Psi = 0. \tag{38}$$

Writing (37) in the form $x' = x\omega^{-1}$,

† P. A. M. Dirac, *Proc. Roy. Soc.* A, **117**, 610 (1928).
‡ W. Pauli, *Handbuch der Physik*, **24**/1.

and noting that

$$\frac{\partial}{\partial x} = \frac{\partial x'}{\partial x} \cdot \frac{\partial}{\partial x'} + \frac{\partial y'}{\partial x} \cdot \frac{\partial}{\partial y'} + \frac{\partial z'}{\partial x} \cdot \frac{\partial}{\partial z'}$$

we see that the Π_j transform according to the rule

$$\Pi = \omega^{-1}\Pi'.$$

Now there are *two* possible ways in which we may discuss the transformation properties of the Dirac equation. We may regard the wavefunction Ψ as an invariant ($\Psi = \Psi'$) and the β_j as the components of a 4-vector. The components of this 4-vector are, of course, matrices. If $\beta = (\beta_1, \beta_2, \beta_3, \beta_4)$ transforms as a 4-vector it transforms like x so that

$$\beta\Pi = \beta'\omega\omega^{-1}\Pi' = \beta'\Pi'$$

and the Dirac equation is transformed to

$$(\textstyle\sum \beta_j' \Pi_j' + imc)\Psi'' = 0, \tag{39}$$

which is of the same form as equation (38).

Alternatively, we can always find a matrix S such that

$$\Pi = \omega^{-1}\Pi' = S^{-1}\Pi'S. \tag{40}$$

If now the β_j are regarded simply as determining the coefficients in the four wave equations (36) and are kept constant, they are exchangeable with S since they act on the inner variable only, so that

$$(S^{-1}\beta\Pi'S)\Psi + imc\Psi = 0.$$

Multiplying on the left by S we obtain

$$(\beta\Pi' + imc)(S\Psi) = 0,$$

which is equivalent to equation (39) if we write

$$\Psi'' = S\Psi.$$

This point of view must be adopted if we consider the Dirac equations as field equations, for then Ψ must be transformed to a new coordinate system in a manner analogous to that in which $\mathbf{E}$ and $\mathbf{H}$ transform in the Maxwell theory.

The form of the matrix S has been determined by Darwin† for some special two-dimensional linear transformations; the results are tabulated below:

(i) *Rotation through an angle α about the z-axis*

$$\omega = \begin{pmatrix} \cos\alpha & \sin\alpha & 0 & 0 \\ -\sin\alpha & \cos\alpha & 0 & 0 \\ 0 & 0 & 1 & 0 \\ 0 & 0 & 0 & 1 \end{pmatrix}, \qquad S = \begin{pmatrix} e^{\frac{1}{2}i\alpha} & 0 & 0 & 0 \\ 0 & e^{-\frac{1}{2}i\alpha} & 0 & 0 \\ 0 & 0 & e^{\frac{1}{2}i\alpha} & 0 \\ 0 & 0 & 0 & e^{-\frac{1}{2}i\alpha} \end{pmatrix}.$$

† C. G. Darwin, *Proc. Roy. Soc.* A, **118**, 654 (1928).

(ii) *Rotation through an angle α about the y-axis*

$$\omega = \begin{pmatrix} \cos\alpha & 0 & -\sin\alpha & 0 \\ 0 & 1 & 0 & 0 \\ \sin\alpha & 0 & \cos\alpha & 0 \\ 0 & 0 & 0 & 1 \end{pmatrix}, \quad S = \begin{pmatrix} \cos\tfrac{1}{2}\alpha & \sin\tfrac{1}{2}\alpha & 0 & 0 \\ -\sin\tfrac{1}{2}\alpha & \cos\tfrac{1}{2}\alpha & 0 & 0 \\ 0 & 0 & \cos\tfrac{1}{2}\alpha & \sin\tfrac{1}{2}\alpha \\ 0 & 0 & -\sin\tfrac{1}{2}\alpha & \cos\tfrac{1}{2}\alpha \end{pmatrix}.$$

(iii) *Uniform relative motion along the z-axis*

$$\omega = \begin{pmatrix} 1 & 0 & 0 & 0 \\ 0 & 1 & 0 & 0 \\ 0 & 0 & \cosh\beta & \sinh\beta \\ 0 & 0 & \sinh\beta & \cosh\beta \end{pmatrix}, \quad S = \begin{pmatrix} \cosh\tfrac{1}{2}\beta & 0 & \sinh\tfrac{1}{2}\beta & 0 \\ 0 & \cosh\tfrac{1}{2}\beta & 0 & -\sinh\tfrac{1}{2}\beta \\ \sinh\tfrac{1}{2}\beta & 0 & \cosh\tfrac{1}{2}\beta & 0 \\ 0 & -\sinh\tfrac{1}{2}\beta & 0 & \cosh\tfrac{1}{2}\beta \end{pmatrix}.$$

These three transformations are all that need be considered since any Lorentz transformation can be built up from them. The matrices S have the peculiar characteristic that their elements involve the angle $\tfrac{1}{2}\alpha$ when the axes of coordinates are rotated through an angle α, so that S is somewhat analogous to the square root of ω. The wave-function Ψ cannot therefore be a tensor. We thus find that the Dirac equation of the electron is invariant under Lorentz transformation and yet it could only be written in tensor form in a highly artificial manner. This is an example of the mathematical principle that the ordinary tensor formalism does not comprise *all* possible representations of the Lorentz group. We shall return to this point later (§ 58 below); for the moment we merely observe that the four wave functions can be split into two pairs, for instance, (Ψ_1', Ψ_4') and (Ψ_2', Ψ_3') in case (i) above, with transformation equations of the form

$$\left.\begin{aligned} \Psi_1' &= a_{11}\Psi_1 + a_{12}\Psi_4 \\ \Psi_4' &= a_{21}\Psi_1 + a_{22}\Psi_4 \end{aligned}\right\}, \tag{41 a}$$

$$\left.\begin{aligned} \Psi_2' &= a_{11}^*\Psi_2 + a_{12}^*\Psi_3 \\ \Psi_3' &= a_{21}^*\Psi_2 + a_{22}^*\Psi_3 \end{aligned}\right\}, \tag{41 b}$$

and with the coefficients a_{ij} satisfying the relation

$$\begin{vmatrix} a_{11} & a_{12} \\ a_{21} & a_{22} \end{vmatrix} = 1. \tag{42}$$

53.4. *The spin of the electron*

If in Dirac's equation (21) we substitute for the α's from equation (29), we obtain the wave equation of the electron in the form

$$\left\{ p_0 + \frac{e}{c}\phi + \rho_1\left(\boldsymbol{\sigma}\cdot\mathbf{p} + \frac{e}{c}\mathbf{A}\right) + \rho_3 mc \right\}\Psi = 0. \tag{43}$$

Multiplying on the left of this equation by the operator

$$-\left(p_0 + \frac{e}{c}\phi\right) + \rho_1\left(\boldsymbol{\sigma}\cdot\mathbf{p} + \frac{e}{c}\mathbf{A}\right) + \rho_3 mc,$$

proceeding as in § 53.1, and making use of the relations (28), we obtain the equation

$$\left[-\left(p_0 + \frac{e}{c}\phi\right)^2 + \left(\boldsymbol{\sigma}.\mathbf{p} + \frac{e}{c}\mathbf{A}\right)^2 + m^2c^2 + \right.$$

$$\left. + \rho_1\left\{\left(\boldsymbol{\sigma}.\mathbf{p} + \frac{e}{c}\mathbf{A}\right)\left(p_0 + \frac{e\phi}{c}\right) - \left(p_0 + \frac{e\phi}{c}\right)\left(\boldsymbol{\sigma}.\mathbf{p} + \frac{e}{c}\mathbf{A}\right)\right\}\right] \Psi = 0.$$

The expression in the curly bracket may be reduced to

$$-\frac{ie\hbar}{c}\left(\boldsymbol{\sigma}.\operatorname{grad}\phi + \frac{1}{c}\frac{\partial\mathbf{A}}{\partial t}\right) = \frac{ie\hbar}{c}(\mathbf{E}.\boldsymbol{\sigma}),$$

where $\mathbf{E}$ is the electric vector of the field. Substituting for $(\boldsymbol{\sigma}.\mathbf{p} + e\mathbf{A}/c)$ from equation (34) and writing

$$\mathbf{H} = \operatorname{curl}\mathbf{A}$$

for the magnetic vector of the field, we obtain finally the wave-equation

$$\left[-\left(p_0 + \frac{e}{c}\phi\right)^2 + \left(\mathbf{p} + \frac{e}{c}\mathbf{A}\right)^2 + m^2c^2 + \frac{e\hbar}{c}(\boldsymbol{\sigma}.\mathbf{H}) + \frac{ie\hbar}{c}\rho_1(\boldsymbol{\sigma}.\mathbf{E}) \right] \Psi = 0.$$

The Hamiltonian on the left-hand side of this equation differs from that of the Klein–Gordon equation by the addition of two terms. Dividing these two extra terms by $2m$ we obtain an expression for the potential energy of the electron due to its spin. The former of the terms in this expression for the potential energy

$$\frac{e\hbar}{2mc}(\boldsymbol{\sigma}.\mathbf{H})$$

shows that the electron possesses a magnetic moment of amount $e\hbar\boldsymbol{\sigma}/2mc$ due to its new degree of freedom. This is precisely the magnetic moment assumed in the Uhlenbeck–Goudsmit model of the spinning electron; in Dirac's theory the electron spin is a direct consequence of the form of the relativistic wave equation for the electron.

The second additional term in the Hamiltonian shows that the electron behaves as though it had an electric moment $ie\hbar\boldsymbol{\sigma}/2mc$, which, being a pure imaginary, does not appear in the spinning electron model. This imaginary quantity only appears when the Hamiltonian (43), which is real, is transformed in a rather artificial way so as to make it resemble the Hamiltonian of the Klein–Gordon theory, and does not appear to be capable of being incorporated into any model of the electron.

We shall now determine the angular momentum operators associated with the Dirac equation; we shall assume that the operator representing the total angular momentum of the electron is the sum of the orbital and the spin angular momentum operators, and that it is a constant of the motion; this means that it commutes with the Hamiltonian of the Dirac equation. If we take **A** to be zero in equation (43) and write $e\phi/c = V(r)$, we see that the Hamiltonian reduces to

$$H = p_0 + V(r) + \rho_1(\boldsymbol{\sigma}.\mathbf{p}) + \rho_3 mc. \tag{44}$$

Now the orbital angular momentum **L** is defined by the equation

$$\mathbf{L} = \mathbf{r} \wedge \mathbf{p}, \tag{45}$$

and satisfies the relations

$$\left.\begin{array}{l} L_x p_x - p_x L_x = 0 \\ L_x p_y - p_y L_x = i\hbar p_z \\ L_x p_z - p_z L_x = i\hbar p_y \end{array}\right\}. \tag{46}$$

Substituting for H from equation (44) we have

$$\begin{aligned} L_x H - H L_x &= \rho_1\{L_x(\boldsymbol{\sigma}.\mathbf{p}) - (\boldsymbol{\sigma}.\mathbf{p})L_x\} \\ &= \rho_1\{\boldsymbol{\sigma}.L_x\mathbf{p} - \mathbf{p}L_x\} \\ &= i\hbar\rho_1\{\sigma_2 p_3 - \sigma_3 p_2\} \end{aligned}$$

by the use of equations (46). Similar equations may be derived for the components L_y and L_z leading to the vector equation

$$\mathbf{L}H - H\mathbf{L} = i\hbar\rho_1(\boldsymbol{\sigma} \wedge \mathbf{p}). \tag{47}$$

Similarly we have

$$\begin{aligned} \sigma_1 H - H\sigma_1 &= \rho_1\{\sigma_1(\boldsymbol{\sigma}.\mathbf{p}) - (\boldsymbol{\sigma}.\mathbf{p})\sigma_1\} \\ &= 2i\rho_1\{\sigma_3 p_2 - \sigma_2 p_3\} \end{aligned}$$

by the help of equations (32). Thus we obtain the equation

$$\boldsymbol{\sigma}H - H\boldsymbol{\sigma} = -2i\rho_1(\boldsymbol{\sigma} \wedge \mathbf{p}). \tag{48}$$

Eliminating the vector product $(\boldsymbol{\sigma} \wedge \mathbf{p})$ between equations (47) and (48) we obtain the equation

$$\mathbf{J}H - H\mathbf{J} = 0, \tag{49}$$

where

$$\mathbf{J} = \mathbf{L} + \tfrac{1}{2}\hbar\boldsymbol{\sigma}. \tag{50}$$

Equation (49) establishes that **J** is a constant of the motion; we can interpret this result by postulating that the electron has a spin angular momentum defined by the equation

$$\mathbf{s} = \tfrac{1}{2}\hbar\boldsymbol{\sigma},$$

or, in terms of the α's,

$$s_x = -\tfrac{1}{2}\hbar i \alpha_2 \alpha_3, \qquad s_y = -\tfrac{1}{2}\hbar i \alpha_3 \alpha_1, \qquad s_z = -\tfrac{1}{2}\hbar i \alpha_1 \alpha_2. \tag{51}$$

It follows at once from these equations that

$$s_x^2 = s_y^2 = s_z^2 = (\tfrac{1}{2}\hbar)^2,$$

in agreement with the spin postulated by Uhlenbeck and Goudsmit, and that the operators satisfy the formal equations

$$s_x s_y = -s_y s_x = \tfrac{1}{2} i\hbar s_z$$

of the Pauli–Darwin theory.

The manner in which the spin comes out in a natural way as a result of setting up the proper relativistic Hamiltonian is one of the major triumphs of Dirac's theory. By contrast, in the Pauli–Darwin theory, the spin had to be added as an additional physical assumption.

53.5. The quantization of the total angular momentum

As a first illustration of the application of Dirac's theory we shall calculate the quantization of the total angular momentum of a single electron. This calculation is an extension, to include the spin of the electron, of the method in the non-relativistic theory by which we classify the states of the electron in terms of the orbital angular momentum. The problem is to determine a wave function Ψ to represent a state in which the square of the total angular momentum and one of the components of the total angular momentum are quantized; i.e. we wish to determine a wave function Ψ satisfying the equations

$$\mathbf{J}^2\Psi = A\Psi, \qquad J_z\Psi = B\Psi, \qquad (52)$$

where A and B are constants and $\mathbf{J}$ is the operator corresponding to the total angular momentum. This is made up of the sum of $\mathbf{L}$, the orbital momentum and $\mathbf{s}$, the spin angular momentum, so that

$$\mathbf{J} = \mathbf{L} + \mathbf{s}.$$

If, for simplicity, we write

$$L_{\pm} = L_x \pm iL_y, \qquad s_{\pm} = s_x \pm is_y,$$

then
$$\mathbf{J}^2 = (\mathbf{L} + \mathbf{s})^2 = \mathbf{L}^2 + \mathbf{s}^2 + (L_+ s_- + L_- s_+ + 2L_z s_z).$$

Now in polar coordinates (cf p. 87)

$$\begin{aligned}
\mathbf{L}^2 &= -\hbar^2\left[\frac{1}{\sin\theta}\frac{\partial}{\partial\theta}\left(\sin\theta\frac{\partial}{\partial\theta}\right) + \frac{1}{\sin^2\theta}\frac{\partial^2}{\partial\phi^2}\right] \\
L_{\pm} &= i\hbar e^{\pm i\phi}\left(\mp i\frac{\partial}{\partial\theta} + \cot\theta\frac{\partial}{\partial\phi}\right) \\
L_z &= -i\hbar\frac{\partial}{\partial\phi}
\end{aligned} \qquad (53)$$

We may therefore write the second of equations (52) in the form

$$\left(i\hbar\frac{\partial}{\partial\phi} + \tfrac{1}{2}\hbar i\alpha_1\alpha_2 + B\right)\Psi = 0. \qquad (52a)$$

Now
$$i\alpha_1\alpha_2\Psi = \begin{pmatrix} -1 & 0 & 0 & 0 \\ 0 & 1 & 0 & 0 \\ 0 & 0 & -1 & 0 \\ 0 & 0 & 0 & 1 \end{pmatrix}\begin{pmatrix} \Psi_1' \\ \Psi_2' \\ \Psi_3' \\ \Psi_4' \end{pmatrix} = \begin{pmatrix} -\Psi_1' \\ \Psi_2' \\ -\Psi_3' \\ \Psi_4' \end{pmatrix},$$

so that equation (52a) may be written as

$$\left(i\hbar\frac{\partial}{\partial\phi} - \tfrac{1}{2}\hbar + B\right)(\Psi_1', \Psi_3') = 0,$$

$$\left(i\hbar\frac{\partial}{\partial\phi} + \tfrac{1}{2}\hbar + B\right)(\Psi_2', \Psi_4') = 0.$$

Similarly the former of the equations (52) when expressed in terms of scalar wave functions takes the form

$$(\mathbf{L}^2 + \tfrac{3}{4}\hbar^2 + \hbar L_z - A)(\Psi_1', \Psi_3') + \hbar L_-(\Psi_2', \Psi_4') = 0,$$

$$(\mathbf{L}^2 + \tfrac{3}{4}\hbar^2 - \hbar L_z - A)(\Psi_2', \Psi_4') + \hbar L_+(\Psi_1', \Psi_3') = 0,$$

where the operators $\mathbf{L}^2$, $L_\pm$, L_z are defined by the equations (53). An inspection of these equations shows that they form two identical sets, one containing only the wave-functions Ψ_1, Ψ_2 and the other only Ψ_3 and Ψ_4. The solution of these differential equations is very similar to that of the equation for the determination of the angular function in the Schrödinger theory of the hydrogenic atom, and will not be reproduced here. The quantized values of $\mathbf{J}^2$ and J_z are found to be

$$A = j(j+1)\hbar^2, \qquad B = m\hbar,$$

where $m = \pm\tfrac{1}{2}, \pm\tfrac{3}{2},\dots$ and $j = \tfrac{1}{2}, \tfrac{3}{2},\dots$ and is such that $j \geqslant |m|$.

The solutions of equations (52) for given choices of m and j are readily found to be

$$\left. \begin{aligned} \Psi_1 &= f(r)\left(\frac{j+1-m}{2j+2}\right)^{\frac{1}{2}}Y_{j+\frac{1}{2},m-\frac{1}{2}}(\theta,\phi) + g(r)\left(\frac{j+m}{2j}\right)^{\frac{1}{2}}Y_{j-\frac{1}{2},m-\frac{1}{2}}(\theta,\phi) \\[2mm] \Psi_2 &= -f(r)\left(\frac{j+1+m}{2j+2}\right)^{\frac{1}{2}}Y_{j+\frac{1}{2},m+\frac{1}{2}}(\theta,\phi) + g(r)\left(\frac{j-m}{2j}\right)^{\frac{1}{2}}Y_{j-\frac{1}{2},m+\frac{1}{2}}(\theta,\phi) \\[2mm] \Psi_3 &= F(r)\left(\frac{j+1-m}{2j+2}\right)^{\frac{1}{2}}Y_{j+\frac{1}{2},m-\frac{1}{2}}(\theta,\phi) + G(r)\left(\frac{j+m}{2j}\right)^{\frac{1}{2}}Y_{j-\frac{1}{2},m-\frac{1}{2}}(\theta,\phi) \\[2mm] \Psi_4 &= -F(r)\left(\frac{j+1+m}{2j+2}\right)^{\frac{1}{2}}Y_{j+\frac{1}{2},m+\frac{1}{2}}(\theta,\phi) + G(r)\left(\frac{j-m}{2j}\right)^{\frac{1}{2}}Y_{j-\frac{1}{2},m+\frac{1}{2}}(\theta,\phi) \end{aligned} \right\}, \quad (54)$$

where $Y_{l,m}(\theta,\phi)$ denotes the surface spherical harmonic

$$Y_{l,m}(\theta,\phi) = (-1)^m\left\{\frac{(2l+1)!(l-m)!}{4\pi.(l+m)!}\right\}^{\frac{1}{2}}P_l^m(\cos\theta)e^{im\phi} \quad (-l \leqslant m \leqslant l).$$

The functions $f(r)$, $g(r)$, $F(r)$, and $G(r)$ are not determined by the equations (52).

53.6. *Darwin's variation principle*

Darwin[†] has shown how to derive both the Maxwell and the Dirac equations from a variation principle

$$\delta S = \delta \iiint L \, dx \, dy \, dz \, dt = 0, \tag{55}$$

where L is given by the equation

$$
\begin{aligned}
L = \frac{\hbar}{2i}\Bigg[& \Psi_1^* \left\{ -\frac{1}{c}\frac{\partial \Psi_1}{\partial t} + \left(\frac{\partial}{\partial x} - i\frac{\partial}{\partial y}\right)\Psi_4 + \frac{\partial \Psi_3}{\partial z} \right\} \\
& + \Psi_2^* \left\{ -\frac{1}{c}\frac{\partial \Psi_2}{\partial t} + \left(\frac{\partial}{\partial x} + i\frac{\partial}{\partial y}\right)\Psi_3 - \frac{\partial \Psi_4}{\partial z} \right\} \\
& + \Psi_3^* \left\{ -\frac{1}{c}\frac{\partial \Psi_3}{\partial t} + \left(\frac{\partial}{\partial x} - i\frac{\partial}{\partial y}\right)\Psi_2 + \frac{\partial \Psi_1}{\partial z} \right\} \\
& + \Psi_4^* \left\{ -\frac{1}{c}\frac{\partial \Psi_4}{\partial t} + \left(\frac{\partial}{\partial x} + i\frac{\partial}{\partial y}\right)\Psi_1 - \frac{\partial \Psi_2}{\partial z} \right\} \Bigg]
\end{aligned}
$$

+complex conjugate of this expression

$$
+ mc(\Psi_1 \Psi_1^* + \Psi_2 \Psi_2^* - \Psi_3 \Psi_3^* - \Psi_4 \Psi_4^*) + \frac{e\phi}{c} \sum_{j=1}^{4} \Psi_j \Psi_j^*
$$

$$
+ \frac{e}{c} A_x (\Psi_1^* \Psi_4 + \Psi_2^* \Psi_3 + \Psi_3^* \Psi_2 + \Psi_4^* \Psi_1)
$$

$$
+ \frac{e}{c} A_y (-i\Psi_1^* \Psi_4 + i\Psi_2^* \Psi_3 - i\Psi_3^* \Psi_2 + i\Psi_4^* \Psi_1)
$$

$$
+ \frac{e}{c} A_z (\Psi_1^* \Psi_3 - \Psi_2^* \Psi_4 + \Psi_3^* \Psi_1 - \Psi_4^* \Psi_2)
$$

$$
- \frac{1}{8\pi c}\left[(\operatorname{curl}\mathbf{A})^2 - \left(\frac{1}{c}\frac{\partial}{\partial t}\mathbf{A} + \operatorname{grad}\phi\right)^2 \right]. \tag{56}
$$

The function L is considered for the purposes of the variation to be a function of the Ψ's, Ψ^*'s, A_x, A_y, A_z, and ϕ. If we vary the function S it is readily seen that the Euler–Lagrange equations yield equations (36) and their complex conjugates and also the equations

$$
\left(\nabla^2 - \frac{1}{c^2}\frac{\partial^2}{\partial t^2}\right)\phi = 4\pi e \sum_{j=1}^{4} \Psi_i \Psi_j^*, \tag{57}
$$

$$
\left(\nabla^2 - \frac{1}{c^2}\frac{\partial^2}{\partial t^2}\right)A_x = -4\pi e (\Psi_1^* \Psi_4 + \Psi_2^* \Psi_3 + \Psi_3^* \Psi_2 + \Psi_4^* \Psi_1), \tag{58}
$$

with two similar equations for A_x and A_y. Comparing these equations with the corresponding equations in the Maxwell–Lorentz theory we

† C. G. Darwin, *Proc. Roy. Soc.* A, **118**, 654 (1928).

find that the electromagnetic effect of the electron can be represented by a charge density $-\rho e$, and a current density $-e\mathbf{j}$, where

$$\rho = (\Psi_1^* \Psi_1 + \Psi_2^* \Psi_2 + \Psi_3^* \Psi_3 + \Psi_4^* \Psi_4), \tag{59}$$

further the components of the probability current are given by the equations

$$\left. \begin{aligned} j_x &= -c(\Psi_1^* \Psi_4 + \Psi_2^* \Psi_3 + \Psi_3^* \Psi_2 + \Psi_4^* \Psi_1) \\ j_y &= +ic(\Psi_1^* \Psi_4 - \Psi_2^* \Psi_3 + \Psi_3^* \Psi_2 - \Psi_4^* \Psi_1) \\ j_z &= -c(\Psi_1^* \Psi_3 - \Psi_2^* \Psi_4 + \Psi_3^* \Psi_1 - \Psi_4^* \Psi_2) \end{aligned} \right\}, \tag{60}$$

provided that the Ψ's are normalized according to the rule

$$\sum_{j=1}^{4} \int \Psi_j \Psi_j^* \, d\tau = 1 \tag{61}$$

to ensure that the total charge shall be $-e$.

With these definitions of ρ, $\mathbf{j}$ it may readily be verified that the continuity equation

$$\frac{\partial \rho}{\partial t} + \operatorname{div} \mathbf{j} = 0 \tag{62}$$

is satisfied.

An interesting interpretation has been given to these results by Breit.† From the first of equations (30) we have that

$$\alpha_1 \Psi = \begin{pmatrix} \Psi_4 \\ \Psi_3 \\ \Psi_2 \\ \Psi_1 \end{pmatrix},$$

and hence that

$$\Psi^* \alpha_1 \Psi = \Psi_1^* \Psi_4 + \Psi_2^* \Psi_3 + \Psi_3^* \Psi_2 + \Psi_4^* \Psi_1.$$

Thus we may write the right-hand side of the first of equations (60) as $\Psi^*(-c\alpha_1)\Psi$. Similarly the right-hand sides of the second and third equations can be written as $\Psi^*(-c\alpha_2)\Psi$, $\Psi^*(-c\alpha_3)\Psi$. Introducing the vector

$$\boldsymbol{\alpha} = (\alpha_1, \alpha_2, \alpha_3)$$

we may therefore write equations (60) in the vectorial form

$$\mathbf{j} = \Psi^*(-c\boldsymbol{\alpha})\Psi. \tag{63}$$

This equation suggests that in the Dirac theory the vector operator $-c\boldsymbol{\alpha}$ represents, in some sense, the *velocity* of the electron. For instance, when we set up the wave equation for the relativistic two-body problem (p. 336), we replace the scalar product $(\mathbf{v}^1 . \mathbf{v}^2)$ occurring in the classical Hamiltonian by $c^2(\boldsymbol{\alpha}^1 . \boldsymbol{\alpha}^2)$; though this substitution is suggested by the analysis given above, its justification lies in the fact that it leads to results which are in agreement with experiment.

† G. Breit, *Proc. Nat. Acad. Sci.* **14**, 553 (1928)

The Dirac theory differs from the Schrödinger theory in that in the latter there is no operator for the velocity, only for the momentum.

54. States of negative energy in Dirac's theory

54.1. *Solution of the Dirac equations for a free particle*

For an electron moving in free space both the vector potential **A** and the scalar potential ϕ are taken as zero in the equations (36). These equations then reduce to the form

$$\left(\frac{1}{c}\frac{\partial}{\partial t}-\frac{imc}{\hbar}\right)\Psi_1'-\left(\frac{\partial}{\partial x}-i\frac{\partial}{\partial y}\right)\Psi_4'-\frac{\partial\Psi_3'}{\partial z}=0,$$

$$\left(\frac{1}{c}\frac{\partial}{\partial t}-\frac{imc}{\hbar}\right)\Psi_2'-\left(\frac{\partial}{\partial x}+i\frac{\partial}{\partial y}\right)\Psi_3'+\frac{\partial\Psi_4'}{\partial z}=0,$$

$$\left(\frac{1}{c}\frac{\partial}{\partial t}+\frac{imc}{\hbar}\right)\Psi_3'-\left(\frac{\partial}{\partial x}-i\frac{\partial}{\partial y}\right)\Psi_2'-\frac{\partial\Psi_1'}{\partial z}=0,$$

$$\left(\frac{1}{c}\frac{\partial}{\partial t}+\frac{imc}{\hbar}\right)\Psi_4'-\left(\frac{\partial}{\partial x}+i\frac{\partial}{\partial y}\right)\Psi_1'+\frac{\partial\Psi_2'}{\partial z}=0.$$

The functions

$$\Psi_k'=C_k\exp\frac{i}{\hbar}(\mathbf{p}.\mathbf{r}-Wt)\quad(k=1,2,3,4),\tag{64}$$

which represent an electron moving in free space with momentum $\mathbf{p}=(p_1,p_2,p_3)$ and energy W, are special solutions of the above differential equations if the relations

$$\left.\begin{array}{l}(W+mc^2)C_1+cp_3\,C_3+c(p_1-ip_2)C_4=0\\(W+mc^2)C_2-cp_3\,C_4+c(p_1+ip_2)C_3=0\\(W-mc^2)C_3+cp_3\,C_1+c(p_1-ip_2)C_2=0\\(W-mc^2)C_4-cp_3\,C_2+c(p_1+ip_2)C_1=0\end{array}\right\}\tag{65}$$

are satisfied. In the equations (65), p_1, p_2, p_3, and W are real and the constants C_k may be complex. Eliminating the quantities C_k from these equations, we obtain as a condition for the existence of non-vanishing solutions of type (64) the determinantal equation

$$\begin{vmatrix}W+mc^2 & 0 & cp_3 & c(p_1-ip_2)\\0 & W+mc^2 & c(p_1+ip_2) & -cp_3\\cp_3 & c(p_1-ip_2) & W-mc^2 & 0\\c(p_1+ip_2) & -cp_3 & 0 & W-mc^2\end{vmatrix}=0,$$

which is easily seen to reduce to the form

$$\{W^2-m^2c^4-c^2|\mathbf{p}|^2\}^2=0.$$

Regarded as an equation for the determination of W this equation has the two double roots

$$W^+ = +c(m^2c^2+\mathbf{p}^2)^{\frac{1}{2}}, \qquad W^- = -c(m^2c^2+\mathbf{p}^2)^{\frac{1}{2}}. \tag{66}$$

Only the positive root W^+ would have any physical significance in the classical theory; in quantum mechanics, as we shall see below, both solutions must be considered.

Since both of the roots are double we may choose two of the constants C_k arbitrarily and determine the remaining two from any two equations of the set (65). Suppose we take W to be the root W^+ and choose C_3 and C_4 to be arbitrary complex constants A and B, say, then from the first and second equations of the set (65) we have the solution

$$\left. \begin{array}{cc} C_1 = -c\dfrac{p_3 A+(p_1-ip_2)B}{W^++mc^2}, & C_2 = -c\dfrac{(p_1+ip_2)A-p_3 B}{W^++mc^2} \\[2mm] C_3 = A, & C_4 = B \end{array} \right\}. \tag{67}$$

The number of electrons per unit volume described by this solution is

$$\Psi\Psi^* = \frac{2W^+(AA^*+BB^*)}{W^++mc^2}.$$

Similarly if we take W to be W^-, $C_1 = C$, $C_2 = D$, we obtain from the third and fourth equations of the set (65) the solution

$$\left. \begin{array}{cc} C_1 = C, & C_2 = D \\[2mm] C_3 = -c\dfrac{p_3 C+(p_1-ip_2)D}{W^--mc^2}, & C_4 = -c\dfrac{(p_1+ip_2)C-p_3 D}{W^--mc^2} \end{array} \right\} \tag{68}$$

which corresponds to

$$\Psi\Psi^* = \frac{2W^-(CC^*+DD^*)}{W^--mc^2}$$

electrons per unit volume.

In each case the four scalar wave-functions Ψ_k are obtained from equation (64).

The existence of solutions of the wave equation for negative energies gave rise to much speculation on their proper interpretation, since states of negative kinetic energy have not been observed. If they were, the acceleration of the electron would be in the *opposite* direction to that of the external force producing it. In the classical relativistic theory this difficulty does not arise, since, though the energy of a free particle in terms of its momentum is given by either of the roots (66), the energy of an electron can only change continuously; thus an electron which initially has positive energy can never reach a state of negative energy, owing to the gap between $\pm mc^2$. In the quantum theory, on the other hand, discontinuous energy transitions are common in applications to practical problems. The possibility of transitions from a positive to a negative energy has been investigated by Klein† and in more detail by Sauter,‡ who found that transition probabilities between states of positive and negative energy are small for the fields occurring in ordinary circumstances. Nevertheless, all theoretical attempts completely to eliminate such transitions have been unsuccessful.

The physical interpretation of the states of negative energy is due to Dirac,§ who formulated the 'hole theory' to avoid the difficulty of an electron making a transition from a positive energy state into one of negative energy. The first basic assumption of the Dirac hole theory is that, in the physical world as we observe it, almost all of the states of negative energy are 'occupied'. In accordance with the Pauli exclusion principle it is assumed that each state is occupied by only one electron. The second assumption is that when all the negative energy states are occupied the distribution of negative energy electrons does not produce an external field and is consequently not observed. The distribution in which all the negative energy states are occupied and all the positive energy states are empty may be taken as a zero point for the measurement of electric charge, momentum, and energy.

If we assume that an external field can remove one of the electrons with negative energy $W = -|W|$ and momentum $\mathbf{p}$ leaving a 'hole' in the distribution of negative energy electrons, then, by the second of our two assumptions, we shall observe the hole as a particle with electronic rest-mass and with its other physical properties given by the equations

$$W_+ = -W = |W|, \qquad e_+ = -e, \qquad \mathbf{p}_+ = -\mathbf{p},$$

where e denotes the electronic charge. A hole in the distribution of negative energy states would thus appear as a particle with positive kinetic energy, which is more in agreement with our concepts of the nature of fundamental particles. Furthermore, the theory predicts that such a particle, though possessing the same mass and numerical charge as the electron, will be *positively* charged. The existence of such particles was confirmed shortly afterwards by C. D. Anderson,‖ who in the course of some observations of tracks produced in a Wilson chamber by cosmic-ray particles in the presence of a strong magnetic field obtained the photograph of a track which could only have been

† O. Klein, *Zeits. f. Physik*, **53**, 157 (1929).

‡ F. Sauter, ibid. **69**, 742 (1931); **73**, 547 (1931).

§ P. A. M. Dirac, *Proc. Roy. Soc.* **126**, 360 (1930); *Quantum Mechanics* (1947), chap. xii.

‖ C. D. Anderson, *Science*, **76**, 238 (1932); **77**, 432 (1933); *Phys. Rev.* **43**, 491 (1933).

produced by a positively charged particle with the same mass and numerical charge as the electron. Subsequent experimental work† has confirmed Anderson's observations of *positrons*, as the new particles are called.

Dirac's hypothesis that the positrons should be identified with holes in the distribution of negative energy states is in agreement with all the experimental facts now at our disposal. In the theory of the positron we have, however, to consider an infinite number of electrons occupying the states of negative energy ranging continuously from $-mc^2$ to $-\infty$. Various attempts‡ have been made to resolve the mathematical difficulty of handling this infinity, but none of them can be regarded as completely satisfactory, though they have all met with some success in certain directions. The theory of holes in its present form, though not yet completely satisfactory, appears nevertheless to be correct in general outline.

54.2. *The production and annihilation of positrons*

The experimental discovery of the existence of positrons in the secondary cosmic rays has led to a search for other sources of positrons. Shortly after Anderson's discovery of the existence of the positron it was found that when certain substances were bombarded by high-speed ions positrons were produced. For example, by bombarding aluminium with α-particles Curie and Joliot§ produced a radioactive isotope of phosphorus which then disintegrated into a stable isotope of silicon with the emission of a positron. Perhaps the most spectacular discovery was that positrons can be produced by the passage of hard γ-rays through matter. This process can be interpreted on the hole theory in a simple manner. If the field of the γ-ray causes an electron in a state of negative energy $(-|W|, \mathbf{p})$ to jump to a state of positive energy $(W', \mathbf{p}')$, then the transition results in the creation of a pair consisting of an electron of energy $W = W'$ and momentum $\mathbf{p}'$ and a positron of energy $W_+ = |W|$ and momentum $-\mathbf{p}$. This phenomenon is called *pair production*. If the energy of the γ-ray is $h\nu$, then, since for the creation of a pair an energy equal to $2mc^2$ is necessary to give the particles the correct rest energy, it follows that for the process to occur we must have
$$h\nu > 2mc^2.$$

† L. Meitner and Philipp, *Naturwiss.* **21**, 286 (1933); J. Chadwick, P. M. S. Blackett, and G. P. S. Occhialini, *Proc. Roy. Soc.* A, **144**, 235 (1934); *Nature*, **131**, 473 (1933); I. Curie and F. Joliot, *Comptes Rendus*, **196**, 1581 (1933); *J. de Physique*, **4**, 494 (1933).

‡ P. A. M. Dirac, *Proc. Camb. Phil. Soc.* **30**, 150 (1934); W. Heisenberg, *Zeits. f. Physik*, **90**, 209 (1934); V. Weisskopf, *Kgl. Dansk. Vid. Selsk.* **14**, 6 (1934).

§ I. Curie and F. Joliot, *Comptes Rendus*, **198**, 254, 408, 559 (1934).

Substituting the known values of the electronic mass and the constants h, c, we find that for pair production to occur the γ-ray must have energy in excess of $1 \cdot 02$ Mev. and therefore a wave-length less than $0 \cdot 012$ A. The excess energy $h\nu - 2mc^2$ appears as the kinetic energy of the positron and the electron. The cross-section for the creation of a positive electron with energy W_+ and a negative one with energy W_- has been calculated by Bethe and Heitler.† In the case where all the energies are very much greater than the rest energy mc^2 of the electron, but not so great that the screening of the Coulomb field by the outer electrons is appreciable, the cross-section for the creation of a positron of energy between W_+ and $W_+ + dW_+$ and an electron of energy W_- ($= h\nu - 2mc^2 - W_+$) is found to be

$$\phi_{W_+} \, dW_+ = 4\bar{\phi} \, dW_+ \frac{W_+^2 + W_-^2 + \tfrac{2}{3}W_+ W_-}{(h\nu)^3} \left(\log \frac{2W_+ W_-}{mc^2 h\nu} - \frac{1}{2} \right), \qquad (69)$$

where $\bar{\phi}$ is defined in terms of the nuclear charge Z by the equation

$$\bar{\phi} = \frac{Z^2 e^4}{137 m^2 c^2}.$$

For the case of complete screening and high energies the corresponding formula is

$$\phi_{W_+} \, dW_+ = 4\bar{\phi} \, dW_+ \left[\frac{W_+^2 + W_-^2 + \tfrac{2}{3}W_+ W_-}{(h\nu)^3} \log \frac{183}{Z^{\frac{1}{3}}} - \frac{W_+ W_-}{9(h\nu)^3} \right]. \qquad (70)$$

The total number of pairs created in a process of this type can be determined in the cases of negligible and complete screening by integrating equations (69) and (70) over all possible values of W_+. In this way we obtain for the cross-sections for pair formation

$$\phi = \bar{\phi} \left(\frac{28}{9} \log \frac{Z h\nu}{mc^2} - \frac{218}{27} \right),$$

$$\phi = \bar{\phi} \left(\frac{28}{9} \log \frac{183}{Z^{\frac{1}{3}}} - \frac{2}{27} \right).$$

Corresponding results can be obtained‡ by numerical integration in the case of energies for which the screening is partial. The theory of pair formation developed in this way has been compared with experimental data§ and found to be in good agreement with the observed results.

Pairs can be formed in several other ways. They can be formed during the passage through matter of a proton or an α-particle whose

† H. A. Bethe and W. Heitler, *Proc. Roy. Soc.* A, **146**, 83 (1934); H. A. Bethe, *Proc. Camb. Phil. Soc.* **30**, 524 (1934).
‡ Loc. cit. and H. R. Hulme and J. C. Jaeger, *Proc. Roy. Soc.* A, **153**, 443 (1936).
§ W. Heitler, *Quantum Theory of Radiation*, pp. 201–2 (Oxford, 1944).

kinetic energy exceeds twice the rest energy of an electron,† or by the motion of an electron through the field of a nucleus.‡ Furthermore, an electron pair can be created in the field of a nucleus by a γ-ray emitted by the nucleus itself,§ or by the action of two light quanta whose total energy exceeds $2mc^2$. Finally, if an electron of energy greater than $7mc^2$ collides directly with an electron at rest an electron pair can be created.‖

Since a pair consisting of a positron and an electron can be created we would expect that they can also be destroyed. In the hole theory this would correspond to the transition of an electron from a state of positive energy to a hole in the distribution of electrons in negative energy states. The energy of the positron and the electron is given out in the form of radiation. The most common process of annihilation is that in which a positron combines with a free or lightly bound electron and their energy is taken away in the form of two photons. If the momenta of the colliding particles are equal and opposite the photons have equal frequencies, but if the electron is at rest the two photons have different frequencies. Since the energies of the colliding particles must exceed $2mc^2$, a simple calculation shows that the wave length of the annihilation radiation must in the former case be less than 0·024 A. The cross-section for such a process in which a positron of energy W_+ collides with an electron at rest has been calculated by Dirac,†† who derives the formula

$$\phi = \frac{\pi e^4}{m^2 c^2} \frac{1}{\gamma+1} \left[\frac{\gamma^2+4\gamma+1}{\gamma^2-1} \log\{\gamma+\sqrt{(\gamma^2-1)}\} - \frac{\gamma+3}{\sqrt{(\gamma^2-1)}} \right], \qquad (71)$$

where γ denotes the ratio W_+/mc^2. For very high energies this equation reduces to the simple form

$$\phi = \frac{\pi e^4}{\gamma m^2 c^2} [\log 2\gamma - 1]. \qquad (72)$$

This theory of two-quanta annihilation has been verified experimentally by Klemperer.‡‡

An alternative process is the combination of a positron and an electron near a nucleus with the emission of a single photon which acts as a carrier for the total energy of the two particles. The case which can be calculated most easily is that in which the electron is bound

† W. Heitler and L. Nordheim, *Journ. d. Phys.* **5**, 449 (1934).
‡ For references see W. Heitler, op. cit., p. 203.
§ W. Heitler, op. cit., p. 204.
‖ F. Perrin, *Comptes Rendus*, **197**, 1100, 1302 (1934).
†† P. A. M. Dirac, *Proc. Camb. Phil. Soc.* **26**, 361 (1930).
‡‡ O. Klemperer, ibid. **30**, 347 (1934).

in the K-shell of an atom; the formula for the cross-section of this process corresponding to equation (71) is

$$\phi_k = \frac{4\pi e^4 Z^5}{137^4 m^2 c^2} \frac{1}{(\gamma+1)^2(\gamma^2-1)^{\frac{1}{2}}}\left[\gamma^2 + \frac{2}{3}\gamma + \frac{4}{3} - \frac{\gamma+2}{(\gamma^2-1)^{\frac{1}{2}}}\log\{\gamma+(\gamma^2-1)^{\frac{1}{2}}\}\right],$$

(73)

where as before the energy of the positron is $W_+ = \gamma mc^2$. For large energies this reduces to

$$\phi_k = \frac{4\pi e^4 Z^5}{137^4 m^2 c^2 \gamma}\left[1 - \frac{1}{\gamma^2}\log 2\gamma\right].$$

(74)

A comparison of the formulae (72) and (74) shows that the cross-section for the annihilation of one photon is always smaller than that for the annihilation of two. The maximum value of the ratio ϕ_k/ϕ occurs when γ is approximately equal to 10; in lead this gives

$$\phi_k/\phi = 0\cdot20.$$

54.3. Relativistic theory of the Compton effect

One of the most striking proofs of the fact that the states of negative energy arising from Dirac's equation must be considered as well as those with positive energy is provided by the relativistic theory of the Compton effect.[†] The radiation process considered in the Compton effect is the collision of a quantum of light of momentum $\mathbf{k}_0$ with a free electron of rest-mass m which is initially at rest. In calculating the transition probability from this initial state to a final state in which the electron has a momentum $\mathbf{p}$ and the light quantum a momentum $\mathbf{k}$ we must consider intermediate states in which the energy is not conserved though the momentum is. It is found that the only possible processes are the following: the electron absorbs the quantum $\mathbf{k}_0$ and acquires the momentum $\mathbf{p}' = \mathbf{k}_0$ and then emits a quantum $\mathbf{k}$ in the transition to the final state; alternatively, the electron first emits a quantum $\mathbf{k}$ changing its momentum to $\mathbf{p}'' = -\mathbf{k}$ and then absorbs the quantum $\mathbf{k}_0$ in the transition to the final state.

Now to each of the values $\mathbf{p}$ of the momentum of the electron there are altogether four states corresponding to the two directions of spin and the positive and negative values of the energy. If we take the negative energy states as intermediate states as well as the positive ones we obtain for the differential cross-section the Klein–Nishina formula[‡]

$$d\phi = \tfrac{1}{4}r_0^2\, d\Omega\, \frac{k^2}{k_0^2}\left[\frac{k_0}{k} + \frac{k}{k_0} - 2 + 4\cos^2\Theta\right],$$

(75)

† O. Klein and Y. Nishina, *Zeits. f. Physik*, **52**, 853, 869 (1929).

‡ W. Heitler, *Quantum Theory of Radiation*, 2nd ed., § 16 (Oxford, 1944).

where Θ is the angle between the directions of polarization of $\mathbf{k}$ and $\mathbf{k}_0$ and r_0 denotes the classical electronic radius e^2/mc. If θ denotes the angle between $\mathbf{k}_0$ and $\mathbf{k}$, the relativistic relation between energy and momentum and the conservation of energy and momentum lead to the equation

$$k = \frac{mc^2}{mc^2 + k_0\,c(1 - \cos\theta)}\,k_0. \tag{76}$$

If the primary radiation is unpolarized and of intensity I_0 the intensity of the scattered radiation at a distance R from the scattering electron is then readily shown to be $I(\theta)\,d\Omega$, where $I(\theta)$ is given by the formula

$$I(\theta) = \tfrac{1}{2}I_0\left(\frac{r_0}{R}\right)^2 \frac{1}{\{1 + \gamma(1 - \cos\theta)\}^3}\left\{1 + \frac{\gamma^2(1 - \cos\theta)^2}{(1 + \cos^2\theta)\{1 + \gamma(1 - \cos\theta)\}}\right\} \tag{77}$$

and $\gamma = k_0/mc$. The intensity distribution for a radiation cf wavelength $0 \cdot 14$ A ($\gamma = 0 \cdot 173$) in carbon has been measured by Friedrich and Goldhaber,[†] and it is found that the curve for $I(\theta)/I_0$ derived from these measurements is, within the limits of the experimental error, in exact agreement with that determined from the above equation.

The total scattering may be obtained from equation (77), by integrating over θ, and the results compared with the experimental values. It is found that the theoretical curve so determined agrees well with the experimental values at least for energies up to $10mc^2$.[‡] On the other hand, other relativistic wave equations, such as the Klein–Gordon equation, lead to results which are not in agreement with the experimental measurements. The Klein–Nishina formula may be regarded as proved, at least for energies in the range considered, and its exactness considered as direct evidence in favour of the Dirac theory of the electron, when the negative energy states are treated with the same weight as those of positive energy. For, if we entirely disregard the intermediate states of negative energy, the formula we obtain for the Compton scattering is appreciably different from the Klein–Nishina formula and is no longer in agreement with the experimental evidence.

55. The relationship of Dirac's equations to previous theories

The fact that in practical problems two of the scalar wave-functions Ψ_k ($k = 1, 2, 3, 4$) have usually greater magnitude than the remaining pair enables us to develop the Dirac wave equations in an approximate

† W. Friedrich and G. Goldhaber, *Zeits. f. Physik*, **44**, 700 (1927).
‡ W. Heitler, loc. cit., p. 160.

manner which brings out their relation to the non-relativistic theories of Schrödinger, Pauli, and Darwin considered in previous chapters.

If we wish to find a periodic solution

$$\Psi_k = \chi_k(x, y, z)e^{-iWt/\hbar}$$

of the scalar wave equations (36), then we have to solve the system of equations

$$\left.\begin{array}{l} (W-e\phi+mc^2)\chi_1+c(\Pi_1-i\Pi_2)\chi_4+c\Pi_3\chi_3 = 0 \\ (W-e\phi+mc^2)\chi_2+c(\Pi_1+i\Pi_2)\chi_3-c\Pi_3\chi_4 = 0 \\ (W-e\phi-mc^2)\chi_3+c(\Pi_1-i\Pi_2)\chi_2+c\Pi_3\chi_1 = 0 \\ (W-e\phi-mc^2)\chi_4+c(\Pi_1+i\Pi_2)\chi_1-c\Pi_3\chi_2 = 0 \end{array}\right\}. \tag{78}$$

Now in the case of positive energy states, if the velocity of the electron is small in comparison with the velocity of light, W is approximately equal to the rest energy mc^2 of the electron; therefore

$$\frac{1}{c}(W-e\phi+mc^2) \sim 2mc.$$

Substituting from this equation into the first two equations of the above set we obtain immediately in the case $\mathbf{A} = 0$,

$$\left.\begin{array}{l} \chi_1 = -\dfrac{\hbar}{2mci}\left\{\left(\dfrac{\partial}{\partial x}-i\dfrac{\partial}{\partial y}\right)\chi_4+\dfrac{\partial\chi_3}{\partial z}\right\} \\ \chi_2 = -\dfrac{\hbar}{2mci}\left\{\left(\dfrac{\partial}{\partial x}+i\dfrac{\partial}{\partial y}\right)\chi_3-\dfrac{\partial\chi_4}{\partial z}\right\} \end{array}\right\}. \tag{79}$$

If we substitute these values of χ_1 and χ_2 into the third equation of the set (78), we find that χ_3 satisfies the equation

$$\nabla^2\chi_3+\frac{2m}{\hbar^2}(W-mc^2-e\phi)\chi_3 = 0. \tag{80}$$

Now if W is nearly equal to mc^2, the quantity $W-mc^2$ represents the kinetic energy W' so that χ_3 is a solution of the non-relativistic Schrödinger equation

$$\left\{\nabla^2+\frac{2m}{\hbar^2}(W'-V)\right\}\chi = 0. \tag{81}$$

The same result holds for χ_4. It is clear from equations (79) that $|\chi_1|$ and $|\chi_2|$ are small compared with $|\chi_3|$ and $|\chi_4|$; thus, in a first approximation, they can be neglected in the expressions (59), (60) for the charge and current density. We then have approximately

$$\rho = \Psi_3^*\Psi_3+\Psi_4^*\Psi_4.$$

These results provide an approximate solution of the Dirac equations (36); if Ψ is a solution of the non-relativistic Schrödinger equation (81), then the following are approximate solutions of (36):

$$\Psi_3' = -C_1\Psi, \qquad\qquad \Psi_4' = -C_2\Psi,$$

$$\Psi_1' = \frac{C_2(\Pi_1-i\Pi_2)+C_1\Pi_3}{2mc}\Psi, \qquad \Psi_2' = \frac{C_1(\Pi_1+i\Pi_2)-C_2\Pi_3}{2mc}\Psi,$$

where C_1, C_2 are arbitrary constants and Π_1, Π_2, Π_3 are interpreted in the usual way as operators.

For negative energy states the roles of Ψ_3', Ψ_4' and Ψ_1', Ψ_2' are reversed.

To show more fully the relation of the Dirac equations to the non-relativistic theory of Pauli and Darwin, we introduce the two wave-functions†

$$\bar{\chi}_1 = e^{imc^2t/\hbar}\begin{pmatrix}\Psi_1'\\\Psi_2'\\0\\0\end{pmatrix}, \qquad \bar{\chi}_2 = e^{imc^2t/\hbar}\begin{pmatrix}\Psi_3'\\\Psi_4'\\0\\0\end{pmatrix}. \qquad (82)$$

The Dirac wave-function Ψ can then be written in the form

$$\Psi = \begin{pmatrix}\Psi_1'\\\Psi_2'\\\Psi_3'\\\Psi_4'\end{pmatrix} = (\bar{\chi}_1-\Lambda\bar{\chi}_2)e^{imc^2t/\hbar}, \qquad (83)$$

where Λ denotes the matrix

$$\Lambda = i\alpha_1\alpha_2\alpha_3 = \begin{pmatrix}0 & 0 & -1 & 0\\0 & 0 & 0 & -1\\-1 & 0 & 0 & 0\\0 & -1 & 0 & 0\end{pmatrix}. \qquad (84)$$

Differentiating both sides of equation (83) with respect to the time, we obtain

$$i\hbar\frac{\partial\Psi}{\partial t} = \left\{mc^2(\bar{\chi}_1-\Lambda\bar{\chi}_2)+i\hbar\left(\frac{\partial\bar{\chi}_1}{\partial t}-\Lambda\frac{\partial\bar{\chi}_2}{\partial t}\right)\right\}e^{-imc^2t/\hbar}. \qquad (85)$$

Now Ψ satisfies the Dirac equation

$$\left[i\hbar\frac{\partial}{\partial t}+e\phi+c\sum_{j=1}^{3}\alpha_j\Pi_j+\alpha_4 mc^2\right]\Psi = 0, \qquad (86)$$

and since

$$\sigma_1\begin{pmatrix}\chi_1\\\chi_2\end{pmatrix} = \begin{pmatrix}0 & 1\\1 & 0\end{pmatrix}\begin{pmatrix}\chi_1\\\chi_2\end{pmatrix} = \begin{pmatrix}\chi_2\\\chi_1\end{pmatrix}$$

and

$$\Lambda\begin{pmatrix}\chi_2\\\chi_1\\0\\0\end{pmatrix} = -\begin{pmatrix}0\\0\\\chi_2\\\chi_1\end{pmatrix},$$

---

† We consider here the case of positive energy states only; the analysis is similar for negative energy states, cf. E. L. Hill and R. Landshoff, *Rev. Mod. Phys.* **10**, 120 (1938).

we may write
$$\alpha_1 \bar{\chi}_1 = -\Lambda\sigma_1 \bar{\chi}_1,$$

or, in general,
$$\alpha_k \bar{\chi}_1 = -\Lambda\sigma_k \bar{\chi}_1, \qquad \alpha_4 \bar{\chi}_1 = \bar{\chi}_1, \tag{87}$$

where $k = 1, 2, 3$. Similarly

$$\alpha_k \Lambda\bar{\chi}_2 = -\sigma_k \bar{\chi}_2, \qquad \alpha_4 \Lambda\bar{\chi}_2 = -\Lambda\bar{\chi}_2. \tag{88}$$

Substituting from equations (85), (87), and (88) into the Dirac equation (86) we obtain

$$\left\{ c\sum_{j=1}^{3} \Pi_j \sigma_j \bar{\chi}_2 + i\hbar\frac{\partial\bar{\chi}_1}{\partial t} + (2mc^2 + e\phi)\bar{\chi}_1 \right\} +$$

$$+ \Lambda\left\{ c\sum_{j=1}^{3} \Pi_j \sigma_j \bar{\chi}_1 + i\hbar\frac{\partial\bar{\chi}_2}{\partial t} + e\phi\bar{\chi}_2 \right\} = 0.$$

Since the operator Λ and the unit operator are independent, each of the expressions in brackets must vanish. In this way we obtain the equations

$$\left(i\hbar\frac{\partial}{\partial t} + 2mc^2 + e\phi \right)\bar{\chi}_1 + c(\boldsymbol{\sigma}.\boldsymbol{\Pi})\bar{\chi}_2 = 0, \tag{89}$$

$$\left(i\hbar\frac{\partial}{\partial t} + e\phi \right)\bar{\chi}_2 + c(\boldsymbol{\sigma}.\boldsymbol{\Pi})\bar{\chi}_1 = 0, \tag{90}$$

where we have written

$$(\boldsymbol{\sigma}.\boldsymbol{\Pi}) = \sum_{j=1}^{3} \sigma_j \Pi_j.$$

Now we can write equation (89) symbolically as

$$\bar{\chi}_1 = -\frac{(\boldsymbol{\sigma}.\boldsymbol{\Pi})\bar{\chi}_2}{2mc[1 + \{i\hbar(\partial/\partial t) + e\phi\}/2mc^2]},$$

showing that $\bar{\chi}_1$ is given approximately by the equation

$$\bar{\chi}_1 = -\frac{1}{2mc}(\boldsymbol{\sigma}.\boldsymbol{\Pi})\bar{\chi}_2 + \frac{1}{4m^2c^2}\left(i\hbar\frac{\partial}{\partial t} + e\phi \right)(\boldsymbol{\sigma}.\boldsymbol{\Pi})\bar{\chi}_2. \tag{91}$$

Substituting from equation (91) into equation (90) we obtain

$$i\hbar\frac{\partial\bar{\chi}_2}{\partial t} = \mathfrak{H}\bar{\chi}_2,$$

where
$$\mathfrak{H} = -e\phi + \frac{1}{2m}(\boldsymbol{\sigma}.\boldsymbol{\Pi})^2 - \frac{1}{4m^2c^2}(\boldsymbol{\sigma}.\boldsymbol{\Pi})\left(i\hbar\frac{\partial}{\partial t} + e\phi \right)(\boldsymbol{\sigma}.\boldsymbol{\Pi}). \tag{92}$$

Now from equation (34)

$$(\boldsymbol{\sigma}.\boldsymbol{\Pi})^2 = \boldsymbol{\Pi}^2 + \frac{\hbar e}{c}(\boldsymbol{\sigma}.\operatorname{curl}\mathbf{A}) = \boldsymbol{\Pi}^2 + \frac{\hbar e}{c}(\boldsymbol{\sigma}.\mathbf{H}),$$

since by Maxwell's equations $\mathbf{H} = \operatorname{curl}\mathbf{A}$. Furthermore,

$$\left(i\hbar\frac{\partial}{\partial t}+e\phi\right)(\boldsymbol{\sigma}.\boldsymbol{\Pi}) = (\boldsymbol{\sigma}.\boldsymbol{\Pi})\left(i\hbar\frac{\partial}{\partial t}+e\phi\right)+i\hbar(\boldsymbol{\sigma}.\mathbf{E})$$

and

$$(\boldsymbol{\sigma}.\boldsymbol{\Pi})(\boldsymbol{\sigma}.\mathbf{E}) = (\mathbf{E}.\mathbf{H})+\frac{\hbar}{i}\operatorname{div}\mathbf{E}-i(\boldsymbol{\sigma}.\mathbf{E}\wedge\mathbf{H})+\hbar(\boldsymbol{\sigma}.\operatorname{curl}\mathbf{E})$$

$$= (\mathbf{E}.\mathbf{H})-i(\boldsymbol{\sigma}.\mathbf{E}\wedge\mathbf{H})-\frac{\hbar}{c}\left(\boldsymbol{\sigma}.\frac{\partial\mathbf{H}}{\partial t}\right),$$

since $\qquad \operatorname{div}\mathbf{E} = 0, \quad\text{and}\quad \operatorname{curl}\mathbf{E} = -\dfrac{1}{c}\dfrac{\partial\mathbf{H}}{\partial t}.$

Substituting these results into equation (92) we obtain

$$\mathfrak{H} = \frac{1}{2m}\left[\boldsymbol{\Pi}^2+\frac{\hbar e}{c}(\boldsymbol{\sigma}.\mathbf{H})\right]\left[1-\frac{1}{2mc}\left(i\hbar\frac{\partial}{\partial t}+e\phi\right)\right]-e\phi-$$
$$-\frac{i\hbar}{4m^2c^2}\left[(\mathbf{E}.\mathbf{H})-i(\boldsymbol{\sigma}.\mathbf{E}\wedge\mathbf{H})-\frac{\hbar}{c}\left(\boldsymbol{\sigma}.\frac{\partial\mathbf{H}}{\partial t}\right)\right].$$

To this degree of approximation we may write $(\boldsymbol{\sigma}.\boldsymbol{\Pi})^2/2m$ for $\left(i\hbar\dfrac{\partial}{\partial t}+e\phi\right)$ so that we have finally for the Hamiltonian $\mathfrak{H}$ the equation

$$\mathfrak{H} = \mathfrak{H}_s+\mathfrak{H}'_s+\frac{\hbar e}{2mc}(\boldsymbol{\sigma}.\mathbf{H})-\frac{\hbar e}{4m^2c^2}(\boldsymbol{\sigma}.\mathbf{E}\wedge\mathbf{H})-$$
$$-\frac{i\hbar}{4m^2c^2}\left\{(\mathbf{E}.\mathbf{H})-\frac{\hbar}{c}\left(\boldsymbol{\sigma}.\frac{\partial\mathbf{H}}{\partial t}\right)\right\},$$

where $\mathfrak{H}_s$ denotes the Hamiltonian operator of the non-relativistic Schrödinger equation, viz.

$$\frac{1}{2m}\boldsymbol{\Pi}^2-e\phi$$

and $\hbar e(\boldsymbol{\sigma}.\mathbf{H})/2mc$ is the energy produced by the spin of the electron in an external field. The term

$$\mathfrak{H}'_s = -\frac{1}{8m^3c^2}\left[\boldsymbol{\Pi}^2+\frac{\hbar e}{c}(\boldsymbol{\sigma}.\mathbf{H})\right]^2$$

is a relativistic correction term. The fourth term

$$\frac{\hbar e}{4m^2c^2}(\boldsymbol{\sigma}.\mathbf{E}\wedge\mathbf{H})$$

is the term attributed by Thomas† to the spin orbit coupling. The remaining terms have no counterpart in the non-relativistic theory.

† L. H. Thomas, *Phil. Mag.* 3, 1 (1927).

56. Solutions of Dirac's equation

56.1. *Rectilinear motion of an electron*

We now consider the motion of an electron parallel to the x-axis in a field that is a function of x only. We suppose that the vector potential **A** is zero everywhere and that $e\phi = -V(x)$. The wave function may be written in the form

$$\Psi = \chi(x)\exp\frac{i}{\hbar}(p_2 y + p_3 z - Wt). \tag{93}$$

Substituting this expression into the Dirac equation (9) we obtain

$$\left[-i\hbar\alpha_1\frac{d}{dx} + \frac{W-V(x)}{c} + \alpha_2 p_2 + \alpha_3 p_3 + \alpha_4 mc\right]\chi(x) = 0.$$

Written in terms of four scalar functions $\chi_\mu(x)$ ($\mu = 1, 2, 3, 4$), this equation becomes

$$-i\hbar\frac{d\chi_1}{dx} + \frac{W-V(x)}{c}\chi_4 + ip_2\chi_1 - p_3\chi_2 - mc\chi_4 = 0,$$

$$-i\hbar\frac{d\chi_2}{dx} + \frac{W-V(x)}{c}\chi_3 - ip_2\chi_2 + p_3\chi_1 - mc\chi_3 = 0,$$

$$-i\hbar\frac{d\chi_3}{dx} + \frac{W-V(x)}{c}\chi_2 + ip_2\chi_3 - p_3\chi_4 + mc\chi_2 = 0,$$

$$-i\hbar\frac{d\chi_4}{dx} + \frac{W-V(x)}{c}\chi_1 - ip_2\chi_4 + p_3\chi_3 + mc\chi_1 = 0.$$

If we substitute the expressions

$$\chi_2 = \frac{ip_3}{k}\phi_2, \qquad\qquad \chi_3 = -\frac{ip_3}{k}\phi_2,$$

$$\chi_1 = \phi_1 + a\phi_2, \qquad\qquad \chi_4 = \phi_1 + b\phi_2$$

into the second and third equations of this set of differential equations, we find that they reduce to

$$\frac{d\phi_2}{dx} - \frac{i}{\hbar}\cdot\frac{W-V(x)}{c}\phi_2 + \frac{k}{\hbar}\phi_1 + \frac{k}{\hbar}\left(a + \frac{p_2+imc}{k}\right)\phi_2 = 0,$$

$$\frac{d\phi_2}{dx} - \frac{i}{\hbar}\cdot\frac{W-V(x)}{c}\phi_2 + \frac{k}{\hbar}\phi_1 + \frac{k}{\hbar}\left(b - \frac{p_2+imc}{k}\right)\phi_2 = 0.$$

These equations can be written in the form

$$\frac{d\phi_2}{dx} - \frac{i}{\hbar}\cdot\frac{W-V(x)}{c}\phi_2 + \frac{k}{\hbar}\phi_1 = 0 \tag{94}$$

if a, b are chosen according to the equations

$$a = -(p_2+imc)/k, \qquad b = (p_2+imc)/k.$$

With these values of a, b inserted in the expressions for χ_1, χ_4 we substitute for the χ's in the first and fourth equations of the original set. Taking account of the equation (94) we find that both equations reduce to

$$\frac{d\phi_1}{dx} + \frac{i}{\hbar} \cdot \frac{W - V(x)}{c} \phi_1 + \frac{k}{\hbar} \phi_2 = 0. \qquad (95)$$

We have thus reduced the problem to that of solving the two first-order differential equations (94) and (95). When the functions ϕ_1 and ϕ_2 are determined from these equations, the scalar wave functions are obtained from the relations

$$\Psi_1^{\cdot} = \left\{ \phi_1(x) - \frac{p_2 - imc}{k} \phi_2(x) \right\} \exp\frac{i}{\hbar}(p_2 y + p_3 z - Wt),$$

$$\Psi_2^{\cdot} = \frac{ip_3}{k} \phi_2(x) \exp\frac{i}{\hbar}(p_2 y + p_3 z - Wt),$$

$$\Psi_3^{\cdot} = -\frac{ip_3}{k} \phi_2(x) \exp\frac{i}{\hbar}(p_2 y + p_3 z - Wt),$$

$$\Psi_4^{\cdot} = \left\{ \phi_1(x) + \frac{p_2 + imc}{k} \phi_2(x) \right\} \exp\frac{i}{\hbar}(p_2 y + p_3 z - Wt).$$

The case of a uniform field $V(x) = ax$ has been treated by Sauter,[†] that of a simple harmonic oscillator, $V(x) = \omega x^2$, by Nikolsky,[‡] and that in which $V(x)$ is a polynomial of any degree in x, or in $1/x$, by Plesset.[§]

56.2. *The energy levels of the hydrogen atom*

The most important success of the Dirac theory, apart from the solution of the problem of the spin of the electron, has been the derivation of the fine structure of the energy levels of an electron moving in the Coulomb field of a single nucleus. Dirac,[||] using the methods of non-commutative algebra, showed that Sommerfeld's fine structure formula for the energy levels of the hydrogen atom was a natural consequence of the use of the relativistic wave equation. The same result was later derived by Darwin[††] and by Gordon by more familiar methods; we shall follow the latter treatments here.

The Coulomb field of an electron moving in the field of a nucleus of atomic number Z may be derived from the potentials

$$\mathbf{A} = 0, \qquad \phi = Ze^2/r.$$

† F. Sauter, *Zeits. f. Physik*, **69**, 742 (1931).
‡ K. Nikolsky, ibid. **62**, 677 (1930).
§ M. S. Plesset, *Phys. Rev.* (2) **41**, 278 (1932).
|| P. A. M. Dirac, *Proc. Roy. Soc.* A, **117**, 610 (1928).
†† C. G. Darwin, ibid. **118**, 654 (1928); W. Gordon, *Zeits. f. Physik*, **48**, 11 (1928).

We substitute from these equations into equations (36); introducing polar coordinates r, θ, ϕ defined by the equations

$$x = r\sin\theta\cos\phi, \qquad y = r\sin\theta\sin\phi, \qquad z = r\cos\theta,$$

we obtain

$$\frac{\partial}{\partial x} + i\frac{\partial}{\partial y} = e^{i\phi}\left[\sin\theta\frac{\partial}{\partial r} + \frac{\cos\theta}{r}\frac{\partial}{\partial\theta} + i\frac{\partial}{r\sin\theta\,\partial\phi}\right],$$

$$\frac{\partial}{\partial x} - i\frac{\partial}{\partial y} = e^{-i\phi}\left[\sin\theta\frac{\partial}{\partial r} + \frac{\cos\theta}{r}\frac{\partial}{\partial\theta} - i\frac{\partial}{r\sin\theta\,\partial\phi}\right],$$

$$\frac{\partial}{\partial z} = \cos\theta\frac{\partial}{\partial r} - \sin\theta\frac{\partial}{r\partial\theta}.$$

We thus obtain for the scalar wave functions the following equations:

$$\left(i\hbar\frac{\partial}{\partial t} + \frac{Ze^2}{r} + mc^2\right)\Psi_1' - i\hbar ce^{-i\phi}\left(\sin\theta\frac{\partial}{\partial r} + \frac{\cos\theta}{r}\frac{\partial}{\partial\theta} - \frac{i}{r\sin\theta}\frac{\partial}{\partial\phi}\right)\Psi_4' - $$
$$- i\hbar c\left(\cos\theta\frac{\partial}{\partial r} - \sin\theta\frac{\partial}{r\partial\theta}\right)\Psi_3' = 0,$$

$$\left(i\hbar\frac{\partial}{\partial t} + \frac{Ze^2}{r} + mc^2\right)\Psi_2' - i\hbar ce^{i\phi}\left(\sin\theta\frac{\partial}{\partial r} + \frac{\cos\theta}{r}\frac{\partial}{\partial\theta} + \frac{i}{r\sin\theta}\frac{\partial}{\partial\phi}\right)\Psi_3' + $$
$$+ i\hbar c\left(\cos\theta\frac{\partial}{\partial r} - \sin\theta\frac{\partial}{r\partial\theta}\right)\Psi_4' = 0,$$

$$\left(i\hbar\frac{\partial}{\partial t} + \frac{Ze^2}{r} - mc^2\right)\Psi_3' - i\hbar ce^{-i\phi}\left(\sin\theta\frac{\partial}{\partial r} + \frac{\cos\theta}{r}\frac{\partial}{\partial\theta} - \frac{i}{r\sin\theta}\frac{\partial}{\partial\phi}\right)\Psi_2' - $$
$$- i\hbar c\left(\cos\theta\frac{\partial}{\partial r} - \sin\theta\frac{\partial}{r\partial\theta}\right)\Psi_1' = 0,$$

$$\left(i\hbar\frac{\partial}{\partial t} + \frac{Ze^2}{r} - mc^2\right)\Psi_4' - i\hbar ce^{i\phi}\left(\sin\theta\frac{\partial}{\partial r} + \frac{\cos\theta}{r}\frac{\partial}{\partial\theta} + \frac{i}{r\sin\theta}\frac{\partial}{\partial\phi}\right)\Psi_1' + $$
$$+ i\hbar c\left(\cos\theta\frac{\partial}{\partial r} - \sin\theta\frac{\partial}{r\partial\theta}\right)\Psi_2' = 0.$$

In these equations we substitute

$$\Psi_\mu' = \bar{\Psi}_\mu(r, \theta, \phi)\exp(-iWt/\hbar) \quad (\mu = 1, 2, 3, 4), \tag{96}$$

and express the function $\bar{\Psi}_\mu$ in terms of F, f, G, g by equations (54). As a result we obtain, after some reduction, the system of differential equations

$$\left.\begin{aligned}
\frac{df}{dr} + \left(j + \frac{3}{2}\right)\frac{f}{r} + \frac{i}{\hbar c}\left(W + \frac{Ze^2}{r} - mc^2\right)G &= 0 \\
\frac{dG}{dr} - \left(j - \frac{1}{2}\right)\frac{G}{r} + \frac{i}{\hbar c}\left(W + \frac{Ze^2}{r} + mc^2\right)f &= 0
\end{aligned}\right\} \tag{97}$$

$$\left.\begin{aligned}
\frac{dF}{dr}+\left(j+\frac{3}{2}\right)\frac{F}{r}+\frac{i}{\hbar c}\left(W+\frac{Ze^2}{r}+mc^2\right)g &= 0 \\
\frac{dg}{dr}-\left(j-\frac{1}{2}\right)\frac{g}{r}+\frac{i}{\hbar c}\left(W+\frac{Ze^2}{r}-mc^2\right)F &= 0
\end{aligned}\right\}. \qquad (98)$$

The differential equations for the four functions f, g, F, G thus fall naturally into two pairs. Consequently for each permissible value of W we can find two independent solutions for the Ψ-function by equating to zero either of the pairs of functions (f, G) or (F, g).

The solution of the pair of equations (98) is similar to that of a pair (97), so we shall consider in detail only the solutions of (97) here. If we make the substitutions

$$\zeta = Ze^2/\hbar c, \quad \epsilon = mc^2/W, \quad \lambda = mc(1-\epsilon^2)^{\frac{1}{2}}/\hbar, \quad \rho = 2\lambda r,$$

$$\left.\begin{aligned}
f(r) &= i(1-\epsilon)^{\frac{1}{2}}e^{-\frac{1}{2}\rho}\rho^{\gamma-1}\{f_1(\rho)-f_2(\rho)\} \\
G(r) &= (1+\epsilon)^{\frac{1}{2}}e^{-\frac{1}{2}\rho}\rho^{\gamma-1}\{f_1(\rho)+f_2(\rho)\}
\end{aligned}\right\}, \qquad (99)$$

the pair of equations (97) is transformed to

$$\left.\begin{aligned}
\frac{df_1}{d\rho} &= \left\{1-\frac{1}{\rho}\left(\gamma+\frac{\zeta\epsilon}{\sqrt{(1-\epsilon^2)}}\right)\right\}f_1+\frac{1}{\rho}\left\{j+\frac{1}{2}-\frac{\zeta}{\sqrt{(1-\epsilon^2)}}\right\}f_2 \\
\frac{df_2}{d\rho} &= \frac{1}{\rho}\left\{j+\frac{1}{2}+\frac{\zeta}{\sqrt{(1-\epsilon^2)}}\right\}f_1-\frac{1}{\rho}\left\{\gamma-\frac{\zeta\epsilon}{\sqrt{(1-\epsilon^2)}}\right\}f_2
\end{aligned}\right\}. \qquad (100)$$

If we assume the functions $f_1(\rho)$, $f_2(\rho)$ to be given by power series of the form

$$f_1(\rho) = \sum_{s=0}^{\infty} c_s \rho^s, \qquad f_2(\rho) = \sum_{s=0}^{\infty} d_s \rho^s,$$

then substituting for the functions in equation (100) and equating powers of ρ^{s-1} we obtain the recurrence formulae

$$\left.\begin{aligned}
c_s\left(\gamma+s+\frac{\zeta\epsilon}{\sqrt{(1-\epsilon^2)}}\right)-d_s\left(j+\frac{1}{2}-\frac{\zeta}{\sqrt{(1-\epsilon^2)}}\right) &= c_{s-1} \\
c_s\left(j+\frac{1}{2}+\frac{\zeta}{\sqrt{(1-\epsilon^2)}}\right)-d_s\left(\gamma+s-\frac{\zeta\epsilon}{\sqrt{(1-\epsilon^2)}}\right) &= 0
\end{aligned}\right\} \qquad (101)$$

for the coefficients c_s, d_s. Since we are considering only positive powers of ρ we may take $s = 0$, $c_1 = 0$ in equation (101) to obtain the equations

$$\left(\gamma+\frac{\zeta\epsilon}{\sqrt{(1-\epsilon^2)}}\right)c_0-\left(j+\frac{1}{2}-\frac{\zeta}{\sqrt{(1-\epsilon^2)}}\right)d_0 = 0,$$

$$\left(j+\frac{1}{2}+\frac{\zeta}{\sqrt{(1-\epsilon^2)}}\right)c_0-\left(\gamma-\frac{\zeta\epsilon}{\sqrt{(1-\epsilon^2)}}\right)d_0 = 0.$$

The necessary and sufficient condition for non-vanishing solutions of the type (99) is therefore

$$\begin{vmatrix} \gamma+\dfrac{\zeta\epsilon}{\sqrt{(1-\epsilon^2)}} & -j-\dfrac{1}{2}+\dfrac{\zeta}{\sqrt{(1-\epsilon^2)}} \\[3mm] j+\dfrac{1}{2}+\dfrac{\zeta}{\sqrt{(1-\epsilon^2)}} & -\gamma+\dfrac{\zeta\epsilon}{\sqrt{(1-\epsilon^2)}} \end{vmatrix} = 0.$$

Regarded as an equation in γ this determinantal equation has two roots, equal in magnitude but of opposite sign. Discarding the negative root since it would lead to wave functions which behave as r^{-n} $(n > 1)$ in the neighbourhood of $r = 0$ and hence give a divergent integral for $\int |\Psi|^2 \, d\tau$, we find that the value of γ is given by the positive root

$$\gamma = \{(j+\tfrac{1}{2})^2 - \zeta^2\}^{\frac{1}{2}}. \tag{102}$$

Since $j \geqslant 1$ and $\zeta = Z(e^2/\hbar c) = Z/137 < 1$, it follows that γ is always real.

Eliminating d_s from equations (101) we obtain the recurrence relation

$$c_s = \frac{\gamma+s-\zeta\epsilon/\sqrt{(1-\epsilon^2)}}{(\gamma+s)^2-(j+\tfrac{1}{2})^2+\zeta^2} c_{s-1}.$$

If the function $f_1(\rho)$ is to be a polynomial of the type $\sum\limits_{s=0}^{n'-1} c_s \rho^s$ in which the last term does not vanish, then we must have

$$\gamma+n'-\frac{\zeta\epsilon}{\sqrt{(1-\epsilon^2)}} = 0.$$

Regarded as an equation in ϵ this equation has roots

$$\epsilon = \pm\frac{\gamma+n'}{\sqrt{\{\zeta^2+(\gamma+n')^2\}}}.$$

Taking the positive root of this equation and defining the principal quantum number, n, by the equation

$$n = n'+j+\tfrac{1}{2},$$

we obtain

$$W = mc^2\left\{1+\frac{\zeta^2}{(n-j-\tfrac{1}{2}+\gamma)^2}\right\}^{-\frac{1}{2}}. \tag{103}$$

Subtracting the rest mass of the electron and substituting for ζ and γ we obtain Sommerfeld's fine structure formula

$$W' = mc^2\left[\left\{1+\frac{Z^2e^4/\hbar^2c^2}{[n-j-\tfrac{1}{2}+\{(j+\tfrac{1}{2})^2-Z^2e^4/\hbar^2c^2\}^{\frac{1}{2}}]^2}\right\}^{-\frac{1}{2}}-1\right]. \tag{104}$$

For small values of $Ze^2/\hbar c$ this formula reduces to the non-relativistic formula

$$W' = -\frac{Z^2me^4}{2\hbar^2}\frac{1}{n^2}.$$

The analytical forms for the functions $f_1(\rho)$ and $f_2(\rho)$ can be determined easily; it is found that when W is given by equation (103) f_1 and f_2 are given by the formulae

$$\left.\begin{aligned} f_1(\rho) &= {}_1F_1(1-n', 2\gamma+1; \rho) \\ f_2(\rho) &= -\frac{\gamma+n'+(j+\frac{1}{2})\epsilon}{n'\epsilon}{}_1F_1(-n', 2\gamma+1; \rho) \end{aligned}\right\}, \tag{105}$$

where the hypergeometric function ${}_1F_1$ is defined by

$$_1F_1(\alpha, \beta; x) = \sum_{n=0}^{\infty} \frac{\Gamma(\beta)\Gamma(\alpha+n)}{\Gamma(\alpha)\Gamma(\beta+n)}\frac{x^n}{n!}.$$

If we substitute for f_1, f_2 from equation (105) into equation (99) and transform back to the original variables, it can be verified easily that

$$|G| \gg |f|. \tag{106}$$

The solution of the pair of differential equations (98) may be carried out in a similar way. If we write

$$F = i\sqrt{(1+\epsilon)}.\,e^{-\frac{1}{2}\rho}\rho^{\gamma-1}\{F_1(\rho)-F_2(\rho)\}, \quad g = \sqrt{(1-\epsilon)}.\,e^{-\frac{1}{2}\rho}\rho^{\gamma-1}\{F_1(\rho)+F_2(\rho)\}$$

and proceed as before, we find that the condition (102) and the Sommerfeld formula (103) are obtained once more, and that

$$F_1(\rho) = -\frac{\gamma+n'-(j+\frac{1}{2})\epsilon}{\gamma+n'+(j+\frac{1}{2})\epsilon}f_2(\rho), \qquad F_2(\rho) = f_1(\rho). \tag{107}$$

Corresponding to equation (106) we then have the relation

$$|F| \gg |g|. \tag{108}$$

56.3. *Motion of an electron in a uniform magnetic field*†

Consider the motion of an electron moving in a uniform magnetic field H in the z-direction. Then the potentials are given by

$$\phi = 0, \qquad A = (-\tfrac{1}{2}Hy, \tfrac{1}{2}Hx, 0),$$

so that the Dirac equation (43) reduces to

$$[p_0+\rho_1\{\sigma_x(p_x-\omega y)+\sigma_y(p_y+\omega x)+\sigma_z p_z\}+\rho_3 mc]\Psi = 0,$$

where we have written $\omega = eH/2c$. If we assume that the wave function Ψ is independent of z and write

$$\Psi = \phi(x)\exp\frac{i}{\hbar}(\omega xy+\eta y-Wt),$$

we find that ϕ satisfies the equation

$$\left[\frac{W}{c}+\rho_1\{\sigma_x p_x+\sigma_y(2\omega x+\eta)\}+\rho_3 mc\right]\phi = 0.$$

† L. D. Huff, *Phys. Rev.* (2), **38**, 501 (1931).

Substituting $x' = x + \eta/2\omega$ and writing out the four component equations we obtain the system of ordinary differential equations

$$\frac{\hbar}{i}\frac{d\phi_4}{dx'} - 2i\omega x'\phi_4 + \left(\frac{W}{c} + mc\right)\phi_1 = 0,$$

$$\frac{\hbar}{i}\frac{d\phi_3}{dx'} + 2i\omega x'\phi_3 + \left(\frac{W}{c} + mc\right)\phi_2 = 0,$$

$$\frac{\hbar}{i}\frac{d\phi_2}{dx'} - 2i\omega x'\phi_2 + \left(\frac{W}{c} - mc\right)\phi_3 = 0,$$

$$\frac{\hbar}{i}\frac{d\phi_1}{dx} + 2i\omega x'\phi_1 + \left(\frac{W}{c} - mc\right)\phi_4 = 0.$$

Eliminating ϕ_1 between the first and last of this set of equations and writing

$$\xi = 2x'(\omega/\hbar)^{\frac{1}{2}}, \qquad \nu = \frac{1}{4\omega\hbar}\left(\frac{W^2}{c^2} - m^2c^2\right)$$

we obtain the differential equation for a harmonic oscillator

$$\frac{d^2\phi_4}{d\xi^2} + (\nu + \tfrac{1}{2} - \tfrac{1}{4}\xi^2)\phi_4 = 0, \tag{109}$$

whose solution may be written (cf. Appendix, § 2)

$$\phi_4 = aD_\nu(\xi) = ae^{-\frac{1}{4}\xi^2}H_\nu(\xi),$$

where $H_\nu(\xi)$ is the Hermite polynomial of order ν.

Similarly if we eliminate ϕ_4 between the first and last equations of the set we obtain $\phi_1 = bD_{\nu-1}(\xi)$. The two solutions are not, however, independent. Substituting the two expressions for ϕ_1, ϕ_4 into the first equation of the set we obtain a relation between a, b. In this way we obtain

$$\phi_4(x') = aD_\nu(\xi), \qquad \phi_1(x') = ia\frac{W/c - mc}{2(\hbar\omega)^{\frac{1}{2}}}D_{\nu-1}(\xi)$$

as the expressions for the functions ϕ_1 and ϕ_4.

It can be shown in a similar manner that

$$\phi_2(x') = iC,$$

where C is an arbitrary constant.

The current densities in the field are given by

$$j_x = -\Psi^*\alpha_x\Psi = -(1 + c^2p^2)(\phi_1^*\phi_4 + \phi_4^*\phi_1),$$

$$j_y = -\Psi^*\alpha_y\Psi = i(1 + c^2p^2)(\phi_4^*\phi_1 - \phi_1^*\phi_4)$$

$$= (1 + c^2p^2)aa^*D_\nu D_{\nu-1}\frac{W/c - mc}{(\hbar\omega)^{\frac{1}{2}}},$$

where $$p^2 = W^2/c^2 - m^2c^2.$$

From the properties of the D-functions it follows that j_y is negative for some values of x; this is apparently a consequence of the spin, since the corresponding expression in the Schrödinger theory turns out to be always positive.†

Using the results (cf. Appendix, § 3)

$$\int_0^\infty D_\nu(\xi)D_{\nu-1}(\xi)\,d\xi = \frac{2^\nu\pi}{\{\Gamma(\tfrac{1}{2}-\tfrac{1}{2}\nu)\}^2}, \qquad \int_0^\infty \xi D_\nu(\xi)D_{\nu-1}(\xi)\,d\xi = \left(\frac{\pi}{2}\right)^{\frac{1}{2}}\nu!$$

we find that the average x-coordinate of the current defined by

$$\bar{x} = \int_0^\infty xj_y\,dx\Big/\int_0^\infty j_y\,dx$$

has the value
$$\bar{x} = \frac{1}{4}\left(\frac{\hbar}{\omega}\right)^{\frac{1}{2}}\frac{\{(\tfrac{1}{2}\nu)!\}^2}{\nu!}2\nu(2\pi)^{\frac{1}{2}}. \tag{110}$$

Now the classical value of this quantity is

$$\bar{x} = \pi r/4,$$

where $r = cp/eH$. The quantum mechanical value reduces to this if we use Stirling's formula

$$n! = (2\pi n)^{\frac{1}{2}}\left(\frac{n}{e}\right)^n.$$

The error in the Stirling formula is of the order $1/\nu$, i.e. 10^{-8} to 10^{-10}, so that the deviation of the classical formula from that given by the Dirac theory is entirely negligible.

56.4. *The scattering of fast electrons by a nucleus*

If a beam of electrons with velocity comparable to that of light falls on a single atomic nucleus, Dirac's equation of the electron must be used to calculate the scattering. We have in fact to find a solution $\Psi = (\Psi_1, \Psi_2, \Psi_3, \Psi_4)$ of this equation which represents an incident plane wave and a scattered wave, and thus which has the asymptotic form

$$\Psi_k \sim C_k e^{ipz/\hbar}+u_k(\theta,\phi)\frac{e^{ipr/\hbar}}{r} \quad (k=1,2,3,4) \tag{111}$$

for large values of r. The constants C_k are not all arbitrary constants; it follows from equation (67) that if we take

$$C_3 = A, \qquad C_4 = B,$$

where A, B are arbitrary complex quantities, then

$$C_1 = -\frac{Ap}{p+mc}, \qquad C_2 = \frac{Bp}{p+mc}, \tag{112}$$

† G. E. Uhlenbeck and L. A. Young, *Phys. Rev.* **36**, 1721 (1930).

where we have written p for W/C. We shall choose A, B such that $AA^*+BB^* = 1$. As already noted the scattered current depends on $u_3(\theta,\phi)$ and $u_4(\theta,\phi)$ only, so that, if $I(\theta)nt\sin\theta\,d\theta d\phi$ is the proportion of the original beam scattered in a given solid angle, we have

$$I(\theta) = |u_3(\theta,\phi)|^2+|u_4(\theta,\phi)|^2.$$

Furthermore, if we take the direction of the spin to mean the direction referred to axes with respect to which the electron is at rest, then

$$-\frac{B}{A} = e^{i\omega}\cot\tfrac{1}{2}\chi, \tag{113}$$

where χ, ω are the spherical polar angles of the spin direction.

Now it can be shown that the general solution of the form (111) is given by

$$\left.\begin{aligned}u_3(\theta,\phi) &= Af(\theta)-Bg(\theta)e^{-i\phi}\\u_4(\theta,\phi) &= Bf(\theta)+Ag(\theta)e^{i\phi}\end{aligned}\right\}, \tag{114}$$

where $f(\theta)$ and $g(\theta)$ are functions of θ alone and depend on the form of the potential function $V(r)$ describing the interaction between the electron and the nucleus. Thus

$$\begin{aligned}I(\theta) = (AA^*+BB^*)\{f(\theta)f^*(\theta)+g(\theta)g^*(\theta)\}+\\+\{f(\theta)g^*(\theta)-f^*(\theta)g(\theta)\}\{A^*Be^{-i\phi}-AB^*e^{i\phi}\}, \tag{115}\end{aligned}$$

so that if A, B satisfy the equations (112) and (113) we have

$$I(\theta) = |f(\theta)|^2+|g(\theta)|^2+D(\theta)\sin\chi\sin(\omega-\phi), \tag{116}$$

where the function $D(\theta)$ is defined by the relation

$$D(\theta) = i\{f(\theta)g^*(\theta)-f^*(\theta)g(\theta)\} \tag{117}$$

and χ, ω determine the direction of the spin axis of the incident electrons.

If the incident beam is unpolarized so that the spin axes are pointing in all directions, we average over all possible directions of the spin axis and obtain

$$\bar{I} = |f(\theta)|^2+|g(\theta)|^2. \tag{118}$$

In the general case the function P will depend on the polarization of the incident beam, and even if the incident beam is unpolarized the scattered beam will in general possess a polarization.

The functions $f(\theta)$ and $g(\theta)$ for scattering by an atomic nucleus with inverse square law field

$$V(r) = Ze^2/r$$

may be determined† from Gordon's solution of the Dirac equation for

† Cf. N. F. Mott, *Proc. Roy. Soc.* A, **124**, 425 (1929).

the hydrogen atom (§ 56.2 above) and from the asymptotic expansion

$$F(\alpha; \beta; z) \sim \begin{cases} \dfrac{\Gamma(\beta)}{\Gamma(\beta-\alpha)}(-z)^{-\alpha} & (\mathscr{R}(\beta-2\alpha) > 0) \\[2ex] \dfrac{\Gamma(\beta)}{\Gamma(\alpha)}e^z z^{\alpha-\beta} & (\mathscr{R}(\beta-2\alpha) < 0) \end{cases}$$

and $|\arg(-z)| < \pi$, $|\arg z| < \pi$. For the details of the calculation the reader is referred to the original paper; we shall only give the result here. The functions $f(\theta)$ and $g(\theta)$ are such that

$$I(\theta) = |f(\theta)|^2 + |g(\theta)|^2$$

$$= \frac{Z^2 c^2 r_0^2}{4\beta^2}(1-\beta^2)\left\{\operatorname{cosec}^4\tfrac{1}{2}\theta - \beta^2\operatorname{cosec}^2\tfrac{1}{2}\theta + \pi\alpha\beta\frac{\cos^2\tfrac{1}{2}\theta}{\sin^3\tfrac{1}{2}\theta} + O(\alpha^2)\right\} \quad (119)$$

and

$$fg^* - f^*g = \frac{Z^2 r_0^2}{\beta^3}(1-\beta^2)^{\frac{3}{2}}i\alpha \operatorname{cosec}\theta \log(\operatorname{cosec}\tfrac{1}{2}\theta), \qquad (120)$$

where m, v, e denote the mass, velocity, and charge of the electron, Z the atomic number of the scattering nucleus, and $\alpha = Ze^2/\hbar c$, $\beta = v/c$, and $r_0 = e^2/mc^2$.

The formulae (119) and (120) determining the total scattering and the polarization of the scattered beam are calculated with neglect of radiative forces which are appreciable for fast electrons.

If we let $\beta \to 0$ in equation (119) we obtain the non-relativistic formula

$$I(\theta) = \left(\frac{Ze^2}{2mv^2}\right)^2 \operatorname{cosec}^4\tfrac{1}{2}\theta.$$

Now the number of particles N scattered in the angular range (θ_1, θ_2) is

$$nt\int_0^{2\pi} d\phi \int_{\theta_1}^{\theta_2} I(\theta)\sin\theta\, d\theta,$$

so that substituting for $I(\theta)$ from (119) we obtain the formula

$$N = \pi nt\left(\frac{Ze^2}{mc^2}\right)^2\frac{1-\beta^2}{\beta^4}\left[\cot^2\tfrac{1}{2}\theta_1 - \cot^2\tfrac{1}{2}\theta_2 - 2\beta^2\log\frac{\sin\tfrac{1}{2}\theta_2}{\sin\tfrac{1}{2}\theta_1} + \right.$$

$$\left. + 2\pi\alpha\beta(\sin\tfrac{1}{2}\theta_1 - \sin\tfrac{1}{2}\theta_2 + \operatorname{cosec}\tfrac{1}{2}\theta_1 - \operatorname{cosec}\tfrac{1}{2}\theta_2) + O(\alpha^2)\right], \quad (121)$$

which reduces to the well-known result

$$N = \pi nt\left(\frac{Ze^2}{mv^2}\right)^2(\cot^2\tfrac{1}{2}\theta_1 - \cot^2\tfrac{1}{2}\theta_2)$$

in the non-relativistic approximation $\beta \to 0$.

For large values of Z and *small* angles, θ, we have approximately

$$I(\theta) = \left(\frac{Ze^2}{2mv^2}\right)^2 (1-\beta^2)\operatorname{cosec}^4 \tfrac{1}{2}\theta.$$

For large values of Z and large angles there is no simple formula for the scattering cross-section. The scattering has, however, been calculated for gold at a scattering angle of $90°$ and for various velocities. We can express the scattering at $90°$ in the two forms

$$I(\theta) = \left(\frac{Ze^2}{2mv^2} \operatorname{cosec}^2 \tfrac{1}{2}\theta\right)^2 (1-\beta^2)R \tag{122}$$

or

$$I(\theta) = \left(\frac{Ze^2}{2mv^2} \operatorname{cosec}^2 \tfrac{1}{2}\theta\right)^2 S, \tag{123}$$

where R and S are numerical factors which are functions of v/c. The values of R, S are given in tabular form below:

TABLE 9

β	0·2	0·3	0·4	0·5	0·6	0·7	0·8	0·9	1·0
R	1·1	1·2	1·4	1·6	1·9	2·2	2·6	3·0	3·4
S	1·0	1·1	1·1	1·2	1·2	1·1	0·9	0·5	0

There have been a number of experimental investigations of scattering of fast electrons by nuclei, mostly by the method of the expansion chamber. A review of the position in 1938 was given by Champion.† For more recent work, see Randels‡ and co-workers. Scattering has been investigated in H, N, F, A, Kr, I, Xe, and Hg, for energies usually up to about 3 Mev., though for xenon recent investigations have gone up to 12 Mev. Except for some early work on mercury, discrepancies with theory are seldom as great as 2, and may be due to experimental error. However, there is little work on large angle scattering with heavy elements.

56.5. *The polarization of electrons by double scattering*

In § 53.4 we saw that formally the electron has a magnetic moment of magnitude $e\hbar/2mc$. When the electron is bound in an atom this magnetic moment cannot be observed directly; all that can be observed is the magnetic moment of the atom as a whole, or the splitting of the spectral lines which we may attribute to the magnetic moment of the electron. It is natural then to inquire if a *free* electron possesses a magnetic moment and if there is any experiment by which we may

† F. C. Champion, *Rep. Prog. Phys.* **5**, 356 (1938).
‡ R. G. Randels, K. T. Chao, and H. R. Crane, *Phys. Rev.* **68**, 64 (1945).

determine this moment. It can readily be seen that a magnetic moment $e\hbar/2mc$ can never be observed directly, for instance, by the use of a magnetometer.† Suppose, for example, that the free electron whose spin is to be observed is at a distance r from a magnetometer. Then the magnetic field due to the spin moment is of order

$$e\hbar/mcr^3$$

and the magnetic field due to the motion of the electron is of order

$$\frac{ev}{c}\frac{1}{r^2}.$$

If the effect of the spin is to be observable it must be greater than the uncertainty in the field due to the electronic motion, so that we must have

$$\frac{\hbar}{mr} > \Delta v, \quad \text{or} \quad \frac{\hbar}{m\Delta v} > r, \tag{124}$$

where Δv is the uncertainty in our knowledge of v. Now by the uncertainty principle we cannot observe both r and v at the same time; the uncertainties of our knowledge of r and v are related by the equation

$$\Delta r\Delta v > \hbar/m. \tag{125}$$

Substituting from this equation into equation (124) we find

$$\Delta r > r,$$

showing that such an experiment will be impossible, since the uncertainty in the position of the electron under observation would exceed the distance of the electron from the magnetometer. In other words, the uncertainty in the field we want to measure would have to be greater than the field itself. The only way in which we can hope to detect the magnetic moment of a free electron is by obtaining a *polarized* beam, that is, a beam in which all the spin axes are pointing in the same direction or at any rate more in one direction than another. A Stern–Gerlach experiment would appear to be the obvious way of producing such a beam of electrons, but here again it can be shown by means of the uncertainty principle that this is impossible. It appears certain that the magnetic moment of a free electron can never be observed in any experiment based on the classical conception of an electron magnet.

The idea that an unpolarized beam of electrons (i.e. one in which the spin axes are pointing in all directions at random) scattered from a

† The argument is due to N. Bohr; cf. N. F. Mott and H. S. W. Massey, *Theory of Atomic Collisions*, p. 42 (Oxford, 1933).

target might be partly polarized was first put forward by Mott.† This polarization could be measured by allowing the scattered beam to fall on a second target. By projecting an unpolarized beam of electrons on to a foil thin enough to ensure single scattering, and allowing some of the scattered electrons to fall on a second thin foil, we should be

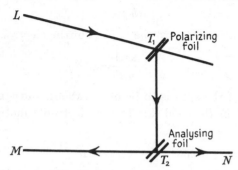

FIG. 65. Experiment for producing and detecting electronic polarization.

able to detect an asymmetrical scattering about the direction in which the beam falls on the second target. The theory of such an experiment was developed by Mott,† making use of the Dirac wave equations for the electron.

Suppose the initial beam LT_1 (cf. Fig. 65) is represented by

$$\Psi_3 = Ae^{ipz/\hbar}, \qquad \Psi_4 = Be^{ipz/\hbar},$$

then the direction of the spin axis of the scattered beam is determined, according to equation (113), by the ratio of the amplitudes of the two components of the wave function of the scattered beam which, according to equation (114), are

$$Af(\theta_1) - Bg(\theta_1), \qquad Ag(\theta_1) + Bf(\theta_1),$$

where θ_1 is the angle between the incident electron beam and the scattered beam. Rotating our axes through an angle θ_1 so that $T_1 T_2$ becomes the axis of z we find the beam of electrons is represented by

$$\Psi_3 = [\{Af(\theta_1) - Bg(\theta_1)\}\cos\tfrac{1}{2}\theta_1 + \{Ag(\theta_1) + Bf(\theta_1)\}\sin\tfrac{1}{2}\theta_1]e^{ipz/\hbar},$$
$$\Psi_4 = [\{Ag(\theta_1) + Bf(\theta_1)\}\cos\tfrac{1}{2}\theta_1 - \{Af(\theta_1) - Bg(\theta_1)\}\sin\tfrac{1}{2}\theta_1]e^{ipz/\hbar}.$$

By making use of equation (115) and averaging over all directions of the spin axis of the initial beam LT_1, we can obtain the number of electrons scattered by the second target in a given direction (θ_2, ϕ_2). We are interested primarily in the asymmetry in the scattering about the line $T_1 T_2$. For prescribed values of θ_1 and θ_2 a straightforward

† N. F. Mott, *Proc. Roy. Soc.* A, **124**, 425 (1929); **135**, 429 (1932).

calculation shows that the number of electrons scattered per unit solid angle is proportional to
$$1 - \delta \cos \phi_2, \tag{126}$$
where
$$\delta = 2 \frac{\{f(\theta_1)g^*(\theta_1) - f^*(\theta_1)g(\theta_1)\}\{f(\theta_2)g^*(\theta_2) - f^*(\theta_2)g(\theta_2)\}}{\{f(\theta_1)f^*(\theta_1) + g(\theta_1)g^*(\theta_1)\}\{f(\theta_2)f^*(\theta_2) + g(\theta_2)g^*(\theta_2)\}}. \tag{127}$$

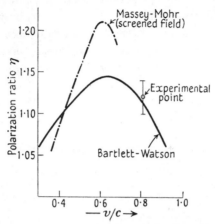

Fig. 66. Theoretical values for the polarization ratio for gold, together with an experimental point.

By means of these equations and the equations (119) and (120) derived for $f(\theta)$, $g(\theta)$, we can estimate the order of magnitude of the effect to be expected in the double-scattering experiment outlined above. If we take both of the angles θ_1 and θ_2 to be 90° we have approximately
$$\delta = 11.2\alpha^2 \frac{\beta^2(1-\beta^2)}{2-\beta^2} \quad \left(\beta = \frac{v}{c}\right). \tag{128}$$

Differentiating the right-hand side of this equation with respect to β and equating it to zero, we find that δ has a maximum when $\beta = 0.764$; for this value of the velocity of the incident electrons we obtain
$$\delta = \left(\frac{Z}{96}\right)^2.$$

Calculations of δ, without using any approximation, were carried out for gold ($Z = 79$) by Mott (loc. cit.) and repeated by Bartlett and Watson,[†] who have calculated somewhat more accurately the rather slowly convergent series involved. Massey and Mohr[‡] have made the calculation for the self-consistent field of the gold atom. These results are shown in Fig. 66, compared with the experimental ratio obtained

† J. H. Bartlett and R. E. Watson, *Phys. Rev.* **56**, 612 (1939).
‡ H. S. W. Massey and C. B. O. Mohr, *Proc. Roy. Soc.* A, **177**, 341 (1941).

by Skull, Chase, and Myers.† No asymmetry was obtained for aluminium, in agreement with theory.

57. The relativistic wave equation for two electrons

57.1. *Equations of Eddington and Breit*

Until now we have considered only the relativistic motion of a single electron moving in an external field, and no attempt has been made to discuss the interactions between two or more electrons. At the time of writing no complete relativistic theory has been formulated for the discussion of problems in which the interaction of two or more elementary particles is taken into account. Such a theory depends on a proper treatment of the interaction of a number of charged particles with an electromagnetic field. The difficulties encountered in formulating a completely satisfactory theory of quantum electrodynamics appear at the moment to be so formidable that their resolution may be expected only along lines rather different from those so far attempted. For this reason quantum electrodynamics will not be discussed in this book;‡ we shall merely indicate the results relating to the interaction between two electrons which have been derived from this source.

The first attempts to set up a relativistic wave equation for two electrons, similar to Dirac's equation for a single electron, were made by Eddington§ and Gaunt‖. In the classical theory the energy of interaction between two electrons is

$$\frac{e^2}{r_{12}}\left[1 - \frac{\mathbf{v}^1 \cdot \mathbf{v}^2}{c^2}\right], \qquad (129)$$

where $\mathbf{v}^1$, $\mathbf{v}^2$ denote the velocities of the two particles and r_{12} the distance between them. The first term of this expression refers to the electrostatic energy and the other to the magnetic. Gaunt and Eddington replace this energy by

$$\frac{e^2}{r_{12}}[1 - \boldsymbol{\alpha}^1 \cdot \boldsymbol{\alpha}^2],$$

and so obtain the wave equation

$$0 = \left\{\Pi_0 + \sum_{j=1}^{3}(\alpha_j^1\,\Pi_j^1 + \alpha_j^2\,\Pi_j^2) + (\alpha_4^1 + \alpha_4^2)m_0 c + \frac{e^2}{cr}(\boldsymbol{\alpha}^1 \cdot \boldsymbol{\alpha}^2)\right\}\Psi, \quad (130)$$

where the wave-function Ψ has sixteen components which may be denoted by

$$\Psi_{mn} \quad (m, n = 1, 2, 3, 4),$$

† C. G. Skull, C. T. Chase, and F. E. Myers, *Phys. Rev.* **63**, 29 (1943).

‡ For a discussion, see P. A. M. Dirac, *Quantum Electrodynamics*; *Comm. Dub. Inst. Adv. Stud.* A, **1** (1943); A, **3** (1946).

§ A. S. Eddington, *Proc. Roy. Soc.* A, **122**, 358 (1929).

‖ J. A. Gaunt, *Proc. Roy. Soc.* A, **122**, 513 (1929); *Phil. Trans.* A, **228**, 151 (1929).

the suffix m referring to the electron denoted by 1, n to that denoted by 2. The matrices α_j^1, α_j^2, are the usual Dirac matrices, but now they operate on the first and second suffixes respectively. As before

$$\Pi_j^1 = \frac{\hbar}{i}\frac{\partial}{\partial x_j^1} + \frac{e}{c}A_j^1, \qquad \Pi_j^2 = \frac{\hbar}{i}\frac{\partial}{\partial x_j^2} + \frac{e}{c}A_j^2, \qquad (131)$$

A^1, A^2 denoting the potentials of electrons 1 and 2 disregarding their interaction, and

$$\Pi_0 = -\frac{\hbar}{ic}\frac{\partial}{\partial t} + \frac{e}{c}(\phi^1+\phi^2) - \frac{e^2}{cr}, \qquad (132)$$

$$\Pi_0 = -i\Pi_4. \qquad (133)$$

It was, however, shown by Breit† that the consequences of equation (130) are unreasonable. Making use of the quantum theory of the electromagnetic field developed by Pauli and Heisenberg, Breit has investigated the form of the Hamiltonian for two electrons. The wave equation corresponding to this Hamiltonian is found to be

$$\left[\Pi_0 + \boldsymbol{\alpha}^1.\boldsymbol{\Pi}^1 + \boldsymbol{\alpha}^2.\boldsymbol{\Pi}^2 + (\alpha_4^1+\alpha_4^2)m_0c + \right.$$
$$\left. + \frac{e^2}{2cr}\left\{(\boldsymbol{\alpha}^1.\boldsymbol{\alpha}^2) + \frac{(\boldsymbol{\alpha}^1.\mathbf{r})(\boldsymbol{\alpha}^2.\mathbf{r})}{r^2}\right\}\right]\Psi = 0. \quad (134)$$

This equation of Breit's is not exact. It does not hold when the velocities of the electrons are too great or when the distance between them is too large, since the potentials are not retarded. With a slight modification, however, this equation has been shown to explain, with a fair degree of accuracy, the observed facts of the hyperfine structure of the helium spectrum.‡

The Breit equation (134) has been derived by Nikolsky§ using Dirac's theory of quantum electrodynamics.‖ In this theory the Hamiltonian of the system of two electrons is the simple sum of the two Hamiltonians for the single electrons. No interaction terms are required in the Hamiltonian, the interaction being introduced by a wave-function Ψ' which is a function not only of the coordinates of the two electrons but also of the variables describing the field. The interaction energy follows as a consequence of the quantization of the field.

The Breit equation for two electrons is satisfactory only when corrections of the order $(v/c)^2$ to the non-relativistic terms are required;

† G. Breit, *Phys. Rev.* (2), **34**, 553 (1929).
‡ Ibid.; **36**, 383 (1930); **39**, 616 (1932); **51**, 248 (1937); **53**, 153 (1938).
§ K. Nikolsky, *Phys. Zeits. d. Sowjetunion*, **2**, 447 (1932–3).
‖ P. A. M. Dirac, *Proc. Roy. Soc.* A, **136**, 453 (1932).

v denotes the velocity of either electron. It is fortunate that an equation correct to this order should be sufficient for calculating the stationary states of two extranuclear electrons and that the present gaps in our knowledge of quantum electrodynamics do not make the calculation of spectroscopic energies impossible. It appears that the approximation to terms of order v/c is sufficient for the rough treatment of energy levels while the approximation to $(v/c)^2$ apparently gives a satisfactory account of their fine structure.

57.2. *The correspondence method of Møller*

We have noted above that the general theory of the interaction of two electrons can only be based on a proper theory of quantum electrodynamics. An important class of problems can, however, be solved in a more elementary way. The method is due to Møller.†

In these problems one considers two electrons initially in states with wave-functions $\Psi_i(\mathbf{r})$, $\chi_i(\mathbf{r})$. These are taken to be Dirac functions, and thus correspond to definite spin directions. We require to calculate the probability that a transition occurs to a state in which the two electrons are in states with wave-functions Ψ_f, χ_f. The transition occurs under the interaction of the electrons alone. Using non-relativistic quantum mechanics it is of course possible to calculate the transition probability to any power of the interaction. The relativistic theory given here gives an answer to the first power only, and is adequate when this is sufficient.

The method is as follows. First one forms the charge and current densities associated with the transition of *one* of the electrons, in the sense of Chapter X, § 46. Using the Dirac theory, these are

$$\rho = \rho_{fi}e^{-2\pi i\nu_{if}t}+\text{complex conjugate},$$
$$\mathbf{j} = \mathbf{j}_{fi}e^{-2\pi i\nu_{if}t}+\text{complex conjugate},\tag{135}$$

where ν_{if} denotes the transition frequency $(W_i-W_f)/h$, and

$$\rho_{fi} = -e\Psi_f^*\Psi_i,$$
$$\mathbf{j}_{fi} = ce\Psi_f^*\,\boldsymbol{\alpha}\Psi_i.\tag{136}$$

One then writes down the scalar and vector potentials of the electromagnetic field that such a transition would produce. These are given, as in § 46, by the equations

$$\left(\nabla^2-\frac{1}{c^2}\frac{\partial^2}{\partial t^2}\right)\Phi = -4\pi\rho,$$
$$\left(\nabla^2-\frac{1}{c^2}\frac{\partial^2}{\partial t^2}\right)\mathbf{A} = -\frac{4\pi}{c}\mathbf{j}.\tag{137}$$

† C. Møller, *Zeits. f. Physik*, **70**, 780 (1931); *Ann. der Physik*, **14**, 531 (1932).

We take the solution corresponding to retarded potentials (i.e. to an outgoing wave). These are

$$
\left.
\begin{aligned}
\Phi &= -e \int \frac{\Psi_f^*(r')\Psi_i(r')e^{2\pi i \nu_{fi}\{|\mathbf{r}-\mathbf{r}'|/c-t\}}}{|\mathbf{r}-\mathbf{r}'|}\,d\tau' \\
\mathbf{A} &= e \int \frac{\Psi_f^*(r')\boldsymbol{\alpha}\Psi_i(r')e^{2\pi i \nu_{fi}\{|\mathbf{r}-\mathbf{r}'|/c-t\}}}{|\mathbf{r}-\mathbf{r}'|}\,d\tau'
\end{aligned}
\right\}. \tag{137 a}
$$

We then allow these potentials to act on the second electron, and calculate by the ordinary methods of perturbation theory the probability per unit time that the electron will make a transition to a state χ_f. Owing to the term $e^{-2\pi i \nu_{fi} t}$ in the formulae (137 a) for Φ and $\mathbf{A}$, the transition probability will be zero unless energy for the whole system is conserved.

In the Hamiltonian for the second electron the perturbing term is (cf. equation (19))

$$
\frac{e}{c}\{\Phi+(\boldsymbol{\alpha}\,.\,\mathbf{A})\}.
$$

To calculate the probability that after a time t a transition has taken place from the state χ_i to the state χ_f we make use of formula (10) of Chapter X. This in our case may be written

$$
\frac{\rho(W)t}{\hbar}\left| \int\!\!\int \Psi_f^*(r_1)\chi_f^*(r_2)\frac{e^2\{1+(\boldsymbol{\alpha}_1\boldsymbol{\alpha}_2)\}}{|\mathbf{r}_1-\mathbf{r}_2|}e^{2\pi i \nu_{fi}|\mathbf{r}_1-\mathbf{r}_2|/c}\Psi_i(r_1)\chi_i(r_2)\,d\tau_1\,d\tau_2 \right|^2 \tag{138}
$$

It is here assumed that all the wave functions are normalized to unity and that $\rho(W)\,dW$ is the number of states of the final system in the energy interval dW.

This formula cannot be correct, because if we make $c \to \infty$ (non-relativistic case) it does not tend to the correct non-relativistic result, using antisymmetrical wave functions. We must therefore replace it by

$$
\frac{\rho(W)t}{\hbar}\left| \int\!\!\int \left[\Psi_f(r_1)\chi_f(r_2)-\Psi_f(r_2)\chi_f(r_1)\right]\frac{\{1+(\boldsymbol{\alpha}_1\boldsymbol{\alpha}_2)\}}{|\mathbf{r}_1-\mathbf{r}_2|}\times \right.
$$
$$
\left. \times\, e^{2\pi i\,\nu_{fi}|\mathbf{r}_1-\mathbf{r}_2|/c}\left[\Psi_i(r_1)\chi_i(r_2)-\Psi_i(r_2)\chi_i(r_1)\right]d\tau_1\,d\tau_2 \right|^2. \tag{139}
$$

This expression has the correct symmetry; but it will be appreciated that the derivation does not depend on any very consecutive argument.

57.3. *Collisions between two fast charged particles*

The method outlined above was first applied by Møller[†] to the discussion of the non-radiative collision between two free electrons.

† Loc. cit.

The accuracy of Møller's calculations is of the same order as that of the first approximation in Born's method, so that for fast particles his results neglect terms of order $e^2/\hbar c$ in comparison with unity. They should, however, be exact to all orders of v/c.

In his treatment of the problem Møller refers the scattering to a Lorentz frame of reference in which the centre of gravity of the two electrons is at rest and their momenta are equal and opposite. The angle of scattering, θ^*, in this frame is related to the observed angle of scattering, θ, by the formula

$$\theta^* = \cos^{-1}\frac{2-(\gamma+3)\sin^2\theta}{2+(\gamma-1)\sin^2\theta}, \tag{140}$$

where γ is given in terms of the relative velocity of the two electrons before collision by the equation

$$\gamma = \left(1-\frac{v^2}{c^2}\right)^{-\frac{1}{2}}.$$

For Ψ_i, Ψ_f, χ_i, χ_f Møller takes plane waves. He finds that the cross-section for scattering between angles θ, $\theta+d\theta$ is

$$I(\theta)\,d\theta = 4\pi\left(\frac{e^2}{m_0 v^2}\right)^2\frac{\gamma+1}{\gamma^2}\left[\frac{4}{(1-\mu^2)^2}-\frac{3}{(1-\mu^2)}+\frac{(\gamma-1)^2}{4\gamma^2}\left\{1+\frac{4}{1-\mu^2}\right\}\right], \tag{141}$$

where we have written, for convenience

$$\mu = \cos\theta^*. \tag{142}$$

This formula, it will be noted, contains no terms in $\hbar$, the Planck constant.

It is of some interest to compare Møller's formula (141) with others of a similar nature. For low velocities equation (141) reduces to the form

$$I(\theta)\,d\theta = 4\pi\left(\frac{e^2}{m_0 v^2}\right)^2\Big\{(\operatorname{cosec}^4\theta+\sec^4\theta-\operatorname{cosec}^2\theta\sec^2\theta)-$$
$$-\frac{v^2}{c^2}(4\operatorname{cosec}^4\theta+3\sec^4\theta-2\operatorname{cosec}^2\theta\sec^2\theta-3\sec^2\theta)\Big\}\sin 2\theta\,d\theta. \tag{143}$$

Now the corresponding formula for the scattering of *slow* β-particles ($v/c \ll 1$) by electrons is (cf. § 24.4)

$$I(\theta)\,d\theta = 4\pi\left(\frac{e^2}{m_0 v^2}\right)^2\{\operatorname{cosec}^4\theta+\sec^4\theta-\operatorname{cosec}^2\theta\sec^2\theta\cos U\}\sin 2\theta\,d\theta, \tag{144}$$

where $$U = \frac{2e^2}{\hbar v}\log\cot\theta. \tag{145}$$

If $e^2/\hbar c$ is small enough to allow us to put $U = 0$, while v/c is small enough to be neglected, the two formulae are equivalent. This is the case if
$$1/137 \ll v/c \ll 1.$$

The scattering of fast β-rays by electrons up to angles of about $12°$ has been investigated experimentally by Williams and Terroux† and by Williams.‡ Instead of measuring the angles of scattering they measured the energy of the recoil electrons; for v/c ranging from 0.60 to 0.97 along a track of length 18 metres they observed about seventy branches with energies between 7,500 and 40,000 volts. This number they compared with the effective cross-section§ for loss of energy between Q, $Q+dQ$, namely,
$$2\pi \frac{e^4}{m_0 v^2} \frac{dQ}{Q^2},$$

which may be deduced from Møller's formula for small angles. At the higher velocities the observed scattering was roughly twice that predicted by this formula, but the ratio diminished as v/c decreased.

A more direct attempt to verify Møller's formula (141) has been made by Champion,‖ who from the analysis of about 650 m. of track of fast β-particles in nitrogen, photographed by the expansion method, obtained 250 collisions with atomic electrons in which the angle of scattering lies between $10°$ and about $30°$. The values of the ratio v/c ranged from 0.82 to 0.92. The number of particles scattered into the ranges $10°$–$20°$, $20°$–$30°$, $> 30°$ was measured and the corresponding theoretical values obtained from Møller's formula by numerical integration. The results are shown in Table 10.

TABLE 10

Angular range	Number scattered	
	Observed	Calculated
$> 30°$	10	13
$20°$–$30°$	26	30
$10°$–$20°$	214	230
Total	250	273

It will be seen that the observed values and those calculated from Møller's formula are in good agreement; it should, however, be noted

---

† E. J. Williams and F. R. Terroux, *Proc. Roy. Soc.* A, **126**, 289 (1929).
‡ E. J. Williams, ibid. **130**, 328 (1930).
§ N. Bohr, *Phil. Mag.* **25**, 10 (1913); **30**, 58 (1915).
‖ F. C. Champion, *Proc. Roy. Soc.* A, **137**, 688 (1932).

that most of the observed scattering angles were less than 30° when the contribution of the spin to Møller's formula is very small.

The theoretical analysis has been extended by Møller† to the case when a quantum is emitted in the collision of two fast charged particles. The cross-section for such a process is calculated first by means of the correspondence method of Møller and then by means of the quantum electrodynamics of Heisenberg and Pauli,‡ and Dirac;§ the same result is obtained by both methods. The formula for the case in which one of the colliding particles is infinitely heavy corresponds to that derived by Bethe and Heitler‖ for the radiation emitted in the collision of a fast charged particle with an atomic nucleus.

The methods of quantum electrodynamics have been employed by Hulme†† to investigate the interaction of a particle in the nucleus of an atom with an electron in the K-shell (a case of some interest in the theory of internal conversion of γ-rays). Hulme's results show that for *bound* particles Møller's correspondence method gives the correct result if we take the retarded potentials due to the transition where the first particle jumps down, and then consider these as perturbing the second particle. For *free* particles, however, we may take either the advanced or the retarded potentials, or we may put the results in a symmetrical form by taking the mean of the two, without affecting the result.

57.4. *The relativistic theory of the Auger effect*

If a K-electron is ejected from an atom, an outer electron, e.g. an L-electron, can fall into the K-shell giving up its energy in one of two ways:

(a) By radiation, a process which gives rise to the X-ray emission lines.

(b) By transferring its energy to one of the outer electrons, which is thereby ejected from the atom. This process is known as the Auger effect. Experimental investigations have been made of the ratio between the number of γ-quanta and the number of Auger electrons.

In calculating the probability of the Auger transition, one treats the process as a transition to a state of equal energy of the system comprised by the two electrons. The formalism is thus exactly that of the foregoing section, and one uses equation (139).

† C. Møller, *Proc. Roy. Soc.* A, **152**, 481 (1935).
‡ W. Heisenberg and W. Pauli, *Zeits. f. Physik*, **56**, 1 (1929); **59**, 168 (1929).
§ P. A. M. Dirac, *Proc. Roy. Soc.* A, **136**, 453 (1932).
‖ H. A. Bethe and W. Heitler, ibid. **146**, 85 (1934).
†† H. R. Hulme, ibid. **154**, 487 (1936).

The probability of the internal conversion of the K-series radiation for gold arising from the interaction of the $L_I L_I$, $L_I L_{II}$, and $L_I L_{III}$ shells has been calculated by Massey and Burhop† in this way. Two approximations arise in the course of the calculations:

   (i) The problem is treated as one of two electrons only, the perturbation by these of the wave functions of the other atomic electrons being neglected.

 (ii) Screened hydrogen-like wave functions are used for the atomic electrons.

The second approximation is probably quite accurate, since it is known that it gives satisfactory results in the discussion of the non-relativistic theory of the Auger effect.‡ The error in the first approximation cannot be estimated until the wave functions of electrons in an atom ionized in an inner shell are found (say, by the method of the self-consistent field).

Details of the calculation are as follows:

Suppose that an electron in the L-shell falls into an empty K-level and that the energy given up raises a second L-electron to a state of the continuous spectrum. If we denote by Ψ_i, Ψ_f the Dirac wave functions of the initial and final states of the ejected electron and by χ_i, χ_f those of the other electron, we find that if Ψ_f is normalized to represent one emitted electron per unit time the number of transitions per unit time is given by

$$\left| \frac{1}{\hbar} \int \Psi_f^* \{ -e\phi - e\rho_1(\mathbf{a}.\boldsymbol{\sigma}) \} \Psi_i \, d\tau \right|. \tag{146}$$

In this equation ρ_1 and $\boldsymbol{\sigma}$ are the usual Dirac operators. The equations defining $\mathbf{a}$, ϕ are analogous to equations $(137\,a)$, viz.

$$\left. \begin{aligned} \phi &= - \int \frac{e}{|\mathbf{r}-\mathbf{r}'|} e^{2\pi i \nu_{fi} |\mathbf{r}-\mathbf{r}'|/c} \chi_f^* \chi_i \, d\tau' \\ \mathbf{a} &= \int \frac{e}{|\mathbf{r}-\mathbf{r}'|} e^{2\pi i \nu_{fi} |\mathbf{r}-\mathbf{r}'|/c} \chi_f^* \rho_1 \boldsymbol{\sigma} \chi_i \, d\tau' \end{aligned} \right\}. \tag{147}$$

Substituting from equations (147) into equation (146) we obtain for the probability per unit time of a transition

$$|A_{fi}|^2 = \left| \frac{1}{\hbar} \int \frac{e}{|\mathbf{r}-\mathbf{r}'|} \exp\left(\frac{2\pi i \nu_{fi} |\mathbf{r}-\mathbf{r}'|}{c} \right) \{ \rho\rho' - \mathbf{j}.\mathbf{j}' \} \, d\tau d\tau' \right|^2, \tag{148}$$

where we have written, for convenience,

$$\rho = -e\chi_f^* \chi_i, \qquad \mathbf{j} = e\chi_f^* \rho_1 \boldsymbol{\sigma} \chi_i,$$
$$\rho' = -e\Psi_f^* \Psi_i, \qquad \mathbf{j}' = e\Psi_f^* \rho_1 \boldsymbol{\sigma} \Psi_i.$$

† H. S. W. Massey and E. H. S. Burhop, *Proc. Roy. Soc.* A, **153**, 661 (1936).
‡ E. H. S. Burhop, ibid. **148**, 272 (1935).

From these definitions it follows immediately that $(\rho, \mathbf{j})$ are time-independent charge density and current vector for the $L \to K$ transition, and that $(\rho', \mathbf{j}')$ are the same quantities for the $L \to \infty$ transition (∞ denoting a state of the continuous spectrum).

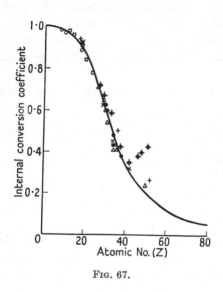

FIG. 67.

The formula (148) does not take the Pauli exclusion principle into account. To do this we introduce the quantity $|B_{fi}|^2$ analogous to (148) but with the final states interchanged. The possibility of electron exchange is then taken into account if we take the total probability of occurrence of the double transition per unit time to be

$$|A_{fi} - B_{fi}|^2. \tag{149}$$

The application of formulae (148) and (149) to the calculation of the probability of the Auger transitions $L_I, L_I \to K, \infty$; $L_I, L_{II} \to K, \infty$; $L_I, L_{III} \to K, \infty$ has been carried out by Massey and Burhop for gold. The detailed calculations show the relativistic effects to be of considerable importance for gold; the K-series internal conversion coefficient being increased by a factor of two. The relative intensity of the above three transitions is given in the non-relativistic approximation by the ratio $1:1\cdot14:2\cdot28$, while the relativistic theory gives a ratio $1:5\cdot5:5\cdot3$. If these conclusions were tested experimentally we should have some insight into the validity, not only of Dirac's equation for the single electron, but also of its approximate extension to two electrons; no experimental confirmation of these results has so far been adduced.

The theoretical values of the internal conversion (ratio of electrons to X-ray quanta) coefficient are shown by the full line in Fig. 67. The values for elements of high atomic number are deduced from the theory developed by Massey and Burhop, those for low atomic numbers from the paper by Burhop cited above, and from a paper by Pincherle.†
There is satisfactory agreement between the theoretical curve and the points determined experimentally.

57.5. *The internal conversion of γ-rays*

It is well known that a γ-ray emitted from the nucleus of a radio-active atom may be absorbed by one of the outer electrons with the production of a secondary β-ray. The intensity of the resultant β- and γ-rays may be observed and the proportion of γ-rays reabsorbed in the atomic system calculated; this ratio is known as the *internal conversion coefficient*. A theoretical estimate of this quantity was first made by Swirles‡ and Fowler§ using non-relativistic wave mechanics. Swirles replaces the nuclear mechanism emitting the γ-ray by an oscillating Hertzian dipole, radiating classically. The radiation field set up by such an oscillator produces photoelectric transitions in the planetary electrons which are then discussed on the Schrödinger theory. The values of the internal conversion coefficient found in this way were not in agreement with the experimental values. The process has since been treated at length by various authors‖ using relativistic quantum mechanics and a field of the type suggested by Swirles.

Suppose that after a radioactive transformation the product nucleus is left in an excited state and then falls to one of lower energy with the emission of a γ-ray or the ejection of an extranuclear electron. Let $g \, dt$ denote the probability that in a time dt the nucleus makes such a transition between two given states with the emission of a γ-ray, and $b_B \, dt$ the probability that the same nuclear transition occurs with the ejection of an extra-nuclear electron from some X-ray level of the atom. Thus corresponding to each level $K, L_I, L_{II},...$ we have the

† L. Pincherle, *Nuovo Cimento*, **12**, 81 (1935).
‡ B. Swirles, *Proc. Roy. Soc.* A, **116**, 491 (1927); **121**, 447 (1928).
§ R. H. Fowler, ibid. **129**, 1 (1930).
‖ H. R. Hulme, ibid. **138**, 643 (1932); H. M. Taylor and N. F. Mott, ibid. **138**, 665 (1932); **142**, 215 (1933); H. M. Hulme, N. F. Mott, J. R. Oppenheimer, and H. M. Taylor, ibid. **155**, 315 (1936); J. B. Fisk, ibid. **143**, 674 (1933); C. D. Ellis and N. F. Mott, ibid. **139**, 369 (1933); J. B. Fisk and H. M. Taylor, ibid. **146**, 178 (1934); N. F. Mott, *Ann. Inst. Henri Poincaré*, **4**, 207 (1933); *Handbuch der Physik*, **24**, 809 (1933); J. C. Jaeger and H. R. Hulme, *Proc. Roy. Soc.* **148**, 708 (1935).

probabilities b_K, b_{L_I}, $b_{L_{II}}$... and the total probability per unit time of the ejection of an electron from *any* shell is

$$b = b_K + b_{L_I} + b_{L_{II}} + \dots .$$

The internal conversion coefficient is then defined by

$$\alpha = \frac{b}{b+g},$$

since $b+g$ is the total probability per unit time that the transition takes place. The internal conversion coefficients for the various levels are defined by

$$\alpha_K = \frac{b_K}{b+g}, \qquad \alpha_L = \frac{b_L}{b+g},$$

etc., and the ratio of the number of observed γ-rays to the number of K-electrons is

$$\frac{\alpha_K}{1-\alpha}.$$

The choice of the name 'internal conversion coefficient' is unfortunate since we now regard the emission of electrons as due to direct inter-action between the nucleus and the atom rather than to the emission and subsequent reabsorption of a γ-ray. The relativistic theory includes the effects of direct interaction as well as those of γ-ray emission and reabsorption; in fact, no sharp distinction can be made between them.

In making the calculations, the unperturbed system is taken to be an electron under the influence of a central charge Ze. We then have

$$\mathbf{A} = 0, \qquad A_0 = Ze/r. \tag{150}$$

To determine the perturbing potentials we must make some assumption about the field which is to represent the γ-ray emitted by the nucleus. Suppose the perturbing field is represented by

$$\left. \begin{aligned} A_0 &= \mathfrak{A}_0 e^{-2\pi i \nu t} + \mathfrak{A}_0^* e^{2\pi i \nu t} \\ \mathbf{A} &= \mathfrak{A} e^{-2\pi i \nu t} + \mathfrak{A}^* e^{2\pi i \nu t} \end{aligned} \right\}, \tag{151}$$

and suppose that Ψ_0 represents the normalized wave function of an extranuclear electron for the ground state, and Ψ_f that of a possible final state, determined by Dirac's wave equation (19) with $\mathbf{A}$ and A_0 given by equation (151). Then the probability per unit time that an electron is ejected because of the field (151) is given by

$$b = \sum_f \left(\frac{1}{\hbar}\right)^2 \left| \int \Psi_f^* \{-e\mathfrak{A}_0 - e(\mathfrak{A} \cdot \rho_1 \sigma)\} \Psi_0 \, d\tau \right|^2, \tag{152}$$

where Ψ_f is normalized so that one electron crosses unit area per unit time and the summation is taken over all possible final states. The functions Ψ_0, Ψ_f have already been determined (§ 56.2 above) so that once $\mathfrak{A}_0$ and $\mathfrak{A}$ have been prescribed the problem reduces to that of calculating the matrix elements occurring in the series (152).

The number of possible fields (151) is, of course, infinite; the various types considered with the corresponding forms of $\mathfrak{A}$, $\mathfrak{A}_0$ are exhibited in Table 11. In this table B is a constant and q denotes $2\pi\nu/c$.

For the dipole radiation the energy radiated by the field is

$$g_0 = \frac{2\pi B^2 \nu}{3\hbar c}, \tag{153}$$

so that for dipole radiation and K-conversion we obtain

$$\frac{b_K}{g} = \frac{\alpha_K}{1-\alpha} = \frac{3\hbar c}{8\pi\nu B^2} \sum_f \left| \frac{1}{\hbar} \int \Psi_f^* \{e\mathfrak{A}_0 + e\rho_1(\mathfrak{A}.\boldsymbol{\sigma})\}\Psi_0 \, d\tau \right|^2, \tag{154}$$

where Ψ_0 is the wave function of the K-state. Since both $\mathfrak{A}_0$ and $|\mathfrak{A}|$ are proportional to B, the unknown constant B is not involved in this expression. Taylor and Mott† showed that the number of quanta escaping from the atom differs from $g_0 \, dt$ (the number of quanta ejected in the absence of the outer electrons) only by a factor of order of magnitude $1/137$ which may be neglected, and is not $(g_0 - b) \, dt$ as was previously supposed. The effect of the extranuclear electrons is thus to *increase* the total nuclear transition probability per unit time.

The evaluation of the matrix elements involved in equation (154) has been carried out using the wave-functions Ψ_f, Ψ_0, which are the exact solutions of the relativistic wave equation for an unscreened nuclear field of potential Ze/r. The possible sources of error are thus:

(i) the assumption that the dipole, quadripole, or other field used is the correct one;

(ii) the neglect of screening;

(iii) the use in the integrations (152) and (154) of the dipole and quadripole forms for the field of the γ-ray at all distances from the centre of the atom; this is obviously incorrect within the nucleus ($r < 10^{-12}$ cm.).

The second of these errors is probably not important since the energy of the ejected electron, even for soft γ-rays (~ 150 kV.) is always much greater than the difference between the screened and unscreened potential energies anywhere in the atom. The third source should not introduce an error greater than the small fraction

$$\kappa = \frac{\text{radius of nucleus}}{\text{wave-length of } \gamma\text{-ray}}, \tag{155}$$

unless the field within the nucleus is unexpectedly great.

† H. M. Taylor and N. F. Mott, *Proc. Roy. Soc.* A, **142**, 215 (1933).

TABLE 11

Investigators	Type	$\mathfrak{U}_0$	$\mathfrak{U}_x$	$\mathfrak{U}_y$	$\mathfrak{U}_z$
H. R. Hulme	Dipole	$\dfrac{B\cos\theta}{r}\left(1-\dfrac{1}{iqr}\right)e^{iqr}$	0	0	$\dfrac{B}{r}e^{iqr}$
H. M. Taylor and N. F. Mott	Quadripole	$-\dfrac{2B}{r}P_2(\cos\theta)\times\left(1-\dfrac{3i}{qr}-\dfrac{3}{q^2r^2}\right)e^{iqr}$	0	0	$-\dfrac{3B}{r}\cos\theta\left(1-\dfrac{i}{qr}\right)e^{iqr}$
	Magnetic dipole	0	$\dfrac{B}{r}P_1^1(\cos\theta)\sin\phi\times\left(1-\dfrac{i}{qr}\right)e^{iqr}$	$-\dfrac{B}{r}P_1^1(\cos\theta)\cos\phi\times\left(1+\dfrac{i}{qr}\right)e^{iqr}$	0
J. B. Fisk and H. M. Taylor	Magnetic quadripole	0	$\dfrac{B}{r}P_2^1(\cos\theta)\sin\phi\times\left(1+\dfrac{3i}{qr}-\dfrac{3}{q^2r^2}\right)e^{iqr}$	$-\dfrac{B}{r}P_2^1(\cos\theta)\cos\phi\times\left(1+\dfrac{3i}{qr}-\dfrac{3}{q^2r^2}\right)e^{iqr}$	0

Conversion in the K-shell. The results of the calculations for dipole, quadripole, and magnetic dipole radiation are shown in Fig. 68. Magnetic quadripole and octopole radiation give considerably higher values. Experimental points are shown on the same diagram.

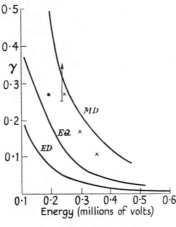

FIG. 68*a*.

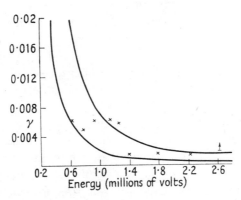

FIG. 68*b*.

Conversion in the L-shell. The internal conversion coefficients for quadripole and dipole radiation are identical for very hard radiation ($h\nu \to \infty$). For dipole radiation Hulme has shown that in this limit

$$\alpha_K : \alpha_{L_I} : \alpha_{L_{II}} : \alpha_{L_{III}} = 6 \cdot 7 : 1 : 0 \cdot 0086 : 0 \cdot 044$$

and that for $h\nu = 7 \cdot 2 \times 10^5$ eV.

$$\alpha_K : \alpha_{L_I} = 7 \cdot 0 : 1.$$

Fisk has shown that for quadripole radiation this ratio remains practically unaltered down to energies of order $h\nu = 2\cdot5 \times 10^5$ eV.

The ratio α_K/α_{L_I} has been estimated by Ellis[†] for a number of lines and found to be roughly in agreement with the theoretical value $7\cdot0$. Gray and O'Leary[‡] find that for RaD in the ultra-soft region $(h\nu = 0\cdot475 \times 10^5)$

$$\frac{\alpha_{L_I}}{1-\alpha_{L_I}} = 2\cdot2.$$

For dipole radiation the theoretical value is $1\cdot8$ and for quadripole $2\cdot75$.

The experimental determination of the internal conversion coefficient is open to appreciable errors, but the data seem to exhibit the following features:

(i) The experimental values plotted against $h\nu$ may be fitted to *two* smooth curves.

(ii) These two curves have the same general *form* as the theoretical curves for dipole and quadripole radiation, but in the soft γ-ray region $(h\nu < 3 \cdot 10^5 \,\text{eV.})$ the theoretical values are more than 50 per cent. too small.

A detailed analysis of the experimental results for elements of odd mass number shows that for ordinary dipole transitions $(\Delta Z = 1)$ the magnetic quadripole terms are weak in comparison with the electric dipole terms, the ratio of the intensities being of order κ^4, where κ is defined by equation (155). Even for the hardest γ-rays this ratio is only about 10^{-4}, so that we should expect transitions for which $\Delta l = 1$ to have almost exactly the theoretical coefficient derived on the assumption that the field is due to a dipole. In the quadripole transitions $(\Delta l = 0)$ the intensities of the magnetic dipole and electric quadripole terms are of the same order, while the magnetic octopole terms are negligible. The ratio of the intensity of the magnetic dipole terms to the electric quadripole terms varies roughly as the square of the wavelength of the γ-ray and consequently increases for softer γ-rays. Thus if the soft γ-rays arise from transitions between the various states of a multiplet level, then the internal conversion coefficient in the region of long wave-lengths approximates to the theoretical magnetic dipole internal conversion coefficient curve, and in the region of short wavelengths should fall below this, and lie near to the corresponding theoretical curve for electric quadripole radiation.

† E. Rutherford, J. Chadwick, C. D. Ellis, *Radiations from Radioactive Substances*, p. 362 f.

‡ J. A. Gray and A. J. O'Leary, *Nature*, **123**, 568 (1929).

58. The Dirac equations in spinor form

We noted in § 53.6 that although Dirac's equation for the electron is invariant under a Lorentz transformation, it can only be written in a tensor form in an artificial way, because of the fact that all the representations of the Lorentz group are not included in the tensor formalism. The necessary extension of the tensor calculus—the spinor calculus—was given by van der Waerden;† with this calculus the equations may be written in an automatically covariant form.

Any pair of quantities (ξ_1, ξ_2) which transform according to the formulae

$$\xi_1' = a_{11}\xi_1 + a_{12}\xi_2, \qquad \xi_2' = a_{21}\xi_1 + a_{22}\xi_2, \tag{156}$$

where the coefficients a_{ij} satisfy the condition

$$\begin{vmatrix} a_{11} & a_{12} \\ a_{21} & a_{22} \end{vmatrix} = 1, \tag{157}$$

is called a spinor of the first rank and is denoted by ξ_k $(k = 1, 2)$. Similarly any two numbers which transform like

$$\eta_1' = a_{11}^*\eta_1 + a_{12}^*\eta_2, \qquad \eta_2' = a_{21}^*\eta_1 + a_{22}^*\eta_2 \tag{158}$$

form a spinor which we shall denote by $\eta_{\dot{r}}$ $(\dot{r} = 1, 2)$.

The contravariant spinors of the first rank ξ^k, $\eta^{\dot{r}}$ are defined by the relations

$$\xi^1 = \xi_2, \qquad \xi^2 = -\xi_1,$$
$$\eta^{\dot{1}} = \eta_{\dot{2}}, \qquad \eta^{\dot{2}} = -\eta_{\dot{1}},$$

which ensure that the scalar products $\xi^k \xi_k$, $\eta^{\dot{r}}\eta_{\dot{r}}$ are invariant.

From these two types of spinors we can build up spinors of higher rank. Thus any four quantities transforming like the products $\xi_1\xi_1$, $\xi_1\xi_2$, $\xi_2\xi_1$, $\xi_2\xi_2$ form a spinor of the second rank which we shall denote by ξ_{kl}. Similarly second rank spinors of the type $\eta_{\dot{r}\dot{s}}$ can be defined. We may also define 'mixed' spinors of the second rank as quantities transforming like a product of a ξ and an η denoted by $\zeta_{\dot{r}k}$. Analogously we can define spinors of higher rank. The main rules of operation of spinor calculus are that it is not necessary to fix the relative position of dotted and undotted indices of the same spinor, and that the complex conjugate of any spinor equation is obtained by replacing all the dotted indices by undotted indices and vice versa. Two identities of great use in spinor analysis are

$$a_k b^k = -a^k b_k; \tag{159}$$
$$a_k b_m c^k + a_m b^k c_k + a^k b_k c_m = 0; \tag{160}$$

† B. van der Waerden, *Gött. Nacht.* 1929, 100. See also O. Laporte and G. E. Uhlenbeck, *Phys. Rev.* (2), **37**, 1380 (1931).

their proof follows at once from the definitions. These rules also hold for dotted suffixes.

We now introduce a spinor operator $\partial_{\dot{s}l}$ defined by the equations

$$\partial_{\dot{1}}^{\dot{1}} = \partial_{\dot{2}1} = \frac{\partial}{\partial x_1} + i\frac{\partial}{\partial x_2},$$

$$-\partial_{\dot{2}}^{\dot{2}} = \partial_{\dot{1}2} = \frac{\partial}{\partial x_1} - i\frac{\partial}{\partial x_2},$$

$$-\partial_{\dot{1}}^{\dot{2}} = \partial_{\dot{1}1} = \frac{\partial}{\partial x_3} - \frac{\partial}{\partial x_4},$$

$$-\partial_{\dot{2}}^{1} = -\partial_{\dot{2}2} = \frac{\partial}{\partial x_3} + \frac{\partial}{\partial x_4}.$$

Now it is obvious from the transformation equations (41) and (42) that the four scalar wave-functions $\Psi_1, \Psi_2, \Psi_3, \Psi_4$ of the Dirac theory form two spinors of the first rank which we shall denote by $\Psi_{\dot{m}}$ and χ_l. The analogue of the four-vector A_μ ($\mu = 1, 2, 3, 4$) will now be a mixed spinor $\phi_{l\dot{m}}$. It follows immediately that the Dirac equations may be written in the spinor form†

$$m_0 c\chi_l - p_l^{\dot{\sigma}} \Psi_{\dot{\sigma}} = 0, \tag{161}$$

$$m_0 c\Psi_{\dot{m}} + p_{\dot{m}}^{\lambda} \chi_\lambda = 0, \tag{162}$$

where we have introduced the abbreviation

$$p_l^{\dot{m}} = \frac{\hbar}{i}\partial_l^{\dot{m}} + \phi_l^{\dot{m}}. \tag{163}$$

Eliminating χ_l from (161) and (162) we obtain

$$m_0^2 c^2 \Psi_{\dot{m}} + p_{\dot{m}}^{\lambda} p_\lambda^{\dot{\sigma}} \Psi_{\dot{\sigma}} = 0. \tag{164}$$

Now by means of the identities (159) and (160) we have

$$p_{\dot{m}}^{\lambda} p_\lambda^{\dot{\sigma}} \Psi_{\dot{\sigma}} = -\tfrac{1}{2}p^{\dot{\sigma}\lambda}p_{\dot{\sigma}\lambda}\Psi_{\dot{m}} + \tfrac{1}{2}p_{\dot{\sigma}\lambda}p_{\dot{m}}^{\lambda}\Psi^{\dot{\sigma}} - \tfrac{1}{2}p_{\dot{m}}^{\lambda}p_{\dot{\sigma}\lambda}\Psi^{\dot{\sigma}},$$

and from the definition (163) of $p_l^{\dot{s}}$ we have

$$p_{\dot{\sigma}\lambda}p_{\dot{m}}^{\lambda}\Psi^{\dot{\sigma}} - p_{\dot{m}}^{\lambda}p_{\dot{\sigma}\lambda}\Psi^{\dot{\sigma}} = \frac{\hbar}{i}\Psi^{\dot{\sigma}}g_{\dot{m}\dot{\sigma}},$$

where $g_{\dot{m}\dot{\sigma}}$ is defined by

$$g_{\dot{m}\dot{\sigma}} = \partial_{\dot{\sigma}\lambda}\phi_{\dot{m}}^{\lambda} + \partial_{\dot{m}\lambda}\phi_{\dot{\sigma}}^{\lambda}. \tag{165}$$

Thus the second-order wave equation (164) reduces to the form

$$\frac{1}{2}\left(\frac{\hbar}{i}\partial^{\dot{\sigma}\lambda} + \phi^{\dot{\sigma}\lambda}\right)\left(\frac{\hbar}{i}\partial_{\dot{\sigma}\lambda} + \phi_{\dot{\sigma}\lambda}\right)\Psi_{\dot{m}} - m_0^2 c^2\Psi_{\dot{m}} = \frac{\hbar}{2i}g_{\dot{m}\dot{\sigma}}\Psi^{\dot{\sigma}}. \tag{166}$$

† The summation convention is used throughout, i.e. when a suffix occurs twice the sum is taken
$$\left(p^{\dot{\sigma}}\Psi_{\dot{\sigma}} \equiv \sum_{\dot{\sigma}} p_l^{\dot{\sigma}}\Psi_{\dot{\sigma}}\right).$$

The left-hand side of this equation is identical with that of the spinor form of the Klein–Gordon wave equation. The term on the right-hand side represents the spin correction.

In the spinor notation the Darwin Lagrangian (56) may be written in the form

$$L = \frac{\hbar}{i}\{\Psi^{\dot{\mu}}\partial^{\lambda}_{\dot{\mu}}\Psi^{\circ}_{\lambda} - \chi^{\dot{\mu}}\partial^{\lambda}_{\dot{\mu}}\chi_{\lambda} - \Psi^{\lambda}\partial^{\dot{\mu}}_{\lambda}\Psi^{\circ}_{\dot{\mu}} + \chi^{\lambda}\partial^{\dot{\mu}}_{\lambda}\chi_{\dot{\mu}}\} +$$
$$+ 2m_0 c(\Psi^{\circ}_{\lambda}\chi^{\lambda} + \Psi^{\circ}_{\dot{\sigma}}\chi^{\dot{\sigma}}) + \phi^{\dot{\mu}\lambda}(\Psi^{\circ}_{\dot{\mu}}\Psi_{\lambda} + \chi_{\dot{\mu}}\chi_{\lambda}) - \tfrac{1}{2}g^{\dot{\mu}\dot{\rho}}g_{\dot{\mu}\dot{\rho}}, \quad (167)$$

where the quantities $g_{\dot{\mu}\dot{\rho}}$ are defined by equation (165).

Considering L as a function of Ψ, χ, ϕ and their derivatives, and forming the Euler–Lagrange equations as before, we obtain the Dirac equations in spinor form together with the Maxwell equations with the Dirac current. In this way we obtain spinor expressions for the current and the charge density.

59. Relativistic wave equations for particles of spin greater than a half

Relativistic wave equations for particles of any spin have been derived by Dirac[†] and by Pauli and Fierz,[‡] on the assumption that each of the scalar wave functions satisfies, in the absence of interaction, the generalized second-order wave equation. The resulting equations connect two irreducible spinors but may be split by a suitable transformation into two sets. The simplest case in the Dirac scheme (apart from the Dirac equations of the electron) is that for a particle with twice the electronic spin. In this case we have for a particle of non-zero mass m_0 in the absence of an electromagnetic field the spinor equations

$$\sum_{\kappa} p^{\dot{\alpha}\kappa}A_{\kappa\lambda} = \sqrt{2}\,m_0\,B^{\dot{\alpha}}_{\lambda}, \qquad \sum_{\dot{\alpha}} p_{\dot{\alpha}\kappa}B^{\dot{\alpha}}_{\lambda} = \frac{m_0}{\sqrt{2}}A_{\kappa\lambda}. \qquad (168)$$

These equations relating the field quantities $B^{\dot{\alpha}}_{\lambda}$, $A_{\kappa\lambda}$ are analogous to the Maxwell–Lorentz equations of the electromagnetic field, an essential difference being that all the quantities are here assumed to be complex. The transition of these equations from spinor to tensor form has been effected by Kemmer[§] who showed that there are four possible ways of writing the equations (168) in tensor form. They are

$$\frac{\partial\phi}{\partial x_{\alpha}} = \kappa\chi_{\alpha}, \qquad \sum_{\alpha=1}^{4}\frac{\partial\chi^{\alpha}}{\partial x_{\alpha}} = \kappa\phi, \qquad (169)$$

† P. A. M. Dirac, *Proc. Roy. Soc.* A, **155**, 447 (1936).

‡ W. Pauli and Fierz, *Helv. Phys. Acta*, **12**, 3, 297 (1939); *Proc. Roy. Soc.* A, **173**, 211 (1939).

§ N. Kemmer, ibid. **166**, 173.

$$\frac{\partial \phi_\beta}{\partial x_\alpha} - \frac{\partial \phi_\alpha}{\partial x_\beta} = \kappa \chi_{\alpha\beta}, \qquad \sum_{\alpha=1}^{4} \frac{\partial \chi^{\alpha\beta}}{\partial x_\alpha} = \kappa \phi^\beta, \qquad (170)$$

$$\frac{\partial \phi_{\beta\gamma}}{\partial x_\alpha} - \frac{\partial \phi_{\alpha\gamma}}{\partial x_\beta} + \frac{\partial \phi_{\alpha\beta}}{\partial x} = \kappa \chi_{\alpha\beta\gamma}, \qquad \sum_{\alpha=1}^{4} \frac{\partial \chi^{\alpha\beta\gamma}}{\partial x_\alpha} = \kappa \phi^{\beta\gamma} \qquad (171)$$

$$\text{(with } \phi_{\alpha\beta} = -\phi_{\beta\alpha}\text{)},$$

and finally

$$\frac{\partial \phi_{\beta\gamma\delta}}{\partial x_\alpha} - \frac{\partial \phi_{\alpha\gamma\delta}}{\partial x_\beta} + \frac{\partial \phi_{\alpha\beta\delta}}{\partial x_\gamma} - \frac{\partial \phi_{\alpha\beta\gamma}}{\partial x_\delta} = \kappa \chi_{\alpha\beta\gamma\delta}, \qquad \sum_{\alpha=1}^{4} \frac{\partial \chi^{\alpha\beta\gamma\delta}}{\partial x_\alpha} = \kappa \phi^{\beta\gamma\delta},$$

$$(172)$$

with
$$\phi_{\alpha\beta\gamma} = -\phi_{\beta\alpha\gamma} = -\phi_{\alpha\gamma\beta}. \qquad (173)$$

In all these equations α, β, γ, δ run from 1 to 4 and

$$\kappa = m_0 c/\hbar.$$

It is immediately obvious that equations (169) are equivalent to the Klein–Gordon equation

$$\sum_{\alpha=1}^{4} \frac{\partial^2 \phi}{\partial x_\alpha^2} = \kappa^2 \phi. \qquad (174)$$

Equations (170) are those proposed earlier by Proca[†] for Bose–Einstein particles (i.e. particles of spin one). The analogous equations (171) and (172) had not been considered prior to Kemmer's analysis. From these equations Kemmer develops four inequivalent possible forms of field theory for Bose–Einstein particles.

It was pointed out by Kemmer[‡] and Duffin[§] that the Proca equations (170) could be written in the form

$$\sum_{\nu,\mu} (\delta_{\alpha\nu}\delta_{\beta\mu} - \delta_{\alpha\mu}\delta_{\beta\nu}) \frac{\partial \phi_\nu}{\partial x_\mu} = -\kappa \chi_{\alpha\beta}, \qquad \sum_\mu \frac{\partial \chi_{\mu\beta}}{\partial x_\mu} = \kappa \phi^\beta;$$

if then we construct a column matrix Ψ whose ten elements are the components of the vector ϕ and the distinct components of the tensor $\chi_{\alpha\beta}$, the Proca equations assume the form

$$\sum_{\mu=1}^{4} \frac{\partial}{\partial x_\mu} (\beta_\mu \Psi) + \kappa \Psi = 0; \qquad (175)$$

here the β_μ satisfy the relations

$$\beta_\mu \beta_\nu \beta_\rho + \beta_\rho \beta_\nu \beta_\mu = \beta_\mu \delta_{\nu\rho} + \beta_\rho \delta_{\mu\nu}, \qquad (176)$$

which are analogous to the relations $\alpha_\mu \alpha_\nu + \alpha_\nu \alpha_\mu = 2\delta_{\mu\nu}$ in the Dirac theory.

† J. Proca, *J. Phys. Radium* (vii), **7**, 347 (1936).
‡ N. Kemmer, *Proc. Roy. Soc.* A, **173**, 91 (1939).
§ R. J. Duffin, *Phys. Rev.* **54**, 1114 (1938).

The algebra defined by the equation (176) has been examined in detail by Kemmer.† Just as in the case of the algebra defined by the Dirac α-operators there are 16 linearly independent quantities among the four α's and their multiple products, in the algebra of the β-operators there are 126 independent elements of the algebra formed from the multiple products of the four β's and the unit matrix. The β's may be represented by 10×10 Hermitian matrices.‡

A question which arises naturally out of these investigations is whether the behaviour of elementary particles of *any* integral or half-integral spin can always be described by an equation of the type

$$\{p_k \alpha^k + \chi\}\Psi = 0, \tag{177}$$

where the p_k are the usual differential operators, χ is a constant, and the quantities α^k are four matrices describing the spin properties of the particle. This problem has been investigated by Bhabha,§ who succeeded in showing that for particles of spin greater than 1 the equations of Dirac, Pauli, and Fierz cannot be written in the form (177). Bhabha postulates that *the fundamental equations of the elementary particles must be first-order equations of the form* (177) *and that all properties of the particles must be derivable from these without the use of any further subsidiary conditions.* As a result of this assumption it is found that the scalar wave functions do not satisfy a second-order wave equation as in the theory of Dirac, Pauli, and Fierz, but Bhabha considers his assumption to be more logical than theirs. He finds that each component of the wave function satisfies an equation of order greater than two which can be written in the form of products of the operators of the usual second-order equation. A consequence of these equations is that we must interpret every particle of spin greater than one as possessing not one but several values of the rest mass. These states of higher rest mass are a necessary feature of the theory. It is shown that these higher values of the rest mass are simple rational multiples of the lowest mass. For example, particles of spin $\frac{3}{2}$, if they exist in nature at all, would be expected to appear with two values of the rest mass, m and $3m$, the former being the stable rest mass. Particles of spin 2 should they exist, would appear with rest masses m, $2m$.

---

† N. Kemmer, *Proc. Camb. Phil. Soc.* **39**, 189 (1943); see also E. Schrödinger, *Proc. Roy. Irish Acad.* **48**, A, 135 (1943).

‡ N. Kemmer, loc. cit.

§ H. J. Bhabha, *Rev. Mod. Phys.* **17**, 200 (1945).

XII
MATRIX MECHANICS

60. Introduction

In this book we have employed the methods of wave mechanics as developed by Schrödinger and others. Although these methods are the most suitable for the applications of the theory to the simpler problems of physics and chemistry they were not the first to be put forward to replace the older quantum theory of Bohr and Sommerfeld. The first system of equations designed to that end was set up slightly earlier by W. Heisenberg and developed by Born, Jordan, and Dirac. Because of the fact that the quantities occurring in this system of equations obeyed the laws of matrix algebra, the theory became known as 'matrix mechanics'. This formulation of quantum mechanics is mathematically equivalent to wave mechanics, but since it is sometimes more convenient to make use of the results in the matrix form we give here a very brief outline of the foundations of matrix mechanics without going into the detailed solution of special problems. The relation of the Heisenberg equations to the Schrödinger equation is also indicated.

The theory of matrix mechanics was developed from the phenomenological point of view; from the beginning Heisenberg adopted the principle that only physical quantities which are actually observable should be incorporated in the new theory. Heisenberg proposed to build up a theory solely in terms of observable properties of atomic systems such as the frequencies, intensities, and polarizations of the radiations emitted by such systems and omitting concepts of doubtful observability such as the positions and velocities of electrons. The relation of matrix mechanics to classical mechanics is more direct than that of the Schrödinger theory because the transition from the classical theory to the quantum theory is made here at an earlier stage. The transition from classical dynamics to the Schrödinger wave mechanics corresponds to a later stage in the development of the classical theory; indeed, Schrödinger's method consists in replacing the Hamilton–Jacobi equation of classical theory by a wave equation suitable for the discussion of atomic processes.

We shall begin by recalling some of the results of classical mechanics.

61. The classical Poisson bracket

In classical mechanics a dynamical system possessing n degrees of freedom is completely specified by the generalized coordinates q_i and the generalized momenta p_i $(i = 1, 2, ..., n)$. Any other dynamical variables of the system, say, F, G,..., can be expressed uniquely as functions of these generalized coordinates and momenta. From any two such dynamical variables F, G the expression

$$\sum_{i=1}^{n} \left(\frac{\partial F}{\partial q_i} \frac{\partial G}{\partial p_i} - \frac{\partial F}{\partial p_i} \frac{\partial G}{\partial q_i} \right) \tag{1}$$

may be formed; such a quantity will be called a *classical Poisson bracket* and be denoted by $[F, G]$. It follows immediately from the definition that

$$[F, p_i] = \frac{\partial F}{\partial q_i}, \qquad [F, q_i] = -\frac{\partial F}{\partial p_i}, \tag{2}$$

so that in classical mechanics the differentials with respect to the variables q_i, p_i may be replaced by a Poisson bracket. In particular we may write Hamilton's canonical equations

$$\dot{q}_i = \frac{\partial H}{\partial p_i}, \qquad \dot{p}_i = -\frac{\partial H}{\partial q_i} \tag{3}$$

in the form $\qquad \dot{q}_i + [H, q_i] = 0, \qquad \dot{p}_i + [H, p_i] = 0. \tag{4}$

The importance of the Poisson bracket in classical mechanics arises from the fact that it is invariant under a contact transformation. It follows at once from the form (4) of Hamilton's canonical equations that they too are invariant under a contact transformation.

The equations (4) may be generalized for any dynamical variable, F, which does not contain the time explicitly; thus

$$\dot{F} = \sum_{i=1}^{n} \left(\frac{\partial F}{\partial q_i} \dot{q}_i + \frac{\partial F}{\partial p_i} \dot{p}_i \right) = \sum_{i=1}^{n} \left(\frac{\partial F}{\partial q_i} \frac{\partial H}{\partial p_i} - \frac{\partial F}{\partial p_i} \frac{\partial H}{\partial q_i} \right) = [F, H]. \tag{5}$$

Many of the most interesting and useful properties of the classical Poisson brackets follow immediately from the definition (1). For example, the equations

$$\left.\begin{array}{c} [p_r, p_s] = [q_r, q_s] = 0 \\ [q_r, p_s] = \delta_{rs} \end{array}\right\} \tag{6}$$

are readily established. The dynamical variables occurring in classical mechanics can usually be expressed as polynomials (or power series) in the coordinates q_i and the momenta p_i, so that Poisson brackets involving them can be calculated from rules of the type

$$[F, G_1 + G_2] = [F, G_1] + [F, G_2], \tag{7}$$

$$[F, G_1 G_2] = [F, G_1] G_2 + G_1 [F, G_2], \tag{8a}$$

$$[F_1 F_2, G] = [F_1, G] F_2 + F_1 [F_2, G], \tag{8b}$$

all of which follow from the definition (1).

62. The quantum Poisson bracket

We shall now investigate the analogue of the Poisson bracket in quantum mechanics. To do this we consider some of the properties of the classical Poisson bracket to see which of them may reasonably be taken over into the formalism of quantum mechanics. It follows immediately from $(8a)$ that

$$[F_1F_2, G_1G_2] = [F_1F_2, G_1]G_2 + G_1[F_1F_2, G_2]$$

and from $(8b)$ that the right-hand side reduces to

$$[F_1, G_1]F_2G_2 + F_1[F_2, G_1]G_2 + G_1[F_1, G_2]F_2 + G_1F_1[F_2, G_2].$$

Similarly by applying the theorems in the reverse order we can show that

$$[F_1F_2, G_1G_2] = [F_1, G_1]G_2F_2 + G_1[F_1, G_2]F_2 + F_1[F_2, G_1]G_2 + F_1G_1[F_2, G_2].$$

Equating these two values of the Poisson bracket $[F_1F_2, G_1G_2]$ we obtain the relation

$$\frac{F_1G_1 - G_1F_1}{[F_1, G_1]} = \frac{F_2G_2 - G_2F_2}{[F_2, G_2]}. \tag{9}$$

In classical mechanics this result is trivial since the numerator of each fraction vanishes identically; but we have seen that in quantum mechanics where the dynamical variables are in general operators, $FG - GF$ is not always zero. In such a theory we might then interpret equation (9) as meaning that the Poisson bracket $[F, G]$ is proportional to the expression $FG - GF$. The constant of proportionality in a special case was first calculated by Dirac[†], who considered the expression $FG - GF$ of the quantum theory and found the corresponding formula of the classical theory to which it must tend in the limit for large quantum numbers. In the classical theory the F and G are functions of the generalized coordinates and momenta of a multiply periodic system. Dirac found that *for large quantum numbers $FG - GF$* corresponded to the expression $i\hbar[F, G]$ of classical mechanics. Generalizing this result he *postulated* that the equation

$$FG - GF = i\hbar[F, G] \tag{10}$$

holds in all circumstances. Equation (10) is the basic axiom of the quantum mechanics formulated by Dirac and can have no formal proof. Its sole justification is that its use leads to results which are consistent with the experimental evidence and that it reduces to the classical equation

$$FG = GF \tag{11}$$

† P. A. M. Dirac, *Proc. Roy. Soc.* A, **109**, 642 (1925).

in the limiting case $\hbar \to 0$. It is assumed that the Poisson bracket $[F, G]$ is calculated formally as in classical mechanics and obeys the same laws as the classical bracket; equation (10) then supplies information about the difference between the two products FG, GF of the two dynamical variables F and G in the quantum theory.

The quantum Poisson bracket is defined by the relation

$$[F, G] = \frac{1}{i\hbar}(FG - GF); \tag{12}$$

it can easily be verified that it has the following properties

$$[F, F] = 0, \tag{13}$$

$$[F, c] = 0 \quad (c, \text{ scalar}), \tag{14}$$

as well as the properties (7) and (8).

63. Angular momentum relations for a single electron

To illustrate the method of calculation of Poisson brackets in quantum mechanics we shall evaluate the brackets corresponding to certain of the dynamical variables connected with the motion of a single electron. If the electron has coordinates (q_1, q_2, q_3) and linear momenta (p_1, p_2, p_3), we assume that the relations

$$[q_i, q_j] = [p_i, p_j] = 0, \qquad [q_i, p_j] = \delta_{ij} \quad (i, j = 1, 2, 3) \tag{15}$$

of classical mechanics hold good in quantum theory.

In classical mechanics we define the angular momentum **m** of a single electron by the vector equation

$$\mathbf{m} = \mathbf{q} \times \mathbf{p},$$

so that its components are

$$(m_1, m_2, m_3) = (q_2 p_3 - q_3 p_2, q_3 p_1 - q_1 p_3, q_1 p_2 - q_2 p_1).$$

From the definition of **m** it follows that

$$[m_3, q_1] = [q_1 p_2 - q_2 p_1, q_1]$$
$$= [q_1, q_1]p_2 + q_1[p_2, q_1] - [q_2, q_1]p_1 - q_2[p_1, q_1],$$

using the rules (7) and (8). If we assume the relations (15), each of the Poisson brackets vanishes except $[p_1, q_1] = -[q_1, p_1] = -1$, so that

$$[m_3, q_1] = q_2.$$

Similar calculations lead to the results

$$
\begin{array}{lll}
[m_1, q_1] = 0 & [m_1, q_2] = q_3 & [m_1, q_3] = -q_2 \\
[m_2, q_1] = -q_3 & [m_2, q_2] = 0 & [m_2, q_3] = q_1 \\
[m_3, q_1] = q_2 & [m_3, q_2] = -q_1 & [m_3, q_3] = 0.
\end{array} \tag{16}
$$

Writing $r^2 = q_1^2 + q_2^2 + q_3^2$ and making use of equations (8) and (16) we obtain the result

$$[m_1, r^2] = q_1[m_1, q_1] + [m_1, q_1]q_1 + q_2[m_1, q_2] + [m_1, q_2]q_2 +$$
$$+ q_3[m_1, q_3] + [m_1, q_3]q_3$$
$$= 0,$$

giving the relations

$$[m_1, r^2] = [m_2, r^2] = [m_3, r^2] = 0. \tag{17}$$

Now it can easily be shown from the definition of a Poisson bracket in classical mechanics (equation (1) above) that, if $[F, G] = 0$ for any two dynamical variables F, G, then $[F, \phi(G)] = 0$, where $\phi(G)$ is any function of G. If we assume this result to be carried over into the quantum theory we have from (17)

$$[m_1, \phi(r)] = [m_2, \phi(r)] = [m_3, \phi(r)] = 0. \tag{18}$$

Corresponding to the set (16) we have the set

$$\left. \begin{array}{lll} [m_1, p_1] = 0 & [m_1, p_2] = p_3 & [m_1, p_3] = -p_2 \\ [m_2, p_1] = -p_3 & [m_2, p_2] = 0 & [m_2, p_3] = p_1 \\ [m_3, p_1] = p_2 & [m_3, p_2] = -p_1 & [m_3, p_3] = 0 \end{array} \right\}. \tag{19}$$

These identities may be easily proved; for instance,

$$[m_3, p_1] = [q_1 p_2 - q_2 p_1, p_1]$$
$$= [q_1, p_1]p_2 + q_1[p_2, p_1] - [q_2, p_1]p_1 - q_2[p_1, p_1]$$
$$= p_2.$$

By a method similar to that employed in establishing the relations (17) we can show that

$$[m_1, p^2] = [m_2, p^2] = [m_3, p^2] = 0, \tag{20}$$

and hence that

$$[m_1, \chi(p)] = [m_2, \chi(p)] = [m_3, \chi(p)] = 0, \tag{21}$$

where $\chi(p)$ is a function of p.

For an electron moving under the action of a central force the Hamiltonian function, H, may be written in the form

$$H = \frac{1}{2\mu} p^2 + V(r),$$

where μ denotes the mass of the electron. Hence by equations (18) and (21) we have

$$[m_1, H] = [m_2, H] = [m_3, H] = 0. \tag{22}$$

Furthermore, from the definition of the angular momentum we have

$$[m_1, m_2] = [m_1, q_3 p_1 - q_1 p_3]$$
$$= [m_1, q_3]p_1 + q_3[m_1, p_1] - [m_1, q_1]p_3 - q_1[m_1, p_3]$$
$$= q_1 p_2 - q_2 p_1 = m_3.$$

In this way we establish the relations

$$[m_1, m_2] = m_3, \qquad [m_2, m_3] = m_1, \qquad [m_3, m_1] = m_2, \qquad (23)$$

from which we may readily deduce

$$[m_1, \mathbf{m}^2] = [m_2, \mathbf{m}^2] = [m_3, \mathbf{m}^2] = 0. \qquad (24)$$

We have established the relations (16) to (24) by means of the formal properties of Poisson brackets in classical mechanics. It is also of interest to note that they can be established simply if we make the assumption, implicit in the Schrödinger theory, that

$$p_i = \frac{\hbar}{i} \frac{\partial}{\partial q_i}.$$

We then have
$$m_3 = \frac{\hbar}{i} \left(q_1 \frac{\partial}{\partial q_2} - q_2 \frac{\partial}{\partial q_1} \right),$$

and so, by equation (12),

$$[m_3, q_1]\Psi = \frac{1}{\hbar i}(m_3 q_1 - q_1 m_3)\Psi$$
$$= -\left[\left(q_1 \frac{\partial}{\partial q_2} - q_2 \frac{\partial}{\partial q_1} \right)(q_1 \Psi) - q_1 \left(q_1 \frac{\partial \Psi}{\partial q_2} - q_2 \frac{\partial \Psi}{\partial q_1} \right) \right].$$

The right-hand side reduces to $q_2 \Psi$, so that the effect of operating on the wave-function Ψ by $[m_3, q_1]$ is equivalent to multiplying it by q_2. This may be written formally as

$$[m_3, q_1] = q_2$$

in agreement with the relations (16). The other relations can be established in a similar way.

64. The angular momentum of a system of electrons

If the dynamical system consists of several electrons, then the angular momentum of the system is taken to be the vector sum of the angular momenta of the individual electrons. Thus, if there are n particles with angular momenta $\mathbf{m}^{(i)}$ ($i = 1, 2, ..., n$) the total angular momentum of the system is defined by the vector equation

$$\mathbf{M} = \sum_{i=1}^{n} \mathbf{m}^{(i)}.$$

If $i \neq j$ then it follows at once from the definitions that

$$[q_1^{(i)}, q_1^{(j)}] = 0, \qquad [m_1^{(i)}, m_2^{(j)}] = 0 \tag{25}$$

for $i, j = 1, 2, ..., n$. Now for any particle i

$$[M_1, q_2^{(i)}] = \sum_{j=1}^{n} [m_1^{(j)}, q_2^{(i)}] = [m_1^{(i)}, q_2^{(i)}] = q_3^{(i)}.$$

In this way it may be established that, for $i = 1, 2, ..., n$,

$$\left. \begin{array}{lll} [M_1, q_1^{(i)}] = 0 & [M_1, q_2^{(i)}] = q_3^{(i)} & [M_1, q_3^{(i)}] = -q_2^{(i)} \\ [M_2, q_1^{(i)}] = -q_3^{(i)} & [M_2, q_2^{(i)}] = 0 & [M_2, q_3^{(i)}] = q_1^{(i)} \\ [M_3, q_1^{(i)}] = q_2^{(i)} & [M_3, q_2^{(i)}] = -q_1^{(i)} & [M_3, q_3^{(i)}] = 0 \end{array} \right\}. \tag{26}$$

The relations

$$\left. \begin{array}{lll} [M_1, p_1^{(i)}] = 0 & [M_1, p_2^{(i)}] = p_3^{(i)} & [M_1, p_3^{(i)}] = -p_2^{(i)} \\ [M_2, p_1^{(i)}] = -p_3^{(i)} & [M_2, p_2^{(i)}] = 0 & [M_2, p_3^{(i)}] = p_1^{(i)} \\ [M_3, p_1^{(i)}] = p_2^{(i)} & [M_3, p_2^{(i)}] = -p_1^{(i)} & [M_3, p_3^{(i)}] = 0 \end{array} \right\} \tag{27}$$

$(i = 1, 2, ..., n)$ corresponding to the set of equations (19) can be established in a similar fashion.

Furthermore,

$$[M_1, M_2] = \left[\sum_{i=1}^{n} m_1^{(i)}, \sum_{j=1}^{n} m_2^{(j)} \right] = \sum_{i,j=1}^{n} [m_1^{(i)}, m_2^{(j)}].$$

Now by definition

$$[m_1^{(i)}, m_2^{(j)}] = m_3^{(i)} \delta_{ij},$$

so that

$$[M_1, M_2] = \sum_{i=1}^{n} m_3^{(i)} = M_3,$$

giving one of the relations of the set

$$[M_1, M_2] = M_3, \qquad [M_2, M_3] = M_1, \qquad [M_3, M_1] = M_2, \tag{28}$$

the others being established in the same way.

Finally, if $\mathbf{M}^2$ is defined by

$$\mathbf{M}^2 = M_1^2 + M_2^2 + M_3^2,$$

it can be shown from equations (28) that

$$[M_1, \mathbf{M}^2] = [M_2, \mathbf{M}^2] = [M_3, \mathbf{M}^2] = 0, \tag{29}$$

also that

$$[M_i, H] = [H, \mathbf{M}^2] = 0 \quad (i = 1, 2, 3). \tag{29a}$$

Thus the angular momentum identities hold not only for a single electron but also for a system of electrons.

65. The equations of motion

We have seen that in classical mechanics the Hamiltonian equations of motion (3) may be written, in terms of the classical Poisson brackets, in the form (4). We now postulate that in quantum mechanics the equations of motion are of the same form except that now the classical Poisson bracket is replaced by the quantum Poisson bracket defined by equation (12). In this way we obtain the equations of motion

$$\dot{q}_j = \frac{i}{\hbar}(Hq_j - q_j H), \qquad \dot{p}_j = \frac{i}{\hbar}(Hp_j - p_j H) \qquad (30)$$

$(j = 1, 2, ..., n)$ for a system with n degrees of freedom. In addition to the equations of motion we require new quantum conditions to replace the conditions

$$\oint p_j \, dq_j = n_j h \qquad (31)$$

of the Bohr theory of the atom. These are obtained by assuming that the Poisson brackets involving the coordinates q_i and the momenta p_i have the same values as in the classical theory. Combining the classical equations (6) with the definition (12) of a quantum Poisson bracket we obtain the quantum conditions

$$\left. \begin{array}{l} q_j q_k - q_k q_j = 0 \\ p_j p_j - p_k p_j = 0 \\ q_j p_k - p_k q_j = i\hbar \, \delta_{jk} \end{array} \right\}. \qquad (32)$$

This method of deriving the quantum conditions (32) is due to Dirac;† they have also been derived from (31) by a method making use of the correspondence principle.‡

The variation with time of any dynamical variable which does not contain the time explicitly is taken to be defined by the classical equation (5) with the Poisson bracket replaced by its quantum analogue (12), i.e.

$$\dot{F} = [F, H] = \frac{1}{\hbar i}(FH - HF). \qquad (33)$$

For this reason any dynamical variable, α, which satisfies the equation

$$i\hbar[\alpha, H] = \alpha H - H\alpha = 0 \qquad (34)$$

is called a *constant of the motion*. For example, equations (22) show that the components of the angular momentum of a single electron are constants of the motion for a central field of force. The Hamiltonian is itself a constant of the motion.

66. Matrix mechanics

So far we have not specified the nature of the entities q_j, p_j satisfying the commutation relations (32), though it is obvious from the third of these equations that they are not ordinary numbers. We have seen

† P. A. M. Dirac, *Proc. Roy. Soc.* A, **109**, 642 (1925).
‡ M. Born, W. Heisenberg, and P. Jordan, *Zeits. f. Phys.* **35**, 557 (1925).

previously, however,‡ that an equation of this type is satisfied if we take

$$p_j = \frac{\hbar}{i} \frac{\partial}{\partial q_j}$$

and interpret it as meaning that the effect of applying the operator $q_j p_j - p_j q_j$ to a function of the p's and q's is merely that of multiplying by $i\hbar$. We can, however, interpret the quantities q_j, p_j in quite a different way. In the classical theory the coordinate q in any system varying periodically with the time with period ν can be represented by a Fourier series of the type

$$q = \sum_{j=-\infty}^{\infty} q(j)e^{2\pi i j\nu t},$$

where, to ensure that the coordinate q is real, the coefficients $q(j)$ must satisfy the relations

$$q^*(j) = q(-j) \tag{35}$$

for all values of j. In the quantum theory the classical frequencies $j\nu$ are replaced by the spectral frequencies ν_{nm} which satisfy the equations

$$\nu_{nm} + \nu_{mk} = \nu_{nk}, \tag{36}$$

$$\nu_{nn} = 0, \tag{37}$$

$$\nu_{mn} = -\nu_{nm}. \tag{38}$$

In setting up a matrix formulation of quantum mechanics, therefore, we form, instead of the Fourier series, the matrix of which the elements are

$$(m|q|n)e^{2\pi i\nu_{mn}t}. \tag{39}$$

The quantities $(m|q|n)$ replace the numbers $q(j)$ of the classical theory. The matrix element (39) corresponds to the transition of the system from the state m to the state n.

Since $\nu_{nn} = 0$ for all n, it follows that the elements along the leading diagonal of this matrix are constant with regard to the time. Furthermore, if the matrix is to represent a *real* coordinate, then corresponding to (35) we must have

$$(m|q|n) = (n|q|m)^*. \tag{40}$$

Matrices with this type of symmetry are called *Hermitian*; all the coordinate matrices of quantum mechanics are assumed to be of this type. The matrix with elements $(n|q|m)^*$ is called the Hermitian conjugate of q and is usually denoted by $q^\dagger$. A Hermitian matrix is thus one satisfying the equation

$$q^\dagger = q.$$

If we have two coordinate matrices

$$q_1 = ||(m|q_1|n)e^{2\pi i\nu_{mn}t}||,$$

$$q_2 = ||(m|q_2|n)e^{2\pi i\nu_{mn}t}||,$$

‡ p. 36 above.

then by the law of matrix multiplication their product is

$$q_1 q_2 = \left\| \sum_k (m|q_1|k)e^{2\pi i \nu_{mk}t}(k|q_2|n)e^{2\pi i \nu_{kn}t} \right\|$$

$$= \left\| \sum_k (m|q_1|k)(k|q_2|n)e^{2\pi i \nu_{mn}t} \right\|$$

by equation (36). On the other hand,

$$q_2 q_1 = \left\| \sum_k (m|q_2|k)(k|q_1|n)e^{2\pi i \nu_{mn}t} \right\|,$$

so that in general $q_1 q_2 \neq q_2 q_1$. In the case $q_1 q_2 = q_2 q_1$ the matrices q_1, q_2 are said to commute.

The elements of the matrices $q_1 q_2$ and $q_2 q_1$ have the same time factors $e^{2\pi i \nu_{mn}t}$ as q_1 and q_2. The exponential time factors are usually omitted from the matrices; it is to be understood that when an element is written $(m|q|n)$ it means $(m|q|n)e^{2\pi i \nu_{mn}t}$. For the equation (33) to have any meaning in matrix mechanics it is necessary to define the differentiation of a matrix with respect to the time t. We will assume that the time derivative $\dot{q}$ is represented by the matrix

$$\dot{q} = ||2\pi i \nu_{mn}(m|q|n)e^{2\pi i \nu_{mn}t}|| \tag{41}$$

obtained by differentiating each of the elements of the matrix q with respect to t. If the matrix q is constant throughout time, all the elements of $\dot{q}$ must vanish.

Now by its definition $\nu_{nn} = 0$, so that whatever the value of $(n|q|n)$ the diagonal elements of the matrix $\dot{q}$ will be zero; but ν_{mn} $(m \neq n)$ is not zero, so that the non-diagonal elements of the matrix $\dot{q}$ can only be zero if

$$(m|q|n) = 0 \quad (m \neq n).$$

In other words, the matrix q is a diagonal matrix of the form

$$\begin{pmatrix} (1|q|1) & 0 & 0 & . & . & . \\ 0 & (2|q|2) & 0 & . & . & . \\ 0 & 0 & (3|q|3) & . & . & . \\ . & . & . & . & . & . \end{pmatrix} = (n|q|n)\,\delta_{mn}.$$

Since the Hamiltonian is constant during the motion it must be represented by a diagonal matrix

$$(i|H|j) = H_i \delta_{ij}. \tag{42}$$

It follows immediately that any matrix which commutes with H is a diagonal matrix, for if α is such a matrix

$$0 = (m|\alpha H - H\alpha|n) = \sum_k \{(m|\alpha|k)(k|H|n) - (m|H|k)(k|\alpha|n)\}$$

$$= (H_n - H_m)(m|\alpha|n),$$

which is satisfied only if

$$(m|\alpha|n) = \alpha_n \delta_{mn}.$$

67. The solution of special problems

The solution of any problem in matrix mechanics is complete when a set of matrices $(m|q_j|n)$ has been constructed to represent the dynamical variables q_j satisfying the conditions:

(i) The matrices are of Hermitian type.

(ii) They are such that the Hamiltonian matrix derived from these matrices is diagonal.

(iii) They satisfy the commutation relations (32).

The further conditions are summed up in the equations of motion

$$\dot{F} = \frac{1}{i\hbar}(FH - HF)$$

satisfied by any dynamical variable F.

In the condition (iii) δ_{ij} is interpreted as the infinite matrix

$$\delta_{ij} = \begin{pmatrix} 1 & 0 & 0 & . & . & . \\ 0 & 1 & 0 & . & . & . \\ 0 & 0 & 1 & . & . & . \\ . & . & . & . & . & . \end{pmatrix}.$$

δ_{ij} is known as the Kronecker delta.

To illustrate the use of the matrix method we shall discuss two simple problems in which the purpose is to obtain matrix representations of constants of the motion in diagonal form, thus obtaining their allowed values in quantum mechanics.

(a) Rigid body rotating about a fixed axis

Consider the motion of a rigid body capable of rotating about a fixed axis. If the body is free from external forces its angular momentum p_θ and its total energy H remain unaltered during the motion. Since the angular momentum is a constant of the motion, we may represent it by a diagonal matrix

$$(j|p_\theta|k) = p_j \delta_{jk}. \tag{43}$$

If the angular displacement of the body is denoted by θ, then the configuration of the dynamical system is repeated whenever θ is increased by $2n\pi$, where n is any integer. In the equation

$$\frac{\partial F}{\partial \theta} = [F, p_\theta] = \frac{i}{\hbar}(p_\theta F - F p_\theta),$$

we may replace F by $e^{in\theta}$ and obtain

$$(p_\theta e^{in\theta} - e^{in\theta} p_\theta) = n\hbar e^{in\theta},$$

or, in matrix form,

$$\sum_k \{(j|p_\theta|k)(k|e^{in\theta}|l) - (j|e^{in\theta}|k)(k|p_\theta|l)\} = n\hbar(j|e^{in\theta}|l).$$

Using the fact that $(j|p_\theta|k)$ is of the form (43) we find that the sum on the right reduces to a simple multiple of $(j|e^{in\theta}|l)$ to give the relation

$$p_j - p_l = n\hbar,$$

showing that $\qquad\qquad p_j = (j+\alpha)\hbar,$

where j is an integer and α is a constant. To show that α is, in fact, zero we need only note that positive and negative values of j in this equation relate to opposite senses of rotation, but to the same numerical value of the angular momentum; that is,

$$(j+\alpha)\hbar = -(-j+\alpha)\hbar$$

or $\qquad\qquad\qquad \alpha = 0.$

Finally $\qquad\qquad\qquad p_j = j\hbar,$

a result which can readily be established by the methods of wave mechanics.

(b) The harmonic oscillator

Suppose that the coordinate of the particle is specified by a matrix q with elements

$$(j|q|k) = (j|a|k)e^{2\pi i\nu_{jk}t}. \tag{44}$$

The Hamiltonian of a harmonic oscillator is of the form

$$H = \frac{1}{2\mu}p^2 + \tfrac{1}{2}\kappa q^2.$$

The canonical equations are then

$$\dot{q} = p/\mu, \qquad \dot{p} = -\kappa q. \tag{45}$$

Eliminating p from these equations, substituting for q from equation (44), and writing $\kappa = 4\pi^2\nu_0^2\mu$, we obtain

$$4\pi^2(\nu_0^2 - \nu_{jk}^2)(j|a|k) = 0.$$

This equation is satisfied if we take

$$(j|a|k) = 0 \quad (k \neq j\mp 1),$$
$$\nu_{j,j+1} = -\nu_0, \qquad \nu_{j,j-1} = \nu_0. \tag{46}$$

Now from the former of equations (45) we have for the matrix p

$$(j|p|k) = 2\pi i\mu\nu_{jk}(j|a|k)e^{2\pi i\nu_{jk}t}, \tag{47}$$

so that

$$(j|pq-qp|m) = 2\pi i\mu \sum_k (\nu_{jk} - \nu_{km})e^{2\pi i(\nu_{jk}+\nu_{km})t}(j|a|k)(k|a|m),$$

and by the commutation rule (32) this must equal $-i\hbar\,\delta_{jm}$. Substituting $m = j$, making use of equations (46), and of the result

$$\nu_{jk} = -\nu_{kj},$$

we obtain

$$(j|a|j+1)(j+1|a|j)-(j|a|j-1)(j-1|a|j) = \frac{\hbar}{4\pi\mu\nu_0},$$

which may be written

$$|(j+1|a|j)|^2-|(j|a|j-1)|^2 = \frac{\hbar}{4\pi\mu\nu_0}.$$

If we assume that $|(1|a|0)|^2$ is the first non-vanishing term of the series we obtain

$$|(j|a|j-1)|^2 = \frac{j\hbar}{4\pi\mu\nu_0},$$

so that the matrix q has elements

$$(j|q|k) = 0 \quad (k \neq j\pm 1),$$

$$(j|q|j-1) = \sqrt{\left(\frac{j\hbar}{4\pi\mu\nu_0}\right)}e^{2\pi i(\nu_0 t+\beta_{j,j-1})},$$

$$(j|q|j+1) = \sqrt{\left(\frac{(j+1)\hbar}{4\mu\pi\nu_0}\right)}e^{-2\pi i(\nu_0 t+\beta_{j,j+1})},$$

where the β's are arbitrary.

The elements of the matrix p are then deduced from equation (47).

For the energy levels of the system we have

$$\begin{aligned}
(n|H|n) &= \frac{1}{2\mu}(n|\dot{q}^2+4\pi^2\nu_0^2 q^2|n) \\
&= 4\pi^2\mu \sum_m (\nu_{mn}^2+\nu_0^2)|(m|a|n)|^2 \\
&= 4\pi^2\mu\nu_0^2\{|(n-1|a|n)|^2+|(n+1|a|n)|^2\} \\
&= (n+\tfrac{1}{2})h\nu_0.
\end{aligned}$$

68. Canonical transformations

Suppose a dynamical system is completely specified by a set of coordinates q_j and momenta p_j which may be represented by Hermitian matrices. If now the coordinates are transformed to Q_j and the momenta to P_j in such a way that the matrices of the new coordinates and momenta are related to those of the old by the matrix equations

$$Q_j = Sq_j T, \qquad P_j = Sp_j T,$$

then
$$[Q_j, P_k] = S(q_j TSp_k-p_k TSq_j)T.$$

Now the old coordinates and momenta satisfy the commutation relations (32); it follows from this last equation that the new coordinates

will satisfy relations of this type if the matrices S, T satisfy the equations
$$ST = TS = 1,$$
i.e. if T is the inverse, S^{-1}, of S. Thus the transformation
$$Q_j = Sq_j\,S^{-1}, \qquad P_j = Sp_j\,S^{-1} \tag{48}$$
preserves the form of the commutation relations (32) and is called a canonical transformation; it plays a role in the quantum theory analogous to that of a contact transformation in classical·mechanics.

The matrix S must also be of such a nature that the coordinate Q_j is real. Writing out equation (48) we have
$$(m|Q_j|n) = \sum_{k,l} (m|S|k)(k|q|l)(l|S^{-1}|n),$$
$$(n|Q_j|m)^* = \sum_{k,l} (n|S|l)^*(l|q|k)^*(k|S^{-1}|m)^*.$$
The two are equal if and only if
$$(l|S^{-1}|n) = (n|S|l)^*,$$
i.e. if $$S^{-1} = S^\dagger$$
or $$SS^\dagger = 1. \tag{49}$$
For the coordinates Q_j to be real the matrix S of the transformation (48) has therefore to be a unitary matrix.

Furthermore, since
$$P_j^2 = P_j P_j = Sp_j\,S^{-1}Sp_j\,S = Sp_j^2\,S^{-1},$$
$$P_j^3 = P_j P_j^2 = Sp_j\,S^{-1}Sp_j^2S^{-1} = Sp_j^3S^{-1}, \text{ etc.}$$
it follows by induction that if $F(p,q)$ is a dynamical variable which is a function of p_j, q_j which can be expanded in powers of p_j, q_j, then in the new system of coordinates
$$F(P,Q) = SF(p,q)S^{-1},$$
and in particular the Hamiltonian transforms according to the rule
$$H(P,Q) = SH(p,q)S^{-1}.$$

69. Perturbation theory in matrix mechanics

A perturbation theory can be developed in matrix mechanics just as in wave mechanics, and it is often found in applications to particular problems that the matrix method gives the required result more quickly or in a more elegant form. Suppose that the Hamiltonian function of the dynamical system depends on the value of a parameter ϵ whose deviation from zero denotes the amount of the perturbation, and that this function can be expanded in ascending powers of ϵ in the form
$$H(p,q) = H_0(p,q) + \sum_{n=1} \epsilon^n H_n(p,q). \tag{50}$$

The problem to be solved in matrix mechanics is the determination of matrices p, q which satisfy the commutation relations (32) and which are such that
$$H(p,q) = W, \tag{51}$$
where W is a diagonal matrix. We suppose that the motion of the unperturbed system ($\epsilon = 0$) has been solved; i.e. we have determined matrices p_0, q_0 satisfying the commutation relations and such that
$$H_0(p_0,q_0) = W_0, \tag{52}$$
where W_0 is a (known) diagonal matrix.

We shall confine ourselves to a discussion of the case in which the dynamical system is uniquely specified by a single coordinate q, though the analysis may readily be extended to systems with more degrees of freedom. We assume that the matrix W can be expanded in the form
$$W = W_0 + \sum_{n=1} \epsilon^n W_n \tag{53}$$
reducing to W_0 when $\epsilon = 0$.

Transform the variables p_0, q_0 to p, q by means of the equations
$$p = S p_0 S^{-1}, \qquad q = S q_0 S^{-1},$$
where S is a unitary matrix. Then, since p_0, q_0 satisfy the commutation relations (32), so also do p, q. Furthermore,
$$H(p,q) = S H(p_0,q_0) S^{-1}, \tag{54}$$
so that by equation (51),
$$S H(p_0,q_0) = W S. \tag{55}$$
Writing
$$S = S_0 + \sum_{n=1} \epsilon^n S_n \tag{56}$$
and substituting from (50), (53), and (56) into equation (55) and equating powers of ϵ, we have
$$\left.\begin{aligned}
S_0 W_0 - W_0 S_0 &= 0 \\
(S_1 W_0 - W_0 S_1) - (W_1 S_0 - S_0 H_1) &= 0 \\
(S_0 H_2 - W_2 S_0) + (S_1 H_1 - W_1 S_1) + (S_2 W_0 - W_0 S_2) &= 0 \\
\cdots \cdots \cdots \cdots \cdots \cdots \cdots \cdots \cdots
\end{aligned}\right\}, \tag{57}$$
remembering that $H_0 = W_0$.

From the first of these equations we have
$$\sum_k \{(m|S_0|k)(k|W_0|n) - (m|W_0|k)(k|S_0|n)\} = 0,$$
which reduces to
$$(m|S_0|n)(W_{0n} - W_{0m}) = 0,$$
since W_0 is a diagonal matrix. If the unperturbed system is non-degenerate, $W_{0m} \neq W_{0n}$ unless $m = n$; thus $(m|S_0|n)$ is zero if $m \neq n$,

so that S_0 is a diagonal matrix. To determine the diagonal elements we must now make use of the fact that S is unitary, i.e.

$$(S_0 + \epsilon S_1 + \epsilon^2 S_2 + ...)(S_0^\dagger + \epsilon S_1^\dagger + \epsilon^2 S_2^\dagger + ...) = 1,$$

whence

$$S_0 S_0^\dagger = 1, \qquad S_0 S_1^\dagger + S_1 S_0^\dagger = 0, \qquad S_0 S_2^\dagger + S_1 S_1^\dagger + S_2 S_0^\dagger = 0.$$
$$(58)$$

From the first of the equations (58) we see that $(n|S_0|n)$ is of the form $e^{i\alpha_n}$ which can be absorbed into the usual (unwritten) time factor. We thus may write

$$(m|S_0|n) = \delta_{mn}. \tag{59}$$

Substituting this value for $(m|S_0|n)$ in the second of equations (57) we have

$$(m|S_1|n)(W_{0n} - W_{0m}) = (m|W_1|n) - (m|H_1|n), \tag{60}$$

from which it follows that H_1 is *not* a diagonal matrix and also that

$$(n|W_1|n) = (n|H_1|n). \tag{61}$$

Also from equation (60) we have for $m \neq n$

$$(m|S_1|n) = \frac{(m|H_1|n)}{W_{0m} - W_{0n}}. \tag{62}$$

To find the diagonal elements $(n|S_1|n)$ we make use of the second of equations (58); since S_0 is a unit matrix this reduces to

$$S_1 + S_1^\dagger = 0,$$

giving

$$(n|S_1|n) + (n|S_1^*|n) = 0,$$

i.e.

$$(n|S_1|n) = 0.$$

From the third of equations (57) we have on substituting for the matrix elements of S_0, H_0

$$(m|W_2|n) = (m|H_2|n) + \sum_k (m|S_1|k)(k|H_1|n) + (m|W_1|m)(m|S_1|n) + $$
$$+ (m|S_2|n)(W_{0m} - W_{0n}).$$

Putting $m = n$ and substituting from equation (62) for $(m|S_1|k)$ we obtain an expression for $(n|W_2|n)$. Writing

$$W_n = W_{0n} + \epsilon(n|W_1|n) + \epsilon^2(n|W_2|n) + O(\epsilon^3)$$

we have finally

$$W_n = W_{0n} + \epsilon(n|H_1|n) + \epsilon^2 \left\{ (n|H_2|n) + \sum \frac{(n|H_1|k)(k|H_1|n)}{W_{0k} - W_{0n}} \right\} + O(\epsilon^3),$$
$$(63)$$

which is of the same form as equation (25) of Chapter III.

70. Dirac's generalization of matrix mechanics

It is well known that eigenvalues of a certain operator may contain a continuous sequence of values as well as the discrete ones; for example, in the case of the energy this accounts for the existence of the continuous spectrum. To account for phenomena of this type in matrix mechanics we must extend our matrix calculus to include systems in which the elements of the matrices will have indices which are continuous in one region and assume only certain discrete values in another. The methods developed by Dirac[†] to deal with this problem will now be illustrated in a simple case—that in which the dynamical system possesses one degree of freedom; the extension to systems with more degrees of freedom is purely formal.

The first point to be observed is that in any region in which the indices vary in a continuous fashion the elements of a matrix $(\xi_1|f|\xi_2)$ are each functions of the two variables ξ_1 and ξ_2. In this region the matrix law of multiplication becomes

$$(\xi_1|fg|\xi_2) = \int (\xi_1|f|\xi_3)\,d\xi_3(\xi_3|g|\xi_2), \tag{64}$$

the integration being taken over all the values of ξ_3 in the continuous range. In the case of mixed ranges the product will be the sum of an integral and a sum over discrete values. In the continuous case the place of the unit matrix is taken by the *Dirac δ-function* which is defined by the following relations

$$\delta(x) = 0 \quad (x \neq 0), \qquad \int\limits_{-\infty}^{\infty} \delta(x)\,dx = 1. \tag{65}$$

From this definition the following properties may be derived directly or as a result of an integration by parts

$$\int\limits_{-\infty}^{\infty} f(\xi)\delta(\alpha-\xi)\,d\xi = f(\alpha), \tag{66}$$

$$\int\limits_{-\infty}^{\infty} f(\xi)\delta'(\alpha-\xi)\,d\xi = f'(\alpha), \tag{67}$$

$$\int\limits_{-\infty}^{\infty} \delta(\alpha-\xi)\delta(\beta-\xi)\,d\xi = \delta(\alpha-\beta). \tag{68}$$

From equations (64) and (66) it follows at once that

$$(\xi_1|f|\xi_2) = \int \delta(\xi_1-\xi_3)\,d\xi_3(\xi_3|f|\xi_2),$$

† P. A. M. Dirac, *Proc. Roy. Soc.* A, **113**, 621 (1927).

which shows that in the continuous range the elements of the unit matrix are
$$(\xi_1|1|\xi_2) = \delta(\xi_1 - \xi_2).$$

Similarly the elements of the diagonal matrix

$$\begin{pmatrix} \xi & 0 & 0 & . & . & . \\ 0 & \xi' & 0 & . & . & . \\ 0 & 0 & \xi'' & . & . & . \\ . & . & . & . & . & . \end{pmatrix}$$

are
$$(\xi|\alpha|\xi') = \xi\,\delta(\xi - \xi').$$

If we write
$$(\xi|\beta|\xi') = \frac{\hbar}{i}\delta'(\xi - \xi'),$$

then it follows immediately from the definition (64) that

$$(\xi|\alpha\beta - \beta\alpha|\xi') = \frac{\hbar}{i}\int \{\xi\,\delta(\xi - \xi'')\delta'(\xi'' - \xi') - \xi''\delta'(\xi - \xi'')\delta(\xi'' - \xi')\}\,d\xi''.$$

Integrating the second term by parts and the first by the rule (68) we have

$$(\xi|\alpha\beta - \beta\alpha|\xi') = -\frac{\hbar}{i}\int \delta(\xi - \xi'')\delta(\xi'' - \xi')\,d\xi'' = i\hbar\,\delta(\xi - \xi'),$$

which may be written in the form

$$\alpha\beta - \beta\alpha = i\hbar$$

to show that α and β are canonical conjugates.

The fundamental problem of the generalized matrix mechanics is the discovery of a transformation of the coordinate system which leads to a diagonal matrix for the Hamiltonian of the system. Suppose, for instance, that we have a representation in which the generalized coordinates and momenta are of the form

$$(\xi|q|\xi') = \xi\,\delta(\xi - \xi'), \qquad (\xi|p|\xi') = \frac{\hbar}{i}\delta'(\xi - \xi').$$

Suppose we change the coordinates and momenta to $(\eta|Q|\eta')$ and $(\eta|P|\eta')$ by a transformation

$$q = SQS^{-1}, \qquad p = SPS^{-1}$$

to make the Hamiltonian function H a diagonal matrix, say $W_\eta\,\delta(\eta - \eta')$. Then, by (54),
$$H(p,q)S = SH(P,Q)$$

that is,
$$\int (\xi|H(p,q)|\xi')\,d\xi'(\xi'|S|\eta) = \int (\xi|S|\eta')\,d\eta'(\eta'|H|\eta)$$
$$= \int (\xi|S|\eta')\,d\eta'\,W_\eta\,\delta(\eta - \eta').$$

The integral on the right-hand side can be evaluated immediately to give

$$\int (\xi|H|\xi')\,d\xi'(\xi'|S|\eta) = W_\eta(\xi|S|\eta). \tag{69}$$

Equation (69) is Dirac's generalized form of the Schrödinger equation.[†] It assumes a simpler form when the Hamiltonian $H(q,p)$ is an *algebraic function* of the variables p, q; for from equations for p, q and the results (66) and (67)

$$\int (\xi|q|\xi')\,d\xi'(\xi'|S|\eta) = \xi(\xi|S|\eta),$$

$$\int (\xi|p|\xi')\,d\xi'(\xi'|S|\eta) = \frac{\hbar}{i}\frac{\partial}{\partial\xi}(\xi|S|\eta),$$

from which it follows by induction that, if $f(q,p)$ is an algebraic function of p, q,

$$\int (\xi|f|\xi')\,d\xi'(\xi'|S|\eta) = f\left(\xi,\frac{\hbar}{i}\frac{\partial}{\partial\xi}\right)(\xi|S|\eta). \tag{70}$$

Applying this result to equation (69), writing $\eta = n$ and $(\xi|S|\eta) = S_n(\xi)$, we have

$$\left\{H\left(\xi,\frac{\hbar}{i}\frac{\partial}{\partial\xi}\right) - W_n\right\}S_n(\xi) = 0, \tag{71}$$

which is the usual Schrödinger equation. The elements of the transformation matrix S, which leads to a representation in which the Hamiltonian H is a diagonal matrix, are the eigenfunctions $S_n(\xi)$.

The elements of the matrix representing any other dynamical variable F are given by the formula

$$(\eta|F|\eta') = \int (\eta|S^{-1}|\xi')\,d\xi' \int (\xi'|F(q,p)|\xi'')\,d\xi''(\xi''|S|\eta')$$

$$= \int (\eta|S^{-1}|\xi')\,d\xi'\,F\left(\xi',\frac{\hbar}{i}\frac{\partial}{\partial\xi'}\right)(\xi'|S|\eta')$$

by equation (70), provided, of course, that F is an algebraic function of the p and q. Now from the condition (49) we have

$$(\eta|S^{-1}|\xi') = (\xi'|S|\eta)^*,$$

so that writing $\eta = n$, $(\xi|S|\eta) = S_n(\xi)$ we have

$$(n|F|n') = \int S_n^*(\xi)F\left(\xi,\frac{\hbar}{i}\frac{\partial}{\partial\xi}\right)S_{n'}(\xi)\,d\xi.$$

[†] P. A. M. Dirac, *Quantum Mechanics*, 2nd ed., p. 116.

APPENDIX

PROPERTIES OF ORTHOGONAL FUNCTIONS

1. Introduction

A SET of complex functions $\Psi_n(x)$ of the real variable x is said to be *orthogonal* in the interval $\alpha \leqslant x \leqslant \beta$, if all the functions of the set are such that the integral

$$\int_\alpha^\beta |\Psi_n(x)|^2 \, dx$$

exists for all values of n, and if

$$\int_\alpha^\beta \Psi_m^*(x) \Psi_n(x) \, dx = 0 \quad (m \neq n).$$

The quantities α and β may be zero, finite, or $\pm\infty$. The simplest functions of this type defined in the interval $-\pi \leqslant x \leqslant \pi$ are $\cos nx$, $\sin nx$, where n is an integer. The most important property of orthogonal functions is that under certain conditions we may expand any arbitrary function $f(x)$ as a series of the type

$$f(x) = \sum_n a_n \Psi_n(x)$$

analogous to Fourier series. Using the orthogonal property it follows immediately that the coefficients a_n are given by the formula

$$a_n = \frac{\int_\alpha^\beta f(x) \Psi_n^*(x) \, dx}{\int_\alpha^\beta \Psi_n(x) \Psi_n^*(x) \, dx}.$$

If, for all values of n,

$$\int_\alpha^\beta |\Psi_n(x)|^2 \, dx = 1,$$

the functions $\Psi_n(x)$ are said to be *normalized*; in this case the formula for the coefficients a_n becomes

$$a_n = \int_\alpha^\beta f(x) \Psi_n^*(x) \, dx.$$

Orthogonal polynomials are of great importance in quantum mechanics. The theory of such polynomials has been treated in great detail by Szegö.† No such rigorous treatment will be attempted in this

---

† G. Szegö, *Orthogonal Polynomials* (American Math. Soc. Coll. Publ. XXIII, New York, 1939).

appendix; we shall confine ourselves to the derivation of such properties of orthogonal polynomials as are useful in the solution of certain elementary problems of wave mechanics.

2. Hermite polynomials and functions

In quantum mechanics the Hermite polynomials arise in the solution of the Schrödinger equation for the linear harmonic oscillator. It was shown in § 11 that, in this instance, the wave equation could be reduced to the form

$$\frac{d^2\Psi}{dy^2} + (\lambda - y^2)\Psi = 0. \tag{1}$$

We have to determine the values of the parameter λ which lead to solutions which tend to zero exponentially as y tends to infinity. The solution was obtained by making the substitution

$$\Psi = e^{-\frac{1}{2}y^2}H(y), \tag{2}$$

and it was shown that if $\lambda = 2n+1,$ $\tag{3}$

then $H(y)$ is a polynomial of the form

$$H_n(y) = \sum_{s=0}^{n} A_s y^s \quad (A_n \neq 0). \tag{4}$$

Substituting from equation (4) into the equation

$$\frac{d^2H}{dy^2} - 2y\frac{dH}{dy} + 2nH = 0 \tag{5}$$

obtained from p. 51 by putting $\lambda = 2n+1$, we obtain the recurrence relation

$$A_{s-2} = \frac{s(s-1)}{2(s-n-2)}A_s$$

for the coefficients of y. Taking A_n to be 2^n, we obtain the solution

$$H_n(y) = 2^n\left[y^n - \frac{n(n-1)}{4}y^{n-2} + \frac{n(n-1)(n-2)(n-3)}{4.8}y^{n-4} - \dots\right]. \tag{6}$$

The polynomial defined by equation (6) is called a *Hermite polynomial*, and the corresponding function

$$\Psi_n(y) = e^{-\frac{1}{2}y^2}H_n(y)$$

is called a *Hermite function*.

From the form (6) of the Hermite polynomial it is readily verified directly that

$$H_n(y) = (-1)^n e^{y^2}\frac{d^n e^{-y^2}}{dy^n}. \tag{7}$$

Differentiating both sides of this equation with respect to y we obtain the recurrence relation

$$H'_n(y) = 2yH_n(y) - H_{n+1}(y). \tag{8}$$

A second differentiation yields

$$H_n''(y) = 2yH_n'(y)+2H_n(y)-H_{n+1}'(y). \tag{9}$$

Now $H_n(y)$ is a solution of equation (5), so that

$$H_n''(y) = 2yH_n'(y)-2nH_n(y). \tag{10}$$

An expression for $H_{n+1}'(y)$ in terms of $H_{n+2}(y)$ and $H_{n+1}(y)$ can be obtained from equation (8) by replacing n by $n+1$; it is

$$H_{n+1}'(y) = 2yH_{n+1}(y)-H_{n+2}(y). \tag{11}$$

Eliminating $H_n''(y)$, $H_n'(y)$, and $H_{n+1}'(y)$ from equations (8) to (11), we obtain the recurrence formula

$$2yH_{n+1}(y) = H_{n+2}(y)+2(n+1)H_n(y). \tag{12}$$

The first two Hermite polynomials can be determined readily from equation (7); the remaining ones can then be found by repeated use of equation (12). In this way we find for the first eleven polynomials:

$H_0(y) = 1,$

$H_1(y) = 2y,$

$H_2(y) = 4y^2-2,$

$H_3(y) = 8y^3-12y,$

$H_4(y) = 16y^4-48y^2+12,$

$H_5(y) = 32y^5-160y^3+120y,$

$H_6(y) = 64y^6-480y^4+720y^2-120,$

$H_7(y) = 128y^7-1344y^5+3360y^3-1680y,$

$H_8(y) = 256y^8-3584y^6+13440y^4-13440y^2+1680,$

$H_9(y) = 512y^9-9216y^7+48384y^5-80640y^3+30240y,$

$H_{10}(y) = 1024y^{10}-23040y^8+161280y^6-403200y^4+302400y^2-30240.$

3. Integrals involving Hermite functions

To determine the normalization factors of the eigenfunction of the linear harmonic oscillator we require to know the value of the integral

$$I(m,n) = \int_{-\infty}^{\infty} \Psi_n(y)\Psi_m(y)\,dy = \int_{-\infty}^{\infty} e^{-y^2}H_m(y)H_n(y)\,dy. \tag{13}$$

The proof that $I(m,n)$ vanishes unless $m = n$ follows at once from the fact that the function $\Psi_n(y)$ satisfies the differential equation

$$\frac{d^2\Psi_n}{dy^2}-y^2\Psi_n+(2n+1)\Psi_n = 0,$$

so that

$$\int_{-\infty}^{\infty} \Psi_m(y)\Psi_n(y)\,dy = \frac{1}{2(n-m)} \int_{-\infty}^{\infty} (\Psi_m'' \Psi_n - \Psi_n'' \Psi_m)\,dy,$$

which is zero unless $m = n$.

In particular, $I(n, n+2) = 0$, so that from equation (12) it follows that

$$\int_{-\infty}^{\infty} 2ye^{-v^2}H_n(y)H_{n+1}(y)\,dy = 2(n+1)I(n, n). \tag{14}$$

Now the left-hand side of this equation may be written

$$\int_{-\infty}^{\infty} 2ye^{v^2}\frac{d^n e^{-v^2}}{dy^n}\frac{d^{n+1}e^{-v^2}}{dy^{n+1}}\,dy = \int_{-\infty}^{\infty} e^{v^2}\left(\frac{d^{n+1}e^{-v^2}}{dy^{n+1}}\right)^2 dy,$$

which gives the recurrence formula

$$I(n+1, n+1) = 2(n+1)I(n, n).$$

Now

$$I(0, 0) = \int_{-\infty}^{\infty} e^{-v^2}\,dy = \sqrt{\pi},$$

so that by induction we arrive at the formula

$$I(n, n) = 2^n n!\,\sqrt{\pi}. \tag{15}$$

Thus the normalized eigenfunctions of the Schrödinger equation

$$\frac{d^2\Psi}{dx^2} + \frac{2m}{\hbar^2}(W - \tfrac{1}{2}px^2)\Psi = 0$$

are

where

$$\left.\begin{aligned}\Psi_n(x) &= \frac{\alpha^{\frac{1}{2}}}{2^{\frac{1}{2}n}(n!)^{\frac{1}{2}}\pi^{\frac{1}{4}}} e^{-\frac{1}{2}\alpha^2 x^2}H_n(\alpha x),\\[4pt]\alpha &= (2mp/\hbar^2)^{\frac{1}{4}}.\end{aligned}\right\} \tag{16}$$

The matrix element $(n|x|m)$ for the harmonic oscillator is, by definition, given by the equation

$$\int_{-\infty}^{\infty} \Psi_n(x)x\Psi_m(x)\,dx = \frac{1}{\alpha(2^{n+m}\pi n!\,m!)^{\frac{1}{2}}} \int_{-\infty}^{\infty} ye^{-v^2}H_n(y)H_m(y)\,dy.$$

Making use of the recurrence formula (12) we find that

$$\int_{-\infty}^{\infty} ye^{-v^2}H_n(y)H_m(y)\,dy = \tfrac{1}{2}I(n, m+1) + nI(m, n-1),$$

and hence by use of the orthogonality relation that

$$(n|x|m) = 0$$

unless $m = n \pm 1$. Putting $m = n+1$ and inserting the value of $I(n+1, n+1)$ as given by equation (15), we have finally

$$(n|x|n+1) = \sqrt{\left(\frac{n+1}{2\alpha^2}\right)}. \tag{17}$$

4. Laguerre polynomials

Closely related to the Hermite polynomials are the Laguerre polynomials which may be defined by the equation

$$L_k^n(\xi) = \frac{d^n}{d\xi^n}\left[e^\xi \frac{d^k}{d\xi^k}(\xi^k e^{-\xi}) \right]. \tag{18}$$

A comparison of equations (7) and (18) shows that the Hermite polynomials can be reduced to Laguerre polynomials with parameters $n = \pm\frac{1}{2}$. Conversely, Laguerre polynomials can, to a certain extent, be reduced to Hermite polynomials, by the relation[†]

$$L_{k-n}^n(\xi) = \frac{(-1)^k \Gamma(k+n+1)}{(2n)!\, \pi^{\frac{1}{2}} \Gamma(n+\frac{1}{2})} \int_{-1}^{1} (1-x^2)^{n-\frac{1}{2}} H_{2k}(x\xi^{\frac{1}{2}})\, dx \quad (n > -\tfrac{1}{2}). \tag{19}$$

The Laguerre polynomials are most easily calculated directly from the definition (18); the first ten polynomials are found to be:

$L_0^0(\xi) = 1,$

$L_1^0(\xi) = 1-\xi, \qquad L_1^1(\xi) = -1,$

$L_2^0(\xi) = 2-4\xi+\xi^2, \qquad L_2^1(\xi) = -4+2\xi, \qquad L_2^2(\xi) = 2,$

$L_3^0(\xi) = 6-18\xi+9\xi^2-\xi^3, \qquad L_3^1(\xi) = -18+18\xi-3\xi^2,$

$L_3^2(\xi) = 18-6\xi, \qquad L_3^3(\xi) = -6.$

It also follows directly from equation (18) that $L_k^n(\xi)$ is a solution of the ordinary differential equation

$$\xi\frac{d^2y}{d\xi^2} + (n+1-\xi)\frac{dy}{d\xi} + (k-n)y = 0. \tag{20}$$

Now if we write $\qquad x = \tfrac{1}{2}\xi, \qquad g = \xi^{l+1}G,$

we find that the equation

$$\frac{d^2g}{dx^2} - 2\frac{dg}{dx} + \left\{\frac{\alpha}{x} - \frac{l(l+1)}{x^2}\right\}g = 0 \tag{21}$$

occurring in the theory of the hydrogen atom (equation (18) of Chapter II) is transformed to

$$\xi\frac{d^2G}{d\xi^2} + [2(l+1)-\xi]\frac{dG}{d\xi} + (\tfrac{1}{2}\alpha-1-l)G = 0, \tag{22}$$

† A. W. Uspensky, *Ann. Math.* (2), **28**, 593 (1927).

which is identical with equation (20) if we choose

$$n = 2l+1, \qquad k = 2l+s,$$

where s is a positive integer and $\alpha = 2(l+s)$. Thus the solution of equation (21) may be written in the form

$$g = (2x)^{l+1} L_{2l+s}^{2l+1}(2x). \tag{23}$$

The integral $\qquad I_{n,n';k,k'}^{p} = \int\limits_{0}^{\infty} \xi^{p} e^{-\xi} L_{k}^{n}(\xi) L_{k'}^{n'}(\xi) \, d\xi$

is of importance in wave mechanics; its value is given by the following formula due to Schrödinger

$$I_{n,n';k,k'}^{p} = (-1)^{k+k'} k! \, k'! \, (p-n)! \times$$

$$\times \sum_{s=0}^{\sigma} \frac{(p+s)!}{s! \, (k-n-s)! \, (p-k+s)! \, (k'-n'-s)! \, (p'-k'+s)!}, \tag{24}$$

where σ is the smaller of the two integers $k-n$, $k'-n'$.

In determining the normalization factors for the eigenfunctions of the hydrogen atom we require the value of the integral

$$\int\limits_{0}^{\infty} \xi^{2l+2} e^{-\xi} \{L_{2l+s}^{2l+1}(\xi)\}^{2} \, d\xi.$$

In this instance $k-n = k'-n' = s-1$ and all the terms in the sum on the right-hand side of equation (24) vanish except those for which s takes on the values $s-1$, $s-2$. Equation (24) then yields for the value of this integral

$$\int\limits_{0}^{\infty} \xi^{2l+2} e^{-\xi} \{L_{2l+s}^{2l+1}(\xi)\}^{2} \, d\xi = \frac{2(l+s)\{(2l+s)!\}^{3}}{(s-1)!}. \tag{25}$$

5. The Legendre polynomials

An equation of great importance in mathematical physics is the Legendre equation

$$(1-\mu^{2}) \frac{d^{2}y}{d\mu^{2}} - 2\mu \frac{dy}{d\mu} + l(l+1)y = 0, \tag{26}$$

in which l is a constant (but not necessarily an integer). If we wish to obtain polynomial solutions of this equation of the form

$$y = \sum_{s=0}^{n} a_{s} \mu^{s} \quad (a_{n} \neq 0), \tag{27}$$

then substituting from equation (27) into equation (26) and equating to zero the coefficient of μ^{n} we obtain the relation

$$a_{n}[n(n+1) - l(l+1)] = 0. \tag{28}$$

Since by hypothesis $a_n \neq 0$, it follows that polynomial solutions of equation (26) of the type (27) are only possible if l is a positive integer. Substituting from (27) into (26) and equating coefficients of μ^s we obtain the recurrence formula

$$a_{s+2} = \frac{(s-l)(s+l+1)}{(s+1)(s+2)} a_s \tag{29}$$

for the coefficients a_s, whence we derive the polynomial solution

$$P_n(\mu) = \sum_{s=0}^{\sigma} \frac{(-1)^s (2n-2s)!}{2^n s! (n-s)! (n-2s)!} \mu^{n-2s}, \tag{30}$$

where the integer σ is $\frac{1}{2}n$ or $\frac{1}{2}(n-1)$ according as n is an even or an odd integer. $P_n(\mu)$ is called the Legendre polynomial of degree n. From this definition of the Legendre polynomial we deduce the Rodrigues formula

$$P_n(\mu) = \sum_{s=0}^{\sigma} \frac{(-1)^s}{2^n s! (n-s)!} \frac{d^n}{d\mu^n} (\mu^{2n-2s})$$

$$= \frac{1}{2^n n!} \frac{d^n}{d\mu^n} \sum_{s=0}^{\sigma} \frac{(-1)^s n!}{s! (n-s)!} \mu^{2n-2s}$$

$$= \frac{1}{2^n n!} \frac{d^n}{d\mu^n} (\mu^2 - 1)^n. \tag{31}$$

6. Integral expression for the Legendre polynomial

If we assume Cauchy's theorem in the form

$$\frac{1}{2\pi i} \int_C \frac{f(\zeta)}{\zeta - \mu} d\zeta = f(\mu),$$

where $f(\zeta)$ is an analytical function of the complex variable in a certain domain R which includes the point $\zeta = \mu$, and where the integral is taken along a closed contour C which includes $\zeta = \mu$ and lies wholly within the domain R, then by differentiating both sides of the equation l times with respect to μ we obtain the result

$$\frac{d^l}{d\mu^l} f(\mu) = \frac{l!}{2\pi i} \int_C \frac{f(\zeta)}{(\zeta - \mu)^{l+1}} d\zeta.$$

Substituting the function $(\zeta^2 - 1)^l$ for $f(\zeta)$ we obtain, by an application of Rodrigues' formula,

$$P_l(\mu) = \frac{2^{-l}}{2\pi i} \int_C \frac{(\zeta^2 - 1)^l}{(\zeta - \mu)^{l+1}} d\zeta. \tag{32}$$

Equation (32) is known as Schlaefli's formula for the Legendre polynomial. Using the identity

$$\frac{2^{-l-1}(\zeta^2-1)^{l+1}}{(\zeta-\mu)^{l+2}} - 2^{-l}\mu\frac{(\zeta^2-1)^l}{(\zeta-\mu)^{l+1}} = \frac{2^{-l}(\zeta^2-1)^l}{(\zeta-\mu)^{l+1}} - \frac{2^{-l-1}}{l+1}\frac{d}{d\zeta}\left(\frac{\zeta^2-1}{\zeta-\mu}\right)^{l+1}$$

and noting that if the second term on the right-hand side of this identity is integrated round a contour of the type specified at the beginning of this section it gives a zero contribution, we arrive at the relation

$$P_{l+1}(\mu) - \mu P_l(\mu) = \frac{2^{-l}}{2\pi i}\int\frac{(\zeta^2-1)^l}{(\zeta-\mu)^l}\,d\zeta.$$

Differentiating both sides of this equation with respect to μ we obtain the recurrence formula

$$P'_{l+1}(\mu) - \mu P'_l(\mu) = (l+1)P_l(\mu). \tag{33}$$

In a similar fashion we can establish that

$$(l+1)P_{l+1}(\mu) - (2l+1)\mu P_l(\mu) + lP_{l-1}(\mu) = 0. \tag{34}$$

Differentiating this last equation with respect to μ and substituting for $P'_{l+1}(\mu)$ from equation (33), we obtain the relation

$$\mu P'_l(\mu) - P'_{l-1}(\mu) = lP_l(\mu). \tag{35}$$

Elimination of $\mu P'_l(\mu)$ from equations (33) and (35) yields the result

$$P'_{l+1}(\mu) - P'_{l-1}(\mu) = (2l+1)P_l(\mu), \tag{36}$$

and finally the elimination of P'_{l-1} from (35) by means of equation (33) with $l-1$ written for l gives

$$(\mu^2-1)P'_l(\mu) = l\mu P_l(\mu) - lP_{l-1}(\mu). \tag{37}$$

Now the expressions for $P_0(\mu)$ and $P_1(\mu)$ can be derived immediately from either of equations (30) and (31); they are found to be 1 and μ respectively. The expressions for $P_n(\mu)$ $(n \geqslant 2)$ then follow by repeated applications of the recurrence formula (34). In this way we obtain for the first six Legendre polynomials:

$$P_0(\mu) = 1, \qquad\qquad P_3(\mu) = \tfrac{1}{2}(5\mu^3 - 3\mu),$$
$$P_1(\mu) = \mu, \qquad\qquad P_4(\mu) = \tfrac{1}{8}(35\mu^4 - 30\mu^2 + 3),$$
$$P_2(\mu) = \tfrac{1}{2}(3\mu^2 - 1), \qquad\qquad P_5(\mu) = \tfrac{1}{8}(63\mu^5 - 70\mu^3 + 15\mu).$$

7. The associated Legendre polynomials

The equation

$$(1-\mu^2)\frac{d^2y}{d\mu^2} - 2\mu\frac{dy}{d\mu} + \left[l(l+1) - \frac{u^2}{1-\mu^2}\right]y = 0, \tag{38}$$

which reduces to the Legendre equation (26) when $u = 0$, also plays an important role in mathematical physics. By obtaining solutions in series in the same manner as in the last section it is easily verified that polynomial solutions of this equation exist if and only if u and l are integers. In the subsequent analysis we shall assume that this condition is fulfilled and also that $u \leqslant l$.

If we make the substitution

$$y = (1-\mu^2)^{\frac{1}{2}u} \eta$$

in equation (38), we find that the function $\eta(\mu)$ satisfies the differential equation

$$(1-\mu^2)\frac{d^2\eta}{d\mu^2} - 2(u+1)\mu\frac{d\eta}{d\mu} + (l-u)(l+u+1)\eta = 0,$$

and this may be written in the form

$$\frac{d^u}{d\mu^u}\left\{(1-\mu^2)\frac{d^2\zeta}{d\mu^2} - 2\mu\frac{d\zeta}{d\mu} + l(l+1)\zeta\right\} = 0, \quad \eta = \frac{d^u\zeta}{d\mu^u}$$

by the use of Leibnitz's theorem. Now the expression in the bracket on the left-hand side of the former of these two equations is simply the expression which is equated to zero in Legendre's equation (26). Hence if ζ is any solution of the Legendre equation (26), the function

$$y = (1-\mu^2)^{\frac{1}{2}u}\frac{d^u\zeta}{d\mu^u}$$

is a solution of the associated Legendre equation (38). The polynomial form of η corresponding to $\zeta = P_l(\mu)$ leads to the *associated Legendre function* which is thus defined by the relations

$$P_l^u(\mu) = (1-\mu^2)^{\frac{1}{2}u}\frac{d^u P_l(\mu)}{d\mu^u} = \frac{1}{2^l\,l!}(1-\mu^2)^{\frac{1}{2}u}\frac{d^{l+u}}{d\mu^{l+u}}(\mu^2-1)^l, \qquad (39)$$

the second of these expressions being a consequence of the Rodrigues formula (31).

As a result of equation (39) the recurrence formulae for the associated Legendre functions can be determined immediately from those for the Legendre functions. Differentiating equation (34) u times with respect to μ and equation (35) $u-1$ times and eliminating $d^{u-1}P_l(\mu)/d\mu^{u-1}$ from the resulting equations we obtain the relation

$$\mu P_l^u(\mu) = \frac{l+u}{2l+1}P_{l-1}^u(\mu) + \frac{l-u+1}{2l+1}P_{l+1}^u(\mu). \qquad (40)$$

Similarly if we differentiate (36) u times with respect to μ and then multiply by $(1-\mu^2)^{\frac{1}{2}(1+u)}$ we obtain the recurrence formula

$$(1-\mu^2)^{\frac{1}{2}}P_l^u(\mu) = \frac{1}{2l+1}[P_{l+1}^{u+1}(\mu) - P_{l-1}^{u+1}(\mu)]. \qquad (41)$$

The associated Legendre functions can be deduced from the table of Legendre polynomials at the end of §6 by means of the former of the relations (39). In this way we obtain:

$$P_1^1(\mu) = (1-\mu^2)^{\frac{1}{2}},$$

$$P_2^1(\mu) = 3\mu(1-\mu^2)^{\frac{1}{2}}, \quad P_2^2(\mu) = 3(1-\mu^2),$$

$$P_3^1(\mu) = \tfrac{1}{2}(15\mu^2-3)(1-\mu^2)^{\frac{1}{2}}, \quad P_3^2(\mu) = 15\mu(1-\mu^2), \quad P_3^3(\mu) = 15(1-\mu^2)^{\frac{3}{2}},$$

$$P_4^1(\mu) = \tfrac{1}{2}(35\mu^3-15\mu)(1-\mu^2)^{\frac{1}{2}}, \quad P_4^2(\mu) = \tfrac{1}{2}(105\mu^3-15)(1-\mu^2),$$

$$P_4^3(\mu) = 105\mu(1-\mu^2)^{\frac{3}{2}}, \quad P_4^4(\mu) = 105(1-\mu^2)^2,$$

$$P_5^1(\mu) = \tfrac{1}{8}(315\mu^4-210\mu^2+15)(1-\mu^2)^{\frac{1}{2}},$$

$$P_5^2(\mu) = \tfrac{1}{2}(315\mu^3-105\mu)(1-\mu^2),$$

$$P_5^3(\mu) = \tfrac{1}{2}(945\mu^2-105)(1-\mu^2)^{\frac{3}{2}},$$

$$P_5^4(\mu) = 945\mu(1-\mu^2)^2,$$

$$P_5^5(\mu) = 945(1-\mu^2)^{\frac{5}{2}}.$$

8. Integrals involving the associated Legendre functions

If we write
$$I_{l,l'}^{u,u'} = \int_{-1}^{1} P_l^u(\mu)P_{l'}^{u'}(\mu)\,d\mu, \tag{42}$$

then, by equation (39),

$$I_{l,l'}^{u,u} = \frac{(-1)^u}{2^{l+l'}\,l!\,l'!}\int_{-1}^{1}(\mu^2-1)^u\frac{d^{l+u}}{d\mu^{l+u}}(\mu^2-1)^l\frac{d^{l'+u}}{d\mu^{l'+u}}(\mu^2-1)^{l'}\,d\mu$$

$$= \frac{(-1)^{2u+l'}}{2^{l+l'}\,l!\,l'!}\int_{-1}^{1}(\mu^2-1)^{l'}\frac{d^{l'+u}}{d\mu^{l'+\mu}}\left[(\mu^2-1)^u\frac{d^{l+u}}{d\mu^{l+u}}(\mu^2-1)^l\right]d\mu$$

as a result of $l'+u$ integrations by parts. Expanding the second factor in the integrand by Leibnitz's theorem we find

$$I_{l,l'}^{u,u} = \frac{(-1)^{2u+l'}}{2^{l+l'}\,l!\,l'!}\sum_s \frac{(l'+u)!}{s!\,(l'+u-s)!} \times$$

$$\times \int_{-1}^{1}(\mu^2-1)^{l'}\frac{d^{l'+u-s}}{d\mu^{l'+u-s}}(\mu^2-1)^u\frac{d^{l+u+s}}{d\mu^{l+u+s}}(\mu^2-1)^l\,d\mu. \tag{43}$$

Now the term of highest order in the expansion of $(\mu^2-1)^u$ is μ^{2u}, so that $\dfrac{d^{l'+u-s}}{d\mu^{l'+u-s}}(\mu^2-1)^u$ vanishes if $s \geqslant l'-u$. Similarly the second factor in the integrand vanishes if $s \leqslant l-u$. Since the integral is symmetrical there is no loss of generality involved in the assumption that $l \leqslant l'$, but if $l < l'$ the above two relations limiting the values which s is capable of assuming are incompatible, so that

$$I_{l,l'}^{u,u} = 0, \qquad l \neq l'. \tag{44}$$

If $l = l'$, then $s = l - u$ is the only term of the series (43) which gives a non-vanishing contribution to the final result. We then have

$$
\begin{aligned}
I_{l,l'}^{u,u} &= \frac{(-1)^{2u+l}}{2^{2l}(l!)^2} \frac{(l+u)!}{(l-u)!\,(2u)!} \int_{-1}^{1} (\mu^2-1)^l (2u)!\,(2l)!\,d\mu \\
&= \frac{(l+u)!}{(l-u)!} \frac{2}{2l+1}.
\end{aligned}
\tag{45}
$$

The analysis for $I_{l,l'}^{u+1,u-1}$ proceeds along similar lines; again we find that the integral vanishes unless $l = l'$.

By means of the recurrence formula (40) we have

$$\int_{-1}^{1} \mu P_l^u(\mu) P_{l'}^u(\mu)\, d\mu = \frac{l+u}{2l+1} I_{l-1,l'}^{u,u} + \frac{l-u+1}{2l+1} I_{l+1,l'}^{u,u},$$

so that, by equation (44),

$$\int_{-1}^{1} \mu P_l^u(\mu) P_{l'}^u(\mu)\, d\mu = 0 \tag{46}$$

unless $l' = l+1$. When $l' = l\pm 1$ the value of the integral follows immediately from equation (45).

Similarly the recurrence relation (41) yields the formula

$$\int_{-1}^{1} (1-\mu^2)^{\frac{1}{2}u} P_l^u(\mu) P_{l'}^{u\pm1}(\mu)\, d\mu = \frac{1}{2l+1}[I_{l+1,l'}^{u+1,u\pm1} - I_{l-1,l'}^{u+1,u\pm1}], \tag{47}$$

so that this integral also vanishes unless

$$l' = l\pm 1.$$

9. Some expansions involving Legendre functions

From Schlaefli's integral formula (32) for the Legendre polynomial $P_n(\mu)$ and the definition (39) of the associated Legendre function, we see that when m and n are real integers

$$P_n^m(\mu) = \frac{1}{2\pi i} \frac{(n+m)!}{2^n n!} (\mu^2-1)^{\frac{1}{2}m} \int_C \frac{(\zeta^2-1)^n}{(\zeta-\mu)^{n+m+1}}\, d\zeta, \tag{48}$$

where the contour C encloses both of the points $\zeta = 1$ and $\zeta = \mu$. If $\mu > 0$ we may take the contour C to be the circle

$$|\zeta-\mu| = |\surd(\mu^2-1)|.$$

Integrating round this contour we obtain from (48) the equation

$$\frac{1}{2\pi} \int_0^{2\pi} \{\mu+\sqrt{(\mu^2-1)}\cos(\phi-\psi)\}^n \frac{\cos}{\sin} m\phi \, d\phi = \frac{n!}{(n+m)!} \frac{\cos}{\sin} m\psi \, P_n^m(\mu),$$

(49)

from which follows immediately the Fourier expansion

$$\{\mu+\sqrt{(\mu^2-1)}\cos(\phi-\psi)\}^n = P_n(\mu)+2\sum_{m=1}^n \frac{n!}{(n+m)!} P_n^m(\mu)\cos m(\psi-\phi).$$

(50)

Changing n to $-(n+1)$ we obtain the expansion

$$\{\mu'+\sqrt{(\mu'^2-1)}\cos\psi\}^{-n-1} = P_n(\mu')+2\sum_{m=1}^n (-1)^m\frac{(n-m)!}{n!} P_n^m(\mu')\cos m\psi,$$

(51)

where, as noted above, we have assumed n to be an integer.

Applying Parseval's theorem for Fourier series to the series (50) and (51) we find that the series

$$P_n(\mu)P_n(\mu')+2\sum_{m=1}^n (-1)^n\frac{(n-m)!}{(n+m)!} P_n^m(\mu)P_n^m(\mu')\cos m\phi$$

converges to the sum

$$\frac{1}{2\pi} \int_{-\pi}^{\pi} \frac{\{\mu+\sqrt{(\mu^2-1)}\cos(\psi+\phi)\}^n}{\{\mu'+\sqrt{(\mu'^2-1)}\cos\psi\}^{n+1}} \, d\psi.$$

This integral may be evaluated by means of Cauchy's theorem.[†] Its value is found to be $P_n[\mu\mu'+\sqrt{\{(\mu^2-1)(\mu'^2-1)\}}\cos\phi]$. Writing $\mu = \cos\theta$, $\mu' = \cos\theta'$, and

$$\cos\Theta = \cos\theta\cos\theta'+\sin\theta\sin\theta'\cos\phi,$$

we obtain the result

$$P_n(\cos\Theta) = P_n(\cos\theta)P_n(\cos\theta')+2\sum_{m=1}^n \frac{(n-m)!}{(n+m)!} P_n^m(\cos\theta)P_n^m(\cos\theta').$$

(52)

This result is often of value in the solution of problems in quantum mechanics.

Another expansion which is of use in the relativistic theory of the Auger effect[‡] and of the interaction of two electrons in the self-consistent field method[§] is the following:

$$\frac{e^{ik|\mathbf{r}_1-\mathbf{r}_2|}}{|\mathbf{r}_1-\mathbf{r}_2|} = \sum_{n=0}^{\infty} (2n+1)\frac{\zeta_n(kr_b)}{r_b}\frac{\eta_n(kr_a)}{r_a} P_n(\cos\widehat{\mathbf{r}_1\mathbf{r}_2}),$$

(53)

† E. W. Hobson, *The Theory of Spherical and Ellipsoidal Harmonics*, 365–71 (Cambridge, 1931).

‡ H. S. W. Massey and E. H. S. Burhop, *Proc. Roy. Soc.* A, **153**, 661 (1936).

§ B. Swirles, ibid. **157**, 680 (1936).

where r_a is the smaller and r_b the greater of r_1 and r_2 and

$$\left.\begin{aligned}\eta_n(x) &= \sqrt{(\tfrac{1}{2}\pi x)}J_{n+\frac{1}{2}}(x) \\ \zeta_n(x) &= \sqrt{(\tfrac{1}{2}\pi x)}\{iJ_{n+\frac{1}{2}}(x)+(-1)^nJ_{-n-\frac{1}{2}}(x)\}\end{aligned}\right\}. \tag{54}$$

A similar expansion for the real exponential function can also be found; it is

$$\frac{e^{-k|\mathbf{r}_1-\mathbf{r}_2|}}{|\mathbf{r}_1-\mathbf{r}_2|} = \sum_{n=0}^{\infty} \frac{2n+1}{(r_1 r_2)^{\frac{1}{2}}} I_{n+\frac{1}{2}}(kr_a)K_{n+\frac{1}{2}}(kr_b)P_n(\cos \widehat{\mathbf{r}_1\mathbf{r}_2}), \tag{55}$$

where r_a and r_b are defined as before. In equations (54) and (55) the functions $J_m(z)$, $I_m(z)$, and $K_m(z)$ denote the usual Bessel functions in the notation adopted by Watson.†

Partial differentiation of equation (55) with respect to k leads to other expansions of importance:

$$e^{-k|\mathbf{r}_1-\mathbf{r}_2|} = \sum_{n=0}^{\infty} \frac{2n+1}{(r_1 r_2)^{\frac{1}{2}}} p_n(k, r_b; r_a)P_n(\cos \widehat{\mathbf{r}_1\mathbf{r}_2}), \tag{56}$$

$$|\mathbf{r}_1-\mathbf{r}_2|e^{-k|\mathbf{r}_1-\mathbf{r}_2|} = \sum_{n=0}^{\infty} \frac{2n+1}{(r_1 r_2)^{\frac{1}{2}}} q_n(k, r_b; r_a)P_n(\cos \widehat{\mathbf{r}_1\mathbf{r}_2}), \tag{57}$$

where

$$p_n(k, r_b; r_a) - r_b\,I_{n+\frac{1}{2}}(kr_a)K_{n+\frac{1}{2}}(kr_b) - r_a\,I_{n-\frac{1}{2}}(kr_a)K_{n+\frac{1}{2}}(kr_b) \tag{58}$$

and

$$q_n(k, r_b; r_a) = (r_a^2+r_b^2)I_{n+\frac{1}{2}}(kr_a)K_{n+\frac{1}{2}}(kr_b) - $$
$$- \frac{2n}{2n+1}r_a r_b\,I_{n-\frac{1}{2}}(kr_a)K_{n-\frac{1}{2}}(kr_b) - \frac{2(n+1)}{2n+1}r_a r_b\,I_{n+\frac{3}{2}}(kr_a)K_{n+\frac{3}{2}}(kr_b). \tag{59}$$

If formulae for higher powers are needed they may be obtained by further partial differentiations with respect to k. These expansions facilitate the evaluation of certain complicated integrals occurring in the theory of molecular structure.‡

10. Surface spherical harmonics

From the two sets of orthogonal functions $P_l^u(\cos \theta)$ and $e^{iu\phi}$ we can form a third set of functions

$$Y_{l,u}(\theta, \phi) = (-1)^u\left[\frac{2l+1}{2}\frac{(l-u)!}{(l+u)!}\right]^{\frac{1}{2}} P_l^u(\cos \theta)e^{iu\phi}(2\pi)^{-\frac{1}{2}}, \tag{60}$$

which is an orthogonal set on the surface of the unit sphere, i.e. the functions of the set satisfy the integral relation

$$\int_0^{\pi} \sin \theta \, d\theta \int_0^{2\pi} Y_{l,u}^* Y_{l',u'} \, d\phi = \delta_{ll'}\delta_{uu'}. \tag{61}$$

† G. N. Watson, *The Theory of Bessel Functions* (2nd ed., Cambridge, 1944).
‡ C. A. Coulson, *Proc. Camb. Phil. Soc.* **33**, 104 (1937).

The functions $Y_{l,u}(\theta, \phi)$ possess the further property that they are solutions of Laplace's equation in polar coordinates when $\partial/\partial r$ is taken to vanish identically. Furthermore, they satisfy a large number of recurrence relations which may readily be written down from a knowledge of the recurrence relations satisfied by the associated Legendre functions $P_l^u(\cos\theta)$. Some of these results which arise frequently in calculations in quantum mechanics are given below for reference. Their derivation follows directly from the results of the previous sections.

$$\frac{\partial}{\partial\theta} Y_{l,u}(\theta, \phi)$$

$$= -\tfrac{1}{2}\{(l+u)(l-u+1)\}^{\frac{1}{2}} Y_{l,u-1} e^{i\phi} + \tfrac{1}{2}\{(l-u)(l+u+1)\}^{\frac{1}{2}} Y_{l,u+1} e^{-i\phi}, \quad (62)$$

$$(L_x + iL_y) Y_{l,u}(\theta, \phi) = \hbar\{(l-u)(l+u+1)\}^{\frac{1}{2}} Y_{l,u+1}(\theta, \phi), \quad (63)$$

$$(L_x - iL_y) Y_{l,u}(\theta, \phi) = \hbar\{(l+u)(l-u+1)\}^{\frac{1}{2}} Y_{l,u-1}(\theta, \phi), \quad (64)$$

$$L_z Y_{l,u}(\theta, \phi) = m\hbar Y_{l,u}, \quad (65)$$

$$\mathbf{L}^2 Y_{l,u}(\theta, \phi) = l(l+1)\hbar^2 Y_{l,u}(\theta, \phi). \quad (66)$$

NAME INDEX

SUBJECT INDEX

Absorption coefficient, 253.
— of radiation, 253, 255, 265.
Airy integrals, 18.
Alkali atoms, 100.
— halides, 164, 201.
Alpha decay, 17, 22.
— particles scattered by helium, 113.
Analytical wave functions, 142.
Angular momentum, 44, 85, 86, 305, 306, 359–62.
Annihilation of positrons, 275, 313.
Anomalous Zeeman effect, 91, 100.
Associated Legendre polynomials, 382.
Atomic size, 41.
— units, 127.
Auger effect, 342.

Benzene molecule, 198, 200.
Bohr magneton, 88.
— theory of atom, 44.
Bond angles, 194.
Bonding orbits, 199.
Born approximation, 238, 239.
Bose Einstein particles, 354.
Bragg reflection, 212.
Breadth of spectral lines, 268.
Bremsstrahlung, 275.
Brillouin zone, 212.
Butadiene, 200.

Canonical transformations, 368.
Carbon atom, 150.
— molecules, 194.
Centre of force scattering, 234.
Chlorine ion, 140.
Classical Poisson bracket, 356.
— theory of radiation, 275.
Classification of radiation processes, 274.
Coherent scattering of light, 274.
Cohesive forces, 201, 220.
Cold emission, 219.
Collective electron model, 215.
Collisions, 233 et seq.; between electrons and atoms, 242; between fast particles, 339; between identical particles, 113; between molecules, 162.
Colour centres, 226.
Commutation relations, 36, 363.
Complex molecules, 192 et seq.
Compressibility, 202.
Compton effect, 4, 33, 190, 274, 316.
Conduction band, 223.
Conductivity, 222.
Conductors, 214.
Constant of motion, 363.

Contact between metal and insulator, 229; between metal and semi-conductor, 230.
— transformations, 357, 369.
Continuity equation, 259, 294, 309.
Continuous spectrum, 60.
Cosmic ray phenomena, 289.
Coulomb scattering, 114, 241.
Cross-section for radiation processes, 267 et seq.; for collisions, 233.
Crystals, 201, 207, 226, 227.

Darwin's variation principle, 308, 353.
Deflexion of electron beams, 10.
Degenerate states, 49, 72.
Delta function, 95, 277, 372.
Deuteron, 122.
Diamagnetic susceptibility, 141.
Diatomic molecules, 103, 110, 162, 176.
Differential analyser, 125.
Diphenyl, 200.
Dipole moments, 257.
Dirac wave equation, 296, 322, 351; matrices, 298.
Dirac's generalization of matrix mechanics, 372.
Distribution of momentum, 19, 34, 59, 69, 190.
Double scattering of electrons, 332.
Doublet separation, 100.
Dual nature of electrons, 7; of light, 4.

Einstein–Bose statistics, 107.
Einstein coefficients, 253.
Electrical conductivity, 222.
Electron affinities, 204; beams, 10; in a box, 46; spin, 89.
Electronic motion in crystals, 207; in non-metals, 223.
Emission bands, 215.
— of radiation, 253, 258, 265.
Energy levels, 42; by perturbation method, 118; in a magnetic field, 87; of hydrogen atom, 44, 57, 323; of lithium atom, 57.
Energy of a many-electron system, 133.
Ethylene double-streamers, 197.
Exchange integral, 119, 134.
Excitation of atoms by α-particles, 248.
Excited states, 41.
Exciton, 227.
Expansion theorem, 65.

F-centres, 226.
f-sum rule, 169.
Fermi–Dirac statistics, 107.
Field quantization, 259.

CATALOG OF DOVER BOOKS

PHYSICS

General physics

FOUNDATIONS OF PHYSICS, R. B. Lindsay & H. Margenau. Excellent bridge between semi-popular works & technical treatises. A discussion of methods of physical description, construction of theory; valuable for physicist with elementary calculus who is interested in ideas that give meaning to data, tools of modern physics. Contents include symbolism, mathematical equations; space & time foundations of mechanics; probability; physics & continua; electron theory; special & general relativity; quantum mechanics; causality. "Thorough and yet not overdetailed. Unreservedly recommended," NATURE (London). Unabridged, corrected edition. List of recommended readings. 35 illustrations. xi + 537pp. 5⅜ x 8.
S377 Paperbound $2.75

FUNDAMENTAL FORMULAS OF PHYSICS, ed. by D. H. Menzel. Highly useful, fully inexpensive reference and study text, ranging from simple to highly sophisticated operations. Mathematics integrated into text—each chapter stands as short textbook of field represented. Vol. 1: Statistics, Physical Constants, Special Theory of Relativity, Hydrodynamics, Aerodynamics, Boundary Value Problems in Math. Physics; Viscosity, Electromagnetic Theory, etc. Vol. 2: Sound, Acoustics, Geometrical Optics, Electron Optics, High-Energy Phenomena, Magnetism, Biophysics, much more. Index. Total of 800pp. 5⅜ x 8.
Vol. 1 S595 Paperbound $2.00
Vol. 2 S596 Paperbound $2.00

MATHEMATICAL PHYSICS, D. H. Menzel. Thorough one-volume treatment of the mathematical techniques vital for classic mechanics, electromagnetic theory, quantum theory, and relativity. Written by the Harvard Professor of Astrophysics for junior, senior, and graduate courses, it gives clear explanations of all those aspects of function theory, vectors, matrices, dyadics, tensors, partial differential equations, etc., necessary for the understanding of the various physical theories. Electron theory, relativity, and other topics seldom presented appear here in considerable detail. Scores of definitions, conversion factors, dimensional constants, etc. "More detailed than normal for an advanced text . . . excellent set of sections on Dyadics, Matrices, and Tensors," JOURNAL OF THE FRANKLIN INSTITUTE. Index. 193 problems, with answers. x + 412pp. 5⅜ x 8.
S56 Paperbound $2.00

THE SCIENTIFIC PAPERS OF J. WILLARD GIBBS. All the published papers of America's outstanding theoretical scientist (except for "Statistical Mechanics" and "Vector Analysis"). Vol I (thermodynamics) contains one of the most brilliant of all 19th-century scientific papers—the 300-page "On the Equilibrium of Heterogeneous Substances," which founded the science of physical chemistry, and clearly stated a number of highly important natural laws for the first time; 8 other papers complete the first volume. Vol II includes 2 papers on dynamics, 8 on vector analysis and multiple algebra, 5 on the electromagnetic theory of light, and 6 miscellaneous papers. Biographical sketch by H. A. Bumstead. Total of xxxvi + 718pp. 5⅝ x 8⅜.
S721 Vol I Paperbound $2.00
S722 Vol II Paperbound $2.00
The set $4.00

BASIC THEORIES OF PHYSICS, Peter Gabriel Bergmann. Two-volume set which presents a critical examination of important topics in the major subdivisions of classical and modern physics. The first volume is concerned with classical mechanics and electrodynamics: mechanics of mass points, analytical mechanics, matter in bulk, electrostatics and magnetostatics, electromagnetic interaction, the field waves, special relativity, and waves. The second volume (Heat and Quanta) contains discussions of the kinetic hypothesis, physics and statistics, stationary ensembles, laws of thermodynamics, early quantum theories, atomic spectra, probability waves, quantization in wave mechanics, approximation methods, and abstract quantum theory. A valuable supplement to any thorough course or text.
Heat and Quanta: Index. 8 figures. x + 300pp. 5⅜ x 8½.
S968 Paperbound $1.75
Mechanics and Electrodynamics: Index. 14 figures. vii + 280pp. 5⅜ x 8½.
S969 Paperbound $1.75

THEORETICAL PHYSICS, A. S. Kompaneyets. One of the very few thorough studies of the subject in this price range. Provides advanced students with a comprehensive theoretical background. Especially strong on recent experimentation and developments in quantum theory. Contents: Mechanics (Generalized Coordinates, Lagrange's Equation, Collision of Particles, etc.), Electrodynamics (Vector Analysis, Maxwell's equations, Transmission of Signals, Theory of Relativity, etc.), Quantum Mechanics (the Inadequacy of Classical Mechanics, the Wave Equation, Motion in a Central Field, Quantum Theory of Radiation, Quantum Theories of Dispersion and Scattering, etc.), and Statistical Physics (Equilibrium Distribution of Molecules in an Ideal Gas, Boltzmann statistics, Bose and Fermi Distribution, Thermodynamic Quantities, etc.). Revised to 1961. Translated by George Yankovsky, authorized by Kompaneyets. 137 exercises. 56 figures. 529pp. 5⅜ x 8½. S972 Paperbound $2.50

ANALYTICAL AND CANONICAL FORMALISM IN PHYSICS, André Mercier. A survey, in one volume, of the variational principles (the key principles—in mathematical form—from which the basic laws of any one branch of physics can be derived) of the several branches of physical theory, together with an examination of the relationships among them. Contents: the Lagrangian Formalism, Lagrangian Densities, Canonical Formalism, Canonical Form of Electrodynamics, Hamiltonian Densities, Transformations, and Canonical Form with Vanishing Jacobian Determinant. Numerous examples and exercises. For advanced students, teachers, etc. 6 figures. Index. viii + 222pp. 5⅜ x 8½.
S1077 Paperbound $1.75

Acoustics, optics, electricity and magnetism, electromagnetics, magnetohydrodynamics

THE THEORY OF SOUND, Lord Rayleigh. Most vibrating systems likely to be encountered in practice can be tackled successfully by the methods set forth by the great Nobel laureate, Lord Rayleigh. Complete coverage of experimental, mathematical aspects of sound theory. Partial contents: Harmonic motions, vibrating systems in general, lateral vibrations of bars, curved plates or shells, applications of Laplace's functions to acoustical problems, fluid friction, plane vortex-sheet, vibrations of solid bodies, etc. This is the first inexpensive edition of this great reference and study work. Bibliography. Historical introduction by R. B. Lindsay. Total of 1040pp. 97 figures. 5⅜ x 8.
S292, S293, Two volume set, paperbound, **$4.70**

THE DYNAMICAL THEORY OF SOUND, H. Lamb. Comprehensive mathematical treatment of the physical aspects of sound, covering the theory of vibrations, the general theory of sound, and the equations of motion of strings, bars, membranes, pipes, and resonators. Includes chapters on plane, spherical, and simple harmonic waves, and the Helmholtz Theory of Audition. Complete and self-contained development for student and specialist; all fundamental differential equations solved completely. Specific mathematical details for such important phenomena as harmonics, normal modes, forced vibrations of strings, theory of reed pipes, etc. Index. Bibliography. 86 diagrams. viii + 307pp. 5⅜ x 8.
S655 Paperbound **$1.50**

WAVE PROPAGATION IN PERIODIC STRUCTURES, L. Brillouin. A general method and application to different problems: pure physics, such as scattering of X-rays of crystals, thermal vibration in crystal lattices, electronic motion in metals; and also problems of electrical engineering. Partial contents: elastic waves in 1-dimensional lattices of point masses. Propagation of waves along 1-dimensional lattices. Energy flow. 2 dimensional, 3 dimensional lattices. Mathieu's equation. Matrices and propagation of waves along an electric line. Continuous electric lines. 131 illustrations. Bibliography. Index. xii + 253pp. 5⅜ x 8.
S34 Paperbound **$1.85**

THEORY OF VIBRATIONS, N. W. McLachlan. Based on an exceptionally successful graduate course given at Brown University, this discusses linear systems having 1 degree of freedom, forced vibrations of simple linear systems, vibration of flexible strings, transverse vibrations of bars and tubes, transverse vibration of circular plate, sound waves of finite amplitude, etc. Index. 99 diagrams. 160pp. 5⅜ x 8.
S190 Paperbound **$1.35**

LIGHT: PRINCIPLES AND EXPERIMENTS, George S. Monk. Covers theory, experimentation, and research. Intended for students with some background in general physics and elementary calculus. Three main divisions: 1) Eight chapters on geometrical optics—fundamental concepts (the ray and its optical length, Fermat's principle, etc.), laws of image formation, apertures in optical systems, photometry, optical instruments etc.; 2) 9 chapters on physical optics—interference, diffraction, polarization, spectra, the Rayleigh refractometer, the wave theory of light, etc.; 3) 23 instructive experiments based directly on the theoretical text. "Probably the best intermediate textbook on light in the English language. Certainly, it is the best book which includes both geometrical and physical optics," J. Rud Nielson, PHYSICS FORUM. Revised edition. 102 problems and answers. 12 appendices. 6 tables. Index. 270 illustrations. xi +489pp. 5⅜ x 8½.
S341 Paperbound **$2.45**

PHOTOMETRY, John W. T. Walsh. The best treatment of both "bench" and "illumination" photometry in English by one of Britain's foremost experts in the field (President of the International Commission on Illumination). Limited to those matters, theoretical and practical, which affect the measurement of light flux, candlepower, illumination, etc., and excludes treatment of the use to which such measurements may be put after they have been made. Chapters on Radiation, The Eye and Vision, Photo-Electric Cells, The Principles of Photometry, The Measurement of Luminous Intensity, Colorimetry, Spectrophotometry, Stellar Photometry, The Photometric Laboratory, etc. Third revised (1958) edition. 281 illustrations. 10 appendices. xxiv + 544pp. 5½ x 9¼.
S319 Clothbound **$10.00**

EXPERIMENTAL SPECTROSCOPY, R. A. Sawyer. Clear discussion of prism and grating spectrographs and the techniques of their use in research, with emphasis on those principles and techniques that are fundamental to practically all uses of spectroscopic equipment. Beginning with a brief history of spectroscopy, the author covers such topics as light sources, spectroscopic apparatus, prism spectroscopes and graphs, diffraction grating, the photographic process, determination of wave length, spectral intensity, infrared spectroscopy, spectrochemical analysis, etc. This revised edition contains new material on the production of replica gratings, solar spectroscopy from rockets, new standard of wave length, etc. Index. Bibliography. 111 illustrations. x + 358pp. 5⅜ x 8½.
S1045 Paperbound **$2.00**

FUNDAMENTALS OF ELECTRICITY AND MAGNETISM, L. B. Loeb. For students of physics, chemistry, or engineering who want an introduction to electricity and magnetism on a higher level and in more detail than general elementary physics texts provide. Only elementary differential and integral calculus is assumed. Physical laws developed logically, from magnetism to electric currents, Ohm's law, electrolysis, and on to static electricity, induction, etc. Covers an unusual amount of material; one third of book on modern material: solution of wave equation, photoelectric and thermionic effects, etc. Complete statement of the various electrical systems of units and interrelations. 2 Indexes. 75 pages of problems with answers stated. Over 300 figures and diagrams. xix +669pp. 5⅜ x 8.
S745 Paperbound **$2.75**

Catalogue of Dover Books

SUPERFLUIDS: MACROSCOPIC THEORY OF SUPERCONDUCTIVITY, Vol. I, Fritz London. The major work by one of the founders and great theoreticians of modern quantum physics. Consolidates the researches that led to the present understanding of the nature of super-conductivity. Prof. London here reveals that quantum mechanics is operative on the macro-scopic plane as well as the submolecular level. Contents: Properties of Superconductors and Their Thermodynamical Correlation; Electrodynamics of the Pure Superconducting State; Relation between Current and Field; Measurements of the Penetration Depth; Non-Viscous Flow vs. Superconductivity; Micro-waves in Superconductors; Reality of the Domain Structure; and many other related topics. A new epilogue by M. J. Buckingham discusses developments in the field up to 1960. Corrected and expanded edition. An appreciation of the author's life and work by L. W. Nordheim. Biography by Edith London. Bibliography of his publica-tions. 45 figures. 2 Indices. xviii + 173pp. 5⅝ x 8⅜. S44 Paperbound **$1.45**

SELECTED PAPERS ON PHYSICAL PROCESSES IN IONIZED PLASMAS, Edited by Donald H. Menzel, Director, Harvard College Observatory. 30 important papers relating to the study of highly ionized gases or plasmas selected by a foremost contributor in the field, with the assistance of Dr. L. H. Aller. The essays include 18 on the physical processes in gaseous nebulae, covering problems of radiation and radiative transfer, the Balmer decrement, electron temperatures, spectrophotometry, etc. 10 papers deal with the interpretation of nebular spectra, by Bohm, Van Vleck, Aller, Minkowski, etc. There is also a discussion of the intensities of "forbidden" spectral lines by George Shortley and a paper concern-ing the theory of hydrogenic spectra by Menzel and Pekeris. Other contributors: Goldberg, Hebb, Baker, Bowen, Ufford, Liller, etc. viii + 374pp. 6⅛ x 9¼. S60 Paperbound **$2.95**

THE ELECTROMAGNETIC FIELD, Max Mason & Warren Weaver. Used constantly by graduate engineers. Vector methods exclusively: detailed treatment of electrostatics, expansion meth-ods, with tables converting any quantity into absolute electromagnetic, absolute electrostatic, practical units. Discrete charges, ponderable bodies, Maxwell field equations, etc. Introduc-tion. Indexes. 416pp. 5⅜ x 8. S185 Paperbound **$2.00**

THEORY OF ELECTRONS AND ITS APPLICATION TO THE PHENOMENA OF LIGHT AND RADIANT HEAT, H. Lorentz. Lectures delivered at Columbia University by Nobel laureate Lorentz. Unabridged, they form a historical coverage of the theory of free electrons, motion, absorption of heat, Zeeman effect, propagation of light in molecular bodies, inverse Zeeman effect, optical phenomena in moving bodies, etc. 109 pages of notes explain the more advanced sections. Index. 9 figures. 352pp. 5⅜ x 8. S173 Paperbound **$1.85**

FUNDAMENTAL ELECTROMAGNETIC THEORY, Ronold P. King, Professor Applied Physics, Harvard University. Original and valuable introduction to electromagnetic theory and to circuit theory from the standpoint of electromagnetic theory. Contents: Mathematical Description of Matter—stationary and nonstationary states; Mathematical Description of Space and of Simple Media—Field Equations, Integral Forms of Field Equations, Electromagnetic Force, etc.; Transformation of Field and Force Equations; Electromagnetic Waves in Unbounded Regions; Skin Effect and Internal Impedance—in a solid cylindrical conductor, etc.; and Electrical Circuits—Analytical Foundations, Near-zone and quasi-near zone circuits, Balanced two-wire and four-wire transmission lines. Revised and enlarged version. New preface by the author. 5 appendices (Differential operators: Vector Formulas and Identities, etc.). Problems. Indexes. Bibliography. xvi + 580pp. 5⅜ x 8½. S1023 Paperbound **$2.75**

Hydrodynamics

A TREATISE ON HYDRODYNAMICS, A. B. Basset. Favorite text on hydrodynamics for 2 genera-tions of physicists, hydrodynamical engineers, oceanographers, ship designers, etc. Clear enough for the beginning student, and thorough source for graduate students and engineers on the work of d'Alembert, Euler, Laplace, Lagrange, Poisson, Green, Clebsch, Stokes, Cauchy, Helmholtz, J. J. Thomson, Love, Hicks, Greenhill, Besant, Lamb, etc. Great amount of docu-mentation on entire theory of classical hydrodynamics. Vol I: theory of motion of frictionless liquids, vortex, and cyclic irrotational motion, etc. 132 exercises. Bibliography. 3 Appendixes. xii + 264pp. Vol II: motion in viscous liquids, harmonic analysis, theory of tides, etc. 112 exercises, Bibliography. 4 Appendixes. xv + 328pp. Two volume set. 5⅜ x 8.
S724 Vol I Paperbound **$1.75**
S725 Vol II Paperbound **$1.75**
The set **$3.50**

HYDRODYNAMICS, Horace Lamb. Internationally famous complete coverage of standard refer-ence work on dynamics of liquids & gases. Fundamental theorems, equations, methods, solutions, background, for classical hydrodynamics. Chapters include Equations of Motion, Integration of Equations in Special Gases, Irrotational Motion, Motion of Liquid in 2 Dimen-sions, Motion of Solids through Liquid-Dynamical Theory, Vortex Motion, Tidal Waves, Surface Waves, Waves of Expansion, Viscosity, Rotating Masses of liquids. Excellently planned, ar-ranged; clear, lucid presentation. 6th enlarged, revised edition. Index. Over 900 footnotes, mostly bibliographical. 119 figures. xv + 738pp. 6⅛ x 9¼. S256 Paperbound **$3.25**

HYDRODYNAMICS, H. Dryden, F. Murnaghan, Harry Bateman. Published by the National Research Council in 1932 this enormous volume offers a complete coverage of classical hydrodynamics. Encyclopedic in quality. Partial contents: physics of fluids, motion, turbulent flow, compressible fluids, motion in 1, 2, 3 dimensions; viscous fluids rotating, laminar motion, resistance of motion through viscous fluid, eddy viscosity, hydraulic flow in channels of various shapes, discharge of gases, flow past obstacles, etc. Bibliography of over 2,900 items. Indexes. 23 figures. 634pp. 5⅜ x 8. S303 Paperbound **$2.75**

Mechanics, dynamics, thermodynamics, elasticity

MECHANICS, J. P. Den Hartog. Already a classic among introductory texts, the M.I.T. professor's lively and discursive presentation is equally valuable as a beginner's text, an engineering student's refresher, or a practicing engineer's reference. Emphasis in this highly readable text is on illuminating fundamental principles and showing how they are embodied in a great number of real engineering and design problems: trusses, loaded cables, beams, jacks, hoists, etc. Provides advanced material on relative motion and gyroscopes not usual in introductory texts. "Very thoroughly recommended to all those anxious to improve their real understanding of the principles of mechanics." MECHANICAL WORLD. Index. List of equations. 334 problems, all with answers. Over 550 diagrams and drawings. ix + 462pp. 5⅜ x 8.
S754 Paperbound **$2.00**

THEORETICAL MECHANICS: AN INTRODUCTION TO MATHEMATICAL PHYSICS, J. S. Ames, F. D. Murnaghan. A mathematically rigorous development of theoretical mechanics for the advanced student, with constant practical applications. Used in hundreds of advanced courses. An unusually thorough coverage of gyroscopic and baryscopic material, detailed analyses of the Coriolis acceleration, applications of Lagrange's equations, motion of the double pendulum, Hamilton-Jacobi partial differential equations, group velocity and dispersion, etc. Special relativity is also included. 159 problems. 44 figures. ix + 462pp. 5⅜ x 8.
S461 Paperbound **$2.00**

THEORETICAL MECHANICS: STATICS AND THE DYNAMICS OF A PARTICLE, W. D. MacMillan. Used for over 3 decades as a self-contained and extremely comprehensive advanced undergraduate text in mathematical physics, physics, astronomy, and deeper foundations of engineering. Early sections require only a knowledge of geometry; later, a working knowledge of calculus. Hundreds of basic problems, including projectiles to the moon, escape velocity, harmonic motion, ballistics, falling bodies, transmission of power, stress and strain, elasticity, astronomical problems. 340 practice problems plus many fully worked out examples make it possible to test and extend principles developed in the text. 200 figures. xvii + 430pp. 5⅜ x 8. S467 Paperbound **$2.00**

THEORETICAL MECHANICS: THE THEORY OF THE POTENTIAL, W. D. MacMillan. A comprehensive, well balanced presentation of potential theory, serving both as an introduction and a reference work with regard to specific problems, for physicists and mathematicians. No prior knowledge of integral relations is assumed, and all mathematical material is developed as it becomes necessary. Includes: Attraction of Finite Bodies; Newtonian Potential Function; Vector Fields, Green and Gauss Theorems; Attractions of Surfaces and Lines; Surface Distribution of Matter; Two-Layer Surfaces; Spherical Harmonics; Ellipsoidal Harmonics; etc. "The great number of particular cases . . . should make the book valuable to geophysicists and others actively engaged in practical applications of the potential theory," Review of Scientific Instruments. Index. Bibliography. xiii + 469pp. 5⅜ x 8. S486 Paperbound **$2.25**

THEORETICAL MECHANICS: DYNAMICS OF RIGID BODIES, W. D. MacMillan. Theory of dynamics of a rigid body is developed, using both the geometrical and analytical methods of instruction. Begins with exposition of algebra of vectors, it goes through momentum principles, motion in space, use of differential equations and infinite series to solve more sophisticated dynamics problems. Partial contents: moments of inertia, systems of free particles, motion parallel to a fixed plane, rolling motion, method of periodic solutions, much more. 82 figs. 199 problems. Bibliography. Indexes. xii + 476pp. 5⅜ x 8. S641 Paperbound **$2.00**

MATHEMATICAL FOUNDATIONS OF STATISTICAL MECHANICS, A. I. Khinchin. Offering a precise and rigorous formulation of problems, this book supplies a thorough and up-to-date exposition. It provides analytical tools needed to replace cumbersome concepts, and furnishes for the first time a logical step-by-step introduction to the subject. Partial contents: geometry & kinematics of the phase space, ergodic problem, reduction to theory of probability, application of central limit problem, ideal monatomic gas, foundation of thermo-dynamics, dispersion and distribution of sum functions. Key to notations. Index. viii + 179pp. 5⅜ x 8.
S147 Paperbound **$1.50**

ELEMENTARY PRINCIPLES IN STATISTICAL MECHANICS, J. W. Gibbs. Last work of the great Yale mathematical physicist, still one of the most modern treatments available for advanced students and workers in the field. Covers the basic principle of conservation of probability of phase, theory of errors in the calculated phases of a system, the contributions of Clausius, Maxwell, Boltzmann, and Gibbs himself, and much more. Includes valuable comparison of statistical mechanics with thermodynamics: Carnot's cycle, mechanical definitions of entropy, etc. xvi + 208pp. 5⅜ x 8. S707 Paperbound **$1.45**

PRINCIPLES OF MECHANICS AND DYNAMICS, Sir William Thomson (Lord Kelvin) and Peter Guthrie Tait. The principles and theories of fundamental branches of classical physics explained by two of the greatest physicists of all time. A broad survey of mechanics, with material on hydrodynamics, elasticity, potential theory, and what is now standard mechanics. Thorough and detailed coverage, with many examples, derivations, and topics not included in more recent studies. Only a knowledge of calculus is needed to work through this book. Vol. I (Preliminary): Kinematics; Dynamical Laws and Principles; Experience (observation, experimentation, formation of hypotheses, scientific method); Measures and Instruments; Continuous Calculating Machines. Vol. II (Abstract Dynamics): Statics of a Particle—Attraction; Statics of Solids and Fluids. Formerly Titled "Treatise on Natural Philosophy." Unabridged reprint of revised edition. Index. 168 diagrams. Total of xlii + 1035pp. 5⅜ x 8½.

Vol. I: S966 Paperbound **$2.35**
Vol. II: S967 Paperbound **$2.35**
Two volume Set Paperbound **$4.70**

INVESTIGATIONS ON THE THEORY OF THE BROWNIAN MOVEMENT, Albert Einstein. Reprints from rare European journals. 5 basic papers, including the Elementary Theory of the Brownian Movement, written at the request of Lorentz to provide a simple explanation. Translated by A. D. Cowper. Annotated, edited by R. Fürth. 33pp. of notes elucidate, give history of previous investigations. Author, subject indexes. 62 footnotes. 124pp. 5⅜ x 8.
S304 Paperbound **$1.25**

MECHANICS VIA THE CALCULUS, P. W. Norris, W. S. Legge. Covers almost everything, from linear motion to vector analysis: equations determining motion, linear methods, compounding of simple harmonic motions, Newton's laws of motion, Hooke's law, the simple pendulum, motion of a particle in 1 plane, centers of gravity, virtual work, friction, kinetic energy of rotating bodies, equilibrium of strings, hydrostatics, sheering stresses, elasticity, etc. 550 problems. 3rd revised edition. xii + 367pp. 6 x 9. S207 Clothbound **$4.95**

THE DYNAMICS OF PARTICLES AND OF RIGID, ELASTIC, AND FLUID BODIES; BEING LECTURES ON MATHEMATICAL PHYSICS, A. G. Webster. The reissuing of this classic fills the need for a comprehensive work on dynamics. A wide range of topics is covered in unusually great depth, applying ordinary and partial differential equations. Part I considers laws of motion and methods applicable to systems of all sorts; oscillation, resonance, cyclic systems, etc. Part 2 is a detailed study of the dynamics of rigid bodies. Part 3 introduces the theory of potential; stress and strain, Newtonian potential functions, gyrostatics, wave and vortex motion, etc. Further contents: Kinematics of a point; Lagrange's equations; Hamilton's principle; Systems of vectors; Statics and dynamics of deformable bodies; much more, not easily found together in one volume. Unabridged reprinting of 2nd edition. 20 pages of notes on differential equations and the higher analysis. 203 illustrations. Selected bibliography. Index. xi + 588pp. 5⅜ x 8. S522 Paperbound **$2.45**

A TREATISE ON DYNAMICS OF A PARTICLE, E. J. Routh. Elementary text on dynamics for beginning mathematics or physics student. Unusually detailed treatment from elementary definitions to motion in 3 dimensions, emphasizing concrete aspects. Much unique material important in recent applications. Covers impulsive forces, rectilinear and constrained motion in 2 dimensions, harmonic and parabolic motion, degrees of freedom, closed orbits, the conical pendulum, the principle of least action, Jacobi's method, and much more. Index. 559 problems, many fully worked out, incorporated into text. xiii + 418pp. 5⅜ x 8.
S696 Paperbound **$2.25**

DYNAMICS OF A SYSTEM OF RIGID BODIES (Elementary Section), E. J. Routh. Revised 7th edition of this standard reference. This volume covers the dynamical principles of the subject, and its more elementary applications: finding moments of inertia by integration, foci of inertia, d'Alembert's principle, impulsive forces, motion in 2 and 3 dimensions, Lagrange's equations, relative indicatrix, Euler's theorem, large tautochronous motions, etc. Index. 55 figures. Scores of problems. xv + 443pp. 5⅜ x 8. S664 Paperbound **$2.50**

DYNAMICS OF A SYSTEM OF RIGID BODIES (Advanced Section), E. J. Routh. Revised 6th edition of a classic reference aid. Much of its material remains unique. Partial contents: moving axes, relative motion, oscillations about equilibrium, motion. Motion of a body under no forces, any forces. Nature of motion given by linear equations and conditions of stability. Free, forced vibrations, constants of integration, calculus of finite differences, variations, precession and nutation, motion of the moon, motion of string, chain, membranes. 64 figures. 498pp. 5⅜ x 8. S229 Paperbound **$2.45**

DYNAMICAL THEORY OF GASES, James Jeans. Divided into mathematical and physical chapters for the convenience of those not expert in mathematics, this volume discusses the mathematical theory of gas in a steady state, thermodynamics, Boltzmann and Maxwell, kinetic theory, quantum theory, exponentials, etc. 4th enlarged edition, with new material on quantum theory, quantum dynamics, etc. Indexes. 28 figures. 444pp. 6⅛ x 9¼.
S136 Paperbound **$2.65**

THE THEORY OF HEAT RADIATION, Max Planck. A pioneering work in thermodynamics, providing basis for most later work, Nobel laureate Planck writes on Deductions from Electrodynamics and Thermodynamics, Entropy and Probability, Irreversible Radiation Processes, etc. Starts with simple experimental laws of optics, advances to problems of spectral distribution of energy and irreversibility. Bibliography. 7 illustrations. xiv + 224pp. 5⅜ x 8.
S546 Paperbound **$1.50**

FOUNDATIONS OF POTENTIAL THEORY, O. D. Kellogg. Based on courses given at Harvard this is suitable for both advanced and beginning mathematicians. Proofs are rigorous, and much material not generally avaliable elsewhere is included. Partial contents: forces of gravity, fields of force, divergence theorem, properties of Newtonian potentials at points of free space, potentials as solutions of Laplace's equations, harmonic functions, electrostatics, electric images, logarithmic potential, etc. One of Grundlehren Series. ix + 384pp. 5⅜ x 8.
S144 Paperbound **$1.98**

THERMODYNAMICS, Enrico Fermi. Unabridged reproduction of 1937 edition. Elementary in treatment; remarkable for clarity, organization. Requires no knowledge of advanced math beyond calculus, only familiarity with fundamentals of thermometry, calorimetry. Partial Contents: Thermodynamic systems; First & Second laws of thermodynamics; Entropy; Thermodynamic potentials: phase rule, reversible electric cell; Gaseous reactions: van't Hoff reaction box, principle of LeChatelier; Thermodynamics of dilute solutions: osmotic & vapor pressures, boiling & freezing points; Entropy constant. Index. 25 problems. 24 illustrations. x + 160pp. 5⅜ x 8.
S361 Paperbound **$1.75**

THE THERMODYNAMICS OF ELECTRICAL PHENOMENA IN METALS and A CONDENSED COLLECTION OF THERMODYNAMIC FORMULAS, P. W. Bridgman. Major work by the Nobel Prizewinner: stimulating conceptual introduction to aspects of the electron theory of metals, giving an intuitive understanding of fundamental relationships concealed by the formal systems of Onsager and others. Elementary mathematical formulations show clearly the fundamental thermodynamical relationships of the electric field, and a complete phenomenological theory of metals is created. This is the work in which Bridgman announced his famous "thermomotive force" and his distinction between "driving" and "working" electromotive force. We have added in this Dover edition the author's long unavailable tables of thermodynamic formulas, extremely valuable for the speed of reference they allow. Two works bound as one. Index. 33 figures. Bibliography. xviii + 256pp. 5⅜ x 8. S723 Paperbound **$1.65**

TREATISE ON THERMODYNAMICS, Max Planck. Based on Planck's original papers this offers a uniform point of view for the entire field and has been used as an introduction for students who have studied elementary chemistry, physics, and calculus. Rejecting the earlier approaches of Helmholtz and Maxwell, the author makes no assumptions regarding the naturo of hoat, but bogins with a few empirical facts, and from these deduces new physical and chemical laws. 3rd English edition of this standard text by a Nobel laureate. xvi + 297pp. 5⅜ x 8.
S219 Paperbound **$1.75**

THE MATHEMATICAL THEORY OF ELASTICITY, A. E. H. Love. A wealth of practical illustration combined with thorough discussion of fundamentals—theory, application, special problems and solutions. Partial Contents: Analysis of Strain & Stress, Elasticity of Solid Bodies, Elasticity of Crystals, Vibration of Spheres, Cylinders, Propagation of Waves in Elastic Solid Media, Torsion, Theory of Continuous Beams, Plates. Rigorous treatment of Volterra's theory of dislocations, 2-dimensional elastic systems, other topics of modern interest. "For years the standard treatise on elasticity," AMERICAN MATHEMATICAL MONTHLY. 4th revised edition. Index. 76 figures. xviii + 643pp. 6⅛ x 9¼.
S174 Paperbound **$3.00**

STRESS WAVES IN SOLIDS, H. Kolsky, Professor of Applied Physics, Brown University. The most readable survey of the theoretical core of current knowledge about the propagation of waves in solids, fully correlated with experimental research. Contents: Part I—Elastic Waves: propagation in an extended plastic medium, propagation in bounded elastic media, experimental investigations with elastic materials. Part II—Stress Waves in Imperfectly Elastic Media: internal friction, experimental investigations of dynamic elastic properties, plastic waves and shock waves, fractures produced by stress waves. List of symbols. Appendix. Supplemented bibliography. 3 full-page plates. 46 figures. x + 213pp. 5⅜ x 8½.
S1098 Paperbound **$1.55**

Relativity, quantum theory, atomic and nuclear physics

SPACE TIME MATTER, Hermann Weyl. "The standard treatise on the general theory of relativity" (Nature), written by a world-renowned scientist, provides a deep clear discussion of the logical coherence of the general theory, with introduction to all the mathematical tools needed: Maxwell, analytical geometry, non-Euclidean geometry, tensor calculus, etc. Basis is classical space-time, before absorption of relativity. Partial contents: Euclidean space, mathematical form, metrical continuum, relativity of time and space, general theory. 15 diagrams. Bibliography. New preface for this edition. xviii + 330pp. 5⅜ x 8.
S267 Paperbound **$2.00**

ATOMIC SPECTRA AND ATOMIC STRUCTURE, G. Herzberg. Excellent general survey for chemists, physicists specializing in other fields. Partial contents: simplest line spectra and elements of atomic theory, building-up principle and periodic system of elements, hyperfine structure of spectral lines, some experiments and applications. Bibliography. 80 figures. Index. xii + 257pp. 5⅜ x 8.
S115 Paperbound **$2.00**

THE PRINCIPLE OF RELATIVITY, A. Einstein, H. Lorentz, H. Minkowski, H. Weyl. These are the 11 basic papers that founded the general and special theories of relativity, all translated into English. Two papers by Lorentz on the Michelson experiment, electromagnetic phenomena. Minkowski's SPACE & TIME, and Weyl's GRAVITATION & ELECTRICITY. 7 epoch-making papers by Einstein: ELECTROMAGNETICS OF MOVING BODIES, INFLUENCE OF GRAVITATION IN PROPAGATION OF LIGHT, COSMOLOGICAL CONSIDERATIONS, GENERAL THEORY, and 3 others. 7 diagrams. Special notes by A. Sommerfeld. 224pp. 5⅜ x 8.
S81 Paperbound **$1.75**

EINSTEIN'S THEORY OF RELATIVITY, Max Born. Revised edition prepared with the collaboration of Gunther Leibfried and Walter Biem. Steering a middle course between superficial popularizations and complex analyses, a Nobel laureate explains Einstein's theories clearly and with special insight. Easily followed by the layman with a knowledge of high school mathematics, the book has been thoroughly revised and extended to modernize those sections of the well-known original edition which are now out of date. After a comprehensive review of classical physics, Born's discussion of special and general theories of relativity covers such topics as simultaneity, kinematics, Einstein's mechanics and dynamics, relativity of arbitrary motions, the geometry of curved surfaces, the space-time continuum, and many others. Index. Illustrations, vii + 376pp. 5⅜ x 8.
S769 Paperbound **$2.00**

ATOMS, MOLECULES AND QUANTA, Arthur E. Ruark and Harold C. Urey. Revised (1963) and corrected edition of a work that has been a favorite with physics students and teachers for more than 30 years. No other work offers the same combination of atomic structure and molecular physics and of experiment and theory. The first 14 chapters deal with the origins and major experimental data of quantum theory and with the development of conceptions of atomic and molecular structure prior to the new mechanics. These sections provide a thorough introduction to atomic and molecular theory, and are presented lucidly and as simply as possible. The six subsequent chapters are devoted to the laws and basic ideas of quantum mechanics: Wave Mechanics, Hydrogenic Atoms in Wave Mechanics, Matrix Mechanics, General Theory of Quantum Dynamics, etc. For advanced college and graduate students in physics. Revised, corrected republication of original edition, with supplementary notes by the authors. New preface by the authors. 9 appendices. General reference list. Indices. 228 figures. 71 tables. Bibliographical material in notes, etc. Total of xxiii + 810pp. 5⅜ x 8⅜.
S1106 Vol. I Paperbound **$2.50**
S1107 Vol. II Paperbound **$2.50**
Two volume set Paperbound **$5.00**

WAVE MECHANICS AND ITS APPLICATIONS, N. F. Mott and I. N. Sneddon. A comprehensive introduction to the theory of quantum mechanics; not a rigorous mathematical exposition it progresses, instead, in accordance with the physical problems considered. Many topics difficult to find at the elementary level are discussed in this book. Includes such matters as: the wave nature of matter, the wave equation of Schrödinger, the concept of stationary states, properties of the wave functions, effect of a magnetic field on the energy levels of atoms, electronic spin, two-body problem, theory of solids, cohesive forces in ionic crystals, collision problems, interaction of radiation with matter, relativistic quantum mechanics, etc. All are treated both physically and mathematically. 68 illustrations. 11 tables. Indexes. xii + 393pp. 5⅜ x 8½.
S1070 Paperbound **$2.25**

BASIC METHODS IN TRANSFER PROBLEMS, V. Kourganoff, Professor of Astrophysics, U. of Paris. A coherent digest of all the known methods which can be used for approximate or exact solutions of transfer problems. All methods demonstrated on one particular problem —Milne's problem for a plane parallel medium. Three main sections: fundamental concepts (the radiation field and its interaction with matter, the absorption and emission coefficients, etc.); different methods by which transfer problems can be attacked; and a more general problem—the non-grey case of Milne's problem. Much new material, drawing upon declassified atomic energy reports and data from the USSR. Entirely understandable to the student with a reasonable knowledge of analysis. Unabridged, revised reprinting. New preface by the author. Index. Bibliography. 2 appendices. xv + 281pp. 5⅜ x 8½.
S1074 Paperbound **$2.00**

PRINCIPLES OF QUANTUM MECHANICS, W. V. Houston. Enables student with working knowledge of elementary mathematical physics to develop facility in use of quantum mechanics, understand published work in field. Formulates quantum mechanics in terms of Schroedinger's wave mechanics. Studies evidence for quantum theory, for inadequacy of classical mechanics, 2 postulates of quantum mechanics; numerous important, fruitful applications of quantum mechanics in spectroscopy, collision problems, electrons in solids; other topics. "One of the most rewarding features . . . is the interlacing of problems with text," Amer. J. of Physics. Corrected edition. 21 illus. Index. 296pp. 5⅜ x 8. S524 Paperbound **$1.85**

PHYSICAL PRINCIPLES OF THE QUANTUM THEORY, Werner Heisenberg. A Nobel laureate discusses quantum theory; Heisenberg's own work, Compton, Schroedinger, Wilson, Einstein, many others. Written for physicists, chemists who are not specialists in quantum theory, only elementary formulae are considered in the text; there is a mathematical appendix for specialists. Profound without sacrifice of clarity. Translated by C. Eckart, F. Hoyt. 18 figures. 192pp. 5⅜ x 8.
S113 Paperbound **$1.25**

SELECTED PAPERS ON QUANTUM ELECTRODYNAMICS, edited by **J. Schwinger.** Facsimiles of papers which established quantum electrodynamics, from initial successes through today's position as part of the larger theory of elementary particles. First book publication in any language of these collected papers of Bethe, Bloch, Dirac, Dyson, Fermi, Feynman, Heisenberg, Kusch, Lamb, Oppenheimer, Pauli, Schwinger, Tomonoga, Weisskopf, Wigner, etc. 34 papers in all, 29 in English, 1 in French, 3 in German, 1 in Italian. Preface and historical commentary by the editor, xvii + 423pp. 6⅛ x 9¼. S444 Paperbound **$2.75**

THE FUNDAMENTAL PRINCIPLES OF QUANTUM MECHANICS, WITH ELEMENTARY APPLICATIONS, E. C. Kemble. An inductive presentation, for the graduate student or specialist in some other branch of physics. Assumes some acquaintance with advanced math; apparatus necessary beyond differential equations and advanced calculus is developed as needed. Although a general exposition of principles, hundreds of individual problems are fully treated, with applications of theory being interwoven with development of the mathematical structure. The author is the Professor of Physics at Harvard Univ. "This excellent book would be of great value to every student . . . a rigorous and detailed mathematical discussion of all of the principal quantum-mechanical methods . . . has succeeded in keeping his presentations clear and understandable," Dr. Linus Pauling, J. of the American Chemical Society. Appendices: calculus of variations, math. notes, etc. Indexes. 611pp. 5⅜ x 8. S472 Paperbound **$3.00**

QUANTUM MECHANICS, H. A. Kramers. A superb, up-to-date exposition, covering the most important concepts of quantum theory in exceptionally lucid fashion. 1st half of book shows how the classical mechanics of point particles can be generalized into a consistent quantum mechanics. These 5 chapters constitute a thorough introduction to the foundations of quantum theory. Part II deals with those extensions needed for the application of the theory to problems of atomic and molecular structure. Covers electron spin, the Exclusion Principle, electromagnetic radiation, etc. "This is a book that all who study quantum theory will want to read," J. Polkinghorne, PHYSICS TODAY. Translated by D. ter Haar. Prefaces, introduction. Glossary of symbols. 14 figures. Index. xvi + 496pp. 5⅜ x 8⅜. S1150 Paperbound **$2.75**

THE THEORY AND THE PROPERTIES OF METALS AND ALLOYS, N. F. Mott, H. Jones. Quantum methods used to develop mathematical models which show interrelationship of basic chemical phenomena with crystal structure, magnetic susceptibility, electrical, optical properties. Examines thermal properties of crystal lattice, electron motion in applied field, cohesion, electrical resistance, noble metals, para-, dia-, and ferromagnetism, etc. "Exposition . . . clear . . . mathematical treatment . . . simple," Nature. 138 figures. Bibliography. Index. xiii + 320pp. 5⅜ x 8. S456 Paperbound **$2.00**

FOUNDATIONS OF NUCLEAR PHYSICS, edited by **R. T. Beyer.** 13 of the most important papers on nuclear physics reproduced in facsimile in the original languages of their authors: the papers most often cited in footnotes, bibliographies. Anderson, Curie, Joliot, Chadwick, Fermi, Lawrence, Cockcroft, Hahn, Yukawa. UNPARALLELED BIBLIOGRAPHY. 122 double-columned pages, over 4,000 articles, books, classified. 57 figures. 288pp. 6⅛ x 9¼. S19 Paperbound **$2.00**

MESON PHYSICS, R. E. Marshak. Traces the basic theory, and explicitly presents results of experiments with particular emphasis on theoretical significance. Phenomena involving mesons as virtual transitions are avoided, eliminating some of the least satisfactory predictions of meson theory. Includes production and study of π mesons at nonrelativistic nucleon energies, contrasts between π and μ mesons, phenomena associated with nuclear interaction of π mesons, etc. Presents early evidence for new classes of particles and indicates theoretical difficulties created by discovery of heavy mesons and hyperons. Name and subject indices. Unabridged reprint. viii + 378pp. 5⅜ x 8. S500 Paperbound **$1.95**

Prices subject to change without notice.

Dover publishes books on art, music, philosophy, literature, languages, history, social sciences, psychology, handcrafts, orientalia, puzzles and entertainments, chess, pets and gardens, books explaining science, intermediate and higher mathematics, mathematical physics, engineering, biological sciences, earth sciences, classics of science, etc. Write to:

Dept. catrr.
Dover Publications, Inc.
180 Varick Street, N.Y. 14, N.Y.